Liquid Fuels from Coal

1972

G.K. Goldman

Thirty-Six Dollars

NOYES DATA CORPORATION
Noyes Building
Park Ridge, New Jersey 07656, U.S.A.

FOREWORD

The detailed, descriptive information in this book is based on U.S. patents since the early nineteen forties relating to the production of liquid fuels from coal.

This book serves a double purpose in that it supplies detailed technical information and can be used as a guide to the U.S. patent literature in this field. By giving all the information that is significant, and eliminating legalistic phraseology, this book presents an advanced, technically oriented review of liquid fuels obtained from coal.

The U.S. patent literature is the largest and most comprehensive collection of technical information in the world. There is more practical, commercial, timely process information assembled here than is available from any other source. The technical information obtained from a patent is extremely reliable and comprehensive; sufficient information must be included to avoid rejection for "insufficient disclosure".

The patent literature covers a substantial amount of information not available in the journal literature. The patent literature is a prime source of basic commercially utilizable information. This information is overlooked by those who rely primarily on the periodical journal literature. It is realized that there is a lag between a patent application on a new process development and the granting of a patent, but it is felt that this may roughly parallel or even anticipate the lag in putting that development into commercial practice.

Many of these patents are being exploited commercially. Whether used or not, they offer opportunities for technological transfer. Also, a major purpose of this book is to describe the number of technical possibilities available, which may open up profitable areas of research and development.

These publications are bound in paper in order to close the time gap between "manuscript" and "completed book". Industrial technology is progressing so rapidly that hard cover books do not always reflect the latest developments in a particular field, due to the longer time required to produce a hard cover book.

The Table of Contents is organized in such a way as to serve as a subject index. Other indexes by company, inventor, and patent number help in providing easy access to the information contained in this volume.

CONTENTS AND SUBJECT INDEX

INTRODUCTION   1

1. THE CHEMICAL NATURE OF COAL   2
       Composition   2
       Structure   2
       Comparison with Petroleum   2

2. EXTRACTIVE CONVERSION PROCESSES   4
       Liquid Hydrocarbon Fractions as Extracting Solvents   4
          Production of Hydrogen-Rich Liquid Fuels from Coal   4
          Production of Gasoline by the Extraction of Coal   9
          Conversion of Coal to Hydrogen-Rich Liquid Fuels   13
          Conversion of Coal to Hydrocarbonaceous Products   16
          Utilization of Solvent Extraction as a Means to Convert Coal to Liquid Fuels   20
          Solvent Extraction of Coal   30
          Hydrogen-Donor Solvents in the Liquefaction of Coal   32
          Liquefaction of Coal in a Shell and Tube Extraction Zone   35
          Solvent Extraction Based on Partial Separation of Coal Slurry and Liquid   36
          "Coking" of Liquid Coal Extraction Products to Fuels and Chemicals   38
          Solvent Extraction of Coal in the Presence of Hydrogen Sulfide   41
          Liquefaction of Coal via Solvent Extraction in a Hydrogen Atmosphere   42
          Liquefaction of Coal by Means of Friedel-Crafts Catalysts   45
          Liquefaction Process Using Colloidal Size Coal   47
          Hydrogenated Thianaphthenes for the Extraction of Coal   48
       Solvation and Depolymerization   49
          Solvent Depolymerization of Coal   49
          Hydrogenation of Solvent Extracts   50
          Extraction and Hydrogenation of Coal   53
          Two-Stage Conversion of Coal to Liquid Hydrocarbons   54
       Deashing of Coal   57
          Deashing as a Means to Produce Liquid Hydrocarbons   57
          Deashing in the Presence of Acids   60
          Solvent Processing to Form an Ash-Free Coal   65
          Production of Ash-Free Anode Carbon   69
          Deashing of Coal Without Utilizing Hydrogen   72
       Dual Solvent Systems   75
          Liquefaction of Coal in a Dual Solvent System   75
       Multistage Solvent Extraction Systems   76
          Successive Extraction and Fractional Distillation   76
          Liquefaction of Coal by a Three-Stage Solvent Extraction Process   79
          Two-Stage Solvent Extraction System   85
          Two-Stage Solvent Extraction Utilizing a Solids Filtration System   89
       Microwave and Ultrasonics for Liquefaction and Extraction   92
          Utilizing Microwave Energy for the Liquefaction of Coal   92
          Ultrasonic Treatment as an Aid in the Solvent Extraction and Solubilization of Coal with Quinoline   93
       Thermal Liquefaction of Coal with Solvents   94
       Separation of Coal-Oil Suspensions   96

3. HYDROGENATION PROCESSES   101
       Noncatalytic Hydrogenations   101
          Process for the Hydrogenation of Coal   101
          Partial Hydrogenation of Coal at Elevated Temperatures and Pressures   103
          Hydroconversion of Solid Carbonaceous Materials   106
       Catalytic Hydrogenations   108
          Catalytic Hydrogenation of Carbonized Coal Vapors   108
          Liquid Phase Hydrogenation of Coal   110
          Efficient Catalytic Hydrogenation of Coal Paste   112
          Catalytic Hydrogenation of Coal with Water Recycle   114
          Balanced Hydrogenation of Coal   117

Contents and Subject Index

Hydrogenation of Coal in the Absence of a Pasting Solvent 117
Hydrogenation of Coal in the Presence of Pasting Media 119
Contact Catalysis of Vapors from Destructively Distilled Coal 121
Countercurrent Solvent Extraction with Simultaneous Hydrogenation 123
Rapid Hydrogenation of Coal 124
Solvation and Hydrogenation of Coal in Partially Hydrogenated Hydrocarbon Solvents 128
Liquid Phase Hydrogenation of Pulverized Coal 131
Cyclic Process for Converting Coal into Liquid Products by the Use of Fixed Catalytic Beds 132
Effect of Asphaltene Formation During the Hydrogenation of Coal 134
Use of Hydroconversion Catalysts 135
Spherical Catalysts in Coal Extract Hydrogenation 135
Hydrocracking of Coal Employing a Dual Function Catalytic Adsorbent 138
Hydrogenation and Liquefaction of Coal in the Presence of a Solid Adsorbent 140
Hydroconversion of Coal with a Combination of Catalysts 141
Catalytic Treatment of Carbonaceous Materials 144
Catalyst for the Hydrogenation of Hydrocarbon Materials 145
Highly Porous Catalysts 145
Nickel Carbonyl Catalyst 146
Catalytic Hydroprocessing of Coal with Metal Sulfides and Naphthenates 148
Hydrogenation of Coal Tar in the Presence of Iodine 149
Hydrogenation of Coal Employing Zinc Catalysts 151
Hydrogasification of Carbonaceous Material with Aluminum Chloride 152
Utilization of Friedel-Crafts Catalysts 153
Ebullating Bed Processes 156
Gas-Liquid Contacting Process 156
Catalytic Hydrogenation of Coal in an Ebullating Bed 158
Production of Low Sulfur Fuel Oil from Coal 159
Hydrogen Donor Solvents in Coal Hydrogenation Processes 161
Ebullating Bed Coal Hydrogenation 163
Coal Hydrogenation in a Catalytic Ebullating Bed Reactor 164
Catalytic Hydrogenation in a Series of Ebullating Bed Reactors 166
Low Pressure Hydrogenation of Coal in an Ebullating Bed 167
Coal Hydrogenation Process Utilizing an Expanded Particulate Solids Bed 169
H-Coal Process: Slurry Oil System 172
Hydrocracking of Polynuclear Aromatics in the Presence of a Zinc Halide 174
Quadri-Phase Low Pressure Hydrogenation for Partial Liquefaction of Coal 175
Coal Liquefaction by Low Pressure Hydrogenation 178
Residuum Recovery from Coal Conversion Processes 179
Refining of Coal Hydrogenation Products 182
Jet Fuel Production from Blended Conversion Products 183
Underground Liquefaction of Coal 183

4. CARBONIZATION PROCESSES 186
Thermal Cracking of Coal 186
Production of Motor Fuels by Carbonization of Lignite in the Presence of Alkali 186
Fluidized Process for the Further Carbonization of Carbonaceous Solids 188
Fractional Carbonization of Coal 190
Conversion of Carbonaceous Solids into Volatile Products 191
Treatment of Hydrocarbonaceous Solids 194
Direct Conversion of Carbonaceous Material to Hydrocarbons 196
Preparation of Hydrocarbon Oils by Thermal Cracking of Bituminous Materials 198
Method of Producing Motor Fuel 199
Production of Chemical Products from Coal Carbonization 201
Production of Synthetic Crude Oil from Low Temperature Carbonization of Coal Tars 204
The Hydrovisbreaking of Coal to Motor Fuels 205
Process for Hydrocoking Coal to Liquid Hydrocarbons 208
Process and System for Producing Synthetic Crude from Coal 209
Low Temperature Carbonization for the Production of Synthetic Crude Oil from Coal 211
Method for the Production of Gasoline 211
Depolymerization of Bituminous Coal Utilizing Friable Metal Reactants 212
Pyrolysis of Coal 214
Continuous Distillation of Coal and Other Hydrocarbonaceous Materials and Autogenous Hydrogenation of the Condensible Volatiles 214
Pyrolyzing a Solid or Liquid Hydrocarbonaceous Fuel in a Fluidized Bed 215
Hydrocarbon Fuels by the Pyrolysis of Coal in a Fuel Cell 217
Concomitant Production of Coke 219
Chemical Modification of Coal into Hydrocarbon Oils and Coke 219
Carbonization of Coal to Coke and Recovery of Volatile Constituents 221

COMPANY INDEX 224
INVENTOR INDEX 225
U.S. PATENT NUMBER INDEX 227

INTRODUCTION

Ever since F. Bergius in 1913 demonstrated the formation of petroleum-like hydrocarbons by hydrogenation of coal at high temperatures and pressures, the problem proved to be an intriguing one for chemists, engineers and economists alike.

The crux of the matter rests in the low hydrogen content of coal (about 5 weight percent) which must be raised to about 14% for a typical gasoline. The normally cheap hydrogen becomes expensive when it is used in such quantities. The alternative Fischer-Tropsch synthesis (first published in 1923) which uses enriched synthesis gas from the passage of steam over heated coke, is even more expensive.

Both processes have attained a high degree of technological perfection and become immediately practical when the supply of natural petroleum crudes is cut off, as in case of a global war.

There are many newer processes, especially those worked out under the auspices of the U.S. Office of Coal Research, e.g., the SCR (solvent refined coal) process, "Operation Gasoline", "Project Seacoke", the deashed coal project, the COED (Char Oil Energy Development) process, and the H-Coal process, whose technological details are described in one of the patents excerpted in this book.

At the moment it looks as if future coal to gasoline plants will operate on the principle of contacting crushed coal with selective solvents which act as hydrogen donors to aid in converting it to a liquid or semiliquid phase. Final hydrogenation will be based on the several recent catalytic concepts described in the vast patent literature.

THE CHEMICAL NATURE OF COAL

COMPOSITION

Coal is the fossilized plant life of prehistoric times, especially of the carboniferous period of the paleozic era, about 345,000,000 years ago. It is thought that coal was formed by the decomposition of vegetable matter under almost anaerobic conditions.

With the help of microorganisms, a chemical transformation took place in the presence of stagnant water, resulting in the formation of peat. As the water drained away, the material became buried, and temperatures and pressures increased. Thus the conversion to coal took place, very slowly, extending over many millions of years, leading first to lignite, and then to higher grades, such as soft bituminous coal and finally anthracite. Coals are comprised of carbon, hydrogen, oxygen, sulfur and nitrogen. Coals, oil shale and tar sands represent about 80% of recoverable fossil fuels. The other 20% is petroleum.

STRUCTURE

Structurally coals are composed chiefly of condensed, aromatic rings of high molecular weight. NMR (nuclear magnetic resonance) spectra yield estimates of the distribution of hydrogen atoms between aromatic and nonaromatic structures. About 70% of all carbon atoms are in aromatic rings, but only about 23% of hydrogen atoms are attached to aromatic carbon atoms. These compounds have molecular weights in the order of 10,000. Oxygen, sulfur and nitrogen are combined in chemically functional groups, such as, OH, CO, COOH, NH_2, CN, S, SH etc., which occur as integral parts of the original molecules.

Figure 1.1 may serve as an example of the complex high molecular weight compounds found in the typical cross-bonded structure of highly volatile coal. The S, N and O contents of coal are often greater than 1%, and the oxygen content of lignite is sometimes over 20%. Such heteroatoms cause serious problems in the manufacture of liquid fuels from coal, in addition to the main problem of the successful incorporation of hydrogen atoms, as stated in the Introduction.

COMPARISON WITH PETROLEUM

The main differences between typical analyses of coals and petroleum crudes are shown in the following table.

	Anthracite	Medium volatile bit.	High volatile A bit.	High volatile B bit.	Lignite	Petroleum crude	Gasoline	Toluene
CHEMICAL COMPOSITION OF SOME COALS AND PETROLEUM								
C	93.7	88.4	84.5	80.3	72.7	83–87	86	91.3
H	2.4	5.0	5.6	5.5	4.2	11–14	14	8.7
O	2.4	4.1	7.0	11.1	21.3			
N	0.9	1.7	1.6	1.9	1.2	0.2		
S	0.6	0.8	1.3	1.2	0.6	1.0		
H/C atom ratio	0.31	0.67	0.79	0.82	0.69	1.76	1.94	1.14

Coal analysis on moisture- and ash-free basis. Ash content of coal 3 to 15%.
C-fraction aromatic = 0.7. Aromatic rings per cluster—not over 3. H_{arom}/H_{aliph} = 0.23.
H/C atom ratio of petroleum residua: asphaltenes 1.18, resin 1.47, oil 1.67.

Source: Industrial and Engineering Chemistry (July 1969)

FIGURE 1.1: MOLECULAR STRUCTURE

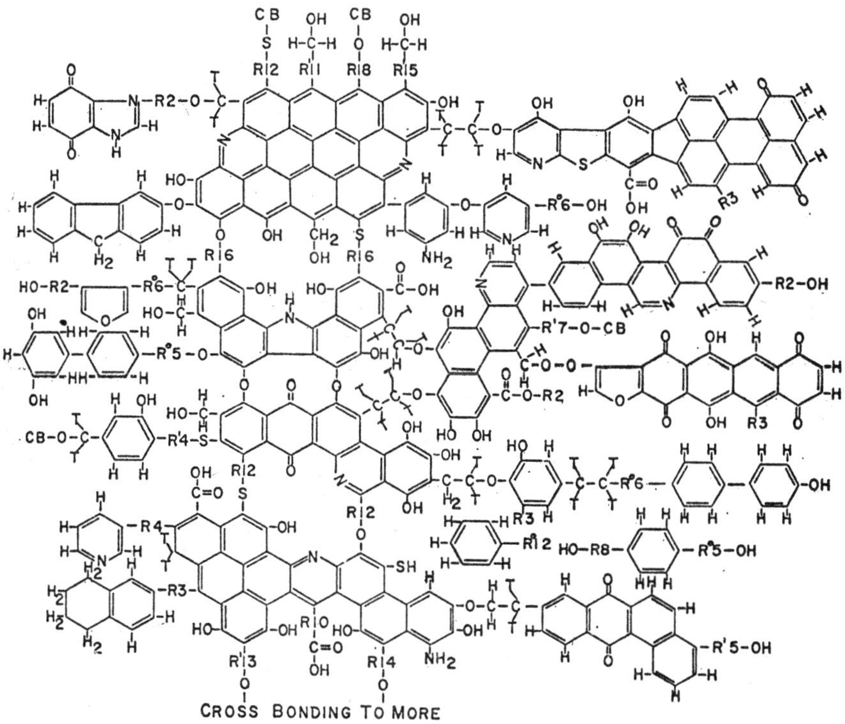

CROSS BONDING TO MORE
HETEROCYCLIC GROUPS

R°N = Alicyclic rings of N carbons.
RN = Alkyl side chain of N carbons.
R'N = Unsaturated alkyl side chain of N carbons.
CB = Cross bonding by O or S to new heterocyclic groups with side chains.
T = Tetrahedral 3 dimensional C—C bonds, C—O bonds and C—S bonds.

Source: M.G. Huntington; U.S. Patent 3,244,615; April 5, 1966

Even prior to Bergius it was known that hydrocarbon gases and liquids, tars and the chemicals derived from these hydrocarbons could be obtained not only from petroleum, but also in some form from coal. Early processes employed destructive distillation for the conversion of coal into these more valuable and useful products. The transformation of coal into a liquid form is a relatively rapid process. This conversion can be carried out in a number of ways, such as formation and extraction of a slurry with a hydrocarbon solvent (for example, a fuel oil), carbonization (thermal cracking to coal tar), catalytic hydrogenation and hydrogenolysis. Many variants and modifications of these processes have been attempted and are described in this book. Modern petroleum refining methods such as silica-alumina cracking and catalytic hydrocracking based on molecular sieves are of course necessary and applicable to the refining of crude oils obtained from coal.

Hydrogenation of liquefied coal is slower than that of petroleum crudes, because of the presence of the polynuclear aromatic structures (see the formula which is more or less an ideogram). The prerequisites and requirements for the manufacture of gasoline from coal may be summed up as follows.

(a) Liquefaction of coal.
(b) Removal of ash, sulfur, nitrogen and oxygen.
(c) Addition of hydrogen, which includes conversion of the polynuclear material (asphaltenes).
(d) Cracking, refining and reforming for raising the octane number.

All of the processes described in this book deal with these problems and give the reader an overall picture of the various achievements apparent from the patent literature.

EXTRACTIVE CONVERSION PROCESSES

LIQUID HYDROCARBON FRACTIONS AS EXTRACTING SOLVENTS

Production of Hydrogen-Rich Liquid Fuels from Coal

E. Gorin; U.S. Patent 3,018,241; January 23, 1962; assigned to Consolidation Coal Company describes a process related to a method for converting coal to liquid hydrocarbons, and, more particularly, to the production of hydrogen-rich liquids suitable for use as feedstock in gasoline manufacturing operations.

The extraction of coal by means of solvents has been proposed as a kind of partial conversion of the coal. In some instances extraction has been accompanied by concurrent hydrogenation as by the use of extrinsic hydrogen, or by concurrent deposition of coke. The difficulty with such concurrent addition of hydrogen or concurrent rejection of carbon in the form of coke is that both are relatively nonselective, that is, not only is the extract subjected to such treatment, but so also is the coal residue. Thus, uncontrolled, indiscriminate, and inefficient redistribution of hydrogen is effected.

Coal extracts contain too many compounds of widely different molecular size to permit complete resolution of their component molecular species. It is sufficient for these purposes to examine the gross characteristics of the extracts in terms of molecular weight. Using benzene as a solvent, it has been found that coal extracts may be separated readily into two fractions, a benzene-soluble and a benzene-insoluble fraction respectively. Surprisingly, the benzene-insoluble fraction has the following characteristics, set forth below, regardless of the conditions, solvent used, or depth of extraction employed in the initial solvent extraction treatment. Average molecular weight, 1,500; melting temperature range, 250° to 350°C. and hydrogen (wt. percent), 5.5 to 6.0.

The entire ultimate analysis of the benzene-insolubles is similar to that of the feed coal except as to oxygen and sulfur. The benzene-solubles, on the other hand, vary in their characteristics depending on the conditions of extraction. In general, however, their molecular weight ranges from 300 to 1,000; and their hydrogen content ranges from 6 to 8 percent by weight.

While the characteristics of the benzene-insoluble fraction of the extract, as set forth above, do not change significantly with increasing coal extraction, the amount of this portion in the extract increases materially with increasing coal extraction, in the absence of coking or hydrogen addition during the solvent extraction. This increase in amount of benzene-insolubles was observed in the case of all solvents tried, but at different rates of increase. It has been found that as the benzene-insoluble fraction of extract increases, the extract becomes correspondingly more difficult to hydrogenate, i.e., higher temperatures and pressures are required to convert substantially all the extract to hydrogen-enriched hydrocarbonaceous liquid. This process provides an improved process for converting bituminous coal, and particularly a highly caking bituminous coal, to a hydrogen-enriched liquid suitable as feedstock for gasoline manufacturing operations.

In this process, the solvent extraction treatment is controlled to yield an extract, under the extraction conditions, which amounts to less than 60 percent by weight of the maf (moisture-free and ash-free) coal. It has been found desirable in certain cases to subject the coal to solvent extraction conditions such that between 60 and 80% by weight of the maf coal is dissolved. However, in such cases it is necessary to separate sufficient benzene-insoluble material from the extract so that less than 65% by weight of the maf coal is recovered as the benzene-soluble rich fraction, as will be more fully explained hereinafter.

Figure 2.1a is a graph showing the relationship of hydrogen transferred from solvent to coal to the depth of extraction. Figure 2.1b is a schematic flow sheet of the process. Referring to Figure 2.1b of the drawings, comminuted coal is introduced into a stirred solvent extraction zone 10 concurrently with 0.5 to 4.0 parts by weight of a solvent. The extraction zone 10 is adapted to confine the coal and the solvent for a residence period from about 5 minutes to 4 hours at elevated pressures and temperatures. The residence period and temperatures are determined by the specific solvent and the desired depth of coal extraction. The pressure is that required to maintain the solvent as a liquid at the selected temperature, generally in the range of 1 to 6,500 psig.

Suitable solvents for the coal in the extraction step are those which are predominantly polycyclic hydrocarbons, preferably partially or completely hydrogenated aromatics, including naphthenic hydrocarbons, which are liquid under the temperature and pressure of extraction. Mixtures of these hydrocarbons are generally employed, and are derived from intermediate or final steps of this process. Those hydrocarbons or mixtures thereof boiling between about 260° and 425°C. are preferred. Examples of suitable solvents are tetralin, decalin, biphenyl and methylnaphthalene. Other types of coal solvent may be added to the abovementioned types for special reasons, but the resulting mixture should be predominantly of the types mentioned, i.e., should constitute more than 50% by weight of the solvent used. Examples of additive solvents are the phenolic compounds, such as phenol, cresols and xylenols.

As stated above, the coal is comminuted, and preferably, but not necessarily, of a fluidizable size, for example, −14 mesh Tyler Standard screen. Up to about 25% depth of extraction, the coal particles retain substantially their original size; beyond 25% extraction, the particles undergo degradation. The coal and the solvent are maintained in intimate contact within the extraction zone 10 until the solvent has dissolved the desired amount of coal, i.e., up to 80% by weight of the maf coal. At least 10 percent by weight of the maf coal should be dissolved since the extract below 10% is essentially benzene-soluble material and therefore does not require the use of this process. To dissolve above about 40% of the maf coal, it is normally necessary that hydrogen be added to the coal. This is usually accomplished by employing hydrogen-transferring solvents such as tetralin or mixtures of hydrocarbons derived from intermediate or final steps of the process. It has been found that as one increases the depth of extraction, the transfer of hydrogen increases rapidly (as is demonstrated by reference to Figure 2.1a of the drawings) such that if the depth of extraction exceeds 80%, the overall process becomes economically prohibitive in terms of the cost of the hydrogen required.

Specifically, at high depths of extraction, the hydrogen does not react exclusively with the new forming extract, but instead produces an increasing amount of gas which is of little value as compared to the extract. In Figure 2.1a the hydrogen transferred (wt. percent of maf coal) to the extract from the solvent is plotted against depth of extraction. As previously stated, as one increases the depth of extraction, each additional increment of extract contains a higher proportion of benzene-insoluble material. Thus, the deeper one extracts, the greater the amount of benzene-insoluble material that must be separated from the extract. In order to minimize the amount of benzene-insolubles that must be separated, it is preferred to conduct the solvent extraction under conditions to yield an extract amounting to less than 60% by weight of the maf coal.

The temperature of the extraction zone should be an elevated temperature between about 100° to 500°C., but in no event high enough to cause appreciable coke formation. In some instances it may be desirable to conduct the extraction in stages at successively higher temperatures until the desired depth of extraction is attained. Instead of a batch system, a continuous countercurrent system may be employed. The particular system used is not material to the practice of this process.

Following extraction, the mixture of solvent, extract, and residue is conducted rapidly, so as to avoid cooling of the mixture, through a conduit 12 to a stirred separation zone 14. The primary function of this zone is to separate the extract into a benzene-insoluble rich fraction and a benzene-soluble rich fraction. This separation may be accomplished by the addition to the separation zone 14 of a paraffinic solvent, e.g., hexane, in a volume ratio of the paraffinic solvent to the extraction solvent between 0.1 and 1.0. Alternatively, the temperature of the separation zone may be lowered below the temperature employed in the solvent extraction zone. Depending upon the coal solvent employed, the temperature of extraction, and the depth of extraction, the act of cooling to low temperature may precipitate most of the benzene-insoluble rich fraction, thereby dispensing with the necessity of adding the precipitating paraffinic solvent.

If a paraffinic solvent is used, it has been found that the solvent is useful as an aid to the subsequent separation of the solids from the liquid. It is important in any event to have determined in advance the amount of benzene-insolubles in the extract so that the precipitation of the desired amount of the extract can be controlled. The larger the amount of benzene-insolubles in the extract, the larger is the amount of precipitating solvent that must be added, or the greater is the difference in temperature between the extraction zone and the separation zone that must be maintained.

From the separation zone 14 a mixture of liquid and solids is discharged through a conduit 16 to a conventional type filtration zone 18, of if desired a centrifuge. The solids are therein separated from the liquid. The liquid phase, consisting of a solution of the benzene-soluble rich fraction of the extract and solvents, i.e., the paraffinic solvent, if used, and the extraction solvent, is conducted through a conduit 20, to a fractionation zone 22 wherein the extraction solvent is recovered and recycled through a conduit 24 to the extraction zone 10; and the precipitating solvent, if used, is recovered and returned through a conduit 26 to the separation zone 14.

The benzene-soluble rich fraction of the extract is separately recovered and conducted through a conduit 28 to a hydrogenation zone 30, the operation of which will be hereinafter described. If desired, some or all of the extraction solvent,

FIGURE 2.1: PRODUCTION OF HYDROGEN-RICH LIQUID FUELS FROM COAL

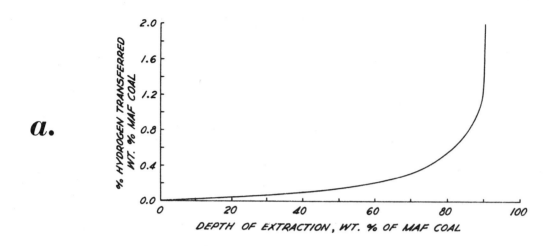

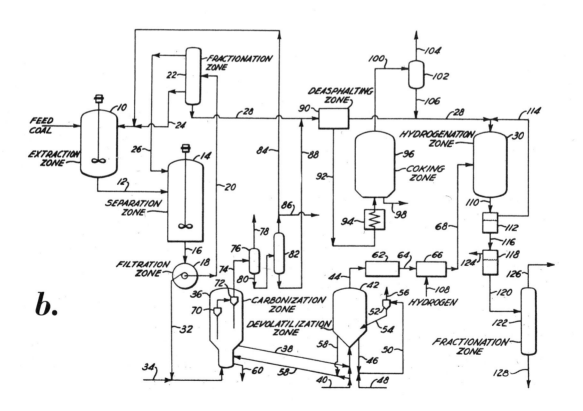

Source: E. Gorin; U.S. Patent 3,018,241; January 23, 1962

instead of being recycled to the extraction zone 10, may be used as a diluent for the benzene-soluble rich fraction in its passage through the hydrogenation zone.

As pointed out earlier, it may be desirable to dissolve up to 80% by weight of maf coal. Depending on the coal employed, the solvent used, as well as other extraction conditions, there may be sufficient benzene-soluble material present in the incremental extracts beyond 60% to justify its recovery. However, to recover this additional benzene-soluble material requires substantial separation of the incremental benzene-insoluble material. It has been found necessary to separate at least sufficient benzene-insoluble material to ensure recovery of less than 65% of the maf coal as the benzene-soluble rich fraction.

The solids from the filtration zone 18, i.e., the residue and the precipitated benzene-insoluble rich fraction of the extract, are discharged into a conduit 32 where they are picked up by a stream of recycle gas, air, or steam entering through a conduit 34 and are carried into a carbonization zone 36. It should be noted at this point that, if desired, the residue from the extraction zone 10 may be separated from the extract as by filtration prior to separating the extract into the benzene-soluble and benzene-insoluble rich fractions. In such a case the residue is sent directly to the carbonization zone 36, and the extract is then introduced into the separation zone 14. The benzene-insoluble rich fraction may then be coked separately or introduced into the carbonization zone 36. The carbonization zone 36 may be any one of the well-known systems for carbonizing carbonaceous solids at low temperatures, i.e., 425° to 760°C.

For example, a bed of solids may be maintained in the zone in a fluidized state by means of the abovementioned carrier gas. The temperature of the carbonization zone may be maintained by any suitable means, for example, by preheating the carrier gas to the appropriate high temperature. It is preferred, however, to burn a portion of the carbonized residue, i.e., char, produced in the carbonization zone 36 to supply the necessary heat. This is accomplished by withdrawing char from the carbonization zone 36 through a conduit 38, and conveying the withdrawn char by means of an inert gas such as recycle gas entering through a conduit 40 into a char devolatilization zone 42. The char is preferably maintained in a fluidized state in this zone at a temperature between about 645° and 945°C. The devolatilization temperature must be higher than any processing temperature to which the solids have been previously exposed. The volatile content of the solids will be driven off as a hydrogen-rich gas which can be recovered through a conduit 44. A typical composition of such gas produced by simply heating char (derived by carbonization at 496°C.) at 870°C. is in percent by volume as follows: H_2, 72.0; H_2S, 0.75; CO_2, 0.81; CO, 13.19; CH_4, 12.15; and N_2, 1.1.

A portion of the devolatilized char is withdrawn from the devolatilization zone 42 through a conduit 46; picked up by air entering through a conduit 48, and lifted through a combustion leg 50. The temperature of the char as a result of the combustion is raised to that sufficient to maintain the temperature in the devolatilization zone 42 when returned through a cyclone separator 52 and a conduit 54 to that zone. Flue gas is removed from the cyclone separator 52 through a conduit 56. Hot char from the devolatilization zone 42 is transferred by a conduit 58 back to the carbonization zone 36 by means of recycle gas from the conduit 40. Net char produced in the carbonization zone is discharged through a conduit 60. The hydrogen-rich gas from the char devolatilization zone 42 is conducted via the conduit 44 to a conversion zone 62 where substantially pure hydrogen is produced by techniques well-known in the art. The resulting hydrogen is conveyed through a conduit 64 to a compressor 66 which compresses the hydrogen to the desired pressure. The compressed hydrogen is conducted to the hydrogenation zone 30 through a conduit 68.

Returning to the carbonization zone 36, the effluent tar vapors are circulated through cyclone separators 70 and 72, which return finely divided solids to the carbonization zone 36. The tar vapors are conducted through a conduit 74 to a condenser 76 where noncondensable gas is discharged through a conduit 78. The gas may be used for manufacture of hydrogen by known methods such as steam reforming or may be used as plant fuel. The tar is carried through a conduit 80 to a fractionation zone 82 in which a liquid fraction boiling below 325°C. and a liquid fraction boiling above 325°C. are recovered. The fraction boiling below 325°C. is discharged through a conduit 84 which leads to the conduit 24 emptying into the extraction zone 10. If desired, however, a portion of the low boiling fraction may be recovered through a conduit 86 and then introduced into a gasoline refining plant. The fraction boiling above 325°C., after suitable treatment (not shown) to remove any solids, if present, is discharged into a conduit 88 which conveys the fraction to the conduit 28 wherein it is commingled with the benzene-soluble rich fraction.

The mixture of the benzene-soluble rich fraction and the tar in conduit 28 contains asphaltic materials or asphaltenes which have an average molecular weight between about 700 and 1,000. In some instances it may be desirable to reduce the asphaltene content. Accordingly, a deasphalting zone 90 may be interposed in the conduit 28 for precipitating at least a portion of the asphaltenes. The deasphalting is accomplished by well-known methods employed in petroleum technology such as the addition of propane, pentane, or hexane. The precipitaed asphaltenes, preferably diluted with a fluxing oil such as a portion of a coker distillate, are conducted through a conduit 92 to a preheater 94 and thence into a coking zone 96 adapted in conventional fashion to coke the asphaltenes at a temperature between about 426° and 760°C. Ash-free coke is discharged through a conduit 98. The coker distillate is removed through a conduit 100 and condensed in a condenser 102, from which noncondensable gases are discharged through a conduit 104. The condensate is carried by a conduit 106 back to the conduit 28 leading to the hydrogenation zone 30. The deasphalting step also removes any residual carbonaceous solids carried over into the benzene-soluble rich fraction of the extract or the tar.

Preferably, however, the mixture of benzene-soluble rich extract and the tar from the fractionation zone 82, recovered via the conduit 88 is introduced directly into the hydrogenation zone 30. In the hydrogenation zone 30, the extract and tar are contacted with hydrogen, preferably in the presence of a hydrogenation catalyst. As previously mentioned, hydrogen is introduced into the hydrogenation zone 30 via the conduit 68; however, if required, additional hydrogen may be introduced into the system through a conduit 108 at the compressor 66. Hydrogenation of the extract and tar can be conducted at pressures of 1,000 to 10,000 psig, preferably about 2,000 to 3,500 psig, a range well below that normally required for direct hydrogenation of coal. The hydrogenation temperature range is about 400° to 600°C., preferably about 410° to 455°C.

The hydrogenation catalyst should be sulfur resistant, e.g., molybdenum or tungsten oxides or sulfides impregnated on a refractory support to permit catalyst regeneration. The support usually will be an alumina-rich material such as pure gamma alumina or alumina composited with other oxides such as silica. Other metals such as nickel or cobalt may be added as catalyst promoters.

The products of hydrogenation are discharged from the hydrogenation zone 30 through a conduit 110, cooled, and passed into a separator 112. Hydrogen-rich gas is separated from the products and recycled through a conduit 114 to the hydrogenation zone 30. The remaining products in the separator 112 are depressurized and then passed via a conduit 116 into a low pressure separator 118. From the low pressure separator 118 the liquid product is carried through a conduit 120 to a fractionation zone 122, while the gaseous product is withdrawn from the separator 118 via a conduit 124. The liquid product is fractionated in the fractionation zone 122 into any desired fractions.

A preferred separation is to fractionate the liquid hydrogenation product into a fraction boiling above 360°C. and a fraction boiling below 360°C. The latter fraction is passed through a conduit 126 to further refining and hydrogenation operations for conversion to gasoline in conventional fashion. The former fraction is passed through a conduit 128 and may be reintroduced into the hydrogenation zone 30 or into the coking zone 96. If desired, portions of both fractions may be introduced into the solvent extraction zone 10, as a portion of the solvent therein.

Example: Pittsburgh seam coking bituminous coal was used as raw material. The coal was subjected to an extraction in a closed vessel with decalin as a solvent at a temperature of 348°C. for 1 hour. Based on 100 pounds of maf coal, 220 pounds of decalin were employed as solvent. The ultimate analysis of the starting coal and the solvent-free extract is as follows:

	maf Coal, Wt. %	Extract, Wt. %
H	5.74	6.45
C	82.26	83.51
N	1.31	1.23
O	8.13	6.81
S	2.56	2.00

The yields of extraction products, based on 100 pounds of maf coal, are as follows:

	Weight of Product (lbs.)
Hydrogen sulfide	0.1
Gas	1.0
Liquor	1.0
Extract	23.0
Solid residue (maf)	74.9

The addition of 50 pounds of hexane to the extract solution precipitated 6.2 pounds of extract of which about 70% by weight was determined to be benzene-insoluble. The remainder of the extract contained about 85% by weight of benzene-soluble material. The precipitated extract and solid residue were carbonized at 510°C., yielding 58.5 pounds of char and 12.6 pounds of tar including the light oil fraction. The total yield of liquid was thus 29.2 pounds.

In the description of the preferred embodiment, the deasphalting step (see 90 of Figure 2.1b) and the coking of the precipitated asphaltenes (see 96 of Figure 2.1b) may be eliminated and, instead, the +360°C. oil from the hydrogenation zone 30 be recycled tharoug that zone. Or as a still further option, the deasphalting step may be eliminated with the +360°C. oil from the hydrogenation zone 30 going to the coker 96. In order to compare these three optional modes of treatment of the hydrogenation feedstock, the abovementioned liquid yield of 29.2 pounds was divided into three aliquot parts which were respectively subjected to the three optional treatments. The first aliquot part, hereinafter called Aliquot A, was treated in accordance with the steps shown in Figure 2.1b, namely, as follows, with the understanding that the yields are reported on the basis of a starting feedstock of 29.2 pounds, that is, the actual yield is multiplied by three.

To Aliquot A was added 20 pounds of hexane per 100 pounds of Aliquot A. The resulting precipitate comprising principally asphaltenic material amounted to 4.6 pounds. The latter was coked in a conventional delayed coking system at 470°C., yielding 2.7 pounds of ash-free coke and 1.4 pounds of coker distillate. The latter was combined with the nonprecipitated portion of the extract from the deasphalting step, making a total of 26.0 pounds, which was then hydrogenated in a fixed bed catalyst system. The catalyst was cobalt molybdate on alumina (15% MoO_3, 3% CoO, 82% Al_2O_3); the temperature was 440° to 454°C., and the pressure 3,500 psig. The liquid hourly space velocity was about 1.0 pound of total feed per pound of catalyst per hour. The hydrogenated products were fractionated and the -360°C. distillate recovered as gasoline feedstock. The +360°C. fraction amounting to 10.4 pounds was recycled through the hydrogenation zone 30. The amount of H_2 consumed was 1.22 pounds.

The second aliquot part, hereinafter designated Aliquot B, was simply sent directly to the hydrogenation zone without any deasphalting or coking treatments. The same hydrogenation conditions were employed as used for Aliquot A. The hydrogenated products likewise were fractionated yielding 25.8 pounds of -360°C. gasoline feedstock and some +360°C. oil which was recycled through the hydrogenation zone. The amount of H_2 consumed was 1.46 pounds.

The third aliquot part, hereinafter designated as Aliquot C, like Aliquot B, was sent directly to the hydrogenation zone and hydrogenated under the same conditions as were the other aliquot parts. The resulting hydrogenated products were similarly fractionated into a -360°C. fraction (23.5 pounds) and a +360°C. fraction (10.6 pounds). The latter was coked in the abovementioned delayed coking system at 468°C., yielding 1.8 pounds of ash-free coke and 8.1 pounds of coker distillate which was mixed with Aliquot C before entering the hydrogenation zone. The results of the above described treatments may be summarized as follows.

TABLE 1: COMPOSITION OF THE SEVERAL FEED MATERIALS

	H	C	N	O	S
Raw extract	6.45	83.5	1.2	6.8	2.0
Extract with benzene-insolubles removed	6.69	83.1	1.0	7.2	2.1
Tar from low temperature carbonization	7.60	83.3	1.0	6.5	1.6
Coker distillate Aliquot A	7.31	86.1	1.0	4.2	1.4
Average recycle oil to hydrogenation zone	9.07	89.9	0.4	0.5	0.1
Total feed to hydrogenation zone (excluding recycle oil):					
Aliquot A	7.24	82.9	0.9	7.0	2.0
Aliquots B and C	7.08	83.1	1.0	6.9	1.9

TABLE 2: FEED COMPOSITION TO HYDROGENATION ZONE AND TOTAL YIELDS

	Aliquot A Case	Aliquot B Case	Aliquot C Case
Wt. percent of feed to hydrogenation zone:			
Extract and tar	71.5	66.7	78.3
Recycle oil	28.5	33.3	21.7
Yield wt. percent of maf coal:			
-360°C. distillate	23.2	25.8	23.5
Gas	1.7	1.8	2.2
Liquor	1.9	2.1	2.1
H_2S	0.5	0.6	0.5
Ash-free coke	2.7	0.0	1.8
H_2 consumption	1.22	1.46	1.34
Lbs. H_2 consumed per 100 lbs. of -360°C. distillate	5.25	5.66	5.69

Production of Gasoline by the Extraction of Coal

E. Gorin; U.S. Patent 3,018,242; January 23, 1962; assigned to Consolidation Coal Company describes a process which relates to the conversion of bituminous coal to a hydrogen-enriched hydrocarbonaceous liquid suitable as feedstock to a gasoline refining plant.

Coal is normally converted to gasoline by a two-step process which comprises initially converting the coal to a hydrogen-enriched hydrocarbonaceous liquid and then converting the latter to gasoline in a conventional type gasoline refining plant.

In accordance with this process, bituminous coal is converted to a hydrogen-enriched hydrocarbonaceous liquid by a process which comprises subjecting the coal to a solvent extraction treatment, whereby a mixture of extract and undissolved coal is obtained. The undissolved coal will sometimes hereinafter be referred to as residue. The solvent extraction is conducted under conditions to yield an extract amounting to between 50 and 70% by weight of maf, i.e., moisture-free and ash-free, coal, hereinafter more fully explained. The extract is separated from the residue and the residue is then introduced into a devolatilization retort from which is recovered a distillate tar and a solid material. The solid material is hereinafter referred to as char. At least a portion of the distillate tar and at least a portion of the extract are subsequently subjected to catalytic hydrogenation under hydrogenation conditions, whereby a hydrogen-enriched hydrocarbonaceous liquid is obtained.

It is generally concluded that as the amount of extract obtained from the solvent extraction of coal increased, the amount of tar recoverable upon subsequent low temperature carbonization of the residue correspondingly decreased. Specifically, it was thought that once the amount of extract exceeded about 50% by weight of the maf coal, essentially no tar remained in the residue. It has been found, however, that a substantial amount of tar remains in the residue even when as much as 70% by weight of the maf coal is recovered as extract.

In order to obtain more than about 40% by weight of the maf coal as extract during the solvent extraction of coal, it is normally necessary that hydrogen be added to the coal. The hydrogen is usually added by employing a so-called "hydrogen-transferring" hydrocarbonaceous solvent such as tetrahydronaphthalene or specific extract hydrogenation products. As the amount of extract obtained by the solvent extraction is continuously increased above about 40%, the amount of hydrogen transferred markedly increases. It is known that the transferred hydrogen usually reacts with the extract as well as unites with carbon contained in the coal to form gas. The gas is generally methane and ethane, these gases being of relatively little value as compared to the extract. It is believed that the hydrogen also reacts with the residue, thereby accounting for the unexpected amount of tar obtained from the residue upon subsequent low temperature carbonization. It is important to note, however, that as the amount of extract approaches 70% by weight of the maf coal the transferred hydrogen tends to produce an increasing amount of gas rather than reacting with the residue. Specifically, once the amount of extract obtained by the solvent extraction of the coal exceeds 70% by weight of the maf coal relatively little, if any, tar is recoverable from the resulting residue upon subsequent low temperature carbonization. In addition, it has been found that when the amount of extract exceeds about 70% by weight of the maf coal the cost of the transferred hydrogen becomes economically prohibitive.

Figure 2.2 is a diagrammatic illustration of the preferred process. The process primarily comprises introducing bituminous coal, such as Pittsburgh Seam coal, in contact with a hydrocarbonaceous solvent in a solvent extraction zone 10, to yield an extract amounting to between 50 and 70% by weight of the maf coal. The extract is a liquid, dissolved in the solvent, at the conditions of extraction. Substantially all of the extract and the hydrocarbonaceous solvent are separated from the residue in a separation zone 18, whereupon a mixture of the extract and the solvent is then introduced into a topping still 24, while the residue is introduced into a low temperature carbonization retort 30. Distillate tar which is recovered from the retort 30 is fractionated in a fractionation zone 36. A portion of the tar is withdrawn from the zone 36 and combined with a portion of the extract in a conduit 28, and the mixture is then introduced into a catalytic hydrogenation zone 42. A hydrogen-enriched hydrocarbonaceous liquid is obtained from the catalytic hydrogenation zone 42, a portion of which is subsequently employed as a gasoline refining plant feedstock.

Solvent Extraction Zone: Bituminous coal is introduced into a conventional type solvent extraction zone 10 via a conduit 12. Preferably, the bituminous coal is a high volatile bituminous coal. By high volatile is meant bituminous coal having a volatile content of greater than about 20% by weight of the maf coal. Hydrocarbonaceous solvent is introduced via a conduit 14 into the solvent extraction zone 10. The coal and the solvent react therein to yield an extract comprising between 50 and 70% by weight of the maf coal. Since the main purpose of this process is to obtain as much hydrogen-enriched hydrocarbonaceous liquid as economically possible from the coal, it is necessary that the extract comprise at least 50% by weight of the maf coal. For reasons previously stated, the amount of extract must not exceed 70% by weight of the maf coal.

A mixture of extract, solvent, and residue is withdrawn from the extraction zone 10 via a conduit 16, and the mixture is then introduced into a conventional type separation zone 18. The above solvent extraction process may be any of the processes commonly employed, e.g., continuous, batch, countercurrent, or staged extraction at a temperature in the range of 300° to 500°C., a pressure in the range of 1 to 6,500 psig, a residence time in the range of one minute to 120 minutes, a solvent to coal ratio of from 0.5:1 to 4:1, and, if desired, a catalyst and/or up to 50 standard cubic feet of hydrogen per pound of maf coal.

Suitable solvents for the coal in the extraction step are those which are predominantly polycyclic hydrocarbons, preferably partially or completely hydrogenated aromatics, including naphthenic hydrocarbons, which are liquid under the temperature and pressure of extraction. Mixtures of these hydrocarbons are generally employed, and are derived from intermediate or final steps of the process. Those hydrocarbons or mixtures thereof boiling between 260° and 425°C. are preferred. Examples of suitable solvents are tetrahydronaphthalene, decalin, biphenyl, methylnaphthalene, and dimethylnaphthalene. Other types of coal solvent may be added to the abovementioned types for special reasons, but the resulting mixture should be predominantly of the types mentioned, that is, should constitute more than 50% by weight of the solvent used. Examples of additive solvents are the phenolic compounds, such as phenol, cresols, and xylenols.

A preferred solvent is a portion of the product obtained from a previous catalytic hydrogenation of extract, normally comprising a blend of two high boiling distillates, preferably a 260° to 325°C. fraction and a 325° to 425°C. fraction, at a feed ratio in the range of 1:1 to 3:1, respectively. The solvent is obtained in this manner primarily to enhance the economics of the over-all process.

Separation Zone and Topping Still: Substantially all of the extract and the solvent are separated from the residue in the conventional type separation zone 18, which is preferably a filtration zone. If desired, however, a cyclone, centrifuge, or a conventional type settling zone may be employed in place of the filtration zone. The residue, substantially free of solvent and extract is withdrawn from the separation zone 18 via a conduit 20, while a mixture of the extract and the solvent is withdrawn via a conduit 22. The solvent and extract mixture is introduced into a conventional type topping still 24. The mixture is separated therein into a first fraction comprising substantially all of the hydrocarbonaceous solvent and some low boiling extract and a second fraction comprising the major portion of the high boiling extract. The separation is usually made at 325°C., corresponding to the boiling point requirements of gasoline refining plant feedstock. The first fraction is withdrawn from the topping still 24 via a conduit 26, part of which is subsequently reintroduced into the extraction zone 10 as a portion of the solvent therein. The rest is preferably introduced into a gasoline refining plant (not shown). The second fraction is withdrawn from the topping still 24 via a conduit 28.

If desired, the extract and solvent mixture obtained from the separation zone 18 may be treated prior to the topping still 24 in a deashing zone wherein solid contaminants which are not removable by mechanical separation methods are removed. If these contaminants are not removed from the extract, they tend to deposit on the catalyst maintained in the catalytic hydrogenation zone, thereby causing a more rapid decrease in the activity of the catalyst than would otherwise be experienced. Such decrease in activity forces resort to more frequent replenishment of the catalyst with either regenerated or fresh catalyst. The deashing zone may be any one of those which are generally employed, e.g., an acid treating zone.

Carbonization Retort: The residue withdrawn from the zone 18 via the conduit 20 is introduced into a conventional type low temperature carbonization retort 30 which is maintained at a temperature in the range of 425° to 760°C. Preferably, the retort 30 is a fluidized low temperature carbonization zone however, if desired, other conventional devolatilization zones may be employed, e.g., a rotary kiln. Solids, i.e., char, are withdrawn from the retort 30 via a conduit 32, while vapors and any solvent that may have adhered to the residue subsequent to the separation zone 18 are withdrawn via a conduit 34. The vapors and any solvent that adhered to the residue are introduced into a conventional type fractionation zone 36. If necessary, the tar vapors and the solvent are freed of any entrained solids before entering the fractionation zone 36 by any suitable means such as an electrostatic precipitator or a micrometallic filter. The material introduced into the fractionation zone 36 is preferably separated therein into a fraction boiling above 325°C., which is withdrawn via a conduit 38, and into a fraction boiling below 325°C., which is withdrawn via a conduit 40. The latter is introduced into a gasoline refining plant (not shown), while the former fraction is combined in the conduit 28 with the extract fraction removed from the topping still 24. The mixture is then introduced into a conventional type catalytic hydrogenation zone 42.

If desired, however, prior to introducing the mixture of extract and tar into the hydrogenation zone all or portions of the mixture may be introduced via a conduit 44, into a conventional type coking zone 46. Coke is recovered from the coking zone 46 via a conduit 48, while a coker distillate is recovered via a conduit 50. The coker distillate is condensed in a condenser 52 from which noncondensable gases are discharged via a conduit 54. The condensate is withdrawn from the condenser via a conduit 56 and then introduced into the hydrogenation zone 42. Coking the mixture of extract and tar tends to enhance the quality of the feed to the hydrogenation zone thereby decreasing the frequency of regeneration of the catalyst.

Hydrogenation Zone: Hydrogen is introduced into the catalytic hydrogenation zone 42 via a conduit 58 in contact with the tar and the extract mixture such that the mixture is hydrogenated therein. Hydrogenation products are withdrawn via a conduit 60, from which is subsequently obtained a hydrogen-enriched hydrocarbonaceous liquid suitable for use as a gasoline refining plant feedstock. A portion of the hydrogenation products may be recovered and thereafter introduced into the solvent extraction zone 10 as a portion of the hydrocarbonaceous solvent. In addition, portions of the higher boiling products of hydrogenation may be reintroduced into the hydrogenation zone and/or introduced into a conventional type coking zone (not shown).

The conditions generally employed during the catalytic hydrogenation of extract are a temperature in the range of 400° to 550°C.; a pressure in the range of 1,000 to 10,000 psig; a hydrogen feed rate of from 5 to 100 standard cubic feet per pound of extract; and a liquid feed rate of from 10 to 100 pounds per cubic foot of reaction volume. The catalytic hydrogenation zone may be any one of the conventional hydrogenation zones employed by those skilled in the art such as a liquid phase

FIGURE 2.2: PRODUCTION OF GASOLINE BY THE EXTRACTION OF COAL

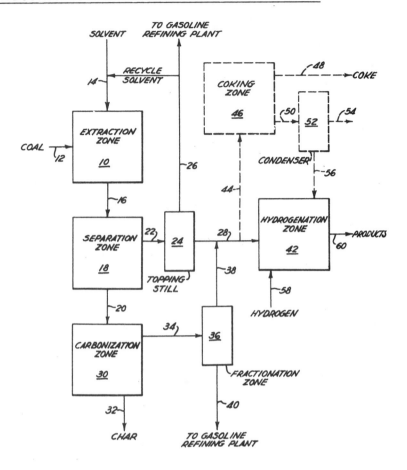

Source: E. Gorin; U.S. Patent 3,018,242; January 23, 1962

or a vapor phase hydrogenation zone employing catalyst in the form of a fixed, gravitating, or fluidized bed therein. In addition, the catalyst may also be dispersed within the mixture of tar and extract in the form of a slurry and then introduced into a slurry phase, catalytic hydrogenation zone such that the catalyst is introduced into, maintained therein, and withdrawn therefrom in the form of a slurry or a suspensoid. Suitable catalysts are, for example, metals of sub-groups 5 to 8 of the periodic chart, preferably oxides or sulfides in combinations thereof. A preferred catalyst is one containing a metal oxide or sulfide of sub-group 6 of the periodic chart, i.e., molybdenum combined with a relatively minor amount of a transition group metal oxide or sulfide such as cobalt. The active hydrocracking metals are preferably supported on a hydrous oxide support such as alumina gel.

Example: The following is an example of the use of the process. Pittsburgh Seam coal was treated in a solvent extraction zone with a solvent recovered from a previous hydrogenation of extract under the following conditions:

Process Conditions

Temperature	380°C.
Pressure	70 psig
Solvent/coal ratio	1.0
Residence time	1.0 hour

The solvent comprised a mixture of a 260° to 325°C. fraction and a 325° to 425°C. fraction in the ratio by weight of 1 to 1 respectively. The yields of the extraction treatment are given on the following page.

Yields	Wt. Percent Original maf Coal
Extract	57.8
Gases + H_2O	7.3
Residue	34.9

The extract was separated from the residue by filtration and the extract then introduced into a topping still, while the residue was carbonized in a fluidized low temperature carbonization retort under the following conditions and giving the following yields:

Process Conditions	
Temperature	510°C.
Residence time	20 minutes
Sweep gas rate	4 cu. ft./lb.

Yields	Wt. Percent maf Residue
Gas + C_4	2.8
Liquor	2.8
Tar + light oil	16.4
Char	78.0

The portion of the extract and the tar plus light oil boiling above 325°C. were introduced in admixture with a catalyst into a liquid phase catalytic hydrogenation zone under the following conditions and giving the following yields:

Process Conditions	
Temperature	441°C.
Pressure	3,500 psig
Residence time (on fresh feed)	2.8 hours
Catalyst	MoS_2

Yields	Wt. Percent Fresh Feed
C_1 to C_3	12.5
C_4	5.2
C_5 to 325°C. distillate	80.6

Conversion of Coal to Hydrogen-Rich Liquid Fuels

In a process developed by E. Gorin; U.S. Patent 3,117,921; January 14, 1964; assigned to Consolidation Coal Company coal is subjected to solvent extraction under conditions to dissolve up to 80 weight percent of the coal (on a moisture-free and ash-free basis). The coal extraction product, which comprises coal extract and undissolved coal residue, is then treated, for example, in a filtration zone, to separately recover coal extract. This extract, which is a solid at room temperature and which is substantially free of hydrocarbons boiling below 400°C., is composed almost entirely of nondistillable, high molecular weight polycyclic aromatics. These polycyclic aromatics differ substantially in their response to hydrogenation treatment at elevated temperatures. It has been observed that if the hydrogenation conditions are dictated by the more refractory components of the extract, then an inordinate amount of coke and gas is produced. Accordingly, in this process the extract is subjected to a prehydrogenation treatment which effects only partial conversion of the extract to a distillable liquid boiling below 325°C. In general, the prehydrogenation is conducted at a temperature between 400° and 470°C. and at a pressure between 500 and 5,000 psig.

However, the conditions may fall somewhat outside these ranges depending on the nature of the extract or on the selection of catalyst, if any. A higher boiling or so-called bottoms portion of the prehydrogenated extract is subjected to carbonization, i.e., coking, at 425° to 760°C., to yield a liquid distillate. A lower boiling portion of the prehydrogenated extract in admixture with at least a portion of the liquid distillate is subsequently hydrogenated to yield hydrogen-enriched liquid fuels.

Referring to Figure 2.3, coal, preferably high volatile bituminous coal, is introduced into a stirred solvent extraction zone 10 concurrently with 0.5 to 4.0 parts by weight of a coal extraction solvent. The extraction zone 10 is adapted to confine the coal and the solvent for a residence period from about 5 min. to 4 hr. at elevated pressures and temperatures.

The residence period and temperatures are determined by the specific solvent and the desired depth of coal extraction. The pressure is preferably that required to maintain the solvent as a liquid at the selected temperature, generally in the range of 1 to 6,500 psig.

Suitable solvents for the coal in the extraction step are those which are predominantly polycyclic, aromatic hydrocarbons, preferably partially or completely hydrogenated aromatics, including completely saturated naphthenic hydrocarbons which are liquid under the temperature and pressure of extraction. Mixtures of these hydrocarbons may be used and are preferably derived from intermediate or final steps of this process. Those hydrocarbons or mixtures thereof boiling between about 260° and 425°C. are especially preferred. Examples of suitable solvents are tetrahydronaphthalene, decalin, biphenyl, methyl-naphthalene, and dimethylnaphthalene. Other types of coal solvent may be added to the abovementioned types for special reasons, but the resulting mixture should be predominantly of the types mentioned. Examples of additive solvents are the phenolic compounds such as phenol, cresols, and xylenols.

The coal and the solvent are maintained in intimate contact within the extraction zone 10 until the solvent has dissolved, i.e., converted the desired amount of coal. Preferably up to 80 weight percent of the maf (moisture-free and ash-free) coal is dissolved, as is further discussed in U.S. Patent 3,018,241. It has been found that the cost of converting more than 80 weight percent of the coal becomes economically prohibitive in terms of the amount of hydrogen transfer that is needed.

In addition, as the depth of coal extraction is increased, each additional increment of coal extract contains a higher proportion of benzene-insoluble material which correspondingly makes the resulting coal extract more difficult to hydrogenate. If desired, however, any depth of coal conversion may be used. In fact, if more than 80 weight percent coal conversion is used, the process becomes even more desirable. It has been found that it is preferred to conduct the solvent extract under conditions to yield an extract amounting to less than 60 weight percent of the maf coal.

The temperature of the extraction zone should be an elevated temperature between about 100° and 500°C., but preferably not high enough to cause appreciable coke formation. In some instances it may be desirable to conduct the coal extraction in stages at successively higher temperatures until the desired depth of extraction is attained. Instead of a batch system, a continuous or a countercurrent system may be employed.

Following extraction, the mixture of solvent, extract, and residue is conveyed through a conduit 12 to a conventional type separation zone 14 such as a filtration zone, sedimentation zone, or centrifugation zone. The extract, which is usually a solid at room temperature and generally contains less than 5 weight percent hydrocarbons boiling below 400°C., is therein separated from the residue. If desired, a portion of the coal extract may be separated with the residue and processed therewith. For example, in U.S. Patent 3,018,241, it is shown that the extract may be cooled or treated with a paraffinic solvent such as hexane to separate the extract into a benzene-soluble rich extract fraction and a benzene-insoluble rich extract fraction. The latter extract fraction may be coked alone or in combination with the residue.

The residue, alone or in combination with a precipitated benzene-insoluble rich extract fraction, is conveyed via a conduit 16 to a drying zone 18 wherein a recycle gas stream entering through a conduit 20 is used to strip any retained solvent therefrom. The effluent stream from the drying zone 18 is passed through a conduit 22 to a pair of cyclone separators 24 and 25 which separate the vapors from the solids. The solids drop into a conduit 26 where they are picked up by a carrier gas and introduced into a carbonization zone 28.

The carbonization zone 28 may be any one of the well-known systems for carbonizing carbonaceous solids at low temperatures, i.e., 425° to 760°C. For example, solids may be maintained in the zone in a fluidized bed by means of the abovementioned carrier gas. The temperature of the carbonization zone may be maintained by any suitable means, for example, by preheating the carrier gas to the appropriate high temperature or by burning a portion of the carbonized residue, i.e., char, produced in the carbonization zone 28. This latter method is accomplished by withdrawing char from the carbonization zone 28 through a conduit 30, and conveying the withdrawn char by means of an inert gas such as recycle gas entering through a conduit 32, into a char devolatilization zone 34. The char is preferably maintained in a fluidized bed in the zone 34 at a temperature between about 645° and 945°C. The devolatilization temperature must be higher than any processing temperature to which the solids have been previously exposed. The volatile content of the solids will be driven off as a hydrogen-rich gas which can be recovered through a conduit 36.

A portion of the devolatilized char is withdrawn from the devolatilization zone 34 through a conduit 38, picked up by air entering through a conduit 40, and lifted through a combustion leg 42. The temperature of the char as a result of the combustion is raised to that sufficient to maintain the temperature in the devolatilization zone 34 when returned through a cyclone separator 44 and a conduit 46 to that zone. Flue gas is removed from the cyclone separator 44 through a conduit 48. Hot char from the devolatilization zone 34 is transferred by a conduit 50 back to the carbonization zone 28 by means of recycle gas from the conduit 32. Net char produced in the carbonization zone 28 is discharged through a conduit 52. The hydrogen-rich gas from the char devolatilization zone 34 is conducted via the conduit 36 to a conversion zone 54 wherein substantially pure hydrogen is produced by techniques well-known in art. The resulting hydrogen may be used, for example, in the subsequent hydrogenation of the extract. Returning to the carbonization zone 28, the effluent tar vapors are circulated through cyclone separators 56 and 58, which return finely divided solids to the carbonization zone 28. The distillate tar vapors are withdrawn from the carbonization zone via a conduit 60 and subsequently fractionated, as more fully explained hereinafter.

Returning now to the coal extract which is separated from the residue in the separation zone 14, the extract is conducted through a conduit 62 to a flash tower 64 wherein at least some of the solvent is flashed off through a conduit 66. The solvent vapors are commingled with solvent vapors from the aforementioned residue drying zone 18 in a conduit 68 which carries the solvent vapors to a condenser 70. Any noncondensable gas is discharged through a conduit 72 while the condensed solvent is returned to the extraction zone 10 via a conduit 74.

The extract is conveyed from the flash tower 64 through a conduit 76 to a preheater 78 which serves to raise the temperature of the extract to about 426° to 468°C. The preheated extract is passed through a mild prehydrogenation zone 80 which serves to add about 0.5 to 2.0 pounds of hydrogen per 100 pounds of feed. The operating conditions are as follows: temperature, 425° to 470°C.; pressure, 500 to 2,500 psig and residence time 5 to 6 minutes, preferred 10 to 30 minutes.

Hydrogen input to the prehydrogenator 80 may be by means of hydrogen transfer from hydrogenated oil derived from a final step of this process. Free hydrogen gas may also be added to aid hydrogenation. The prehydrogenation operation is preferably conducted substantially noncatalytically, or with relatively small amounts of "homogeneous" catalysts, i.e., 0.05 to 1.0 weight percent of a hydrogen halide or its corresponding ammonium salt, i.e., NH_4Cl, NH_4Br, or NH_4I. Inexpensive catalysts such as red mud may also be used if desired. The hydrogenated oil is used in amounts between 1 and 3 parts per part of extract, preferably mixed with solvent from the flash tower 64.

FIGURE 2.3: CONVERSION OF COAL TO HYDROGEN-RICH LIQUID FUELS

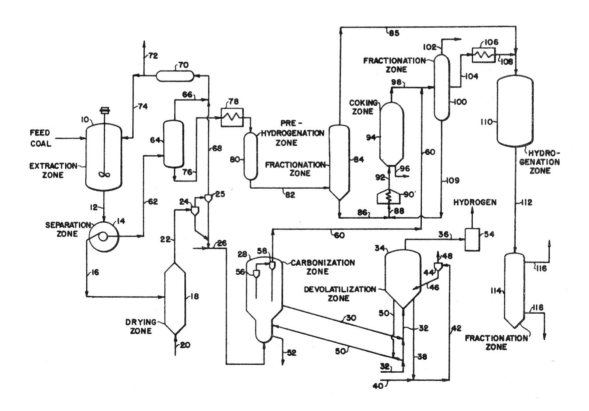

Source: E. Gorin; U.S. Patent 3,117,921; January 14, 1964

The mildly prehydrogenated extract is discharged through a conduit 82 into a fractionation zone 84 which preferably separates the prehydrogenated extract products into a +325°C. and a –325°C. fraction. The latter fraction is withdrawn through a conduit 85 and subseqently hydrogenated. The +325°C. bottoms fraction which still contains nondistillable hydrocarbons is conveyed through a conduit 86 into a conduit 88 to a preheater 90, and then through a conduit 92 to a coking zone 94 operating at 425° to 760°C. Ash-free coke is discharged through a conduit 96. Coker distillate is withdrawn from the coking zone 94 via a conduit 98 and is commingled with the distillate tar vapors withdrawn from the carbonizer 28 via a conduit 60.

The distillate mixture is introduced into a fractionation zone 100. A –300°C. fraction is recovered through a conduit 102 for further refining, if desired, to yield chemicals and low boiling solvents. A 300° to 425°C. fraction is sent through a conduit 104 to a preheater 106. The preheated fraction is withdrawn via a conduit 108 and then admixed in the conduit 85 with the –325°C. fraction of the prehydrogenated extract. The mixture is then introduced into a hydrogenation zone 110. The portion of the distillates boiling above 425°C. is withdrawn from the fractionation zone 100 via a conduit 109 and recycled to the coking zone 94.

In the hydrogenation zone 110, the prehydrogenated extract and tar are contacted with hydrogen, preferably in the presence of a hydrogenation catalyst. Hydrogenation of the extract and tar may be conducted at pressures of about 1,000 to 10,000 psig, preferably about 2,000 to 3,500 psig, a range well below that normally required for direct hydrogenation of coal. The hydrogenation temperature range is about 400° to 600°C., preferably about 410° to 455°C. The hydrogenation catalyst should be sulfur-resistant, e.g., molybdenum or tungsten oxides or sulfides impregnated on a refractory support to permit catalyst regeneration. The support usually will be an alumina-rich material such as pure gamma alumina or alumina composited with other oxides such as silica. Other metals such as nickel or cobalt may be added as catalyst promoters.

The products of hydrogenation are discharged from the hydrogenation zone 110 through a conduit 112, cooled, and passed into a fractionation zone 114 wherein the products are separated into any desired fractions. A preferred separation is to fractionate the hydrogenation product into a fraction boiling above 360°C. and a fraction boiling below 360°C. The latter fraction is passed through a conduit 116 to further refining and hydrogenation operations for conversion to gasoline. The former fraction is passed through a conduit 118 and may be reintroduced into the hydrogenation zone 110 or into the coking zone 94. If desired, portions of both fractions may be introduced into the solvent extraction zone 10 as a part of the solvent therein.

Conversion of Coal to Hydrocarbonaceous Products

E. Gorin and M.B. Neuworth; U.S. Patent 3,120,474; February 4, 1964; assigned to Consolidation Coal Company have found that where coal is prepared by comminution in conventional crushing and grinding equipment, the material will contain a usual random distribution of particles of all sizes down to ultrafines having diameters which are measured in microns. For example, a typical differential and cumulative screen analysis of a comminuted coal suitable for treatment by fluidized low temperature carbonization and for conveying in the form of a slurry is presented in Table 1.

TABLE 1: DIFFERENTIAL AND CUMULATIVE SCREEN ANALYSIS OF COMMINUTED AGGLOMERATING COAL

Tyler Standard Screen Size	Weight Percent Retained on Screen	
	Differential	Cumulative
Retained on:		
8	Trace	Trace
14	0.2	0.2
28	5.7	5.9
48	14.6	20.5
100	28.9	49.4
200	19.9	69.3
325	9.2	78.5
Pan	21.5	100.0

It has been found that a number of advantages exists if only a portion of the comminuted coal is introduced into the solvent extraction zone. Only a particular portion of the comminuted coal should be introduced into the extraction zone, while the remaining comminuted coal should be treated in another manner, as will be further discussed.

In this process, the cominuted coal feedstream is separated into the relatively fine and the relatively coarse coal fractions by employing a zone which simultaneously dries, preheats, and separates.

In most coal conversion processes wherein a continuous solvent extraction zone is employed, the extract obtained from the extraction zone is generally separated from the residue, if any is present, prior to further treatment of the extract. Normally, the separation zone is a conventional type filtration zone. It is economically desirable to employ other conventional type separation zones, such as a hydroclone, centrifuge, or sedimentation zone, in place of the filtration zone. Unfortunately, it has been found that adequate separation of the residue from the extract can usually be effected only with a filtration zone. However, filtration rates which are desirable in a commercial plant filtration zone are normally not attained.

The extraction products consist of a slurry of fine residue particles in a solution of the extraction solvent and the extract, the slurry having a relatively high density and viscosity. The fine residue particles accordingly have a tendency to remain suspended in the extract-solvent solution and, in some instances, enter the filter septum and blind the interstices thereby lowering the filtration rate. To complicate matters even further, it is known that when more than about 40% by weight of the moisture-free and ash-free, i.e., maf, coal is extracted, the individual coal particles tend to degrade. Thus, filtration of the resulting extraction products becomes even more difficult.

It has been found that the filtration rate of the extraction products may be improved by eliminating the relatively fine portion of the comminuted coal fed to the solvent extraction zone. Obviously, this will minimize the concentration of fine residue particles in the extraction product, thereby enhancing filtration and in many instances enabling other conventional type separation zones to be employed. It is not enough, however, just to remove the fine coal particles from the feedstream to the extraction zone, since the fine coal particles are also capable of being converted to valuable hydrocarbonaceous products. It is the combination of minimizing the filtration problem and still converting the fine coal particles to valuable hydrocarbonaceous products which is the important feature of this process. It is economically prohibitive to convert only the relatively coarse fraction of coal to the more valuable hydrocarbonaceous products.

Thus, it was decided to subject the relatively fine coal fraction to carbonization in admixture with the residue. It was discovered that the relatively fine coal particles can be processed to yield a greater quantity of recoverable distillate tar products per unit weight than that recovered not only from the residue particles but also from the larger coal particles that had not been extracted. The higher yield of tar results from the fact that pretreating the fine coal fraction prior to carbonization is not required, as explained below. Thus, in addition to the advantage gained by eliminating the coal fines from the filtration zone, there is a corollary advantage in subjecting the coal fines to carbonization.

It is preferred to use a fluidized low temperature carbonization zone as the devolatilization zone. However, when the coal employed in the process is a highly caking coal, it is generally necessary to preoxidize the coal to prevent the particles from agglomerating in the fluidized low temperature carbonization zone. The preoxidation treatment, unfortunately, severely reduces the tar yield.

It has been discovered that relatively fine coal particles possess a much lower caking tendency than coarse coal in fluidized low temperature carbonization processing. Since the larger particles of coal can be rendered substantially nonagglomerative under fluidized low temperature carbonization conditions (via solvent extraction), the untreated coal fines can be admixed therewith to provide a feed material which is operable under fluidized low temperature carbonization conditions.

It is to be understood that by the phrases "relatively coarse" and "relatively fine", it is intended to distinguish two fractions of the coal feedstream which differ significantly in median particle size. The relatively fine fraction could comprise principally particles capable of passing through a 200 mesh screen; whereas the corresponding relatively coarse fraction would comprise the original coal feedstream from which the relatively fine fraction had been removed. The relatively coarse fraction, of course, may contain significant quantities of particles capable of passing through a 200 mesh screen and the relatively fine fraction could similarly contain significant quantities of particles too large to pass through a 200 mesh screen.

With reference to Figure 2.4, the process comprises introducing comminuted coal into a combination drying, preheating, and separation zone 10 wherein the relatively fine fraction of the coal is separated from the relatively coarse fraction; introducing the relatively coarse fraction into a continuous solvent extraction zone 34 wherein the coal is extracted to produce a mixture of extract and residue; separating the extract and residue mixture in a separation zone 40; and introducing the relatively fine coal fraction and the residue into a devolatilization zone 46.

Comminuted coal, preferably highly caking, high volatile bituminous coal such as Pittsburgh Seam coal, is introduced into a drying, preheating, and separation zone 10 via a conduit 12. The coal had been previously comminuted to a size in the range of about 8 x 0 mesh Tyler Standard screen, and preferably in the range of about 14 x 0 mesh Tyler Standard screen. A fluidized bed 14 of fluidizable size coal particles is established in the zone 10 under the influence of gases flowing upwardly at a velocity of about 0.5 to 2.5 feet per second through the zone from a conduit 16. Where hot gases are employed for effecting drying and preheating, they are provided in sufficient quantity and at a temperature sufficiently high to remove moisture from the coal particles and to heat the dried particles to an elevated temperature in order to minimize the heat input requirements for further coal processing.

Alternatively, heating tube bundles or heating coils 18 may be embedded within the fluidized bed 14 to provide the heat needed for drying and preheating. A heat exchange medium such as hot oil, hot sand and the like may be supplied to the heating element 18 through a conduit 20 and removed for reheating through a conduit 22. Exit temperature of the coal particles from the zone 10 should be from about 120° to 340°C., preferably from about 200° to 290°C. The coal particles should not be subjected to temperatures at which agglomeration will occur during the drying and preheating step. The gases rise through the fluidized bed 14 and are recovered from the zone 10 via a conduit 24 with substantial quantities of relatively fine coal particles entrained therein. The entrained relatively fine coal particles are separated from the gases in a conventional type gas-solids separation device 26 such as a cyclone. Solids-free gases, i.e., waste gases, are eliminated from the cyclone 26 via a conduit 28. Relatively fine coal particles are recovered from the cyclone 26 via a conduit 30. Regulation of the upward linear velocity of the hot gases in the drying, preheating, and separation zone 10 permits control of the fraction of the comminuted coal feedstream which will be entrained and recovered via the conduit 24 as the relatively fine coal fraction.

Referring again to the drying, preheating, and separation zone 10, the relatively coarse particles from the comminuted coal feedstream are not entrained in the fluidizing gases and may be withdrawn from the zone 10 via a conduit 32. The quantity of relatively fine coal particles which are separately treated should be at least about 10% by weight and preferably at least about 20% by weight of the coal feedstream. The quantity of relatively coarse particles which are subjected to solvent extraction should be at least about 50% by weight of the coal feedstream.

In place of the zone 10, any conventional type separation zone may be employed for separating the relatively fine coal fraction from the relatively coarse coal fraction. However, in view of the fact that the coal must be dried and preheated for further treatment in the process, the above method for simultaneously drying, preheating and separating the comminuted coal is desirable.

The relatively coarse coal fraction withdrawn from the zone 10 via the conduit 32 is introduced into a conventional type solvent extraction zone 34 in admixture with a hydrocarbonaceous solvent introduced into the zone 34 via a conduit 36. Commercially, it is desirable that the overall process be continuous; however, if desired, batch or semicontinuous operation may be employed. As previously mentioned, if continuous operation is employed, the coal being introduced into the solvent extraction zone is premixed with the solvent and then introduced into the extraction zone 34 in the form of a coal-solvent slurry.

The coal and solvent react in the extraction zone so that at least a portion of the coal is extracted, the extraction products being withdrawn via a conduit 38. The depth of coal conversion, i.e., the amount of coal that is extracted, is dependent primarily on the purpose of the overall conversion process. If it is desired only to decake the coal for subsequent treatment in a fluidized low temperature carbonization zone, then at least 10% by weight (on a maf basis) of the relatively coarse coal fraction introduced into the extraction zone must be extracted. However, if it is desired to make hydrocarbonaceous liquid products suitable for conversion to gasoline, then the extraction treatment should be such that between about 50 to 70% by weight (on a maf basis) of the relatively coarse fraction introduced into the extraction zone is converted to extract.

The solvent extraction process may be any of the processes commonly employed by those skilled in the art, e.g., at a temperature in the range of about 300° to 500°C., a pressure in the range of 1 to 6,500 psig, a residence time in the range of 1 to 120 minutes, a solvent-to-coal ratio of from 0.5:1 to 4:1, and, if desired, a catalyst or up to 50 standard cubic feet of hydrogen per pound of coal feed may be used. The particular conditions of extraction will be determined by the depth of coal conversion that is desired.

Suitable solvents for the coal in the extraction step are those which are predominantly polycyclic hydrocarbons. These are usually aromatic hydrocarbons which may be partially or completely hydrogenated, including naphthenic hydrocarbons, which are liquid under the temperature and pressure of extraction. Mixtures of these hydrocarbons are generally employed, and are derived from intermediate or final steps of the process. Those hydrocarbons or mixtures thereof boiling between 260° and 425°C. are preferred. Examples of suitable solvents are tetrahydronaphthalene, Decalin, biphenyl, methylnaphthalene, and dimethylnaphthalene. Other types of coal solvent may be added to the abovementioned types for special reasons, but the resulting mixture should be predominantly of the types mentioned, that is, should constitute more than 50% by weight of the solvent used. Examples of additive solvents are the phenolic compounds, such as phenol, cresols, and xylenols.

Substantially all of the extract and the solvent are separated from the residue in a conventional type separation zone 40 which is preferably a filtration zone. If desired, however, a cyclone, centrifuge, or a conventional type settling zone may be employed in place of the filtration zone. The residue, substantially free of solvent and extract, is withdrawn from the separation zone 40 via a conduit 42, while a mixture of the extract and the solvent is withdrawn via a conduit 44.

FIGURE 2.4: CONVERSION OF COAL TO HYDROCARBONACEOUS PRODUCTS

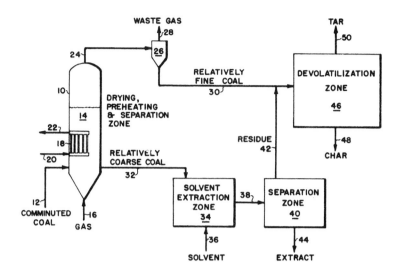

Source: E. Gorin and M.B. Neuworth; U.S. Patent 3,120,474; February 4, 1964

At least a portion of the residue withdrawn from the separation zone 40 via the conduit 42 and at least a portion of the relatively fine coal fraction withdrawn from the cyclone 26 are introduced into a conventional type devolatilization zone 46 which is maintained at a temperature in the range of about 425° to 760°C. It is usually desirable to premix the fine coal and the residue to minimize any tendency of the feed coal to agglomerate. Preferably, the zone 46 is a fluidized low temperature carbonization zone; however, if desired, other conventional devolatilization zones may be employed, e.g., a rotary kiln. Hydrocarbonaceous solids, i.e., char, are withdrawn from the zone 46 via a conduit 48, while tar vapors and any solvent that may have adhered to the residue subsequent to the separation zone 40 are withdrawn via a conduit 50. If necessary, the tar vapors and the solvent are freed of any entrained solids, before being subsequently treated, by any suitable means such as an electrostatic precipitator or a micrometallic filter.

The tar vapors are subsequently condensed so that a distillate tar is obtained. The distillate tar may be introduced in combination with the extract obtained from the separation zone 40 into a conventional type hydrocracking zone (not shown) to produce valuable hydrocarbonaceous liquids suitable for conversion to gasoline in a conventional type gasoline refining plant. However, when less than about 50% by weight (maf basis) of the relatively coarse fraction is converted to extract, it is economically desirable to utilize the extract in applications other than for hydrocracking to gasoline, for example, as a coker feedstock.

Due to the fact that the relatively fine coal particles are subjected directly to devolatilization without any previous solvent extraction, a fraction of the distillate tar recovered from the devolatilization zone will be relatively rich in tar acids, i.e., cresols, phenols, and xylenols. These materials are preferably recovered from the tar prior to admixing the tar fraction with the extract. If desired, a portion of the residue from the separation zone may be employed for other purposes, for example, the residue may be introduced into a conventional type water-gas generator.

Example: High volatile bituminous coal having the following properties is employed in each of the process sequences of this example.

Percent volatile matter	39.3
Percent fixed carbon	47.7
Percent ash	13.0
Heat of combustion, Btu/lb.	12,700
Fischer assay tar yield (percent by weight)	16.6

Sequence A — A sample of the above coal is comminuted to particles having a size consist in the range of 14 x 0 mesh Tyler Standard screen. The comminuted coal is subjected to solvent extraction with crude dimethylnaphthalene for 1 hour at 350°C. Two pounds of solvent are employed for each pound of coal. The resulting mixture of extract and undissolved coal, i.e., residue, is filtered and the recovered residue is then introduced into a fluidized low temperature carbonization zone. The residue is carbonized for 45 minutes at 496°C. Because the residue is substantially noncaking, no treatment such as preoxidation is necessary prior to introducing the residue into the carbonization zone.

Sequence B — A second sample of the same coal is comminuted to particles having a size consist in the range of 14 x 0 mesh Tyler Standard screen. The comminuted coal is introduced into a drying, preheating, and separation zone such as described in the preferred embodiment wherein the comminuted coal is separated by elutriation into a coarse fraction and a fine fraction. The coarse fraction comprises 65% by weight of the comminuted coal, and the fine fraction comprises 35% by weight of the comminuted coal. The coarse fraction which is substantially all coarser than 200 mesh is subjected to solvent extraction and filtration in the same manner as described in Sequence A. Due to the coarser coal employed in the extraction step, a considerably higher filtration rate than in Sequence A is attained. The residue recovered from the filtration zone is combined with the fine fraction (which substantially is all finer than 200 mesh), and the mixture is subjected to fluidized low temperature carbonization as described in Sequence A. The caking characteristics of the mixture are sufficiently low, thereby enabling the mixture to be treated in the fluidized carbonization zone without any pretreatment. Thus a maximum yield of tar is obtained from the fine coal fraction.

Sequence C — A third sample of the above coal is also comminuted as described above, and the comminuted coal is introduced into a fluidized low temperature carbonization zone under the same conditions set forth in Sequence A. However, because the comminuted coal is highly caking, prior to introducing the coal into the carbonization zone, the coal is oxidized. The coal is treated with air for 45 minutes at 405°C. whereby 6.1% by weight of the coal is oxidized. This oxidation treatment renders the coal sufficiently noncaking. The yields of extract, benzene soluble extract, tar, and light oil recovered from the process steps in each of the above sequences are compared in Table 2.

TABLE 2: COMPARISON OF YIELDS FOR VARIOUS PROCESS SEQUENCES

Process Sequence	Step	Feed (MAF Basis) Wt. Percent of Coal	Yields of Liquid Products—Wt. Percent MAF Feed Coal			
			Extract	Benzene Soluble Extract or Tar	Light Oil	Total Benzene Soluble Plus Light Oil
A	Extraction	100 Coal	38.7	18.8	....	18.8
	Carbonization	59.1 Extraction Residue	....	6.7	0.4	7.1
Total Yields in Process			38.7	25.5	0.4	25.9
B	Extraction	65.0 Coarse Coal	25.2	12.2	....	12.2
	Carbonization	38.4 (Extraction Residue)	....	4.4	0.3	4.7
		35.0 Fine Coal	....	8.7	0.5	9.2
Total Yields in Process			25.2	25.3	0.8	26.1
C	Carbonization	100 Coal	....	13.4	0.8	14.2

The most significant comparison between the three sequences is the total yield of benzene-soluble material plus light oil. These materials are the more valuable products on the basis of ease in conversion to valuable hydrocarbonaceous products. The above yields represent close to the maximum that can be achieved without the use of hydrogen, directly or indirectly, for example, by hydrogen transfer from a hydrogen donor solvent.

It is seen that Process Sequences A and B give substantially higher yields than can be achieved by direct carbonization of the coal. The improvement arises largely from obviating the need for pretreatment of the coal which severely reduces the tar yield. It is noted that the yields of benzene-soluble liquid are substantially the same in Sequences A and B. Economically, however, Process Sequence B is preferred because the extraction step is simplified both by virtue of the higher filtration rate achieved and the fact that the extraction plant is reduced in size.

Utilization of Solvent Extraction as a Means to Convert Coal to Liquid Fuels

E. Gorin; U.S. Patent 3,143,489; August 4, 1964; assigned to Consolidation Coal Company provides a process for the conversion of coal to synthetic liquid fuels which comprises a series of sequential, partial conversion steps, each of which is designed to effect most efficiently the incremental addition of hydrogen or the progressive rejection of carbon, as the case may be. In its broadest sense the process comprises:

(1) Coal extraction;
(2) Separation of extract from undissolved coal residue;
(3) A primary catalytic hydrocracking zone;
(4) Catalytic hydrofining; and
(5) A secondary catalytic hydrocracking zone.

In the foregoing listed steps, progressive, incremental addition of hydrogen is effected in the following generalized fashion. In the coal extraction step a small amount of hydrogen is added to the extraction zone either by the use of a hydrogen-transfer solvent or by the introduction of hydrogen gas or both. The purpose of this additional hydrogen is to permit the solvent extraction of up to 80 weight percent of the maf (moisture-free and ash-free) coal. It is obviously desirable (for economic reasons) to recover a major portion of the coal as coal extract. However, coal as such has limited solubility in those solvents which it is practical to use in this process, unless hydrogen is added to partially upgrade the coal. While larger addition of hydrogen will permit greater depths of extraction, it has been found that as the depth of extraction exceeds 80 weight percent, the hydrogen addition required to exceed such depths becomes economically prohibitive, as further explained hereinafter.

The products of extraction are separated in the second step to yield extract and undissolved coal residue. Most of the ash in the feed coal, that is, 99 weight percent or more, is recovered with the residue. The extract is a solid at room temperature and contains very little (in general, less than 5 weight percent) material boiling below 400 °C. The remainder of the extract is substantially nondistillable without decomposition.

It is highly desirable that the extract be free of ash before it or its upgraded products are introduced into the hydrogenation zones, particularly the latter two hydrogenation zones. The presence of such ash constituents, even in amounts as small as hundredths of one percent, seriously affects the activity and selectivity of tha catalysts in the three hydrogenation zones. Deashing can be effected in the separation zone, in a distinctly separate deashing zone, in the primary hydrocracking zone, or in all three of these zones, as will be more fully discussed later. For the moment, it is sufficient to point out that the ash that is left in the coal extract following separation from the residue is quite different in composition from that of the gross ash in the coal feedstock.

The function of the primary catalytic hydrocracking zone is to convert at least a portion of and preferably the major portion of the nondistillable coal extract to an ash-free, distillable hydrocarbonaceous liquid boiling below about 500 °C. Generally the major portion of the distillable hydrocarbonaceous liquid boils in the range of 200° to 400 °C. This partial upgrading treatment is carried out under relatively mild catalytic hydrogenation conditions which are particularly chosen so as to minimize gas and coke formation. These conditions, however, are not sufficiently severe to yield a distillable product which is free of nitrogen, oxygen, and sulfur (i.e., N—O—S) compounds, or to yield a distillable product, the major portion of which boils below about 200 °C., that is, in the gasoline boiling range.

The function of the catalytic hydrofining zone is to remove substantially all of the N—O—S contaminants from the ash-free, distillable hydrocarbonaceous liquid fed thereto. If desired, all of the distillable hydrocarbonaceous liquid obtained from the primary hydrocracking zone may be introduced into the hydrofining zone; preferably, however, only the fraction boiling below about 400 °C. is introduced therein. It is important to note that the hydrofining treatment is designed primarily to remove N—O—S contaminants from the feed material and is not designed to effect any major lowering of the boiling range of the feed material. For example, the major portion of the N—O—S-free effluent hydrofiner products still boils above 200 °C., and generally in the range of 200° to 400 °C.

The function of the secondary catalytic hydrocracking zone is to lower the boiling range of at least the higher boiling fraction of the effluent hydrofiner products. This final, partial upgrading treatment is carried out under hydrogenation conditions and in the presence of an efficient cracking catalyst especially suited for such purpose. The selection of the optimum cracking catalyst in the secondary catalytic hydrocracking zone is permitted because of the previous removal of ash contaminants and N—O—S contaminants and because of the previous conversion of the original nondistillable extract to substantially noncoking, distillable hydrocarbonaceous liquid. In general, the liquid fuel product from the secondary hydrocracking zone boils below 200 °C., that is in the gasoline boiling range. The use of the terms "primary" and "secondary" is merely for convenience of reference and does not mean that the secondary hydrocracking zone is subordinate to the primary hydrocracking zone. The following, with reference to Figure 2.5, is a description of this process. The process comprises the following:

(1) A solvent extraction zone 10 wherein the coal is extracted;
(2) A separation zone 20 wherein the extract is separately recovered from the residue;
(3) A carbonization zone 26 wherein the residue is carbonized to produce a liquid distillate and a solid hydrocarbonaceous solid product, referred to as "char";
(4) A deashing zone 40 wherein at least a portion of the residual ash remaining in the extract subsequent to separation from the residue is removed;
(5) Three primary catalytic hydrocracking zones 50 wherein the extract is converted to distillable hydrocarbonaceous liquid;
(6) A coking zone 68 wherein a portion of the unconverted extract from the primary hydrocracking zones is coked to produce coke and a liquid distillate;
(7) A hydrofining zone 74 wherein N—O—S compounds are removed from distillable hydrocarbonaceous liquid; and
(8) A secondary catalytic hydrocracking zone 84 wherein high boiling N—O—S-free effluent hydrofiner products are converted to gasoline.

Any coal may be used in the process, nonlimiting examples of which are lignite, bituminous coal, and subbituminous coal. Preferably, the coal fed to this process is one having a volatile matter content of at least 20 weight percent, for example, a high volatile bituminous coal such as Pittsburgh Seam coal. A typical composition of a Pittsburgh Seam coal suitable for use in the process is shown in the following table.

Proximate Analysis	Wt. Percent mf* Coal
Volatile matter	39.3
Fixed carbon	47.7
Ash	13.0
	100.0

Ultimate Analysis	Wt. Percent maf Coal
Hydrogen	5.5
Carbon	80.8
Nitrogen	1.4
Oxygen	7.5
Sulfur	4.8
	100.0

*mf means moisture-free.

The feed coal is preferably ground to a finely divided state, for example, minus 14 mesh Tyler Standard screen, and is freed of substantially all extraneous water before introduction into the process.

Coal is introduced into a solvent extraction zone 10 via a conduit 12. Fresh hydrocarbonaceous solvent and recycle solvent are introduced into the extraction zone 10, via conduits 14 and 16, respectively. The coal and the solvent react therein to yield the desired coal extract. The solvent extraction process may be any of the processes commonly used, e.g., continuous, batch, countercurrent, or staged extraction, at a temperature in the range of 300° to 500°C., a pressure in the range of 1 to 6,500 psig, a residence time in the range of 1 to 120 minutes, a solvent to coal ratio of 0.5:1 to 4:1, and, if desired, in the presence of a catalyst and/or up to 50 standard cubic feet of hydrogen per pound of maf coal.

Suitable solvents for the coal in the extraction step are polycyclic, aromatic hydrocarbons which are liquid under the temperature and pressure of extraction. Preferably, at least a portion of the aromatics are partially or completely hydrogenated. Mixtures of the above hydrocarbons are generally used and are derived from intermediate or final steps of the process, for example, from the primary hydrocracking zone products or from the hydrofining zone products. Those hydrocarbons or mixtures thereof boiling between 260° and 425°C. are preferred. A particularly preferred solvent is a portion of the product obtained from the primary catalytic hydrocracking zone. This solvent normally comprises a 325° to 425°C. fraction blended with some lower boiling material.

The coal and the solvent are maintained in intimate contact within the extraction zone 10 until the solvent has extracted, i.e., converted or dissolved, up to 80 weight percent of the maf feed coal. A previously mentioned, in order to attain the above depths of extraction, hydrogen must be added to the coal during extraction. It is preferred to add the hydrogen by the use of a hydrogen-transfer solvent of the types described above.

It has been found that at least 50 weight percent of the maf coal must be extracted in order to attain economic extract yields. It has been found also if more than 80 weight percent of the maf coal is extracted, the cost associated with the nonselective transfer of hydrogen that takes place at those depths becomes prohibitive. Thus, the amount of hydrogen which is added to the coal during extraction is only that amount which is necessary to accomplish the desired coal extraction, i.e., to dissolve up to 80 weight percent and preferably to dissolve between 50 and 80 weight percent of the maf coal.

Following extraction, the mixture of solvent, extract, and residue is conducted rapidly, so as to avoid cooling of the mixture, through a conduit 18 to a separation zone 20. Preferably, the separation zone 20 is a filtration zone; however, if desired, a centrifuge, sedimentation zone, hydroclone and the like may be used. The primary function of the separation zone 20 is to separate the undissolved coal residue from the coal extract. The secondary function of this separation zone is to separate a portion of the benzene-insoluble rich coal extract from the whole extract produced.

The feed coal contains about 13 weight percent ash. When the extraction products are separated, for example, by filtration, more than 99 weight percent of the total ash will remain with the residue. The remaining one percent, however, is of such a finely divided nature, or in fact soluble in the extract, that it can not be removed by filtration and thus passes with the extract (filtrate).

The liquid extraction (filtrate), comprising "recovered extract" and solvent, are withdrawn from the separation zone 20 via a conduit 22. The solid extraction products, comprising undissolved coal residue, ash, and precipitated extract, if

FIGURE 2.5:   UTILIZATION OF SOLVENT EXTRACTION AS A MEANS TO CONVERT COAL TO LIQUID FUELS

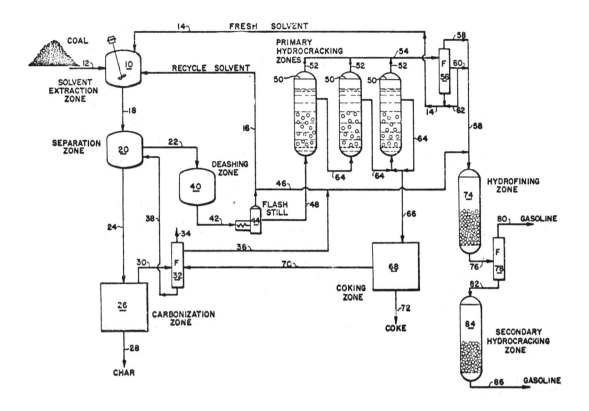

Source: E. Gorin; U.S. Patent 3,143,489; August 4, 1964

any, are withdrawn via a conduit 24.   The extract produced during solvent extraction is sometimes hereinafter referred to as "extract yield".   The recovered extract, which is the extract present in the liquid products (filtrate) recovered from the separation zone, is equal to the extract yield only if no extract is precipitated during the separation of the residue and the extract.

A typical coal extract, produced from a Pittsburgh Seam bituminous coal via solvent extraction with tetrahydronaphthalene solvent at 380°C., 600 psig and a solvent to coal ratio of 2:1, gives the following yields and analysis as shown in the following table.

Analysis of Recovered Coal Extract* Separated from Undissolved Coal Residue via Filtration at 205°C.

Yields	Wt. Percent maf Coal
Conversion	76.5
Extract yield	68.3
Extract precipitate (during filtration)	8.3
Recovered Extract	60.0

Ultimate Analysis (solvent free basis)	Wt. Percent maf Extract
Hydrogen	6.35
Carbon	84.10
Oxygen	6.24
Nitrogen	1.45
Sulfur	1.86
	100.00

*The recovered coal extract contained 0.15 weight percent ash.

The solid extraction products, after drying (not shown) to recover any occluded extraction solvent therefrom (the recovered solvent being recycled to the extraction zone 10), are introduced via the conduit 24 into a conventional type low temperature carbonization zone 26.

The carbonization zone 26 is maintained at a temperature in the range of 425° to 760°C. Preferably, the zone 26 is a fluidized low temperature carbonization zone; however, if desired, other conventional devolatilization zones may be used, e.g., a rotary kiln. Hydrocarbonaceous solids, i.e., char, are withdrawn from the zone 26 via a conduit 28, while a liquid distillate is withdrawn via a conduit 30. Preferably, the liquid distillate of carbonization is separated in a fractionation zone 32, to yield:

(1) A fraction boiling below 230°C. (withdrawn via a conduit 34) which is treated in a conventional tar acid plant (not shown) to recover phenol, cresols, and xylenols;

(2) A fraction boiling between 230° and 325°C. (withdrawn via conduit 36) which is introduced into the hydrofining zone as subsequently explained; and

(3) A bottom fraction boiling above 325°C. (withdrawn via a conduit 38) which is admixed with the extraction products in the separation zone 20.

The liquid distillate usually contains some entrained solids from the low temperature carbonization zone. These solids are concentrated in the bottoms fraction and are removed along with the coal residue in the separation zone 20.

Returning to the recovered extract (the extract obtained from separation zone 20 via the conduit 22), the extract, prior to hydrogenation in the primary catalytic hydrocracking zone, is preferably treated in a deashing zone 40 to remove any remaining ash contained therein. The presence of as little as 0.20 weight percent ash in the extract is sufficient to materially affect the activity and selectivity of hydrogenation catalyst, particularly alumina-based catalyst such as used in the primary catalytic hydrocracking zone. It has been found that the particular ash constituents present in coal extract react with alumina-based catalyst under the elevated temperature and pressure conditions of hydrogenation to cause the surface of the catalyst particle to sinter. A relatively impervious film is formed at the catalyst surface which prevents contact of the extract with the interval catalytically active surface and pore area of the catalyst. The ash that remains in the extract may be removed, at least in part by chemical treatment, for example, with acids.

The following table is a comparison of the ash components present in the gross feed coal and the ash components present in a recovered extract (similar to the extract analyzed in the following table).

Metallic Contaminants (Expressed as Oxides)	Percent by Weight of the Total Contaminants Contained in the Extract	Percent by Weight of the Total Contaminants Contained in the Coal
SiO_2*	20.40	44.30
CaO	15.90	3.80
TiO_2	15.50	1.00
Al_2O_3	10.00	15.20
Fe_2O_3	5.50	21.20
MgO	1.80	1.00
Na_2O	1.00	0.50
K_2O	0.40	1.60
Cr_2O_3	0.23	0.10
V_2O_5	0.04	0.01
Ignition loss**	29.23	11.29
	100.00	100.00

*Silicon is included although it is actually a nonmetallic element.
**The ignition loss is due to subsequent conversion of metal compounds that are stable at the ashing temperature of 1100°F. to the corresponding oxides.

The deashed extract is withdrawn from the deashing zone 40 via a conduit 42 and preferably introduced into a flash still 44 wherein at least a portion of the extraction solvent is separately recovered. The extraction solvent is recycled to the extraction zone 10 via the conduit 16. Because hydrogen-transfer efficiency of recycle solvent is not as high as that of fresh solvent, it is undesirable to recycle to the extraction zone 10 all of the solvent recovered via the flash still 44. Thus, a portion of the recycle solvent stream is conducted via conduit 46 into the hydrofining zone, as hereinafter discussed. The topped extract is withdrawn from the flash still 44 via a conduit 48. Extract, which has preferably been deashed in the zone 40, is introduced via the conduit 48 into the first of a series of staged, dense bed, liquid phase fluidized catalytic hydrocracking zones 50. For convenience purposes, three primary hydrocracking zones are shown; however, if desired, any number may be used. The extract, which as previously mentioned is substantially nondistillable without decomposition, is reacted with hydrogen in the presence of the fluidized catalyst in the primary hydrocracking zones 50 under the following conditions:

Reactor temperature	410 to 475°C.
Reactor pressure (total pressure)	2,500 to 6,000 psig
Hydrogen feed rate	2,000 to 42,000 scf/bbl. feed
Liquid hourly space velocity (individual stage)	0.5 to 3.0 volume/volume/hour

Vaporous products, which are ash-free, are withdrawn from the zones 50 via the conduits 52 and conveyed via a common conduit 54 to a condenser (not shown) wherein noncondensable gases are separately recovered. The condensed vaporous product, i.e., the ash-free, distillable hydrocarbonaceous liquid product, is then introduced into a fractionation zone 56, wherein it is fractionated to yield:

(1) A fraction boiling below 260°C. (withdrawn via a conduit 58) which is subsequently
       catalytically hydrofined;
(2) A fraction boiling between 260° and 325°C. (withdrawn via a conduit 60), the major
       portion of which is subsequently catalytically hydrofined; and
(3) A fraction boiling above 325°C. (withdrawn via the conduit 14) which is introduced
       into the extraction zone 10 as fresh solvent.

Preferably, a portion of the 260° to 325°C. fraction is conveyed via a conduit 62 and introduced into the extraction zone 10 along with the +325°C. fraction, which usually boils below about 500°C. In some instances it may be desirable to further fractionate the +325°C. fraction such that only the 325° to 425°C. fraction is used as extraction solvent while the +425°C. bottoms are recycled to the primary hydrocracking zones 50 to to a coking zone as hereinafter discussed. Obviously, many other variations in the above fractionation of the distillable hydrocarbonaceous liquid may be practiced by those skilled in the art. For example, all of the distillable liquid product may be hydrofined, in which case fresh extraction solvent would be recovered from the hydrofiner products.

To fully appreciate this process, it is important to understand that the nondistillable extract fed to the primary hydrocracking zones is only subjected to sufficient hydrocracking therein to yield a distillable liquid product suitable for subsequent hydrofining. The distillable hydrocarbonaceous liquid product is not completely free of N—O—S compounds, nor does a significant portion thereof boil in the gasoline boiling range, i.e., boil below about 200°C. Generally, the major portion of the distillable hydrocarbonaceous liquid boils in the range of 200° to 400°C.

Returning to the primary hydrocracking zones, the nonvaporized extract is withdrawn from each of the zones 50 (via a conduit 64) and then introduced into the following zones in succession. If desired, however, rather than introduce all of the unconverted extract into the next primary hydrocracking zone, a portion may be recycled to aid in maintaining the hydrocracking catalyst in a fluidized bed. The nonvaporized extract from the last primary hydrocracking zone is preferably recycled to the same zone. In order to prevent any ash buildup in the last primary hydrocracking zone, a portion of the recycle liquid may be conducted into the separation zone 20 wherein the ash will be removed with the residue.

Preferably, substantially all of the recovered extract is converted to the distillable hydrocarbonaceous liquid; however, if desired, a portion of the recycled unconverted extract may be coked, e.g., in a delayed coker to yield a liquid distillate and coke. As shown in the drawing, a portion of the recycled unconverted extract is conveyed via a conduit 66 into any conventional type coking zone 68. Liquid distillate is recovered from the coking zone 68 via a conduit 70 and conveniently fractionated with the liquid distillate of carbonization in the fractionation zone 32. Coke is withdrawn from the coking zone 68 via a conduit 72.

In some instances it may be desirable to maintain the primary hydrocracking zones at different pressures and temperatures, for example, increasing the temperature and possibly the pressure in each succeeding stage. The catalyst may also be the same or different in each of the zones.

Instead of maintaining the catalyst in the form of a fluidized bed in the zones 50, the catalyst may be maintained in the form of a fixed or gravitating bed. The catalyst may also be dispersed within the extract in the form of a slurry and then introduced into a slurry phase primary hydrocracking zone such that the catalyst is introduced into, maintained therein, and withdrawn therefrom, in the form of slurry or a suspensoid.

The catalyst used in the primary hydrocracking zone is a catalytic composite of alumina, an oxide of molybdenum, and at least one oxide from the group of cobalt and nickel. The catalytic base, which is preferably substantially all alumina, may, if desired, contain a small amount of additive components such as silica, which tends to make the catalyst more resistant to high temperatures. Prior to using the catalyst in the primary hydrocracking zone, the catalyst is usually sulfided.

The alumina base is preferably a high surface area material, i.e., greater than 150 square meters per gram, which has a high porosity, i.e., a pore volume greater than 0.3 cubic centimeter per gram, and is prepared in catalytically active form from alumina gel. The alumina base also should preferably be one of the low temperature crystallographic forms commonly characterized as gamma, kappa, or theta. The gamma form is preferred from the point of view of thermal stability against conversion to the relatively inactive high temperature form, namely, alpha. A particularly preferred catalyst is one comprising:

	Wt. Percent of Catalyst	
	Broad	Preferred
Molybdenum oxide	3.50 to 20.00	5.55
Nickel oxide	Total nickel oxide	4.64
	plus cobalt oxide,	
Cobalt oxide	2.00 to 8.00	0.11
Alumina	Remainder	59.70

The ash-free, distillable hydrocarbonaceous liquid product (conduit 58) in admixture with the ash-free distillable fraction from the flash still (conduit 46) and the ash-free distillable liquids of carbonization (from carbonization zone 26 and coking zone 68 via conduit 36) is introduced into a hydrofining zone 74. The feed materials are reacted in the zone 74 with hydrogen in the presence of a catalyst under the following conditions:

	Broad	Preferred
Temperature	340° to 470°C.	380° to 430°C.
Pressure (total pressure)	500 to 4,500 psig	1,000 to 3,000 psig
Hydrogen ratio	1,000 to 10,000 scf/bbl. feed	1,500 to 3,000 scf/bbl. feed
Liquid hourly space velocity	0.2 to 2.0 v./v./hr.	0.5 to 1.5 v./v./hr.

The effluent hydrofiner products, recovered from the zone 74 via a conduit 76, are substantially free of nitrogen, oxygen, and sulfur compounds. The effluent products are fractionated in a fractionation zone 78 into a gasoline fraction boiling below about 193°C. (recovered via a conduit 80) and a secondary hydrocracker zone feedstock boiling above about 193°C. (recovered via a conduit 82). If desired, to increase the octane of the gasoline fraction, the portion of the fraction boiling between about 90° to 193°C. may be catalytically reformed in any of the reforming zones known to those skilled in the art (not shown on flowsheet).

The hydrofining catalyst may be disposed in a fixed stationary bed, or various moving bed or fluidized bed techniques may be used. Generally the fixed bed technique, which is illustrated on the drawing, is most satisfactory. Suitable catalysts may comprise any of the oxides or sulfides of the transitional metals, and especially an oxide or sulfide of a group 8 metal (preferably iron, cobalt, or nickel) mixed with an oxide or sulfide of a Group VIB metal (preferably molybdenum or tungsten). Such catalysts may be used in undiluted form, but normally are supported on an absorbent carrier such as alumina, silica, zirconia, titania, and naturally occurring porous supports, i.e., activated high alumina ores such as bauxite or clays such as bentonite, etc. Preferably, the carrier should display relatively little cracking activity, and hence highly acidic carriers are generally to be avoided. The preferred carrier is activated alumina such as previously described with reference to the primary hydrocracking zone 50.

At least the higher boiling portion of the effluent hydrofiner products are introduced via the conduit 82 into a secondary catalytic hydrocracking zone 84. The hydrofiner products are reacted therein in the presence of a catalyst with hydrogen under the following conditions to produce additional gasoline boiling below about 193°C. (recovered via a conduit 86).

	Broad	Preferred
Reactor temperature	340° to 500°C.	380° to 440°C.
Reactor pressure (total pressure)	500 to 4,500 psig	1,200 to 3,000 psig
Hydrogen ratio	2,000 to 10,000 scf/bbl. feed	3,000 to 6,000 scf/bbl. feed
Liquid hourly space velocity	0.3 to 3.0 v./v./hr.	0.5 to 1.5 v./v./hr.

As in the case of the gasoline recovered from the hydrofining zone 74, to 90° to 193°C. gasoline fraction may be catalytically reformed to increase the octane rating thereof.

Since the nitrogen, sulfur, and oxygen compounds present in the distillable hydrocarbonaceous liquid recovered from primary hydrocracking zone 50 are removed in the hydrofining zone 74, the hydrocracker feedstock is preferably reacted with hydrogen in the secondary hydrocracking zone 84 in the presence of an active cracking catalyst which also exhibits some hydrogenation activity. Suitable catalysts include a mixture of a transition group metal such as cobalt and an oxide of a Group VIB metal such as molybdenum on an acid support such as silica-alumina. Platinum acidic oxide catalysts, for example, those which include between about 0.05 to 2.0 weight percent of the catalyst of at least one metal of the platinum and palladium series deposited upon a synthetic support, are frequently used. Transition group metals in the form of oxides or sulfides, particularly nickel and/or cobalt, may be used without other metals. The synthetic support, i.e., the carrier, can also contain halogens and other materials which are known in the art as promoters for cracking catalysts. The synthetic support can also contain small amounts of alkali metals added for the purpose of controlling the cracking activity of the carrier.

Nonlimiting examples of the synthetically-produced carriers include silica-alumina, silica-zirconia, silica-alumina-zirconia, silica-alumina-thoria, alumina-boria, silica-magnesia, silica-alumina-magnesia, silica-alumina-fluorine and the like. A preferred support is a synthetic composite of silica and alumina.

The following is an illustration of how this process operates in practice. Pittsburgh Seam bituminous coal is reacted with a solvent, which is a 325° to 425°C. fraction (containing some 260° to 325°C. material) recovered from extract primary hydrocracking products, under the following conditions:

Temperature, °C.	380
Pressure, psig	70
Solvent/coal (wt. ratio)	1.0
Residence time, minutes	30

The extraction products, comprising a mixture of solvent, extract, and undissolved coal residue, are filtered at 250°C. whereby a mixture of extract and solvent (filtrate) are separately recovered from the residue.

	Wt. Percent maf Coal
Coal conversion	70.1
Extract yield	66.3
Gas produced during extraction*	3.8
Extract recovered via filtration	61.3

*Gas includes C_1 to C_3 hydrocarbons, H_2S, CO_2, CO and NH_3.

An analysis of the extraction products is shown in the following table.

Analysis of Extraction Products

	Feed Coal, maf Wt. Percent	Recovered Extract maf Wt. Percent	Residue* maf Wt. Percent
H	4.80	6.30	2.90
C	69.80	84.27	59.10
N	1.20	1.15	1.30
O	7.60	6.38	2.80
S	4.30	1.90	5.30
Ash	12.30	0.20	28.60

*Includes occluded extract.

The residue is subsequently carbonized in a fluidized low temperature carbonization zone under these conditions; temperature 510°C. and residence time 20 minutes. The following yields are produced.

	Yields, maf Wt. Percent
Gas + C_4	2.8
Liquor	2.8
Light oil	0.6
Tar	11.1
Char	82.7
	100.0

The recovered extract and the +325°C. tar from carbonization are reacted with hydrogen under these conditions; total pressure was 4,200 psig, with H_2 partial pressure of 3,500 psig; temperature, 427°C.; 4.0 hours residence time on fresh sample;

$CoO-MoO_3$ on Al_2O_3 base was the catalyst. The following yields are produced.

Overall Yields	Wt. Percent Fresh Feed
C_1 to C_3 gas	7.5
C_4	1.8
$C_5/325°C.$	87.25
H_2S, NH_3, and H_2O	10.15
Coke and catalyst	0.25
Ash	0.20
	107.15

A more detailed analysis of the $C_5/325°C.$ fraction is as shown in the following table.

Distillate Analysis	$C_5/260°C.$	$200°/325°C.$	$C_5/325°C.$
Wt. percent of total distillate	8.0	92.0	100.0
Ultimate analysis, wt. percent:			
Hydrogen	14.2	11.5	11.9
Carbon	85.6	88.1	87.7
Nitrogen		0.2	0.2
Sulfur	0.1	0.1	0.1
Oxygen	0.1	0.1	0.1
	100.0	100.0	100.0

The primary hydrocracking product, although not suitable for direct use as gasoline, may be used as diesel fuel, fuel oil, and coker feed to make electrode carbon.

Distillate hydrocarbonaceous liquid boiling below about 325°C., which is obtained from the primary hydrocracking zone, is hydrofined in admixture with a 260° to 325°C. fraction (recovered from carbonization of the residue) under the following yields. Pressure was 1,500 psig; temperature 399°C.; space velocity (WHSV) 0.80 v./v./hr.; $CoO-MoO_3$ on Al_2O_3 base was the catalyst and hydrogen consumption, 988 scf/bbl.

Yields	Weight Percent
C_1	1.2
C_2	0.7
C_3	1.0
C_4	0.3
C_5	0.1
$C_6/93°C.$	2.0
$93°/193°C.$	32.5
$+193°C.$	62.2
	100.0

The following table is a further breakdown of the hydrofiner feed and effluent product.

	Feed	$C_6/93°C.$	$93°/193°C.$	$+193°C.$
API gravity	25	65	45	25
Specific gravity	0.90	0.72	0.80	0.90
Molecular weight	185	95	110	200
Ultimate analysis, wt. percent:				
H	11.2	14.5	13.0	12.0
C	88.2	85.5	87.0	88.0
N	0.2	–	(< 5 ppm)	(< 10 ppm)
O	0.2	–	–	–
S	0.2	–	(< 30 ppm)	(<50 ppm)
	100.0	100.0	100.0	100.0

The portion of the hydrofiner products not suitable for direct use as gasoline may be used as gas oil, jet fuel and the like.

The +193°C. fraction from hydrofining is hydrocracked in a fixed bed hydrocracking zone under the following conditions and giving the following yields. Pressure was 1,800 psig; temperature 399°C.; space velocity (WHSV) 0.96 v./v./hr.; Ni-silica alumina was the catalyst and hydrogen consumption, 2,100 scf/bbl.

Yields	Weight Percent
C_1	0.2
C_2	0.3
C_3	3.9
C_4	9.6
C_5	10.3
C_6/93°C.	44.9
93°/193°C.	34.3
	103.5

A more detailed secondary hydrocracker product breakdown is shown in the following table.

	C_6/93°C.	93°/193°C.
API gravity	65	45
Specific gravity	0.72	0.80
Molecular weight	95	110
Ultimate analysis, wt. percent:		
Hydrogen	15.2	13.0
Carbon	84.8	87.0
	100.0	100.0

The 93° to 193°C. fraction from the secondary hydrocracking zone and the hydrofining zone are catalytically reformed under the following conditions and giving the following yields. Pressure was 350 psig; temperature 482°C.; space velocity (WHSV) 1.8 v./v./hr. and platinum on HF treated alumina gel was the catalyst.

Yields	Weight Percent
H_2	3.03
C_1	0.10
C_2	0.17
C_3	0.20
C_4	0.20
C_5	0.20
C_6/210°C. reformate	96.10
	100.00

Reformer Product Properties

	C_6/210°C. Reformate
API gravity	33.00
Specific gravity	0.85
Molecular weight	115
Ultimate analysis, wt. percent:	
Hydrogen	10.2
Carbon	89.8
	100.0

The following fractions from hydrofining, secondary hydrocracking, and reforming are blended as shown in the following table to give a premium gasoline having a leaded blended octane by the research method (F-1+3 cc TEL) of at least 100.

	Blending RVP	F-1+3 cc TEL
C_3	189.0	120.0
C_4	59.0	103.0
C_5	16.0	88.7
C_6/93°C. (hydrofiner product)	6.0	97.0
C_6/93°C. (hydrocracker product)	6.0	97.0
C_6/210°C. (reforming product)	2.9	104.1

Solvent Extraction of Coal

E.F. Nelson; U.S. Patent 3,505,202; April 7, 1970; assigned to Universal Oil Products Company describes a process for the liquefaction of coal via solvent extraction using a hydrogen-donor selective solvent. The method contacts pulverized coal with a solvent, such as Tetralin, to produce a liquefied coal extract. Hydrocarbons useful as fuel and/or chemicals may be obtained from the liquid coal extract.

This process includes a method for the liquefaction of coal which comprises the steps of: (a) admixing lump bituminous coal with a solvent comprising an at least partially hydrogenated polycyclic hydrocarbon; (b) subjecting said admixture to coal pulverization conditions including a relatively high temperature sufficient to at least partially dissolve coal into the solvent; (c) passing the pulverized coal-solvent product into a digestion zone maintained under conditions sufficient to substantially dissolve the pulverized coal; and (d) recovering liquid coal extract from the digestion zone in high concentration.

The extraction of coal by means of solvent has been proposed by definition as partial conversion of the coal since not only is the coal reacted with the hydrogen which is transferred from the solvent but there is also a solution phenomenon which actually dissolves the coal, which has accepted the hydrogen into the solvent. Therefore, as used herein, the term "liquid coal extract" and "liquefied coal fraction" is intended to include the liquid product which is obtained from the solvent extraction of the coal with the selective solvent, and will be generally described on the basis of being "solvent-free", even though a portion of extract comprises hydrocarbons suitable for use as the solvent. The practice of the process is performed under conditions which increase the kinetics of the reaction while maintaining the components therein in primarily liquid phase; although, in some cases, it may be desirable to practice this process in the presence of a vaporized solvent by using a vaporous pulverization technique.

Suitable solvents for use in the practice of this process in the extraction step are those which are of the hydrogen donor type and are at least partially hydrogenated and include naphthenic hydrocarbons. Preferably, the solvent is one which is in liquid phase at the recommended temperature and pressure for the extraction and pulverization step. Mixtures of the hydrocarbons are generally employed and, preferably, are derived from intermediate or final products obtained from subsequent processing following the practice of this process. Typically, these solvent hydrocarbons or mixture of hydrocarbons boil between about 260° and 425°C. Examples of suitable solvents are tetrahydronaphthalene (Tetralin), decahydronaphthalene (Decalin), biphenyl, methylnaphthalene, dimethylnaphthalene, etc. Other types of solvents which may be added to the preferred solvents of this process for special reasons include phenolic compounds such as phenols, cresols, and xylenols.

It is also to be recognized that in some cases it may be desirable during a subsequent separation step prior to the removal of the solvent from the liquid coal extract to add an antisolvent, such as a saturated paraffinic hydrocarbon like hexane, to aid in the precipitation of tarry and solid residues from the coal extract of this process.

The conditions during the pulverization step may be varied widely. The temperature, of course, may be varied over a relatively broad range from essentially atmospheric temperature to a relatively high temperature. It is distinctly preferred in the practice of this process that the temperature of the coal and the solvent be maintained at a relatively high temperature, say from 300° to 500°C. The pressure, in similar manner, may be varied over an extremely wide range from atmospheric pressure to, say, 10,000 psig with a preferred pressure being about 100 psig or typically about 70 psig.

The operation of the pulverizing equipment is preferably performed so that the oversized material, that is, greater in size than the -8 Tyler screen size, be separated and returned to the apparatus for further pulverizing. The utilization of the closed circuit technique is well-known in the art, and is preferred in the practice of this process. Unless otherwise stated, closed circuit operation of the pulverization equipment is deemed inherent in this process.

The amount of solvent which is used during the pulverization step generally will range from 0.2 to 10 pounds of solvent per pound of coal. Satisfactory results may be obtained in the practice of this process in utilizing approximately equal amounts of solvent to coal on a weight basis. The conditions during the pulverization step should be chosen such that the coarse coal is reduced in size to at least a -8 Tyler screen size and the solvent has a chance to react and dissolve the coal to an extent such that the coal particles are at least partially dissolved in the solvent.

It is an essential feature of this process that the pulverization step be not only a mechanism for reducing the size of the coal, but also be used to at least partially dissolve the coal in the solvent. In other words, as will be more fully evident from the discussions presented hereinafter, the process is in some respects a two-stage solvent extraction step. In the practice of this process the conditions chosen in the pulverization step will be such that from 10 to 40% by weight of the maf coal is dissolved in the solvent with at least an additional 50% by weight being dissolved during the subsequent digestion zone, more fully discussed hereinafter.

Following the size reduction step wherein at least part of the coal has been dissolved in the solvent and the oversized solid materials have been separated, the effluent product comprising solvent, having dissolved therein liquid coal extract, and undissolved solid coal is passed into a digestion zone which is a reaction zone for the substantial conversion of the coal into liquid coal extract. The operating conditions for the digestion zone include a temperature from 300° to 500°C., a pressure from atmospheric to 10,000 psig, a solvent to coal weight ratio from 0.2 to 10, and a residence time from 30 seconds to 5 hours, sufficient to dissolve coal such that a total in excess of 50% by weight of maf coal has been liquefied. It is to be noted that the temperature and pressure conditions during the digestion zone may be the same, may be higher, may be lower, or may be any different conditions over those conditions maintained in the pulverization zone. It has been found satisfactory in the practice of this process that the temperature and pressure in the digestion zone be maintained essentially at the same level as the temperature and pressure maintained in the pulverization zone.

Since the purpose of the digestion zone is to substantially complete the conversion of the coal into a liquid coal extract, it may be desirable to add additional solvent to the zone, add a hydrogen-containing gas to the zone, and/or utilize a catalyst in the digestion zone. The catalyst used may be conventional, may be homogenous or heterogenous and may be introduced in the pulverization zone and/or digestion zone in admixture with the liquid solvent or with the solid coal. Those skilled in the art from a knowledge of the characteristics of the coal, the solvent, and the properties desired for the end-product will know whether or not it may be desirable to use any or all of these additional features in the digestion zone. Conventional hydrogenation catalyst may be desirable, such as palladium on an alumina support, or a cobalt-molybdate catalyst or any other hydrogenation catalyst known to those skilled in the art and applicable to the solvent-coal system environment maintained in the digestion zone including the use of a slurry-catalyst system.

After separation of the solvent and undissolved coal residue and catalyst, if any from the total effluent of the digestion zone, the liquid coal extract is further processed by means known to those skilled in the art such as conventional hydrogenation treatment to convert the liquid coal extract into more valuable products, such as fuel, e.g., gasoline boiling range products, and/or chemicals, such as aromatic hydrocarbons, the utility of which is well-known.

The process is described with reference to Figure 2.6 which is a schematic representation of the apparatus. Coarse coal having an average particle diameter in excess of 0.08" is introduced into the system via line 10. A selective solvent is introduced into admixture with the coarse coal from line 11. The oversized solid material from the pulverizing zone is preferably returned to the pulverizing zone via line 12. The entire admixture of coarse coal and solvent is passed via line 13 into mill 14 which may be the ball mill type.

FIGURE 2.6:   SOLVENT EXTRACTION OF COAL

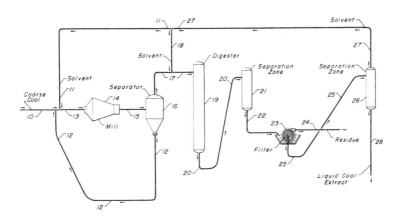

Source: E.F. Nelson; U.S. Patent 3,505,202; April 7, 1970

Suitable pulverization conditions including a temperature from 300° to 500°C. is maintained in mill 14 such that the coarse coal is reduced to an average particle diameter between 0.08" and 0.04" and at least a portion of the coal, say from 10 to 40% by weight is dissolved into the solvent. The effluent from mill 14 containing solvent having dissolved therein the liquid coal extract, undissolved coal of proper small particle size, and undissolved coal of oversize is passed via line 15 into separator 16 which may be of the cyclone type. Conditions are maintained in separator 16 whereby the oversize coal particles, preferably in admixture with at least a portion of the liquid material, is removed via line 12 and returned to mill 14 in a manner previously discussed.

The solvent having dissolved therein the liquid coal extract plus undissolved pulverized coal is passed via line 17 into digestion zone 19 which may be of a jacketed, stirred-type vessel. Added solvent, if any, may be introduced to the system via line 18 in an amount sufficient to maintain the solvent to coal ratios at the desired levels both in digester 19 and mill 14. Control of the solvent dosage to mill 14 will be more fully discussed hereinafter.

The entire effluent from digestion zone 19 is passed via line 20 into first separation zone 21 where conditions are maintained sufficient to begin settling and agglomerating the coal residues and solid materials. As previously mentioned, if desired, by means not shown, an antisolvent such as hexane may be added to zone 21 in an effort to further aid in removing tars and solid materials from the desired solvent and liquid coal extract. An effluent stream from zone 21 is removed via line 22 and passed into filtration zone 23 which is operated in such a manner that the solid coal residue may be withdrawn via line 24 and the solvent-liquid coal extract stream may be withdrawn via line 25. The mother liquor from the filter 23 is passed via line 25 into second separator 26 which may be of a conventional distillation column type. Suitable conditions are maintained therein such that a distillate fraction comprising lean solvent may be withdrawn via line 27 and preferably is returned to admixture with the incoming coarse coal feed from line 10, as previously mentioned.

The remaining liquid coal extract is removed from separator 26 via line 28 for further processing including hydrogenation techniques for upgrading the liquid coal extract to the desired valuable product of motor fuel and/or chemicals. Means (not shown) for removing the antisolvent, if any, may also be incorporated in separation zone 26.

Example 1: A Pittsburg Seam Coal was first pulverized to an average particle diameter of −14 Tyler mesh size. It was treated in a solvent extraction zone with Tetralin solvent under the following conditions: temperature, 380°C.; pressure, 70 psig; solvent/coal, 1.0 and residence time, 1.0 hour. The yield was 57.8% by weight of liquid coal extract (solvent-free) based on the original maf coal. Thus, based on a use of 100 pounds of solvent per 100 pounds of pulverized coal, the prior art obtained 58 pounds of liquid coal extract.

Example 2: A Pittsburg Seam Coal, coarse size, was mixed with an equal weight of Tetralin and subjected to crushing and grinding in a ball mill. After separation and recycle to the mill of the oversize particles, the entire product from the ball mill including solid coal particles of −14 Tyler mesh average particle diameter, liquid extract and solvent, was passed into a digester. The following conditions were maintained for each designated step:

	Ball Mill	Digester
Temperature, °C.	380	380
Pressure, psig	70	70
Solvent/coal ratio	1.0	1.0
Residence time, hours	−	1.0
Liquid coal extract,* percent	17	50**

*Solvent-free basis. **Additional.

This process accomplishes a significant increase in liquid coal extract under substantially the same conditions including the same amount of solvent as used in Example 1. Furthermore, the liquid coal extract obtained from this process contained no more benzene-insoluble material proportionately than that obtained from Example 1.

Hydrogen-Donor Solvents in the Liquefaction of Coal

A similar process described by E.F. Nelson; U.S. Patent 3,505,203; April 7, 1970; assigned to Universal Oil Products Company provides a method for liquefying coal which comprises (a) passing bituminous coal and a hydrogen-rich solvent into an extraction zone under conditions sufficient to convert the coal substantially to liquid coal extract dissolved in solvent having reduced hydrogen content, (b) separating the solvent containing liquid coal extract into a residual fraction, comprising substantially solvent-free liquid coal extract and a fraction comprising solvent having reduced hydrogen content, (c) passing at least a portion of the solvent fraction into a hydrogenation zone under conditions sufficient to increase the hydrogen content of the solvent, thereby producing a hydrogen-rich solvent, and (d) returning hydrogen-rich solvent to the extraction zone as specified.

In the selection of the suitable solvent it must be recognized that the solvent must have the ability to transfer hydrogen to the pulverized coal during the extract step. In other words, it is a requirement that the rich solvent leaving the extraction zone having liquid coal extract dissolved therein has a reduced hydrogen content compared to the hydrogen content of the lean solvent which is added to the extraction zone in admixture with the feed. It has also been explained that another critical feature is the selective hydrogenation of the separated recycle solvent in order to increase its hydrogen content so that hydrogen may be more easily transferred from the solvent to the coal during the extraction step, as previously mentioned.

One of the convenient ways of optimizing the specific hydrotreating operation is to use the J-factor analysis for determining the degree to which hydrogen has been added to the hydrogenation reaction zone feed. This analytical technique permits the characterization of various types of aromatics in a hydrocarbon mixture by means of the J-factor analysis. The technique utilizes mass spectrometer analysis employing a low ionizing voltage. The ionizing voltage is chosen such that only those hydrocarbons to be characterized are ionized while other hydrocarbon types are not ionized under the potential chosen. For example, since compounds more saturated than aromatic hydrocarbons, such as the paraffin hydrocarbons, have an ionization level above 10 volts, the ionization chamber is thus maintained at a potential of about 7 volts so that only the aromatic hydrocarbons are ionized and the saturated compounds will not be observed on the mass spectrum. The mass spectrum reveals molecular ion peaks which correspond to the molecular weight of the aromatic compound. Thus, the technique permits characterization of the aromatic hydrocarbons by means of the general formula C_nH_{2n-J} where J is the herein referred to "J-factor". The following table shows the relationship between the J-factor and the type of aromatic.

J-Factor Number	Type of Aromatic Hydrocarbon
6	Alkyl benzenes and benzene
8	Indanes, Tetralins
10	Indenes
12	Alkyl naphthalenes and naphthalene
14	Acenaphthenes, tetrahydroanthracene
16	Acenaphthalenes, dihydroanthracenes
18	Anthracenes, phenanthrenes

Using this J-factor analysis in characterizing the hydrotreating step allows for the optimum treatment of the solvent to produce a high quality hydrogen enriched solvent for use in converting coal into liquid coal extract. However, as previously mentioned, the important control technique is that a hydrogen content of the initial solvent charged to the extraction zone in admixture with the coal is greater than the solvent leaving the extraction zone having dissolved therein the liquid coal extract. In similar manner, the other control technique is that the hydrogen content of the solvent which has been recovered from the effluent of the extraction zone is less than the hydrogen content of the solvent leaving the hydrogenation zone and being recycled to the extraction zone. The J-factor analysis is simply a convenient means for optimizing the hydrotreating step in the practice of this process.

Referring to Figure 2.7, coarse coal having an average particle diameter generally in excess of 0.08 inch is introduced into the system via line 10. A suitable selective solvent enriched in hydrogen content is introduced into admixture with the coarse coal from line 11, the source of which is more fully discussed hereinafter. As previously mentioned, the oversized solid material from the pulverization zone is also preferably returned to the pulverization zone via line 12. The entire admixture of coarse coal and solvent is passed via line 13 into mill 14 which conventionally may be of the ball mill type.

FIGURE 2.7:   HYDROGEN-DONOR SOLVENTS IN THE LIQUEFACTION OF COAL

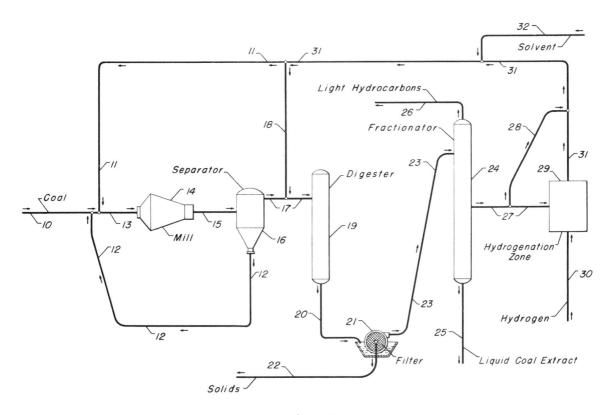

Source: E.F. Nelson; U.S. Patent 3,505,203; April 7, 1970

Suitable pulverization conditions including a temperature of about 380°C., a pressure of about 70 psig, and a solvent to coal weight ratio of about 1 is maintained in mill 14 such that the coarse coal is reduced to an average particle diameter between 0.08 and 0.04 inch and at least a portion of the coal, say, about 17% by weight is dissolved into the solvent.

The effluent from mill 14 containing solvent having dissolved therein the liquid coal extract, undissolved coal of proper small particle size, and undissolved coal of oversize is passed via line 15 into separator 16 which may be of the cyclone type. Conditions are maintained in separator 16 whereby the oversized coal particles, preferably, in admixture with at least a portion of the liquid material is removed via line 12 and returned to mill 14 in a manner previously discussed.

The solvent having dissolved therein the liquid coal extract plus undissolved pulverized coal is passed via line 17 into digestion zone 19 which may be of a jacketed stirred type vessel. Added solvent, if any, may be introduced into the system via line 18 in an amount sufficient to maintain the solvent to coal ratio at the desired level and/or to maintain the hydrogen content of the solvent present in digester 19 at a sufficiently high level. Further, catalyst (from means not shown) may advantageously be used in the digestion step.

The entire effluent from digestion zone 19 is passed via line 20 into filtration zone 21 wherein solid residue is separated from the rich solvent and removed from the system via line 22. The mother liquor comprising solvent having dissolved therein liquid coal extract is removed from filtration zone 21 via line 23. If desired, by means not shown, an antisolvent such as a light hydrocarbon of the hexane type may be added to filtration zone 21 in an effort to further aid in removing tars and solid materials from the desired solvent and liquid coal extract. If an antisolvent is used, then, of course, the material in line 23 also will contain such light hydrocarbon.

The liquid effluent from filtration zone 21 is passed via line 23 into fractionation zone 24 which may be of a conventional distillation column type. Suitable conditions are maintained therein such that a distillate fraction comprising light hydrocarbons may be withdrawn via line 26 and the liquid coal extract may be removed via line 25 for further processing in accordance with the practices known to those skilled in the art, including hydrogenation techniques for upgrading the liquid coal extract to the desired valuable product of motor fuel and/or chemicals. Means (not necessarily shown) for removing the antisolvent, if any, may be also incorporated broadly into fractionation zone 24.

In practice, a material suitable in boiling range as solvent for the coal is withdrawn from fractionation zone 24 via line 27 and passed into hydrogenation zone 29. Hydrogen is introduced into hydrotreater 29 through conduit 30 to supply the required hydrogen. Generally, the hydrotreating step may be carried out by any means known to those skilled in the art of hydrotreating taking into account the previously mentioned J-factor analysis technique for controlling the degree of hydrogenation which is accomplished in hydrotreater 29.

Preferably, hydrotreating catalyst is loaded into a fixed bed, not shown, within the reaction zone. The material in line 27 is mixed with fresh hydrogen from line 30, by means not shown, and recycle gas from a source not shown, heated and passed once-through the fixed bed of catalyst. A hydrotreated effluent is withdrawn from the reaction zone and cooled and introduced into a separator, all by means not shown. The effluent is separated into a normally liquid hydrotreated product and a normally gaseous stream. The normally gaseous stream contains hydrogen and is recycled to the reaction zone by means of a recycle compressor, again by means not shown. The normally liquid product stream may be flashed or stripped to remove dissolved gases, such as hydrogen and hydrogen sulfide or, if desired, this step may be omitted. The sequence of steps and equipment required for hydrogenaeration is well known and have not been shown in detail. All steps and equipment necessary for hydrogenation are embodied in the box shown as hydrogenation zone 29 in the drawing.

The hydrogenation catalyst is preferably sulfur resistant and comprises a silica-alumina support having at least one metal or metal compound of Group VI of the Periodic Table and one metal or metal compound of Group VIII of the Periodic Table. Especially preferable in the practice of this process are those hydrogenation catalysts having tungsten and/or molybdenum along with nickel and/or cobalt on silica-alumina supports. Other supports such as alumina, silica-zirconia, silica-magnesia, faujasite, mordenite, inorganic oxide matrix containing at least one crystalline aluminosilicate, etc. are also suitable. Other metals which are also satisfactory include the noble metals such as platinum or palladium. These latter noble metal catalysts are generally satisfactory without the presence of a Group VIII metal.

The hydrotreating conditions employed in hydrogenation zone 29 are selected to convert the solvent separated from the effluent of the extraction zone to a product having increased hydrogen content such as an aromatic hydrocarbon of the J-8 type, previously defined. Then, correspondingly, the rich solvent separated from the extraction zone has J-12 as the major single type of aromatic hydrocarbon. Therefore, the hydrogenation process variables are controlled to maximize the J-12 to J-8 conversion reaction without substantial conversion of the polycyclic aromatic compounds to monocyclic aromatic compounds of the J-6 type. Suitable pressure ranges are from about 400 to 2,000 psig, preferably, from 600 to 900 psig. Suitable liquid hourly space velocity by weight (LHSV) is from about 0.5 to 20, preferably, from 3 to 10. The hydrogen-to-oil mol ratio may be from 2 to 20, preferably, from 5 to 15. When these conditions are selected, the temperature is then adjusted to maximize the J-12 to J-8 conversion. Normally this temperature will be in the range from 232° to 454°C.

The most straightforward way of obtaining the proper operating conditions is to select the independent variables, conduct a J-factor analysis of the streams flowing in lines 27 and 31, and adjust the temperature to obtain the maximum conversion of J-12 to J-8. If the hydrotreating conditions are too severe, the J-12 type compounds may be converted to the undesirable J-6 compounds.

The properly hydrogen enriched solvent stream is removed from hydrogenation zone 29 via line 31 and returned to the extraction zone via line 11 and/or line 18. Additional suitable solvent, if necessary, may be added to the system from a source not shown via line 32. In addition, for control purposes, a bypass of solvent material around hydrogenation zone 29 may be accomplished by means of line 28. Normally, a small amount of material will always be flowing in line 28 so as to provide flexibility of control on the hydrogen content of the material flowing in line 31.

Liquefaction of Coal in a Shell and Tube Extraction Zone

J.G. Gatsis; U.S. Patent 3,520,794; July 14, 1970; assigned to Universal Oil Products Company describes an apparatus for liquefying coal via solvent extraction. Coal and solvent are introduced into the tubes via a vertical shell and tube extraction zone. The tube is perforated in such a manner that coal extracted may be removed through the perforations into the shell side with the remaining solid material being removed from the tubes. Hydrocarbons useful as fuel and/or chemicals may be obtained from the liquid coal extract.

The process provides a method for liquefying coal which comprises contacting granular coal with a solvent selective for coal in the lower end of at least one smaller conduit disposed concentrically in a larger conduit, passing the coal and solvent upwardly through the smaller conduit under coal extraction conditions; withdrawing liquefied coal and solvent through at least one opening in the upper section of the smaller conduit into the larger conduit in a manner such that solid material is substantially retained in the smaller conduit; removing liquefied coal and solvent from the larger conduit; and removing solid material from the upper end of the smaller conduit.

The method utilizes a reactor consisting of two concentric tubes with the upper section of the inner tube consisting of a perforated or filter element. In operation, the ground coal is mixed with the solvent and the mixture is passed upwardly in the reactor through the inner tube. Preferably, a temperature gradient is applied across the reaction or liquefying zone with the temperature increasing from the bottom of the inner tube to the top of the tube. As the coal proceeds upwardly through the liquefaction zone, the coal is dissolved into the solvent, and as it proceeds through the perforated section of the inner tube, the liquid will pass through the filter and the unreacted coal passed upwardly and out of the extraction zone.

The process may be understood by referring to Figure 2.7, previously described. A portion of the process is shown in more detail in Figure 2.8. This illustrates an apparatus which comprises a vertically disposed shell 33 having at least one conduit 22 extending through the shell in concentric fashion. Means for introducing liquids and solids into the inner tube 22 via line 17 can be by any means known to those skilled in the art. One such means would be a screw conveyor which would carry the feed material through the filter section 23, would compress the solids in the filter section, thereby forcing the liquid through the holes in zone 23 into the space 37 of shell 33. Another method of reaching the same result would be to have a higher pressure in tube 22 than is maintained in space 37. Additionally, the apparatus includes outlet means 21 for withdrawing solid material from the inner tube 22 and outlet means 20 for removing liquid from shell 33.

In addition, there is shown inlet means 34 for introducing hydrogen gas into admixture with the feed material in line 17 and additional outlet means 38 located in the upper section of shell 33 to remove gaseous materials from the effluent which passed through perforations 23 into space 37. In operation, pulverized coal including solvent and catalyst, if desired, is passed via line 17 as a slurry into the lower end of inner tube 22. Hydrogen gas may also be introduced with the feed material via line 34. The entire mixture passes upwardly through inner tube 22 until it reaches filtration zone 23 containing a series of orifice openings having a small enough diameter to prevent the passage through of solid materials having an average diameter of 5 microns or larger.

The liquid coal extract plus solvent, hydrogen gases, and other light gases pass through the perforations in zone 23 into space 37 of shell 33. The insoluble material comprising inorganic material, such as ash, plus any undissolved coal pass out of the system from inner tube 22 via line 21. The material which has passed through filtration zone 23 into space 37 of shell 33 is separated therein with the gaseous materials being removed from shell 33 via line 35. The accumulated liquid coal extract plus solvent is withdrawn from shell 33 via line 20. If desired, a portion of the liquid coal extract may be returned to the digestion zone via line 35. In addition, should there be a significant quantity of undissolved coal in the solid material being removed via line 21, a portion thereof may be returned to the extraction step via line 36.

It is to be noted that the digestion zone comprising shell 33 and the tube 22 is, in effect, of well-known shell and tube design. The embodiment of the process includes the use of at least one tube 22 within shell 33, but may include a plurality of tubes 22 depending upon the design parameters utilized by those skilled in the art. A typical commercial configuration would include a shell having a diameter of 8 feet and containing 1,000 to 5,000, typically 4,000 tubes 22 of from

FIGURE 2.8: LIQUEFACTION OF COAL IN A SHELL AND TUBE EXTRACTION ZONE

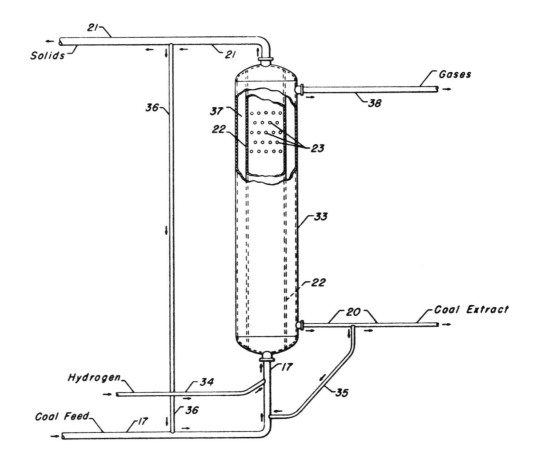

Source: J.G. Gatsis; U.S. Patent 3,520,794; July 14, 1970

2 to 3 inches in diameter. The perforations in zone 23 of tube 22 may be placed in any manner desired. It is distinctly preferred, however, that the perforated area of tube 22 occurs over less than 75% of the length of the conduit. However, the perforations may occur over any portion of tube 22 with the preferred arrangement being that all of the perforations be contained in the upper one-half of tube 22. The diameters of the holes or orifices may range from 5 microns to 0.093 inch in diameter sufficient to prevent the passage therethrough of any significant amount of solid material. The geometry of the hole spacing is not critical to the process.

Solvent Extraction Based on Partial Separation of Coal Slurry and Liquid

E. Gorin, J.A. Phinney and E.H. Reichl; U.S. Patent 3,523,886; August 11, 1970; assigned to the U.S. Secretary of the Interior and Consolidation Coal Company describe a process for making liquid fuel from coal by solvent extraction where the coal is extracted with solvent, and the extract is separated from undissolved coal residue by hydrocyclones where the extract which is the overflow product from the hydrocyclone is catalytically hydrocracked to produce the desired liquid fuel, and the undissolved residue which is the underflow product from the hydrocyclone is carbonized, the improvement comprising maintaining the underflow product as a pumpable slurry containing at least 35% by volume of liquid.

This process is similar in nature to U.S. Patent 3,143,489, but differs in that this process contains an improvement in the separation step of the solvent extraction zone. Instead of substantially completely separating the extra from undissolved residue, only a partial separation is effected to permit the recovery of the residue in the form of a flowable slurry. In order to obtain a flowable slurry, at least 35 volume percent of the slurry must be liquid at the operating temperature. It has been found that such a slurry may be obtained as the underflow from a hydrocyclone suitably operated to produce the desired result. It has also been found that the overflow from such operation of a hydrocyclone will contain more than

95% liquid including both extract and solvent, and even more important, that the solids in such extract overflow are no more harmful to the life of the catalyst in the primary hydrocracking zone than the solids present in extract obtained by substantially complete separation of extract and residue. Thus, the problems associated with the complete separation of liquid extract from the solid residue are avoided. The underflow slurry may be subjected to low temperature carbonization in much the same manner as the dry solids. The increased solids content of the overflow is allowed to build up in the hydrocracking zone, to a point where it is rejected to a coking zone for recovery of any carbon value. The final yield of distillable hydrocarbonaceous liquids is not significantly less than that achieved when complete separation of extract and residue is effected. A lower cost and more operable process is thus provided. In fact, by using a two-stage arrangement of the hydrocyclones incorporating a washing step, as will be shown, the overall recovery of extract is 95%, which is equal to or better than is achieved in the case of complete separation of extract and residue.

Figure 2.9a illustrates the process. Figure 2.9b shows the arrangement of the three hydrocyclones used in the separation. Following extraction, the mixture of solvent, extract and residue is conducted rapidly, so as to avoid cooling of the mixture, through a conduit 18 to a separation zone 20, consisting essentially of hydrocyclones. The hydrocyclones are adapted to operate at elevated temperature, for example 600°F. and at elevated pressures. While such hydrocyclones may be operated so as to effect substantially complete separation of liquid and solids, the improvement accomplished by this process requires operation of the hydrocyclone to assure an underflow which is a flowable slurry. It has been found that at least 35 volume percent of the underflow slurry must be liquid. Only sufficient liquid should be present in the slurry to assure flowability, since more than that unnecessarily diverts extract from transfer to the hydrocracking zone.

The overflow from the hydrocyclone is transferred by a conduit 22 to a solvent recovery zone 21 where solvent is removed by distillation and some of it is recycled through conduit 25 to the extraction zone 10. The balance of the solvent is recycled through conduit 23 to the conduit 18 for readmission to the hydrocyclone. Such recycle to the hydrocyclone helps to control the amount of extract contained in the underflow slurry from the hydrocyclone.

Loss of extract to the carbonization zone may be reduced by using a two-stage arrangement of the hydrocyclones which incorporates a solvent washing step. In such arrangement, two hydrocyclones are connected so that the underflow slurry from the first is introduced into the second hydrocyclone as its feed. Recycle solvent from the solvent recovery zone 21 is introduced into the conduit connecting the two hydrocyclones to dilute the feed to the second hydrocyclone. This solvent removes some of the extract from the second hydrocyclone as part of the overflow, thus reducing the amount of extract in the underflow which goes to the carbonization zone. The overflow from the second hydrocyclone may be returned to join the feed to the first hydrocyclone. Another arrangement, involving three hydrocyclones, is shown in Figure 2.9b.

FIGURE 2.9: SOLVENT EXTRACTION BASED ON PARTIAL SEPARATION OF COAL SLURRY AND LIQUID

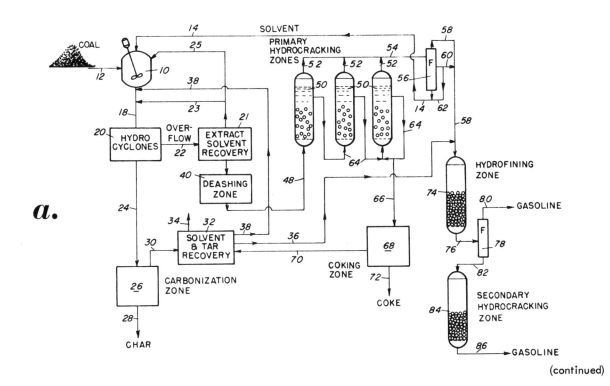

(continued)

FIGURE 2.9: (continued)

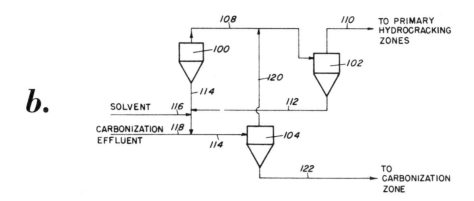

b.

Source: E. Gorin, J.A. Phinney and E.H. Reichl; U.S. Patent 3,523,886; August 11, 1970

The following table summarizes the results of a test program utilizing a 3 inch liquid cyclone at 600°F. and 150 psig on extraction effluent from extraction zone 10.

Coal feed rate, lbs./hr.	1,300	1,300	2,080
Extraction solvent/coal ratio	4.7	3.0	1.5
Cyclone feed:			
Percent solids	6.9	9.9	16.1
Percent extract in solvent	10.7	15.8	27.1
Liquid visc.. cp.	0.35	0.48	1.1
Liquid specific gravity	0.743	0.754	0.780
Feed rate, g.p.m.	18.8	12.7	12.0
Pressure drop, p.s.i.	122	109	96
Cyclone performance:			
Solids in overflow, wt. percent	0.3	1.0	3.3
Solids in underflow, wt. percent	35.5	40.4	34.8
Underflow, wt. percent feed	18.8	22.4	38.7
Solids in solvent-free extract, wt. percent	2.7	6.0	11.1
Percent extract to overflow	86.8	85.0	68.5
Percent solids to underflow	96.7	92.4	87.9
Estimated D_{50}, microns	7.5	13.0	17.0

"Coking" of Liquid Coal Extraction Products to Fuels and Chemicals

E.F. Nelson; U.S. Patent 3,503,864; March 31, 1970; assigned to Universal Oil Products Company describes a process whereby coal is liquefied via solvent extraction. The method contacts pulverized coal with a solvent, passes the coal solvent into a digestion zone, preferably in the presence of hydrogen and a hydrogenation catalyst, and subsequently passes the liquid coal extract into a coking zone for the production of valuable liquid hydrocarbons. The recovered hydrocarbons are useful as fuel and/or chemicals.

The process comprises (a) passing the coal and coal solvent into a pulverization zone under conditions sufficient to reduce the size of coal and to at least partially dissolve the coal; (b) introducing the pulverized coal solvent including dissolved coal into a digestion zone under conditions including the presence of an added hydrogen-containing gas sufficient to substantially dissolve the coal, thereby producing liquid coal extract having increased hydrogen content; (c) passing the liquid coal extract into a reaction zone maintained under coking conditions; (d) withdrawing from the reaction zone coke and hydrocarbons including normally liquid hydrocarbons; and (e) recovering valuable liquid hydrocarbons from the withdrawn hydrocarbons.

The process is based on the theory that having the presence of the hydrogen-rich solvent during the pulverization step of the coal results in a substantial increase in the efficiency of the operation and complementing the subsequent hydrogenation step, i.e., digestion, results in a decreased use of solvent for obtaining at least the same amount of liquid coal extract.

With respect to the benefit gained from having the solvent present during the pulverization step, it is believed that at the point of shear for the crushing and grinding of the coal, the shear site is extremely reactive, and therefore hydrogen can be transferred into that site more easily than if the coal is pulverized prior to contact with the solvent. In addition, the smaller particles of coal which are sheared away from a relatively large lump immediately exposes not only the highly reactive shear site to the solvent, but also exposes an extremely large surface area to the solvent, thereby enabling the resulting small particles of coal to almost immediately dissolve in the solvent and become a part of the liquid coal extract.

Since the purpose of the extraction zone, including the pulverization and digestion zones, is to substantially complete the conversion of the coal into a liquid coal extract, it may be desirable to add to the digestion zone additional solvent or utilize a catalyst in the extraction zone, including specifically a catalyst in the digestion zone. The catalyst used may be conventional, may be homogenous or heterogenous and may be introduced in the pulverization zone and/or digestion zone in admixture with the liquid solvent or with the solid coal. Those skilled in the art, from a knowledge of the characteristics of the coal, solvent and the properties desired for the end product, will know whether or not it may be desirable to use any or all of these features in the digestion zone.

Conventional hydrogenation catalyst may be desirable, such as palladium on an alumina support or a cobalt-molybdate catalyst or any other hydrogenation catalyst known and applicable to the solvent-coal system environment maintained in the digestion zone including the use of a slurry-catalyst system. Hydrogenation in the digestion zone generally accomplishes the following functions: transfer of hydrogen directly to coal molecules; transfer of hydrogen to hydrogen donor molecules; transfer of hydrogen from hydrogen donor molecules to coal molecules; and combinations of the above. Homogenous catalysts may be introduced with the coal, or hydrogen donor compounds, in the pulverization step of the extraction zone. Examples of catalysts suitable include compounds containing tin, nickel, molybdenum, tungsten and cobalt. By way of emphasis, as used here, the term "extraction zone" is intended to include the pulverization step, the digestion step, or the combined pulverization-digestion step.

After separation of gaseous materials, including hydrogen, undissolved coal residue and catalyst, if any, from the total effluent of the digestion zone, the liquid coal extract is passed, preferably in its entirety, into a conventional coking zone. However, if desired, a portion of the total liquid coal extract can be recycled without further treatment to the pulverization zone and/or digestion zone. The coking zone is preferably a delayed coker and comprises a plurality of coke drums. The heated liquid coal extract is passed into a first coking drum where it is decomposed into coke and a vaporous effluent containing normally gaseous hydrocarbons. Following reaction in the first drum, the charge is alternated to a second coking drum and the operation is repeated while the first drum is cooled down and the coke removed therefrom. Coking conditions include a temperature from 400° to 800°C., sufficient to produce coke having a volatile content from 5 to 30% by weight.

Following the coking operation, the effluent is passed, preferably in its vaporous state, directly into separation facilities which typically comprise a fractionation column for the separation of the effluent into valuable liquid hydrocarbons such as normally gaseous hydrocarbons, a relatively light hydrocarbon comprising essentially middle oil, a relatively heavy hydrocarbon comprising materials suitable for use as a coal solvent, and a bottoms fraction comprising residue material which is suitable as fuel. In essence, therefore, the valuable liquid hydrocarbons recovered from the effluent of the coking zone include, for example, gasoline boiling range products and/or chemicals, aromatic hydrocarbon-containing fractions, heavy fuel oil fractions, and the like.

Referring now to Figure 2.10, coarse coal having an average particle diameter generally in excess of 0.08 inch is introduced into the system via line 10. A suitable selective solvent enriched in hydrogen content is introduced into admixture with the coarse coal from line 11. The oversized solid material from the pulverization zone is also preferably returned to the pulverization zone via line 12. The entire admixture of coarse coal and solvent is passed via line 13 into mill 14 which conventionally may be of the ball mill type. Suitable pulverization conditions, including a temperature of about 380°C., a pressure of about 70 psig, and a solvent to coal weight ratio of about 1, are maintained in mill 14 such that the coarse coal is reduced to an average particle diameter between 0.08 and 0.04 inch and at least a portion of the coal, e.g., about 17% by weight is dissolved into the solvent.

The effluent from mill 14 containing solvent having dissolved therein the liquid coal extract, undissolved coal of proper small particle size, and undissolved coal of oversize is passed via line 15 into separator 16 which may be of the cyclone type. Conditions are maintained in separator 16 whereby the oversized coal particles, preferably in admixture with at least a portion of the liquid material, are removed via line 12 and returned to mill 14 in a manner previously discussed.

Solvent having dissolved therein at least a portion of the coal plus undissolved pulverized coal is admixed with hydrogen-containing gas via line 26 and passed via line 17 into digestion zone 19 which may be a jacketed stirred type vessel. Added solvent, if any, may be introduced into the system via line 18 in an amount sufficient to maintain the solvent to coal ratio at the desired level and/or to maintain the hydrogen content of the solvent present in digester 19 at a sufficient high level. Furthermore, hydrogenation catalyst (from means not shown) may advantageously be used in the digestion step. Makeup hydrogen, if any, may be added to the system via line 27. Preferably, the amount of hydrogen present in the digestion zone is from 1,000 to 100,000 standard cubid feet per barrel of coal-solvent entering digester 19 via line 17.

The entire effluent from digestion zone 19 is passed via line 20 into filtration zone 21 where solid residue, including solid hydrogenation catalyst if any, is separated from the liquid material and removed from the system via line 22. Filtration zone 21 preferably is a rotary filter device precoated with conventional filter aids and is typically operated at a pressure of from 50 to 100 psig sufficient to effect removal of substantially all of the suspended solid matter, including undissolved carbonaceous matter. The filter cake is washed and dried by conventional means to recover adsorbed liquid material. The mother liquor, comprising hydrogen gas, if any, and solvent having coal dissolved therein, is removed from filtration zone 21 via line 23. If desired, by means not shown, an antisolvent such as a light hydrocarbon of the hexane type may be added to filtration zone 21 in an effort to further aid in removing tars and solid materials from the desired solvent and liquid hydrocarbons making up the liquid coal extract. If an antisolvent is used, then the material in line 23 will also contain such added light hydrocarbons.

The liquid effluent is passed from filtration zone 21 via line 23 into separator 24 for the separation of the hydrogen gas from the other hydrocarbonaceous material. Although separator 24 has been shown in a position following filtration zone 21, it is within the concepts of the process to arrange for separation of the hydrogen gas prior to filtration zone 21. In other words, another embodiment would include a hydrogen separation zone (not shown) in line 20 between digester 19 and filter 21. However, for purposes of illustration only, separator 24 has been placed between filtration zone 21 and coking unit 29.

In keeping with this illustration, hydrogen gas is removed from separator 24 via line 26 and returned to digester 19, as previously discussed. Separator 24 may also include means, not shown, for the separation of the added light hydrocarbon (antisolvent) which may have been added during the filtration step. Therefore, the liquid coal extract, substantially free of solid matter, hydrogen gas and normally gaseous hydrocarbons, is removed from separator 24 via line 25. The material in line 25 is passed into delayed coking zone 29 which is operated under coking conditions sufficient to produce coke having a volatile content of about 20% by weight. A portion of the liquid coal extract in line 25 may be bypassed around coking zone 29 via line 28 for return to either mill 14 and/or digester 19, if desired. Coke is removed from the coking unit via line 30 and disposed of by means not shown. The effluent of coking zone 29 containing normally liquid hydrocarbons is withdrawn via line 31 and passed into fractionator 33.

FIGURE 2.10: "COKING" OF LIQUID COAL EXTRACTION PRODUCTS TO FUELS AND CHEMICALS

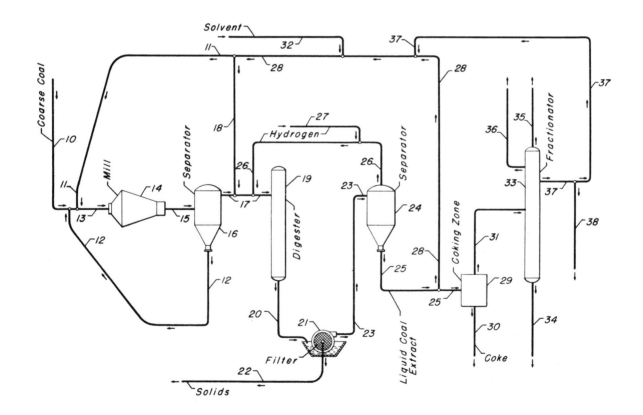

Source: E.F. Nelson; U.S. Patent 3,503,864; March 31, 1970

Fractionator 33 is operated under conditions sufficient to remove normally gaseous hydrocarbon produced during the coking operation from the system via line 35. A relatively heavy hydrocarbon material, such as a kerosene fraction is withdrawn from fractionator 33 via line 36. A relatively heavy hydrocarbon is withdrawn via line 37 and, preferably, comprises sufficient solvation properties for use in the coal liquefaction step previously discussed. Therefore, the material in line 37 is recycled to mill 14 and/or digester 19 via line 28, 11 and/or 18, as discussed hereinabove. A residual fraction comprising heavy fuel oil is withdrawn from fractionator 33 via line 34. Added solvent external of the process may be added to the system via line 32, if desired.

Solvent Extraction of Coal in the Presence of Hydrogen Sulfide

J.G. Gatsis; U.S. Patent 3,503,863; March 31, 1970; assigned to Universal Oil Products Company describes a process for liquefying coal which comprises contacting coal and solvent in the presence of hydrogen sulfide and recovering valuable liquid hydrocarbon products from the resulting liquid coal extract.

It is believed that one of the reasons this process produces such desirable results is that hydrogen sulfide gas acts in some way as a catalytic agent, thereby improving the total conversion of the coal into liquid coal extract, rendering the ash more readily filterable and producing a liquid coal extract having a higher hydrogen content than would otherwise be obtained. Additional benefits may also accrue in the practice of this process by utilizing a hydrogenation catalyst in the solvent extraction zone as well as hydrogen gas and the critical amount of hydrogen sulfide.

The coal preferred for use in the practice of the process is of the bituminous type, such as Pittsburg Seam Coal. More preferably, however, the bituminous coal is a high volatile content coal having a volatile content greater than about 20% by weight of maf coal (moisture and ash-free coal). Although this process will be described with reference to the conversion of bituminous coal to valuable liquid hydrocarbons, it is within the concept of this process to apply to subbituminous coal, lignite, and other solid carbonaceous materials of natural origin. For convenience, therefore, the term "coal" is intended to include all materials within the class consisting of bituminous coal, subbituminous coal, lignite, and other solid carbonaceous materials of natural origin.

Suitable solvents for use in the practice of this process are those which are of the hydrogen-donor type and are at least partially hydrogenated and include naphthalenic hydrocarbons. Preferably, the solvent is one which is in liquid phase at the recommended temperature and pressure for extraction. Mixtures of hydrocarbons are generally employed as the solvent and, preferably, and derived from intermediate or final products obtained from the subsequent processing. Typically, the solvent hydrocarbons or mixtures of hydrocarbons boil between about 260° and 425°C. Examples of suitable solvents are tetrahydronaphthalene (Tetralin), Decalin, biphenyl, methylnaphthalene, dimethylnaphthalene, etc. Other types of solvents which may be added to the preferred solvents of this process for special reasons include phenolic compounds, such as phenols, cresols, and xylenols. It is also to be recognized that in some cases it may be desirable during a subsequent separation step prior to the removal of the solvent from the liquid coal extract to add an antisolvent, such as saturated paraffinic hydrocarbons like hexane, to aid in the precipitation of tarry and solid residue, e.g., ash, from the coal extract of this process.

However, in the selection of a suitable solvent it must be recognized that the solvent must have the ability to transfer hydrogen to the pulverized coal during the extraction step. In other words, it is a requirement that in the absence of added hydrogen, the rich solvent leaving the extraction step having coal dissolved therein must have a reduced hydrogen content compared to the hydrogen content of the lean solvent which is added to the extraction zone. In a preferred embodiment of this process there is embodied the selective hydrogenation of the solvent during extraction in order to increase its hydrogen content so that hydrogen may be more easily transferred from the solvent to the coal during the solvent extraction operation. The essence of this process is based on the discovery that the presence of from 1 to 2% by volume of hydrogen sulfide (based on the amount of hydrogen present) will considerably enhance the efficiency and effectiveness of the conversion of solid coal to liquid coal extract. Preferably, the amount of hydrogen sulfide added will be from 4 to 8% by volume based on hydrogen gas. In the event added hydrogen gas is not present in the extraction zone, the amount of hydrogen sulfide present should be from 10 to 40% based on the amount of coal feed into the solvent extraction zone.

The operating conditions for the solvents extraction zone include a temperature from 250° to 500°C., and pressure from 500 to 5,000 psig, a solvent to coal weight ratio from 0.2 to 10, a residence time from 30 seconds to 5 hours, the presence of hydrogen sulfide gas (previously discussed hereinabove), and, preferably, the presence of hydrogen sufficient to dissolve coal such that a total in excess of 50% by weight of maf coal feed into the solvent extraction zone has been liquefied.

Since the purpose of the extraction zone is to substantially convert coal into liquid coal extract, it may be desirable to add to the extraction zone a catalyst. The catalyst may be conventional, may be homogenous or heterogenous and may be introduced into the pulverization zone and/or extraction zone in admixture with either the liquid solvent or with the solid coal. Those skilled in the art, from a knowledge of the characteristics of the coal, solvent, and of the properties desired for the end product, will know whether or not it may be desirable to use any or all of these features in the solvent extraction zone. If a catalyst is desired, conventional solid hydrogenation catalyst can be satisfactorily utilized, such as nickel-molybdate on an alumina-silica support or a cobalt-molybdate catalyst or any other hydrogenation catalyst known to those skilled in the art and applicable to the solvent-coal system environment maintained in the extraction zone including the use of a slurry-catalyst system.

Hydrogenation in the extraction zone, generally, accomplishes the following functions: transfer of hydrogen directly to coal molecules; transfer of hydrogen to hydrogen-donor molecules; transfer of hydrogen from hydrogen-donor molecules to coal molecules; and various combinations of the above. By way of emphasis, as used herein, the term "extraction zone" is intended to include the pulverization step, the digestion step, or combined pulverization-digestion as is known to those skilled in the art.

After separation of the gaseous materials, including hydrogen, hydrogen sulfide, undissolved coal residue (e.g., ash) and catalyst, if any, from the total effluent of the extraction zone, the liquid coal extract is passed into conventional recovery facilities wherein valuable liquid hydrocarbons are recovered. Typically, these recovery facilities comprise fractionation columns for the separation therein of the liquid coal extract into products such as normally gaseous hydrocarbons, relatively light hydrocarbons comprising essentially middle oil, relatively heavy hydrocarbons comprising materials suitable for use as a coal solvent and a bottoms fraction comprising residue material which is suitable for fuel. In essence, therefore, the valuable liquid hydrocarbons recovered from the liquid coal extract include, for example, gasoline boiling range products and/or chemicals, aromatic hydrocarbon-containing fractions, heavy fuel oil fractions, and the like, the utility of which is well known to those skilled in the art.

The extraction of coal by means of a selective solvent is by definition at least a partial conversion of the coal since not only is the coal reacted with hydrogen which is transferred from the solvent, but is also reacted with the hydrogen which is added during the extraction step. In addition, there is also a solution phenomenon which actually dissolves the coal which has accepted the hydrogen into the solvent. Therefore, as used herein, the terms "liquid coal extract" and "liquid coal fraction" or other words of similar import are intended to include the liquid product which is obtained from the solvent extraction of the coal with the selective solvent in the presence of hydrogen sulfide and generally has been described on the basis of being "solvent-free" even though a portion of the extract comprises hydrocarbons suitable for use as the solvent.

The process is performed under conditions which increase the kinetics of the reaction while maintaining the components therein in primarily liquid phase; although, in some cases, it may be desirable to practice this process in the presence of a vaporized solvent and hydrogen sulfide gas.

Example: This example illustrates the advantage to having hydrogen sulfide present during the solvent liquefaction of coal. An Eastern Kentucky Stoker Coal having the following properties was crushed to an average particle diameter of less than 100 mesh:

	Weight Percent
Ash	3.67
Nitrogen	1.60
Sulfur	1.36
Oxygen	6.99
Free H_2O	1.61
Volatile matter	40.30
Carbon	79.66
Hydrogen	5.55

One part of the crushed coal was mixed with three parts of methylnaphthalene. The mixture was run in a colloid mill for 5 hours thereby producing coal particles having 99% by weight less than 5 microns diameter. 447 grams of the material from the colloid mill was charged to a racker autoclave at a pressure, first of 10 atmospheres of H_2S, and secondly with an additional 90 atmospheres of H_2 thereby obtaining a total pressure of 100 atmospheres. The autoclave was then heated to 390°C. (raising the pressure to 200 atmospheres). These conditions were maintained for 2 hours.

The liquefied coal was recovered from the contents of the autoclave by filtration and distillation (including solvent removal). 80 grams of liquefied coal and 17 grams of solid residue was obtained. The conversion of solid coal to liquid coal was determined from the amount of carbon present in the original coal and the amount of carbon left in the recovered solids. Thus, the amount of carbon in the original coal was 89.02 grams and the amount of carbon in the recovered solids was 11.01 grams resulting in a conversion of solid coal to liquid coal of 87.66% by weight.

Liquefaction of Coal via Solvent Extraction in a Hydrogen Atmosphere

E.F. Nelson; U.S. Patent 3,477,941; November 11, 1969; assigned to Universal Oil Products Company describes a method for the liquefaction of coal via solvent extraction using a hydrogen-donor selective solvent. The method pulverizes coal in the presence of solvent utilizing high velocity impact means situated in a digestion zone which is maintained under coal liquefying conditions. The method includes injecting hydrogen gas into the digestion zone thereby facilitating the conversion of solid coal into liquid coal products. Hydrocarbons useful as fuel and/or chemicals may be obtained from the liquid coal extract.

The process involves the introduction of coal and solvent into an eductor device which is constructed in a manner to propel the admixture through nozzle means against an impact plate with sufficient velocity to fracture the small coal into smaller particles. Preferably, the impact means is physically located inside a digestion vessel which is maintained under coal dissolving conditions including having present liquid solvent which substantially surrounds the impact means. A suitable residence time is maintained in the digestion zone by utilizing the technique of hindered settling whereby the upward velocity of coal and solvent is adjusted so that substantially all of the coal is converted to liquid products prior to being withdrawn from the digestion zone. The hindered settling technique is accomplished by having the impact means located in the lower end of a vertically disposed digestion zone and withdrawing the resulting liquid coal extract and solvent from the upper end thereof.

In the preferred manner of operation there is introduced into the eduction device hydrogen gas which not only acts as a carrying medium for the solvent and coal, but also aids in the conversion of solid coal to liquid coal extract while simultaneously at least partially hydrogenating the solvent present in the digestion zone. In this manner, the solvent is maintained in a desirably high hydrogen content state. The use of the hydrogen gas can be further enhanced by introducing into the digestion zone a suitable hydrogenation catalyst which, preferably, would be introduced into the upper end of the digestion zone. Suitable solvents for use in the practice of this process are those which are of the hydrogen-donor type and are at least partially hydrogenated and include naphthalenic hydrocarbons.

The operating conditions maintained in the digestion zone may be varied widely. The temperature, for example, may be varied essentially from atmospheric temperature to a relatively high temperature. It is distinctly preferred in the practice of this process that the temperature of the coal and the solvent be maintained at a relatively high level, say, from 300° to 500°C. The pressure in similar manner may be varied over an extremely wide range; for example, from atmospheric pressure to, say 10,000 psig with a preferred pressure being about 500 psig. In all cases it is distinctly preferred that the operating conditions be chosen so as to maintain the solvent and dissolved coal in substantially liquid phase. These conditions should also be chosen so as to maintain the digestion zone substantially liquid-full; at least over the volume of the digestion zone where the major portion of the dissolving action takes place. The amount of solvent which is used in the process should be from 0.2 to 10 pounds of solvent per pound of solid coal entering the digestion zone. Satisfactory results may be obtained in utilizing approximately equal amounts of solvent to coal on a weight basis.

As previously mentioned the upwardly flowing solvent in the digestion zone, and, preferably, the upwardly flowing hydrogen gas provided a residence time for the solid coal to be in contact with the solvent through the hindered settling technique. Generally, a residence time from 30 seconds to 5 hours is sufficient and, preferably, the amount of hydrogen gas introduced into the system is sufficient to aid in dissolving the coal and to substantially maintain the hydrogen content of the solvent at substantially the level of the lean solvent. In all cases, the combination of operating conditions should be sufficient so that a total in excess of 50% by weight and, typically, from 70 to 90% by weight of the maf coal has been liquefied. The amount of hydrogen gas necessary to perform this function may range form 1,000 to 100,000 standard cubic feet per barrel of lean solvent entering the system. Typically, however, the amount of hydrogen added to the digestion zone in the preferred embodiment will be in the range from 2,000 to 10,000 standard cubic feet per barrel. However, the amount of hydrogen entering the digestion zone should not be in excess of that which would cause foaming or carryover of solid coal out of the upper end of the digestion zone.

While the purpose of the digestion zone, including the method of adding hydrogen to the digestion zone, is to substantially complete the conversion of the coal into a liquid coal extract, it may also be desirable to add to the digestion zone a hydrogenation catalyst. The catalyst used may be conventional, may be homogenous or heterogenous and may be introduced in the pulverization zone and/or digestion zone in admixture with the liquid solvent or with the solid coal. Those skilled in the art, from a knowledge of the characteristics of the coal, solvent, and the properties desired for the end product will know whether or not it may be desirable to use any or all of these desirable features in the digestion zone. Conventional solid particulate (preferably, finely divided) hydrogenation catalyst may be desirable, such as palladium on an alumina support or a cobalt-molybdate catalyst or any other hydrogenation catalyst known to be applicable to the solvent-coal system environment maintained in the digestion zone.

Hydrogenation in the digestion zone generally accomplishes the following functions: transfer of hydrogen directly to coal molecules; transfer of hydrogen to hydrogen donor molecules; transfer of hydrogen from hydrogen donor molecules to coal molecules; and, combinations of the above. Homogenous catalysts may be introduced with the coal, or hydrogen donor compounds, in the pulverization step prior to the digestion zone. Examples of catalysts suitable include compounds containing tin, nickel, molybdenum, tungsten, and cobalt.

Following the digestion zone, the solvent containing dissolved oil is passed into a separation zone for the recovery therefrom of valuable hydrocarbon products. These products are normal gasoline boiling range products and/or chemicals, aromatic hydrocarbon-containing fractions, heavy fuel oil fractions, and the like, the utility of which is well know by those skilled in the art. As previously mentioned, at least a portion of the coal extract is suitable for use as a coal solvent and may, therefore, be recycled at least in part to the solvent digestion zone as lean solvent therein.

The construction of the impact means may be from any design available. Generally, it should be so constructed so that the extremely high velocities of coal and solvent will cause the substantial fracture of the coal upon impact with the means. The material of construction used for this device may be from any relatively hard material, such as tungsten carbide, stainless steel, alloys of various other types, etc. The only criteria for the material of construction would be that the impact means should not, to any considerable extent, be eroded by the impaction of coal particles on its surface. Desirably, the impact device would be a flat plate constructed a relatively short distance from the end of the nozzle which is being fed with the solvent and coal. Other shapes can, of course, be used, such as a curved surface to direct the crushed coal particles into desired areas of the digestion zone. Other geometric patterns for construction of the impact device can be utilized to influence the flow of solvent and/or solid material within the digestion zone. In addition, the location of the impact means may be either within the digestion zone or immediately outside of the digestion zone. It is distinctly preferred in this process that the impact device be physically located within the digestion zone so that simultaneous liquefaction of the pulverized coal particles may occur.

Referring to Figure 2.11, relatively large diameter solid particulate coal having an average particle diameter in excess of 0.08 inch is introduced in a substantially dry condition into the system from hopper 10. Typically, the temperature of the dry coal is about 300°F. Simultaneously, hot selective solvent enriched in hydrogen content is introduced at a temperature of 750°F. into admixture with the coarse coal via line 11 into eductor 12. Preferably, hot hydrogen also is introduced into eductor 12 at a typical temperature of about 900°F. The entire effluent from eductor 12 passes via conduit 14 which is an appropriate nozzle device into digester vessel 16 at an extremely high velocity and/or pressure. This effluent comprising solvent, coal particles, and hydrogen is propelled against impact means 15 which is a flat plate composed of tungsten carbide. As the solid coal particles impinge against plate 15, the particles are fractured into smaller sized particles which are scattered in random pattern throughout the solvent which is contained in digester 16 and which substantially surrounds impact device 15. In other words, digester 16 is liquid-full of the selective solvent, at least over that portion of digester 16 through which coal is liquefied.

FIGURE 2.11: LIQUEFACTION OF COAL VIA SOLVENT EXTRACTION IN A HYDROGEN ATMOSPHERE

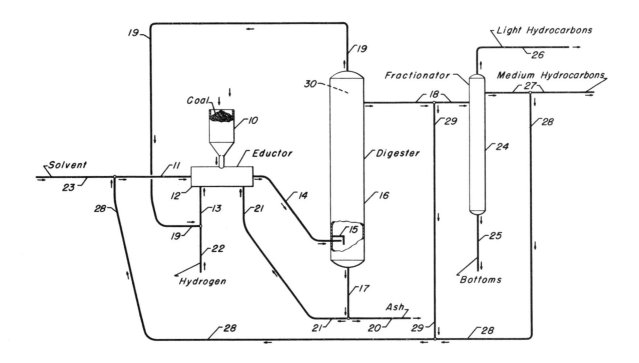

Source: E.F. Nelson; U.S. Patent 3,477,941; November 11, 1969

As the method continues, the coal particles and solvent pass in an upward fashion through digester 16 at a rate which results in the hindered settling of the solid particles thereby providing sufficient residence time for at least a total of 50 weight percent of the maf coal to be converted into liquid coal extract. The solid particles which eventually settle in digester 16 are removed via line 17 and a portion thereof is rejected via line 20 with the remainder passing via line 21 back into eductor 12 for another passage through the impact device. Not shown are optional separation means for the selective recovery of undissolved coal particles which may then be recycled to the eductor as previously described. A liquid coal extract stream containing dissolved coal and solvent is removed from digester 16 at the upper end thereof via line 18. Desirably, a vapor space is maintained at point 30 in digester 16 which provides separation means for unreacted hydrogen gas to be recovered and returned via line 19 to the eductor device 12.

Additional hydrogen gas, if needed, may be introduced into the system via line 22 and added solvent, if needed or desired, may be introduced into the system via line 23. Referring now to the liquid coal extract stream in line 18, this material is passed into fractionator 24 which may be a conventional distillation column type. Suitable conditions are maintained therein such that a distillate fraction comprising light hydrocarbons may be withdrawn via line 26 and a liquid coal extract stream may be removed via line 25 from the bottom of fractionator 24 for further processing in accordance with the practices known to those skilled in the art including processing for upgrading and/or for separating the liquid coal extract to the desirable valuable product of motor fuel and/or chemicals.

In the practice of this process, a material suitable in boiling range as solvent for the coal is withdrawn from fractionator 24 via line 27 and withdrawn from the system for other uses known to those skilled in the art, or in the preferred embodiment of this process, at least a portion thereof is returned to eductor 12 via lines 28 and 11. Still further, if desired, a portion of the withdrawn material in line 18 may also be returned to eductor 12 via lines 29, 28, and 11, respectively.

It was discovered that the utilization of hydrogen gas in the digester 16 permitted the use of less solvent than would otherwise be required. In addition, the presence of an excess of hydrogen gas and solvent at the point of fracturing the coal particles provided a means for a more efficient conversion of the solid coal into liquid coal products.

Liquefaction of Coal by Means of Friedel-Crafts Catalysts

The process described by M.B. Neuworth and L.A. Herédy; U.S. Patent 3,158,561; November 24, 1964; assigned to Consolidation Coal Company relates to the production of coal extract from coal by reacting the coal with phenolic-boron trifluoride complex.

It has been discovered that phenolic-BF_3 complex is a superior treating agent for the recovery of liquid constituents from coal. The phenolic-BF_3 complex does more than merely dissolve those coal constituents that are soluble therein, but the complex actually chemically reacts with coal to depolymerize it, thus forming additional components which are soluble in the complex.

It is to be understood that the term "phenolic-BF_3 complex" as hereinafter used, includes phenol-BF_3 complex; reactive alkyl phenol-BF_3 complexes, e.g., cresol-BF_3 complexes, and xylenol-BF_3 complexes; and reactive halogenated derivatives of the above complexes, e.g., 2-chlorophenol-BF_3 complex, 2,4-dichlorophenol-BF_3 complex, 6-chloro-o-cresol-BF_3 complex and the like. As is well known, only phenolic-BF_3 complexes which have at least one free ortho and/or para position are reactive.

Coal, preferably in a comminuted form, is reacted with a phenolic-BF_3 complex such as phenol-BF_3 complex at a temperature in the range of 50° to 200°C., preferably 70° to 120°C. The reaction is conveniently conducted at autogenous pressures; however, if desired, higher pressures may be used. The solvent is generally used in a weight ratio of solvent to coal in the range of 0.25:1 to 10:1, preferably 0.50:1 to 5:1. Any conventional solvent extraction zone used by those skilled in the art may be employed, e.g., countercurrent, staged, continuous, or batch extraction.

Example: High volatile bituminous coal obtained from the Pittsburgh Seam and having the following typical analysis was used in the following experiment.

Moisture	1.7 wt. %
Volatile matter	38.5 wt. %
Ash	12.6 wt. %
Pyritic sulfur	2.5 wt. %
Ultimate analysis, DMMF*	
H	5.77 wt. %
C	80.36 wt. %
O	10.58 wt. %
N	1.40 wt. %
S	1.89 wt. %

*DMMF means dry mineral matter-free.

The coal was ground to –100 mesh (Tyler Standard screen) and stored under nitrogen until required. Samples were dried in a vacuum oven at 105°C. just prior to reaction. An amount of 1,600 grams of radioactive phenol (the number one carbon position comprises carbon 14), and 400 grams of coal were charged into a five liter three-necked glass reaction flask equipped with stirrer, thermometer, condenser and gas inlet tube. The suspension was stirred and heated to 60° to 70°C. and the introduction of BF_3 was started. The mixture was heated to 100°C. and kept at this temperature until the end of the reaction period. The saturation with BF_3 took about two hours. After this time a very slow stream of BF_3 was bubbled through the system to keep the solution saturated with BF_3. The reaction time was 24 hours.

The first part of the reaction between coal and phenol-BF_3 complex is quite spectacular. Within a period of about 20 min. the suspension becomes very viscous resembling a thixotropic gel due to the swelling and solvation of the coal particles. Shortly after this stage, the viscosity decreases rapidly indicating a further significant disintegration. After this time no individual coal particles can be separated from the mixture either by filtration or by centrifuging. On the other hand, when coal is extracted with phenol at 100°C. under similar conditions but without the addition of BF_3, the phenol solution can be easily separated from the coal particles by filtration, even after a 24 hour extraction period.

After the end of the reaction period, most of the BF_3 and excess phenol were removed by vacuum distillation. When the phenol content of the solution was reduced to about 50 to 60%, the distillation was interrupted and the fluid residue was poured into four liters of analytical reagent grade benzene. Most of the reaction product is insoluble in benzene and precipitates in a granular form which can be filtered easily. The precipitate was filtered, extracted a second time with two liters of hot benzene for 3 hours, and filtered again. The benzene solutions were combined, washed with 15% Na_2CO_3 solution, and distilled. Following the removal of benzene, the solution was vacuum fractionated in a 91 centimeter spinning band column. After the recovery of the radioactive phenol and a smaller fraction consisting mostly of alkyl phenols, a pitch-like residue was left behind (benzene-soluble fraction).

The solid precipitate was stirred with 2 liters of 15% aqueous Na_2CO_3 solution at 100°C. for 8 hours to remove that part of the BF_3 which cannot be removed by vacuum distillation and remains in the residue (about 15% based on the weight of the residue). The benzene insoluble neutralized residue was filtered, dried, and then extracted with two liters of boiling methyl alcohol. After filtration, the extraction was repeated again with a second 2 liters of methyl alcohol. The methanol was evaporated from the solution and the solid residue was obtained (methanol-soluble fraction).

A 50 g. sample of the methanol insoluble residue was extracted with 850 g. phenol at 100°C. for 4 hours. After the addition of 40 g. of Celite, the solution was filtered. The filtrate was concentrated by vacuum distillation and the extract was recovered by pouring the concentrate into a mixture of 80% n-heptane and 20% benzene. The precipitated solid was filtered and dried in a vacuum oven at 160°C. (phenol soluble fraction). The heptane-benzene solution was evaporated and a small amount (about 2% based on coal) of black pitch was recovered. This residue was added to the phenol soluble fraction. The phenol insoluble residue was extracted with 500 grams of pyridine at 100°C. for 4 hours. The solution was concentrated, poured into n-heptane, filtered and dried at 160°C. (pyridine-soluble fraction). The insoluble residue was dried in vacuum at 160°C. (pyridine-insoluble fraction).

All fractions were analyzed for combined phenol content by analyzing for C 14 and comparison with the C 14 assay of the starting phenol. The phenolic hydroxyl content of the various fractions was determined by potentiometric titration in the presence of added 2,6-xylenol using sodium aminoethoxide in pyridine or ethylenediamine. The molecular weights of the benzene-soluble, methanol-soluble, and phenol-soluble fractions were determined ebullioscopically in benzene, benzene-methanol and pyridine, respectively. As a result of the above reaction of coal with phenol-BF_3 complex at 100°C. for 24 hours, about 80 weight percent of the coal dissolved in the complex.

As mentioned above, the reaction product was separated into fractions which were soluble in benzene, methanol, phenol and pyridine respectively. The yields of the various fractions are shown in the following table. The combined yield of soluble fractions and a solvent-insoluble fraction is 122.7% (dry, mineral matter-free coal), indicating a total consumption of 22.7% phenol.

On the basis of a blank experiment made with phenol and BF_3, the amount of self-condensate formed from phenol was calculated to be 4.0% (based on DMMF coal). Consequently, the consumption of phenol in the reaction was 18.7%. The amount of coal components in each fraction adjusted for the combined phenol was calculated and the values are shown in the table on the following page. The yields of benzene, methanol, and phenol solubles are 7.7, 1.8 and 52.0%, respectively. Normally, coal of this type would yield an extract of below 1% when treated with benzene. The combined phenol-soluble extract amounts to 62 weight percent of the coal.

In a blank experiment in which another sample of the same coal was extracted with phenol at 100°C. for 24 hours, the coal extract yield was only 15.5 weight percent. The great increase in coal extract yield when using phenol-BF_3 complex is interpreted as a result of the simultaneous solvent extraction and depolymerization.

Extractive Conversion Processes

Yield and Composition of Coal Reaction Products

	Benzene Soluble	Methanol Soluble	Phenol Soluble	Pyridine Soluble	Insoluble
Total yield, wt. percent DMMF* coal	15.2	4.0	61.2	12.3	30.0
Combined phenol content, wt. percent	49.4	55.7	15.0	10.5	10.5
Coal fraction, wt. percent DMMF coal	7.7	1.8	52.0	11.1	27.0
Ultimate analysis of coal fraction, wt. percent:					
C	85.95	84.06	81.50	79.39	77.11
H	8.04	6.30	5.26	4.39	4.75
O	3.77	4.79	10.04	12.65	14.55
N	0.53	1.58	1.33	1.44	1.52
S	1.70	3.27	1.87	1.89	2.00

*DMMF means dry mineral matter-free.

Liquefaction Process Using Colloidal Size Coal

F.J. Riedl, R.S. Corey and R.E. Syacha; U.S. Patent 3,536,608; October 27, 1970; assigned to Universal Oil Products Company describe a process for liquefying coal which comprises contacting colloidal size coal and solvent in the presence of hydrogen gas and recovering valuable liquid hydrocarbon products from the resulting liquid coal extract.

The coal used in this process is of the bituminous type such as Pittsburg Seam Coal; the bituminous coal is a high volatile content having a volatile content greater than about 20% by weight of maf coal. Although the process is described with reference to the conversion of bituminous coal to valuable liquid hydrocarbons, it is possible to use this process for sub-bituminous coal, lignite and other solid carbonaceous materials of natural origin. For convenience, therefore, the term "coal" is intended to include all materials within the class consisting of bituminous coal, subbituminous coal, lignite, and other solid carbonaceous materials of natural origin.

Suitable solvents for use in the practice of this process are those which are of hydrogen-donor type. Such hydrocarbons are at least partially hydrogenated and include naphthalenic hydrocarbons. Preferably, the solvent is one which is liquid phase at the recommended temperature and pressure for extraction. Mixtures of hydrocarbons are generally employed as the solvent and, preferably, are derived from intermediate or final products obtained from subsequent processing following the practice of this process. Typically, the solvent hydrocarbons or mixtures of hydrocarbons boil between about 260° and 425°C.

Examples of suitable solvents are tetrahydronaphthalene (Tetralin), Decalin, biphenyl, methylnaphthalene, dimethylnaphthalene, etc. Other types of solvents which may be added to the preferred solvents of this process for special reasons include phenolic compounds, such as phenols, cresols, and xylenols. It is also to be recognized that in some cases it may be desirable during a subsequent separation step prior to the removal of the solvent from the liquid coal extract to add an antisolvent such as saturated paraffinic hydrocarbons like hexane to aid in the precipitation of tarry and solid residue, e.g., ash, from the coal extract of this process.

Following the size reduction step wherein the oversized solid materials have been separated from the effluent of the pulverization zone, the coal product (both liquid and solid) is passed into a solvent extraction zone which, in effect, is a reaction zone for the substantial conversion of coal into liquid coal extract. It is within the concept of this process that the pulverization zone and the extraction zone be the same vessel or may be separate vessels, the desirability of which will become evident from the discussion more fully developed hereinbelow.

The operating conditions for the solvent extraction zone include a temperature from 250° to 500°C., a pressure from 500 to 5,000 psig, a solvent to coal ratio from 0.2 to 10, a residence time from 30 seconds to 5 hours, and, preferably the presence of hydrogen gas sufficient to dissolve coal such that a total in excess of 50% by weight of maf coal feed into the solvent extraction zone has been liquefied.

Since the purpose of the extraction zone is to convert coal into liquid coal extract, it may be desirable to add a catalyst to the extraction zone. The catalyst may be conventional, may be homogenous, or heterogenous, and may be introduced into the pulverization zone and/or extraction zone in a mixture either with the liquid solvent or with the solvent coal. Those skilled in the art, from a knowledge of the characteristics of the coal solvent and of the properties desired for the end product will know whether or not it may be desirable to use any or all of these features in the solvent extraction zone. If a catalyst is desired, conventional solid hydrogenation catalysts can be satisfactorily utilized, such as nickel-molybdate on an alumina-silica support, or a cobalt-molybdate catalyst, or any other hydrogenation catalyst known to those skilled in the art and applicable to the solvent-coal system environment maintained in the extraction zone, including the use of a slurry-catalyst system.

It is believed that hydrogenation in the extraction zone generally accomplishes the following functions: transfer of hydrogen directly to coal molecules; transfer of hydrogen to hydrogen-donor molecules; transfer of hydrogen from hydrogen-donor molecules to coal molecules; and various combinations of the above. By way of emphasis, as used herein, the term "extraction zone" is intended to include the pulverization step, the digestion step, or combined pulverization-digestion. After separation of the gaseous materials, including hydrogen, undissolved coal residue (e.g., ash) and catalyst, if any, from the total effluent of the extraction zone, the liquid coal extract is passed into conventional recovery facilities wherein valuable liquid hydrocarbons are recovered.

Example: This example illustrates an advantage to using colloidal size coal during the solvent extraction step. An Eastern Kentucky Stoker Coal having the following properties was crushed to the following sizes: 95% less than 2 microns; 5% greater than 100 microns.

	Weight Percent
Ash	3.67
Nitrogen	1.60
Sulfur	1.36
Oxygen	6.99
Free H_2O	1.61
Volatile matter	40.30
Carbon	79.66
Hydrogen	5.55

One part of the colloidal coal was mixed with solvent and charged to a stirred autoclave, and pressured with hydrogen gas. The liquid coal extract was recovered from the contents of the autoclave by filtration and distillation (including solvent removal). The following results were obtained on two runs:

	Solvent	
	Methylnaphthalene	Tetralin
Pressure, psig, H_2	2,000	2,000
Temperature, °C.	430	430
Solvent/coal ratio	3:1	3:1
Residence time, hours	1	2
Percent conversion, maf coal	71.3	90.0
Percent H_2 in extract	–	7.01

Hydrogenated Thianaphthenes for the Extraction of Coal

L.E. Ruidisch and E.F. Pevere; U.S. Patent 2,681,300; June 15, 1954; assigned to The Texas Company found that a hydrogenated thianaphthene, such as dihydrothianaphthene, is a superior treating agent for the recovery of the liquid components of coal. In this process the coal is digested with the hydrogenated thianaphthene at elevated temperatures to effect recovery of liquid constituents. It is found that the action of the hydrogenated thianaphthene on the coal goes beyond that of a mere solvent effect since the hydrogenated thianaphthenes appear to serve as a carrier of active hydrogen, and a hydrogen exchange reaction in addition to the solvent action takes place so as to produce very high yields of recovered extract.

The coal preferably in a pulverized form is digested with hydrogenated thianaphthene, such as dihydrothianaphthene, at elevated temperatures of the order of 600° to 700°F. The digestion is conducted without release of gas in order to promote the hydrogenating or hydrogen transfer reaction. The solvent is preferably used in weight proportions somewhat in excess of that of the coal.

In a typical example of the process 150 grams of bituminous coal of 10 to 50 mesh and 300 grams of dihydrothianaphthene were charged to a bomb. The bomb was heated in a rocking sleeve heater to 650°F. and held at this temperature for 2 hours. The pressure rose to a maximum of 300 lbs. per square inch indicating the release of hydrogen from the solvent. After cooling, the contents of the bomb were washed out with benzene and the whole mass both solid and liquid was poured into the thimble of a Soxhlet extractor and extracted with benzene. The solids recovered were dried to constant weight. This material which was considered as unextracted coal amounted to 106 grams. The extract was distilled to remove the benzene and the extraction solvent was removed by distillation under reduced pressure. The recovered extract amounted to 41 grams.

Thus the percentage of coal extracted was 29% and the weight percent of the recovered extract based on the coal charge was 27%.

SOLVATION AND DEPOLYMERIZATION

Solvent Depolymerization of Coal

The process by M. Orchin; U.S. Patent 2,476,999; July 26, 1949; assigned to U.S. Secretary of the Interior has been found to improve yields of soluble materials by using solvent vehicles of the bicyclic hydroaromatic series which contain a phenolic hydroxy group. Examples of such compounds which are particularly effective are ortho- and para-cyclohexylphenol and tetrahydronaphthols, such as 1,2,3,4-tetrahydro-5-hydroxynaphthalene.

These solvents normally are employed in about equal parts by weight with the solid carbonizable fuel being extracted, that is a ratio of from 1:1 to 3:2. Under some conditions of operations however the amount of solvent may be increased, although in general it is not necessary or desirable to exceed a ratio of about 4:1.

The extraction is carried out using finely ground or comminuted coal, lignite and the like with the solvent in the desired ratio, under pressures of about 500 lbs./sq. in. and at temperatures of about 400°C. While the pressure may be higher or lower than 500 lbs./sq. in., normally it should not exceed about 1,500 lbs./sq. in. Temperatures may vary from about 250°C. to as high as 450°C., although for typical American bituminous coals it is preferred to operate at approximately 400°C. The operating temperature, in any event, should not exceed that at which there is noticeable pyrolysis of the coal, etc., to be extracted.

This process may be carried out as a batch type operation or in continuous or semicontinuous manner as desired. Either a neutral or reducing atmosphere may be maintained during the extraction. Under these conditions there is no substantial hydrogenation of the extract, the consumption of hydrogen representing from 1 to 2% by weight of the solid material being extracted.

It is not necessary to use substantially pure compounds in this class. Quite satisfactory results may be secured from crude compounds and mixtures, of course, will give equally desirable results. Thus, mixtures of ortho- and paracyclohexylphenol are suitable for the process, as are mixtures of the tetrahydrohydroxynaphthalones. The high boiling tar acid fractions from the hydrogenation of certain coals afford a suitable source from which may be conveniently prepared crude mixtures of these solvents which may be used without further separation and/or purification.

Following the pressure extraction, the solid residual matter is separated from the extract by filtration or centrifuging. The separated solids consist for the most part of the mineral matter, or ash, of the coal or the like starting material, together with unconverted or unextracted starting material. The separation may be effected with or without dilution with the same or other solvents. Such diluents, however, should be chemically similar to the initial solvents, preferably containing a phenolic hydroxyl group in the molecule, as has been found, benzene and similar nonpolar aromatic compounds are likely to precipitate some of the extracted material. Such precipitates, particularly when admixed with ash and unconverted coal, are extremely resistant to solvents, and thus lower the liquefaction yield.

Example: A Bruceton bituminous coal from the Pittsburgh bed was ground to pass 90% through a 100 mesh screen. This coal had the following analysis:

Proximate Analysis	Percent by Weight
Moisture	2.1
Volatile matter	36.0
Fixed carbon	54.7
Ash	7.2

Ultimate Analysis	Percent by Weight
Hydrogen	5.2
Carbon	75.5
Nitrogen	1.5
Sulfur	1.5
Oxygen	9.1
Ash	7.2

One part of the ground coal was admixed with four parts by weight of o-cyclohexylphenol and charged to a stainless steel autoclave containing hydrogen at one atmosphere pressure. The sealed vessel and contents were heated to 400°C. while being rotated to agitate the contents. The pressure due to the vapors of the solvent any any permanent gases present, rose to about 500 lbs./sq. in. After thirty minutes of treatment the contents of the autoclave were discharged and centrifuged to separate extract from the mineral residue (ash) and unconverted coal constituents. The percentage of extraction was determined as 81.6 calculated according to the following formula:

$$\% \text{ extraction} = 100 - \frac{\text{weight of residue } (100 - \% \text{ ash in residue})}{\text{weight of dry, ash-free coal}}$$

When the same coal is extracted under comparable conditions with a solvent comprising naphthalene, phenol and Tetralin (2:1:2) the percentage of extraction was 51.3, while the Tetralin alone the percentage was 49.4.

Hydrogenation of Solvent Extracts

E. Gorin; U.S. Patent 3,162,594; December 22, 1964; assigned to Consolidation Coal Company describe a process for producing distillable hydrocarbonaceous liquid from ash-containing, nondistillable extract obtained by the solvent extraction of coal.

It was found that the coal-extract ash which is below 0.01 micron in diameter, whether soluble or insoluble in the coal extract, is particularly harmful during catalytic hydrocracking of the coal extract. The metallic contaminants found in coal extract are metals which usually appear in the form of compounds, for example, silicates, complex aluminum silicates, sulfates, sulfides, chlorides, and oxides. The metals include sodium, silicon, iron, calcium, magnesium, aluminum, and titanium.

The ash-containing coal extract, at least a portion of which is insoluble in benzene and which contains at least some ash (either soluble or insoluble in the extract) which is smaller than 0.01 micron in diameter, is subjected to hydrogenation. During hydrogenation of the coal extract, hydrogen is added to the extract under conditions such that a product comprising a minor amount of an ash-free, distillable hydrocarbonaceous liquid, which is completely soluble in benzene, and a major amount of an ash-containing, nondistillable hydrocarbonaceous liquid is obtained. The nondistillable hydrocarbonaceous liquid comprises at least 50 weight percent of the coal extract fed to the hydrogenation zone. As a result of the hydrogenation treatment, the nondistillable liquid is more soluble in benzene and contains less ash below 0.01 micron in diameter than the original ash-containing coal extract. At least a portion of the nondistillable liquid subsequently is catalytically hydrocracked to produce additional ash-free, benzene-soluble, distillable hydrocarbonaceous liquid. The distillable hydrocarbonaceous liquid (sometimes referred to as hydrogen-enriched hydrocarbonaceous liquid) from both hydrogenation and hydrocracking is suitable for refining to gasoline.

Referring to Figure 2.12, extract, obtained by treating bituminous coal such as Pittsburgh seam coal in a solvent extraction zone (not shown) wherein at least 35 weight percent of the maf coal is dissolved, is introduced after separation from the residue into a conventional type mixing zone 10 via a conduit 12. Generally, up to 75 weight percent of the extract is insoluble in benzene and the extract contains approximately 0.10 to 0.30 weight percent ash; up to one-half of which is insoluble ash having a particle diameter greater than 0.01 micron. The remaining coal extract ash generally consists of soluble-ash or insoluble-ash having a particle diameter below 0.01 micron.

Catalyst, introduced via a conduit 14, is mixed with the extract in the zone 10 preferably at atmospheric pressure and at a temperature which is sufficient to maintain the extract in the liquid state, generally about 190°C. If lower temperatures are desired, a hydrocarbonaceous solvent may be added to the extract to maintain it in the liquid state. Typical solvents are those which are employed in the solvent extraction zone, for example, tetrahydronaphthalene, Decalin, and various extract hydrogenation and hydrocracking products. Any conventional type catalyst commonly used for hydrogenation of coal extract may be introduced into the mixing zone 10. A mixture of the extract and the catalyst is continuously withdrawn from the mixing zone 10 via a conduit 16 and introduced into a catalytic hydrogenation zone 18.

Hydrogen is introduced into the hydrogenation zone 18 via a conduit 20, wherein it reacts with the extract under the following conditions: 375° to 460°C., 1,000 to 10,000 psig, a hydrogen feed rate in the range of 10 to 50 scf/lb. extract feed, and a liquid feed rate in the range of 20 to 150 lbs./ft.^{3} reaction space. The catalyst concentration in the hydrogenation zone is maintained within the range of 2.5 to 50.0 weight percent, preferably between about 5 and 25 weight percent. As hydrogen and extract react under the above conditions, benzene-insoluble coal extract is converted to benzene-solubles. Correspondingly, soluble-ash and insoluble-ash having a particle diameter below 0.01 micron contained therein is converted to insoluble ash having a particle diameter greater than 0.01 micron.

By nondistillable hydrocarbonaceous liquid, it is meant a liquid which is nondistillable without decomposition such as coal extract. In fact, the nondistillable hydrocarbonaceous liquid is the same as coal extract except for the increased amount of hydrocarbonaceous liquid which is soluble in benzene and the lower amount of ash below 0.01 micron that is contained therein.

A product stream is continuously withdrawn from the catalytic hydrogenation zone 18 via a conduit 22. The product stream comprises catalyst, the distillable hydrocarbonaceous liquid, and the nondistillable hydrocarbonaceous liquid hydrogenation

FIGURE 2.12: HYDROGENATION OF SOLVENT EXTRACTS

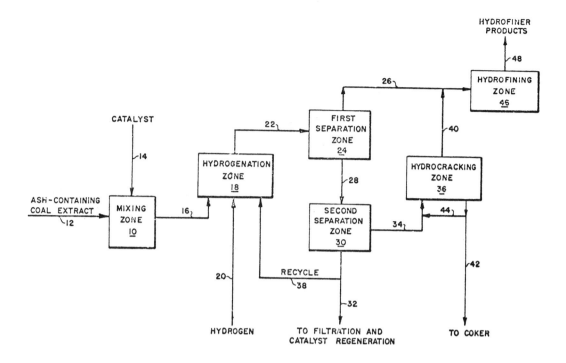

Source: E. Gorin; U.S. Patent 3,162,594; December 22, 1964

product. These products are introduced into a first separation zone 24 wherein the distillable hydrocarbonaceous liquid, which is ash-free and essentially completely soluble in benzene, is separated from the catalyst and the ash-containing, nondistillable hydrocarbonaceous liquid. The distillable liquid is withdrawn from the zone 24 via a conduit 26. Preferably, substantially all of the distillable liquid is subjected to hydrofining as hereinafter explained; however, if desired, portions of the distillable liquid may be used for other purposes, for example, as solvent for the solvent extraction of the coal.

The catalyst and the nondistillable liquid hydrocarbonaceous product are withdrawn from the first separation zone 24 via a conduit 28 and introduced into a second separation zone 30. The separation zone 30 is preferably a sedimentation zone or one which employs centrifugal force as a means of separating, for example, a hydroclone. This type of separation zone is preferred in the nondistillable hydrocarbonaceous liquid in the form of a concentrated slurry. It is desirable to reintroduce at least a portion of the catalyst into the hydrogenation zone; therefore, it is preferred to maintain the catalyst in the form of a concentrated slurry in order to minimize degradation of the individual catalyst particles due to attrition. Catalyst in the form of a concentrated slurry is withdrawn from the separation zone 30 via a conduit 32, while substantially catalyst-free, ash-containing, nondistillable hydrocarbonaceous liquid is withdrawn from the zone 30 via a conduit 34. The latter is preferably introduced into a dense bed, liquid phase fluidized catalytic hydrocracking zone 36.

At least a portion of the concentrated catalyst slurry is reintroduced into the hydrogenation zone 18 via a conduit 38, while the remaining portion is introduced into a filtration zone (not shown). At least a portion of the catalyst obtained from the filtration zone is subsequently treated to remove carbon deposits in a conventional type catalyst regeneration zone. The regenerated catalyst is generally reintroduced into the mixing zone 10. The nondistillable hydrocarbonaceous liquid hydrogenation product separated from the catalyst in the filtration zone is preferably introduced in admixture with the liquid hydrogenation product into the fluidized catalytic hydrocracking zone 36. If desired, however, a portion of the nondistillable liquid may be subjected to coking, for example, to produce electrode carbon and a distillate.

The fluidized catalytic hydrocracking zone 36 preferably contains a plurality of sections, as previously mentioned. Hydrocracking catalyst preferably having a rather narrow size consist within the range of 8 x 100 mesh Tyler Standard screen, e.g., 16 x 24 mesh, 24 x 48 mesh, and 35 x 65 mesh, is introduced in countercurrent flow relationship to the nondistillable hydrocarbonaceous liquid. The hydrocracking zone 36 is maintained under the following conditions: 400° to 550°C., 1,000 to 10,000 psig, a hydrogen feed rate of from 10 to 50 scf/lb. of feed, and a liquid feed rate of from 10 to 150 pounds per cubic feet reaction space. The catalyst employed therein may be any of the catalysts which are commonly used by those skilled in the art for hydrocracking extract, such as metals of subgroups V to VIII of the Periodic Chart, preferably oxides, and combinations thereof. A preferred catalyst is one containing a metal oxide or sulfide of subgroup VI of the Periodic Chart, i.e., molybdenum, combined with a relatively minor amount of a transition group metal oxide or sulfide such as cobalt or nickel. The active hydrocracking metals are preferably supported on a hydrous oxide support such as alumina gel.

As hydrogen and the nondistillable liquid react under the above conditions, a portion of the nondistillable liquid is converted to an ash-free, benzene-soluble, distillable hydrocarbonaceous liquid product which is continuously withdrawn from the zone 36 via a conduit 40. The remaining nondistillable liquid is withdrawn from the zone 36 via a conduit 42. The agglomerated ash passes through the liquid phase, dense fluidized bed of catalyst and is withdrawn from the hydrocracking zone 36 suspended in the unconverted nondistillable liquid product. Preferably, a portion of the ash-containing unconverted nondistillable liquid product is recycled to the zone 36 via a conduit 44; however, if desired, all or portions of the liquid product may be introduced into the hydrogenation zone 18 or introduced into a conventional type coking zone, e.g., a delayed coker (not shown).

The ash-free, distillable liquid product withdrawn via the conduit 40, preferably is admixed with the distillable hydrocarbonaceous liquid hydrogenation product (conduit 26) and the mixture is subjected to hydrofining as hereinafter explained. If desired, however, a portion of the distillate liquids may be used as solvent for the aforementioned solvent extraction of the coal.

Deactivated hydrocracking catalyst is withdrawn (not shown) from the fluidized catalytic hydrocracking zone 36 and preferably at least a portion is introduced into the mixing zone 10 as the hydrogenation catalyst. Normally, catalyst which is too inactive for economic hydrocracking will still be sufficiently active to convert benzene-insolubles to benzene-solubles. Preferably, however, the deactivated hydrocracking catalyst is crushed prior to use in the hydrogenation zone. Crushing the catalyst restores a substantial amount of activity to the hydrocracking catalyst. In fact, the crushed hydrocracking catalyst is sufficiently active to produce, during hydrogenation, a nondistillable hydrocarbonaceous liquid which is substantially completely soluble in benzene and which contains a substantially reduced amount of ash below 0.01 micron in diameter.

If desired, the above overall process may be conducted as a continuous, semicontinuous, or batch operation. Moreover, in place of the fluidized catalytic hydrocracking zone 36 employed in the preferred embodiment, any conventional type of hydrocracking zone may be employed. Naturally, the use of a hydrocracking zone other than a fluidized catalytic hydrocracking zone will result in increased deposition of ash on the catalyst: however, such deposition will be substantially less than the deposition which occurs when the extract is introduced directly into the zone without the prior hydrogenation treatment.

If desired, prior to introducing the ash-containing nondistillable liquid hydrogenation product into the hydrocracking zone, the liquid product may be treated to remove the portion of the insoluble ash having a particle diameter greater than 1.2 microns if any is present, for example, by filtration. The ash-free, distillable hydrocarbonaceous liquid product (conduit 26) is introduced into a hydrofining zone 46. The distillate feed is reacted in the zone 46 with hydrogen in the presence of a catalyst under the following conditions:

	Broad	Preferred
Temperature, °C.	340 to 470	380 to 430
Pressure (total), psig	500 to 4,500	1,000 to 3,000
Hydrogen ratio, scf/bbl. feed	1,000 to 10,000	1,500 to 3,000
LHSV, v./v./hr.	0.2 to 2.0	0.5 to 1.5

The effluent hydrofiner products, recovered from the zone 46 via a conduit 48, are substantially free of nitrogen, oxygen, and sulfur compounds. The effluent products are preferably fractionated to recover a gasoline fraction boiling below about 193°C.

Example: Extract, obtained by the solvent extraction of a Pittsburgh seam coal at 380°C. with tetrahydronaphthalene solvent, was introduced into hydrogenation zone in admixture with a catalyst. The extract contained 0.18 weight percent total ash and 38 weight percent benzene insolubles. Approximately half of the ash was insoluble-ash having a particle diameter greater than 0.01 micron while the remaining portion of the ash was soluble-ash and insoluble-ash having a particle diameter below 0.01 micron. The catalyst was crushed, deactivated hydrocracking catalyst that had been previously employed for hydrocracking a similar extract. The catalyst, when originally introduced into the hydrocracking zone, was an alumina base catalyst containing 13% by weight MoO_3 and 3% by weight CoO. The catalyst was employed in the hydrocracking zone until no further absorption of ash occurred (the catalyst had absorbed 10.5 weight percent ash), at which point the catalyst would normally be discarded. The catalyst was withdrawn from the hydrocracking zone and then regenerated with air in order to remove carbon deposits. The regenerated catalyst was crushed such that substantially all the catalyst particles had a particle diameter with the range of about 0 to 200 microns. The actual particle size distribution of the crushed catalyst was as follows: 50% by weight of the particles were between 147 and 200 microns; 36% by weight of the particles were between 74 and 147 microns and 14% by weight of the particles were between 0 and 74 microns. The conditions of the hydrogenation zone were as follows:

Temperature, °C.	440
Partial pressure of hydrogen, psig	3,500
Hydrogen feed rate, scf/lb. extract	15
Residence time, hr.	1
Catalyst/extract feed ratio	0.046

The products of prehydrogenation were collected and analyzed.

	Yields, Percent by Wt., of Extract Feed
Hydrocarbon gas C_1 to C_4	5.6
Butanes	1.5
C_5 +400°C. distillate oil	35.4
+400°C. nondistillable liquid hydrogenation product	54.2
Hydrogen consumed	4.0

Substantially all of the nondistillable liquid hydrogenation product was soluble in benzene. Furthermore, approximately 90 weight percent of the soluble-ash and insoluble-ash having a particle diameter below 0.01 micron contained in the original extract was converted to insoluble-ash having a particle diameter above 0.01 micron.

Extraction and Hydrogenation of Coal

A. Pott and H. Broche; U.S. Patent 2,308,247; January 12, 1943 describe a process for the extraction followed by hydrogenation of Ruhr type coal. In this process the difficulties encountered in earlier hydrogenations, namely the incomplete hydrogenation of free carbon-like materials, are overcome and maximum throughputs obtained in the hydrogenation of coal extracts, pitch and so forth, by continuously withdrawing a part of the sludge arising in the hot separator and adding it to the crude coal extract solutions before the filtration. In this way the solid substances accumulating in the sludge, such as for example the so-called free carbon from pitch, ash accumulations and the like, are separated off by the filtration of the crude coal extract solutions and get into the ash-containing residual coal of the extraction, with which they are then burned after expulsion of the extraction oils, for example in boiler firings. The oily and reactive portions of the sludge, however, pass into the pure filtrate and, after expulsion of the extraction agent, are together with the coal extracts supplied again to the hydrogenation.

In certain cases, in the common hydrogenation of coal extracts and tar pitches it may be advisable to admix the pitch with the crude coal extract solutions before the filtration so that the ash constituents of the pitch and its portions of so-called free carbon are separated off right from the first and led away together with the ash-containing residual coal of the coal extraction and for example used in firing. In the pure filtrate there are then the ash-free and solid-free, and consequently readily hydrogenated, portions of the pitch together with the coal extract.

After expulsion of the solvent, the mixture of pitch and coal extract is then supplied to the high pressure hydrogenation. In this case also difficultly reactive fractions which have become insoluble accumulating in the sludge can then if desired be drawn off and supplied to the filtration together with the crude coal extract solution. In this way it is possible to obtain maximum throughputs in the high pressure reaction chamber and to maintain at a desired low level the concentration of solid substances, inorganic portions and so forth during the high pressure hydrogenation.

The employment of raised pressures of above 300 atm. gauge pressure, more particularly pressures of 400 to 700 atm. gauge pressure and more, ensures a complete decomposition or degradation of the crude substances introduced. According to this process throughputs are forthwith obtained amounting to 0.3 kg. up to above 1 kg. and more per liter of reaction space per hour. The accompanying diagram represents a flow sheet showing the steps comprised in the process.

Example: A mineral coal from the Ruhr is stirred up with a middle oil which is obtained in the subsequent joint hydrogenation of pitch and mineral coal extract, and is led through a high pressure apparatus at a high temperature. The resulting crude extract solution is released from pressure and cooled down to a lower temperature. To this crude degrade is added a part of the sludge arising in the hot separator of the hydrogenation chamber. Preferably the pitch is also admixed with these crude extract solutions. The mixture of crude degrade, pitch and sludge is then supplied to a pressure filter in which, at a high pressure and temperature, the ash constituents of the pitch and its portions of so-called free carbon are separated off together with the ash-containing residual coal of the coal extraction. In the pure filtrate there are then, together with the coal extract, the portions of the pitch which are free from ash and solid material and consequently readily hydrogenizable. After expulsion of the solvent, the mixture of pitch and coal extract is then mixed with a relatively high boiling oil and supplied to pressure hydrogenation. In this way great outputs of about 1 kg. per liter of reaction space per hour are obtained, and the concentration of solids, inorganic fractions and so forth during the high pressure hydrogenation maintained at the desired low amount.

FIGURE 2.13: EXTRACTION AND HYDROGENATION OF COAL

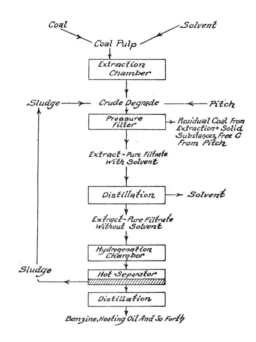

Source: A. Pott and H. Broche; U.S. Patent 2,308,247; January 12, 1943

Two-Stage Conversion of Coal to Liquid Hydrocarbons

B.L. Schulman; U.S. Patent 3,488,279; January 6, 1970; assigned to Esso Research and Engineering Company describes a process whereby coal is hydrogenated to produce liquid products in two stages. The first stage is an initial mild conversion by hydrogen-donor extraction followed by a second stage of catalytic hydrogenation using a cobalt molybdate catalyst and added molecular hydrogen. By this sequence, conversion of oxygen to CO_2 rather than H_2O is maximized, thus more efficiently using the hydrogen to form hydrocarbon products. The liquid products may be hydrocracked in contact with a catalyst similar to that used in catalytic hydrogenation, so that the spent hydrocracking catalyst can be employed as the catalyst in the catalytic hydrogenation stage.

Referring to Figure 2.14, it is seen that the process involves the preparation of a slurry in the zone 100 by admixture of crushed coal introduced by way of line 102 with a hydrogen-donor solvent introduced by way of line 104. The slurry is removed by way of line 106 and is passed into a hydrogen-donor extraction zone 108, wherein the slurry is maintained under conversion conditions, as more specifically set forth hereinafter. The liquid products are separated from the unreacted coal by mechanical separation, such as a hydroclone, and the liquid products are withdrawn from the extraction zone by way of line 110. The gas make is removed by way of line 112 for conversion into hydrogen (e.g., by the water-gas reaction), after removal of any components, such as butanes, pentanes, etc., which have economic values as motor fuels.

The unreacted coal and ash in an oil slurry are removed from the hydrogen-donor extraction zone 108 by way of line 114 and are passed into a catalytic hydrogenation zone 116 where the unreacted coal is contacted with a catalyst introduced

FIGURE 2.14: TWO-STAGE CONVERSION OF COAL TO LIQUID HYDROCARBONS

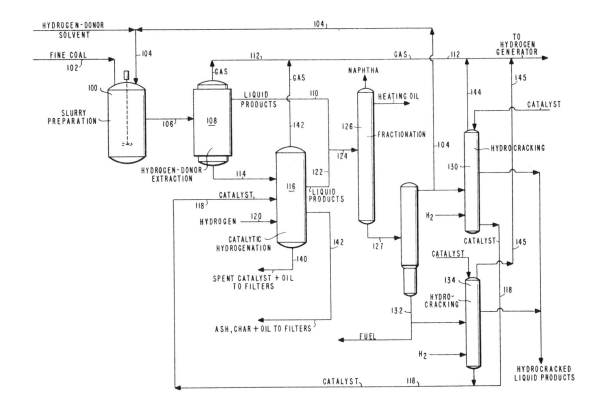

Source: B.L. Schulman; U.S. Patent 3,488,279; January 6, 1970

intermittently or continuously by way of line 118, and hydrogen which is continuously introduced by way of line 120. The hydrogenation is carried out in the liquid phase in the presence of liquid products produced by catalytic hydrogenation of the unreacted coal.

The liquid products from the catalytic hydrogenation zone are withdrawn by way of line 122 and combined with the liquid products from the hydrogen-donor extraction zone and the combined stream is passed by way of line 124 to an atmospheric pressure pipestill 126, where the combined liquid products are fractionated into naphtha and heating oil (e.g., 450° to 600°F.) fractions. Atmospheric tower bottoms are carried by line 127 and introduced into a vacuum pipestill for separation into heavy gas oil (e.g., 600° to 950°F.) and heavy vacuum bottoms (950°+F.). The heavy gas oil is in part recycled to serve as a hydrogen-donor solvent (via line 104) and the remainder is hydrocracked in zone 130, preferably in a fixed-bed catalytic reaction. The heavy bottoms is in part passed to fuel by line 132 and the remainder is hydrocracked in zone 134 in either a fixed bed or liquid-fluidized bed catalytic reaction. Liquid hydrocracked products from both zones are combined for fractionation and recovery of motor fuel and other fractions. Spent catalyst from both hydrocracking zones may be conducted (e.g., by a slurry line 118) intermittently or continuously into zone 116.

Spent catalyst and some occluded oil are removed from the bottom of catalytic hydrogenation zone 116 by way of line 140, and the oil is preferably recovered by filtration. The fine ash and char, plus the occluded oil, are removed from the upper part of the zone 116, and the oil is recovered by filtration. Gas from the catalytic hydrogenation zones is withdrawn by way of line 142 and preferably is combined with the gas make 112 from hydrogen-donor extraction for passage to the hydrogen generator. Likewise, the offgas from the hydrocracking units is passed by way of lines 144 and 145 for admixture with the gas make from the reaction zones or possibly for other treatment to increase the hydrogen purity.

High conversions of coal are achieved in this two-stage process. The first conversion stage is a hydrogen-donor extraction reaction, which eliminates most of the oxygen in the coal as CO_2. The second conversion stage is a catalytic hydrogenation zone which can achieve a high conversion (greater than 90%, based on the unreacted coal which has been charged thereinto) but which tends to react oxygen with hydrogen, an inefficient way to use the expensive hydrogen reactant. The elimination of oxygen in the first stage, however, minimizes the consumption of hydrogen in the catalytic hydrogenation zone since little oxygen remains for reaction with hydrogen.

The first reaction zone is devoted to the hydrogen-donor extraction of the comminuted coal. Reaction conditions in the hydrogen-donor extraction zone include a solvent-to-coal weight ratio of 1:1 to 2:1; a temperature of 700° to 750°F.; a pressure chosen to maintain the solvent predominantly in the liquid phase at the temperature of operation, usually within the range from 50 to 800 psig, preferably about 350 psig (depending on the vapor pressure of the chosen solvent), and an average residence time for the coal in the extraction zone within the range from 0.25 to 2.0 hours, preferably 0.5 hour.

In this first-stage reaction zone, a coal conversion (based on moisture and ash-free coal) is obtained which is suitably within the range from 50 to 85 weight percent, preferably about 80 weight percent. Also, from 70 to 90 weight percent of the oxygen present in the coal will be removed, preferably 85 weight percent. The liquid products obtained are removed from the solvent extraction zone, together with the solvent, and may be fractionally separated therefrom to provide a recycle solvent stream which may be separately hydrogenated before return to the extraction zone, or preferably the solvent and liquid product are passed together through the subsequent treating facilities for hydrocracking. A recycle stream is obtained by fractionation of the hydrocracked products. Hydrogen added in the hydrocracking zone replaces the hydrogen withdrawn in the extraction zone.

A portion of the solvent and liquid products of the hydrogen-donor extraction is separated from the ash and unreacted coal which are present in the effluent from the extraction zone. This may be done mechanically, preferably by using a hydroclone-type separator. The ash and unreacted coal, suitably as a sludge or slurry with a portion of the liquid from the extraction zone, are introduced into a catalytic hydrogenation zone for further conversion of the coal. The catalyst is maintained in the form of a liquid-fluidized bed or is entrained in the liquid stream to avoid the plugging which might occur in a fixed-bed operation.

The liquid which supports the catalyst and acts as a diluent can be supplied by increasing the amount of solvent and extract products carried from the extraction zone with the ash and unreacted coal. However, the liquid is provided by reaction of unreacted coal with hydrogen in the catalytic hydrogenation zone. During startup of the unit, liquid is supplied by solvent and extract from the hydrogen-donor extraction zone.

The weight ratio of the liquid medium to the unreacted coal will be within the range of 1:1 to 4:1, preferably 1:1 to 2:1. Reaction conditions within the catalytic hydrogenation zone will include a temperature of 650° to 850°F., preferably 800°F., a pressure within the range of 1,500 to 3,500 psig, preferably 2,000 psig, and a residence time for the coal within the range from 0.1 to 1 hour, preferably 0.25 hour. Recycle gas, containing more than 75 mol percent hydrogen, is introduced into the reaction zone at a rate of from 25 to 75M scf/ton maf coal, preferably 50M scf/ton.

Example: A subbituminous coal having the proximate and ultimate analyses given in the table below is finely divided to obtain a particle size distribution as shown.

Proximate Analysis	Weight Percent
Moisture	21.20
Ash	8.55
Volatiles	35.55
Fixed carbon	34.70
	100.00

Ultimate Analysis	Weight Percent
Moisture	21.20
Ash	8.55
Hydrogen (ex H_2O)	3.82
Carbon	50.98
Nitrogen	0.74
Sulfur	0.65
Oxygen (ex H_2O)*	14.06
	100.00

*This is equivalent to 20% oxygen based on maf coal.

The finely divided coal described in the previous table is admixed with Tetralin in a weight ratio of solvent to coal of about 2:1. The slurry is admixed in a hydrogen-donor extraction zone at a temperature of about 825°F., and a pressure of about 750 psig, and is reacted for a residence time of 0.5 hour with the hydrogen-donor solvent (Tetralin) to obtain a conversion of the coal of 80 weight percent on a maf basis. In this hydrogen-donor extraction zone, about 85 weight percent of the combined oxygen in the coal is removed in the gas phase, at an H_2O to CO_2 weight ratio of 1.5:1. The liquid products of the hydrogen-donor reaction are removed along with the hydrogen-depleted solvent, and are later separated from the solvent so that the liquid products may be hydrocracked.

The 20% of the coal which is unreacted contains about 12 weight percent O_2 on a maf basis, or only about 15% of the oxygen originally charged with the fresh coal. It (along with ash) is charged to a catalytic hydrogenation zone in contact with a cobalt molybdate catalyst and molecular hydrogen. The hydrogenation is carried out under a temperature of 825°F., a pressure of 2,000 psig, a solids residence time of 0.5 hour, and a hydrogen feed rate of 50M scf/ton maf char fed to reactor.

In this hydrogenation zone, a conversion of the coal feed is carried to 90 to 95 weight percent, and the remaining oxygen is withdrawn mainly as water, the H_2O to CO_2 weight ratio being about 5.0:1. Thus, in the first zone 85% of the oxygen is converted (51% conversion to water, 34% conversion to CO_2), and in the second zone the remaining 15% is converted (12.5% to water, 2.5% to CO_2). The total conversion to CO_2 is 36.5%, compared to only about 16% if catalytic hydrogenation alone is employed. The overall conversion of coal, in both reaction zones, is about 98 to 99 weight percent.

The liquid products withdrawn from the catalytic hydrogenation zone are admixed with the liquid products from the hydrogen-donor extraction and are fractionated, then subjected to hydrocracking in contact with a cobalt-molybdate catalyst. If hydrocracked in a liquid-fluidized bed, the recycle gas rate is 10,000 scf/bbl., at a temperature of about 800°F., and a pressure of 2,000 psig.

The catalyst after having become spent in the hydrocracking unit may be transformed to the catalytic hydrogenation reactor for use in hydrogenating the unreacted coal from the hydrogen-donor extraction zone. By this process, the use of hydrogen-donor extraction in the first stage allows the use of low temperature and relatively low conversion rates to minimize gas yields and maximize removal of oxygen as CO_2, both aspects contributing to the conversion of hydrogen (which desirably will react with the carbonaceous material in the coal to obtain a liquid hydrocarbon product). In the catalytic hydrogenation zone, higher temperatures are employed in order to obtain higher conversion and, by use of a catalyst, good selectivity toward liquid products. Thus, this process provides a superior means for reducing the solid material in coal to liquid products suitable for commercial use.

DEASHING OF COAL

Deashing as a Means to Produce Liquid Hydrocarbons

The process described by E. Gorin; U.S. Patent 3,184,401; May 18, 1965; assigned to Consolidation Coal Company involves the production of hydrogen enriched hydrocarbonaceous products from coal. More particularly, this process relates to a method for removing ash, i.e., metallic contaminants and the like, from ash-containing coal extract prior to catalytic hydrogenation thereof.

U.S. Patent 3,018,242 (see page 9) and U.S. Patent 3,143,489 (see page 20) have shown that valuable liquid products such as gasoline may be derived from coal by initially subjecting the coal to solvent extraction, whereby a mixture of coal extract and undissolved coal residue is obtained. After separating the extract from the residue, the extract is catalytically hydrogenated to yield a hydrogen enriched hydrocarbonaceous liquid suitable for subsequent refining to gasoline, for example via a refining scheme as illustrated in U.S. Patent 3,143,489.

The extract obtained by the solvent extraction of coal, after being separated from the undissolved coal residue, contains a minute, but economically prohibitive, amount of metallic contaminants, sometimes hereinafter referred to as ash. If this ash is not removed from the coal extract, the ash tends to deposit on the catalyst contained in the hydrogenation zone thereby causing a more rapid decrease in the activity of the catalyst than would otherwise be experienced. Such decrease in activity forces resort to more frequent replenishment of the catalyst with either regenerated or fresh catalyst.

While a few methods have been previously suggested for removing ash from coal extract (e.g., U.S. Patent 2,141,615), these methods are economically prohibitive because they all involve deashing the coal extract at a relatively low temperature, generally below 100°C. Since the solvent extraction and catalytic hydrogenation zones are usually operated at a temperature of at least 250°C., and normally 350° to 450°C., the extract must thus be cooled from the relatively high extraction temperature to the relatively low deashing temperature; deashed; and then reheated to the hydrogenation temperature. Obviously it is desirable that the extract be deashed with the minimum amount of, and preferably without any, cooling and reheating.

Deashing at low temperatures, that is, below 100°C., requires the addition of hydrocarbonaceous solvent to the extract in excess of the amount used for solvent extraction in order to render the extract sufficiently fluid for the deashing treatment. The deashing cost is thus increased by the increased volume of liquid that must be treated and by the cost associated with recovering and recycling the additional hydrocarbonaceous solvent. Unfortunately, a method for deashing ash-containing coal extract without the above disadvantages has heretofore not been developed. Accordingly, it is an object of this process to provide an economic method for producing hydrogen-enriched hydrocarbonaceous products from coal via solvent extraction, deashing, and catalytic hydrogenation, which process is free from the aforementioned disadvantages.

In this process ash-containing extract obtained via the solvent extraction of coal is deashed in admixture with a hydrogen-transferring hydrocarbonaceous liquid at a temperature which is at least as high as the temperature at which hydrogen is transferred from the liquid. Normally hydrogen is not transferred from a hydrogen-transferring hydrocarbonaceous liquid below 250°C. The temperature at which hydrogen is transferred from the hydrogen-transferring hydrocarbonaceous liquid is hereinafter referred to as hydrogen-transferring temperature. The resulting deashed extract is subsequently catalytically hydrogenated to yield the desired hydrogen-enriched hydrocarbonaceous product.

When ash-containing extract is deashed without first substantially cooling the extract, for example, at a temperature above 250°C., degradation of the extract occurs such that the resulting deashed extract is more difficult to catalytically hydrogenate and gives poorer hydrogenation yields than extract which has not been deashed. The degradation is manifested by the formation of coke and by the increase in the high molecular weight, hydrogen deficient portion of the extract. The benzene insoluble content of the extract is a measure of this undesirable, high molecular weight extract portion.

For example, when extract is deashed with acidic reagents at above 250°C., not only is coke formed, but the benzene insoluble content of the extract increases from 38 weight percent in the feed extract to more than 90 weight percent in the deashed extract. Surprisingly, however, when the same deashing treatment is conducted at even higher temperatures (above 300°C.), but in the presence of a hydrogen-transferring hydrocarbonaceous liquid, degradation of the extract is not only prevented, but sufficient hydrogen transfer occurs to actually reduce the benzene insoluble content of the treated extract. By deashing ash-containing coal extract by this process the following occurs:

(a) The economically undesirable cooling-reheating cycle is at least markedly minimized.
(b) The necessity for hydrocarbonaceous solvent in excess of the solvent used for solvent extraction is eliminated, as more fully explained hereinafter.
(c) The extract does not undergo harmful degradation during deashing.
(d) The resulting deashed extract is easier to hydrogenate and gives better hydrogenation yields than extract which has not been deashed.
(e) Most importantly, hydrogenation catalyst life is markedly extended when deashed extract is used.

Hydrogen-Transferring Hydrocarbonaceous Liquids: Suitable hydrogen-transferring hydrocarbonaceous liquids are those predominantly polycyclic hydrocarbons which are partially or completely hydrogenated. Polycyclic hydrocarbon mixtures are generally employed, and are preferably derived from intermediate or final steps of the process. Normally the polycyclic hydrocarbons or mixtures thereof boil above 200°C. and preferably between 260° and 425°C.

Partially hydrogenated polycyclic hydrocarbons are the most active and preferred type of hydrogen-transfer liquids. Examples of such materials are the di, tetra, and octa hydro derivatives of anthracene and phenanthrene; tetrahydronaphthalene and alkyl substituted derivatives of the above types of compounds. Completely saturated polycyclic hydrocarbons such as decalin and perhydrophenanthrene are also active as hydrogen-transferring materials although less active than the corresponding partially hydrogenated compounds.

If desired, nonhydrogen-transferring liquids such as naphthalene, anthracene, biphenyl and their alkyl substituted derivatives may be present in admixture with the hydrogen-transferring materials, for example, such is the case when the hydrogen-transferring hydrocarbonaceous liquid is obtained from intermediate or final steps of the process.

While other materials may be admixed with the hydrogen-transferring hydrocarbonaceous liquid during deashing according to the process, it is important that sufficient hydrogen-transferring liquid be present to prevent extract degradation. Normally, the ration of hydrogen-transferring hydrocarbonaceous liquid to extract which is used during deashing varies between 0.5 and 5/1, and preferably between 1 and 2/1.

Specific Deashing Methods: Any deashing process which is suitable for removing at least a portion of the ash contained in coal extract at a temperature above 250°C. is applicable to this process. The essence of this process is that the deashing must be accomplished in the presence of the hydrogen-transferring hydrocarbonaceous liquid when extract is deashed above 250°C. Suitable specific deashing methods are, for example, washing the ash-containing extract with organic or inorganic acids such as described in U.S. Patent 2,141,615. Aqueous solutions of strong inorganic acids such as hydrochloric acid and phosphoric acid are particularly suitable.

The separated extract, with or without the extraction solvent, is conducted with minimal or no cooling into a deashing zone where at least a portion of the ash contained in the extract is removed therefrom. The extract is deashed in the presence of a hydrogen-transferring hydrocarbonaceous liquid.

In no event is the extract cooled below 250°C. As to whether the extract is deashed at substantially the same temperature as extraction or slightly cooled before deashing depends on the specific deashing treatment used. For example, when extract is deashed with a relatively dilute aqueous reagent, it is necessary to cool the extract below the critical point of water, i.e., below 373°C. However, if the extract is deashed with concentrated aqueous or nonaqueous reagents, the deashing may be conducted at substantially the same temperature as the extraction temperature.

As previously mentioned, the extraction solvent itself may supply a portion or all of the hydrogen-transferring liquid. If desired, however, a portion or all of the solvent may be removed from the extract prior to deashing, for example, via distillation, and the extract deashed in admixture with fresh hydrogen-transferring hydrocarbonaceous liquid. Many methods of removing solvent and adding hydrocarbonaceous liquid can be used. The important step, however, is that the extract be deashed in the presence of a hydrogen-transferring hydrocarbonaceous liquid.

If desired, the extract may be deashed without first separating the residue therefrom. Preferably, however, all of the residue and a portion of the extraction solvent is separated from the extract (for recycle to the extraction zone) prior to deashing. Pittsburgh Seam coal is treated in a solvent extraction zone with a solvent recovered from a previous hydrogenation of extract under the following conditions:

Process Conditions

Temperature	380°C.
Pressure	70 psig
Solvent/coal ratio	1.0
Residence time	1.0 hours

The solvent comprises a mixture of a 260° to 325°C. fraction and a 325° to 425°C. fraction in the ratio (by weight) of 1:1, respectively. The yields of the extraction treatment are:

	Weight Percent Original maf* Coal
Extracts	57.8
Gases + H_2O	7.3
Residue	34.9

*maf means moisture-free and ash-free

The extract is separated from the residue by filtration and the extract is then introduced into a topping still while the residue is carbonized in a fluidized low temperature carbonization retort. The solvent boiling below 325°C. is removed in the topping still. The remaining solvent and extract are introduced into a deashing zone where the extract is contacted with aqueous hydrochloric acid (13.5% acid concentration in the aqueous phase) to remove ash therefrom. The extraction solvent that is not removed by topping supplies the desired hydrogen-transferring hydrocarbonaceous liquid. The deashing conditions are as follows:

Process Conditions

Temperature	315°C.
Pressure	1,600 psig
Parts of aqueous phase per part extract	1.0

As a result of the deashing, 60% by weight of the ash contained in the extract is removed. In addition, because of the presence of the hydrogen-transferring hydrocarbonaceous liquid, the extract is not harmed during deashing. The deashed extract is introduced in admixture with a catalyst into a liquid phase catalytic hydrogenation zone under the following conditions and giving the following yields:

Process Conditions

Temperature	441°C.
Pressure	3,500 psig

(continued)

Process Conditions

Residence time (on fresh feed)	2.8 hours
Catalyst	CoO-MoO$_3$ on Al$_2$O$_3$ base

Yields	Wt. Percent Fresh Feed
C$_1$ to C$_3$	12.5
C$_4$	5.2
C$_5$ to 325°C. distillate	80.6

Because of deashing the extract prior to hydrogenation, 620 lbs. of extract per pound of catalyst may be hydrogenated before the catalyst loses 10% of its activity as measured by hydrogen uptake. However, if the extract is not deashed and is hydrogenated under the same conditions, only 75 lbs. of extract per pound of catalyst can be hydrogenated before the catalyst is deactivated to the same extent.

Deashing in the Presence of Acids

The process of E. Gorin, R.T. Struck and C.W. Zielke; U.S. Patent 3,232,861; February 1, 1966; assigned to Consolidation Coal Company describes a method for the removal of ash, i.e., metallic contaminants and the like, from ash-containing coal extract and from catalysts which have been deactivated during catalytic hydrogenation of ash-containing coal extract. More particularly, this process relates to a method for removing particular ash components from ash-containing coal extract.

The metallic contaminants, i.e., ash, contained in petroleum-derived liquids are generally associated with a porphyrin type of molecule or class of compounds which are to a large extent, if not completely, soluble in the petroleum. In contrast, up to 50 weight percent of the metallic contaminants in coal extract, which contaminants have their origin in the coal feedstock, are insoluble, finely divided particles, substantially all of which have a particle diameter between 0.01 and 2.0 microns, thereby making it difficult, if not impossible, to remove the particles by commercial mechanical separation methods. The remaining metallic contaminants in the coal extract have a particle diameter below 0.01 micron and frequently, a major portion of these remaining contaminants actually are soluble in the coal extract.

The metallic contaminants found in coal extract are metals which usually appear in the form of compounds, for example, silicates, complex aluminum silicates, sulfates, sulfides, chlorides and oxides. The metals include sodium, boron, silicon, potassium, iron, calcium, magnesium, aluminum and titanium. The following Table 1 contains a typical analysis of the metallic contaminants present in a coal extract. The extract was obtained by subjecting Pittsburgh Seam bituminous coal to solvent extraction with tetrahydronaphthalene solvent under the following conditions:

Temperature, °C.	380
Pressure, psig	600
Solvent/coal wt. ratio	2
Residence time, min.	52

The extract was separated (by filtration) from the residue and analyzed for metallic contaminants, expressed as oxides. The alkaline oxide ash compounds comprise less than 40 weight percent of the total metal oxides in the ignited extract ash. The ignition loss is due to subsequent conversion of metal compounds that are stable at the ashing temperature of 1100°F. to the corresponding oxides.

TABLE 1

Metallic Contaminants (expressed as oxides)	Percent by Weight of the Total Contaminants Contained in the Extract
SiO$_2$	20.4
CaO, alkaline ash component	15.9
TiO$_2$	15.5
Al$_2$O$_3$	10.0
Fe$_2$O$_3$	5.5
MgO	1.8
Na$_2$O, alkaline ash component	1.0
K$_2$O, alkaline ash component	0.4
Cr$_2$O$_3$	0.23
V$_2$O$_5$	0.04
Ignition loss	29.23

The following, with reference to Figure 2.15 is a description of the process. Any coal may be used in the process. Preferably, the coal is one having a volatile matter content of at least 20 weight percent, for example, a high volatile bituminous coal such as Pittsburgh Seam coal. A typical composition of a Pittsburgh Seam coal suitable for use is shown in Table 2.

TABLE 2

Proximate Analysis	Weight Percent mf* Coal
Volatile matter	39.3
Fixed carbon	47.7
Ash	13.0
	100.0

Ultimate Analysis	Weight Percent maf** Coal
Hydrogen	5.5
Carbon	80.8
Nitrogen	1.4
Oxygen	7.5
Sulfur	4.8
	100.0

*mf means moisture-free
**maf means moisture-free and ash-free

The feed coal is preferably ground to a finely divided state, for example, minus 14 mesh Tyler Standard screen, and is freed of substantially all extraneous water before introduction into the process. Coal is introduced into a solvent extraction zone 10 via a conduit 12. Hydrocarbonaceous solvent is introduced into the extraction zone 10 via a conduit 14. The coal and the solvent react therein to yield the desired coal extract.

FIGURE 2.15: DEASHING IN THE PRESENCE OF ACIDS

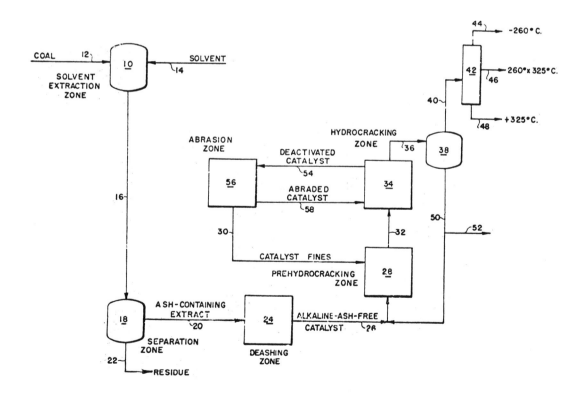

Source: E. Gorin, R.T. Struck and C.W. Zielke; U.S. Patent 3,232,861; February 1, 1966

The solvent extraction process may be any of the processes commonly used in the field, e.g., continuous, batch, counter-current, or staged extraction, at a temperature in the range of 300° to 500°C., a pressure in the range of 1 to 6,500 psig, a residence time in the range of 1 to 120 minutes, a solvent to coal ratio in the range of 0.5 : 1 to 4 : 1 and, if desired, in the presence of a catalyst and up to 50 standard cubic feet of hydrogen per pound of maf coal.

Any of the well-known coal extraction solvents may be used in the extraction zone 10. It is preferred, however, that the solvent be a hydrogen-transferring hydrocarbonaceous liquid. Suitable hydrogen-transferring hydrocarbonaceous liquids are those predominantly polycyclic hydrocarbons which are partially or completely hydrogenated. Polycyclic hydrocarbon mixtures are generally employed and are preferably derived from intermediate or final steps of the process. Normally, the polycyclic hydrocarbons or mixtures thereof boil above 200°C. and preferably between 260° and 425°C. Partially hydrogenated polycyclic hydrocarbons are the most active and preferred type of hydrogen-transfer liquids.

A particularly preferred solvent is a portion of the product obtained from the catalytic hydrocracking zone, as hereinafter more fully explained. This solvent normally comprises a 325° to 425°C. fraction blended with some lower boiling material. The coal and the solvent are maintained in intimate contact within the extraction zone 10 until the solvent has extracted, i.e., converted or dissolved, at least a portion of the coal. Preferably, between 50 and 80 weight percent of the maf (moisture-free and ash-free) feed coal is extracted.

Following extraction, the mixture of solvent, extract, and residue is conducted through a conduit 16 to a separation zone 18 where preferably, substantially all of the residue is separated from the extract and solvent. Normally, the separation zone 18 is a filtration zone; however, if desired, a centrifuge, sedimentation zone, hydroclone and the like may be used. The liquid extraction products (filtrate), comprising ash-containing extract and solvent, are withdrawn from the separation zone 18 via a conduit 20. The residue is recovered via a conduit 22. The separately recovered residue subsequently may be used as boiler fuel or subjected to a fluidized low temperature carbonization process.

The ash-containing coal extract is conducted via the conduit 20 into a deashing zone 24 where at least a portion, and preferably all, of the alkaline ash components are removed from the extract. If desired, at least a portion of the extraction solvent may be removed from the extract prior to introduction into the deashing zone 24. Preferably, however, at least a portion of the extraction solvent is left with the extract during deashing in order to minimize degradation of the coal extract. The extract is treated in the deashing zone 24 to preferentially remove the alkaline ash components, i.e., the compounds of sodium, potassium and calcium. During deashing, some inert ash components will be removed along with the alkaline ash; however, the resulting deashed extract normally contains a much lower proportion of alkaline ash to inert ash than the ash-containing extract feed.

It was found that a substantial portion of the alkaline ash components can be removed simply by contacting the ash-containing coal extract with water. For example, contacting the extract in one or more stages in any conventional type stirred reaction vessel at a temperature between 25° and 370°C., a pressure between 5 and 3,500 psig, and a water to extract ratio (volumetric ratio) between 0.5 and 4.0, for 5 to 120 minutes will normally remove between 65 and 90 weight percent of the alkaline ash components (based on the extract feed) while between 20 and 50 weight percent of the total ash contaminants (based on the extract feed) are removed.

A preferred deashing method is to contact the ash-containing coal extract with a slightly acidic aqueous solution, i.e., an aqueous solution containing sufficient acid to neutralize the alkaline ash components contained in the extract. Normally, less than 0.1 weight percent acid and preferably less than 0.05 weight percent acid is added to the water to form this slightly acidic solution. Preferably, the acid is hydrochloric; however, other mineral acids such as halogen acids and nitric acid are generally suitable, but less attractive economically because of their higher cost. Many other mineral acids such as boric, carbonic, hydrofluoric, phosphoric and sulfuric acids are less suitable because their basic calcium salts are only slightly soluble in water, if at all. Of course, if an excess of the latter acids is used, the calcium acid salts will be formed which are generally more soluble in water. Certain organic acids such as acetic and benzoic may also be used.

By using a slightly acidic aqueous solution to deash the ash-containing coal extract, the number of deashing stages necessary to remove a given amount of alkaline ash is much less than deashing with water alone. For example, between 90 and 96 weight percent of the alkaline ash (based on extract feed) and between 40 and 60 weight percent of the total ash (based on extract feed) is removed from the ash-containing coal extract by washing the extract with a 0.025 weight percent aqueous solution of hydrochloric acid in a first stage and pure water in a second stage. Both stages may be maintained under simular conditions as abovementioned with respect to water alone. Preferably, however, the slightly acidic water treatment is conducted at a temperature between 200° and 300°C., a pressure between 250 and 1,600 psig, for 20 to 60 minutes.

The resulting deashed extract, which still contains inert ash components, is separated from the water or acidified water by simple decantation and is withdrawn from the deashing zone 24 via a conduit 26. The deashed extract contains a much lower proportion of alkaline ash to inert ash than the ash-containing extract feed, and preferably contains no alkaline ash components.

It is important to note that even when slightly acidic water solutions are used to deash the coal extract, the cost associated with such reagents as well as the cost of equipment used to handle such reagents is substantially less than the cost associated with the acid washing deashing schemes used heretofore by prior investigators. Furthermore, the extract normally undergoes little or no degradation due to such water treatment in contrast to the degradation which normally accompanies acid deashing as used heretofore. Of primary importance, however, is the fact that the increase in catalyst life resulting from removing the alkaline ash components more than overcomes the slight added cost associated with removing the alkaline ash. Such is not the case when a substantial portion of the inert ash is removed by washing with highly concentrated acid solutions. At least a portion of the alkaline ash free extract is conveyed by the conduit 26 into a prehydrocracking zone 28, where the extract is hydrocracked in the presence of catalyst fines. These catalyst fines, introduced via a conduit 30, are produced by abrasion of larger hydrocracking catalyst, as is hereinafter more fully explained.

The prehydrocracking zone 28 may be any of the conventional type hydrocracking zones, but preferably the zone 28 is one in which the alkaline ash free extract is treated for purposes of agglomerating the inert ash which is not removed in the deashing zone 24. The agglomerated ash contained in the resulting prehydrocracking products will have less of a deleterious effect on the larger catalyst particles employed in a subsequent hydrocracking zone, as is further discussed by E. Gorin in U.S. Patent 3,162,594. Because the catalyst fines are so small (the catalyst fines normally have a particle diameter below 20 microns), the prehydrocracking zone 28 is operated as a slurry phase or suspensoid type hydrocracking zone. The prehydrocracking products containing the catalyst fines suspended therein are withdrawn from the zone 28 via a conduit 32.

The prehydrocracking zone 28 is preferably maintained at a temperature in the range of 375° to 550°C., a pressure in the range of 1,000 to 10,000 psig, a hydrogen feed rate in the range of 5 to 100 standard cubic feet per pound of feed, and a liquid feed rate in the range of 10 to 150 lbs./ft.^{3} of reaction volume. The catalyst concentration is maintained in the range of 1 to 20 weight percent, and preferably in the range of 3 to 10 weight percent. The prehydrocracking products, suspended catalyst fines, inert ash components and any alkaline ash components not removed during deashing, are conveyed via the conduit 32 into a catalytic hydrocracking zone 34.

The catalytic hydrocracking zone 34 is maintained at a temperature in the range of 400° to 550°C.; a pressure in the range of 1,000 to 10,000 psig; a hydrogen feed rate in the range of 5 to 100 standard cubic feet per pound of feed; and a liquid feed rate in the range of 10 to 150 lbs./ft.^{3} of reaction volume. The catalytic hydrocracking zone 34 may be any one of the conventional type hydrocracking zones used by those skilled in the art where catalyst is maintained in the form of a fixed, gravitating, or fluidized bed therein.

In addition, the catalyst may also be dispersed within the extract in the form of a slurry and then introduced into a slurry phase, catalytic hydrocracking zone such that the catalyst is introduced into, maintained therein, and withdrawn therefrom in the form of a slurry or a suspensoid. Preferably, the catalytic hydrocracking zone 34 is a dense bed, liquid phase fluidized catalytic hydrocracking zone. In this manner the hydrocracking catalysts, which normally have a much larger particle diameter than the catalyst fines (1,600 microns vs. 20 microns or less), are maintained within the hydrocracking zone, and the catalyst fines are removed with the hydrocracking products.

Hydrocracking products containing the catalyst fines suspended therein are withdrawn from the hydrocracking zone 34 and conveyed via a conduit 36 into a hot separation zone 38. Distillable hydrocracking products are withdrawn from the hot separation zone 38 via a conduit 40. These distillable products, after removal of noncondensable gases (not shown), are preferably fractionated in a fractionation zone 42 to yield:

    (1) A fraction boiling below 260°C., which is subsequently refined to gasoline (recovered via a conduit 44).
    (2) A fraction boiling between 260° and 325°C., the major portion of which subsequently is refined to gasoline (recovered via a conduit 46).
    (3) A fraction boiling above 325°C., which is introduced into the extraction zone 10 as makeup solvent (recovered via a conduit 48).

Example: Two coal extracts were prepared from a Pittsburgh Seam bituminous coal by solvent extraction with tetrahydronaphthalene solvent. The conditions of extraction and filtration were adjusted such that in one case a relatively high ash extract was produced, and in the other, a relatively low ash extract was produced. The conditions of extraction used and the ash content of the extracts are listed in Table 3.

TABLE 3

	Extract A	Extract B
Solvent to coal ratio (weight ratio)	2.0	1.5
Extraction temperature (°C.)	380	394
Extraction residence time (min.)	52	28

(continued)

	Extract A	Extract B
Filtration temperature (°C.)	200	264
Extract recovered from filtration (weight percent maf coal)	57.4	74
Ash content of recovered extract (weight percent of extract)	0.13	0.28

Extract A was partially deashed without selective removal of alkaline ash. Extract B was treated for selective removal of alkaline ash components by washing with slightly acidified water in two stages at 90°C. The extract, dissolved in one part of tetrahydronaphthalene and one part of cresol, was washed at 90°C. with two parts of distilled water containing 0.028 weight percent of hydrochloric acid. This washing was followed by washing the extract solution in a second stage with pure water. The total ash and alkaline oxide ash components contained in the deashed extracts A and B are shown in Table 4.

TABLE 4:   ASH CONTENT OF DEASHED EXTRACTS (WEIGHT PERCENT OF EXTRACT)

Deashed Extract	Total Ash	Alkaline Ash ($CaO + K_2O + Na_2O$)
A	0.085	0.015
B	0.12	0.004

Catalyst life studies were made with deashed extracts A and B by individually passing them through a dense bed, liquid phase fluidized catalytic hydrocracking zone under the conditions shown in Table 5. The catalyst used had the following composition:

Catalyst Composition	Weight Percent of Catalyst
Nickel metal	3.65
Molybdenum metal	3.70
Cobalt metal	0.08
Alumina	92.57
	100.00

TABLE 5

	Deashed Extract A	Deashed Extract B
Temperature (°C.)	427	427
Pressure (psig)	3,500	3,500
Space rate (g. extract/g. catalyst/hr.)	3.1	3.4
Total extract passed over catalyst (g./g. catalyst)	393	376

The catalysts used in the above runs were regenerated by burning off the carbon with air at 800°F. They were then tested for activity in an autoclave under the standard test conditions shown in Table 6.

TABLE 6

Temperature, °C.	429
Total pressure, psig	4,200
Hydrogen partial pressure, psig	3,500
Residence time, min.	60
Catalyst/extract (weight ratio)	0.30

The hydrogen consumption is used as a measure of the catalyst activity as shown in Table 7.

TABLE 7

	Hydrogen Consumption (wt. percent of extract)	Activity, percent
Fresh catalyst	5.96	100
Spent catalyst A (used with deashed extract A)	4.65	78
Spent catalyst B (used with deashed extract B)	5.06	85

It is seen in Table 7 that in spite of the lower total ash content of deashed extract A, the spent catalyst A showed a significantly lower activity than the spent catalyst B which was used with deashed extract B. This is attributed to a selective poisoning effect of alkaline oxide, i.e., the alkaline oxide content of deashed extract A was significantly higher than the alkaline oxide content of deashed extract B. (Table 4).

The spent catalysts were then abraded in a rotary drum where 5 to 6 weight percent of the outer surface was removed. The activities of the abraded catalysts were again tested under the standard test conditions of Table 6 except that a lower catalyst to extract weight ratio of 0.05 was used.

TABLE 8

Abraded Spent Catalyst	Hydrogen Consumption (wt. percent extract)
Abraded catalyst A	3.09
Abraded catalyst B	3.33

As can be seen from Table 8, the abraded catalyst B which had been exposed to the deashed extract B, which contained high total ash but low alkaline ash, showed a significantly higher activity than abraded catalyst A. Thus selective poisoning of the alkaline oxides is retained even after the outer ash-rich layer is removed by abrasion. Therefore, by alkaline ash removal plus abrasion, an improved economic catalyst life is obtained.

Solvent Processing to Form an Ash-Free Coal

A process developed by W.C. Bull, L.G. Stevenson, D.L. Kloepper and T.F. Rogers; U.S. Patent 3,341,447; Sept. 12, 1967; assigned to the U.S. Secretary of the Interior and Gulf Oil Corporation relates to the solubilizing of carbonaceous fuels by a solution process into low-ash low-oxygen, low-sulfur fuels.

Figure 2.16 illustrates a continuous embodiment in which a raw feed fuel, such as Kentucky No. 11 coal which has been ground by a suitable means, such as a hammer mill (preferably the coal is finely ground to approximately 80% through 200 mesh, U.S. Standard), is fed by means of a conveyor or the like to an agitated tank 1 where it is mixed with solvent (obtained from previous processing) at a ratio of 1:1 to 4:1 solvent to coal. If desired, the coal solvent slurry in tank 1 may be heated to any suitable temperature which will flash off any moisture which may be present in the coal.

Since the solvent used in this process is derived from the coal being dissolved, its composition may vary, depending on the analysis of the coal being used as feedstock. In general, however, the solvent employed in this process is a highly aromatic solvent obtained from previous processing of fuel, and will generally have a boiling range of 150° to 750°C., a density of 1.1 and a carbon to hydrogen mol ratio in the range from 1.0 to 0.9 to 1.0 to 0.3. Generally, any good organic solvent for coal may be used as the initial startup solvent in the process.

A typical solvent is, for example, middle oil obtained from coal and having a boiling range of 190° to 300°C. A solvent found particularly useful as a startup solvent is anthracene oil or creosote oil having a boiling range of 220° to 400°C. However, the selection of a specific startup solvent is not particularly critical since during the process dissolved fractions of the raw feed fuel form substantial quantities of additional solvent which when added to the solvent originally fed into the system provide a total amount of solvent which is greater than the original amount put in the process. Thus, regardless of what the original solvent may have been, it will lose its identity and approach the constitution of the solvent formed by solution and depolymerization of the raw fuel fed into the process. As a result the composition of the solvent approaches that of the same general composition as the deashed product of the processed feed fuel but of lower molecular weight, with the actual composition in each case determined by the composition of the particular raw feed fuel employed. For this reason the solvent, which is employed, may be broadly defined as that obtained from a previous extraction of raw carbonaceous fuels.

In all events the ratio of solvent to coal in the slurry mixed in slurry tank 1 will be in the range of 0.6:1 to 4:1 with a preferred range of 1:1 to 2.3:1. Ratios of solvent to coal of less than 0.$\overline{6}$:1 (i.e., 0.5:1) produce slurries which are of the consistencies of tar upon dissolution of the coal in the solvent, thus rendering them difficult to move in the system and which frequently cause clogging of the system. Ratios of solvent to coal greater than 4:1 may be used but provide no functional advantage in the solution process and suffer the additional disadvantage of requiring additional energy or work for the subsequent separation of solvent from the deashed coal product for recycling in the system.

As will be appreciated, the more solvent that is introduced into the system the more that must be recovered later on. So, from this standpoint, the lower the ratio that can be used, the better. However, other factors, either economic or those based on processability, may override this consideration and dictate that higher solvent to coal ratios be used. The viscosity of various solvent-coal slurries was measured at 75°C. to obtain clarification of the limits.

FIGURE 2.16:   COAL DEASHING PROCESS SCHEMATIC FLOW DIAGRAM

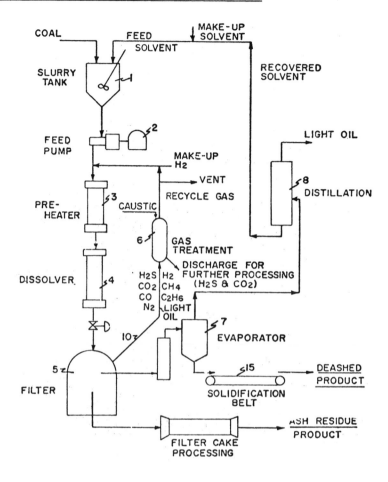

Source: W.C. Bull, L.G. Stevenson, D.L. Kloepper and T.F. Rogers; U.S. Patent 3,341,447; September 12, 1967

It is believed that the following table clearly shows the significance of the 1:1 solvent to coal ratio of the slurry (i.e., 50% coal concentration).

Viscosity of Coal-Solvent Slurry for Various Concentrations of Coal at 75°C.

Percent Coal	Viscosity, cp.
0	4.5
21	11
25	18
33.5	36
35	50
40	90
45.5	260
50	540
55	1,000
63	>10,000

As can be seen in the above table, there is an increase in the viscosity of the coal-solvent slurry when the concentration of coal increases from 50 to 55%. This increase in viscosity causes higher pressure drops in moving the slurries through the system, and also greatly reduces the rate of filtration where employed in the system.

The slurry formed in tank 1 is then fed by means of any suitable method, for example, a positive displacement pump 2, to a preheater 3 and then into a dissolver 4 which is suitably heated to maintain the slurry at its elevated temperature. It is essential in accordance with this process, that hydrogen be added to the slurry ahead of the preheater 3 or dissolver 4 at a partial pressure of at least 500 psi. The hydrogen employed is normally that recycled from previous processing together with any fresh makeup hydrogen required to provide the necessary hydrogen content. Although there is no critical upper limit to the hydrogen pressures employed, for practical reasons, the pressures employed will normally be in the range of 500 to 1,500 psi, with 1,000 psi preferably employed.

The hydrogen pressurized fuel-solvent slurry is heated in the preheaters to rapidly raise the temperature thereof to 370° to 500°C., and preferably 375° to 440°C. The tubes are sized, as to diameter and length, so as to enable the flow of slurry therethrough to be heated to operating temperatures as rapidly as is practical, which in experiments has been obtained as low as 12 to 20 seconds. In general, the preheater will be designed to provide the desired rate of heating to the slurry at a heat flux of not greater than 10,000 Btu/hr./ft.^{2} of tube surface area. Normally in order to maintain good heat transfer, the diameter of the tubes will be sized so as to maintain the slurry in turbulent flow through the preheater.

The length of time in which the solution of the hydrogen pressurized slurry is continued in dissolver 4 is critical to the success of this process. Although the duration of treatment (solution) will vary for each particular carbonaceous fuel treated, it was found that the mechanics of the solution provide an accurate guide for the residence time of the slurry in dissolver 4. In this regard, it was found that the viscosity of the solution obtained during processing of the slurry increases with time in dissolver 4, followed by a decrease in viscosity as this solubilizing of the slurry is continued and then followed by a subsequent increase in the viscosity of the solution on extended holding in the dissolver 4.

One of the criterions used for determining the completion of the solution process, in accordance with this process, is the relative viscosity of the solution formed which is the ratio of the viscosity of the solution to the viscosity of the solvent, as fed, to the process, both viscosities being measured at 210°F. Accordingly, the term Relative Viscosity as used herein is defined as the viscosity at 210°F. of the solution formed divided by the viscosity of the solvent at 210°F. fed to the system, i.e.:

$$\text{Relative Viscosity} = \frac{\text{Viscosity of Solution at 210°F.}}{\text{Viscosity of Solvent at 210°F.}}$$

This Relative Viscosity can be employed for more specific clarification of the residence time for the solution in the dissolver 4. By reference to this Relative Viscosity, it may be noted that as the solubilizing of the slurry proceeds, the Relative Viscosity of the solution first rises above a value of 20 to a point at which the solution is extremely viscous and in a gel-like condition. In fact, if low solvent to coal ratios are used, for example, 0.5:1, the slurry would set up into a gel. After reaching the maximum Relative Viscosity, well above the value of 20, the Relative Viscosity begins to decrease to a minimum after which it again rises to higher values.

It was found essential for the success of this process that the solubilization be allowed to proceed until the decrease in Relative Viscosity (following the initial rise in Relative Viscosity) falls to a value of at least 10 and the resultant solution separated from undissolved residue of the coal before the Relative Viscosity again rises above 10. Normally, the decrease in Relative Viscosity will be allowed to proceed to a value less than 5 and preferably in the range of 1 1/2 to 2.

It may be noted that, during the formation of the solution, the feed fuel depolymerizers in the presence of hydrogen to form fractions which are soluble in the solvent, and it was observed that the depolymerization of the coal during extraction is accompanied by the evolution of hydrogen sulfide, water, carbon dioxide, methane, propane, butane, and other higher hydrocarbons which will comprise part of the atmosphere in the dissolver 4. It was found that the depolymerization of the feed fuel consumes hydrogen up to a weight equivalent to about 2.0% of the weight of the feed fuel (as received), and under preferred conditions, in an amount of 0.5 to 1% of the feed fuel.

Upon completion of the solubilization in dissolver 4, the resultant solution is then charged to a filter 5 for separation of the coal solution from undissolved residue (i.e., mineral matter) of the feed fuel. The filter 5, as shown in the drawing, is a conventional rotary drum pressure filter suitably adapted for pressure let down and venting of gases. It is to be understood that although a rotary drum filter has been described as being utilized in this process, other means of separation may be employed as for example centrifuges and the like.

The gases vented from filter 5 are then passed through a line 10 into a gas treating unit 6 in which hydrogen sulfide and carbon dioxide are scrubbed out in any suitable manner, as for example by caustic solutions. The remaining gas may be given any further treatment desired. The hydrogen sulfide and carbon dioxide free gas recovered is then recycled to the process by feeding to fresh slurry being fed to preheater 3, with all makeup hydrogen being supplied by fresh hydrogen. Analysis of the recovered gases has shown that the overall consumption of hydrogen throughout the system is quite low with the actual consumption of hydrogen being not greater than 2% (based on the feed fuel) and quite often as low as 0.5%.

The filter cake or residue obtained in filter 5 is withdrawn therefrom for additional processing as desired, as for example, solvent recovery, which will be discussed. In practice further processing of the filter cake is desired since, in addition to mineral water, it may contain from between 40 to 50%, by weight, of solvent that can be recovered by pyrolytic distillation. Often this dried filter cake contains about 50% carbon and runs about 7,000 Btu per pound. The further processing of the cake is particularly significant since the coal mineral matter and included solvent may comprise about 10 to 20% of the total weight of the slurry fed to the system. Where the filter cake is comprised of approximately 40 to 50% solvent, the amount of recoverable solvent comprises between 5 to 15% of the original solvent fed into the system. As will be understood, if the filter cake is processed for the recovery of the solvent, the recovered solvent may be recycled into the system for the preparation of additional slurry for feeding into the system.

The filtrate from filter 5 is then pumped at a temperature of 270° to 430°C. through suitable nozzles into a simple vacuum flash evaporator 7 for removal of the majority of the solvent. In accordance with conventional practice, the evaporator will be equipped with a demister to remove any entrained liquid in the vapor, and, also, suitable heaters will be located on the outside of the evaporator to make up for heat losses. The flashed solvent from the evaporator 7 may be passed to a still 8 or recycled directly to the system.

The amount of solvent recovered for recycling to the system will generally comprise a quantity of 85 to 100% of the amount of the solvent originally introduced into the system. This recycled solvent may all come from the evaporator or may be a mixture of solvent from the evaporator and solvent recovered from the filter cake processing. It is to be understood that solvent recovery may be accomplished by a variety of methods, such as wiped film evaporators, and thus such other means may also be employed if desired for recovery of solvent.

The remaining product from evaporator 7, which is liquid at this point may be used as such, or it may be pumped onto a continuous rotating steel belt 15 where it is cooled and solidified. This product, which solidifies upon cooling, is very brittle and breaks into flakes as it finally falls from the belt. Other methods may also be used to recover the product as for example spray cooling or prilling, or, again, if desired the product may be retained in the liquid state and used as such.

This resultant brittle product recovered from evaporator 7 is a hydrocarbon material which has little resemblance to the feed fuel charged into the system. As with the filter cake, a substantial amount of recoverable solvent remains in the product ranging from 15 to 60%. The nature of this product is believed readily evident from the following properties thereof which are set forth in conjunction with corresponding properties of Kentucky No. 11 coal.

Analysis of Process Product Compared with Kentucky No. 11 Coal

	Process Product	Kentucky No. 11 Coal, maf
Carbon, percent	88–89	78.45
Hydrogen, percent	5.0–5.3	5.20
Nitrogen, percent	1.5–1.8	1.19
Sulfur, percent	<1.0	3.74
Oxygen, percent	3.00–3.50	11.40
Volatile matter, percent	15.0–60.0	42.88
Ash, percent	<0.5	7.33
Melting point, °C.	120–280	—
Density, g./cc	1.2–1.3	1.33
Btu/lb.	15,500–16,500	13,978

As can be noted from the above analysis, the percentage of carbon has increased, and the percentages of sulfur and oxygen are substantially lower. The melting point of this product is influenced very strongly by the amount of volatile matter that is left in the product. For example, if a product having about 39% volatile matter and a softening point of 180°C. had been treated so as to leave therein approximately 50% volatile matter, its melting point would be down near 130°C.

Example: Kentucky No. 11 coal, having the same analysis given for it above, was dissolved in a solvent recovered from previous extraction runs (in accordance with this process) under the following conditions:

Process Conditions

Total gas pressure, psig	1,000
Hydrogen in gas, percent	80
Temperature, °C.	410
Solvent : coal ratio	3 : 1

The coal/solvent slurry was heated within 12 to 20 seconds to the reaction temperature of approximately 410°C., and dissolution continued until the Relative Viscosity resultant of the solution rose and then dropped to 3.43. Thereafter, the solution was filtered at this Relative Viscosity from the undissolved residue of the coal, followed by treatment of the filtrate to separate recycle solvent from the product. The resultant product had the analysis shown on the following page.

Carbon, percent	88.16
Hydrogen, percent	5.23
Sulfur, percent	1.17
Nitrogen, percent	1.54
Oxygen, percent	3.42
Ash, percent	0.48
Volatile matter, percent	36.6
Melting point, °C.	220
Density, g./cc	1.24
Btu/lb.	15,768

Production of Ash-Free Anode Carbon

W.J. Bloomer and S.W. Martin; U.S. Patent 3,379,638; April 23, 1968; assigned to The Lummus Company and Great Lakes Carbon Corporation describe the production of useful carbonaceous matter from coal and more particularly relates to the production of substantially ash-free coke from a coal selected from the group consisting of bituminous coal, sub-bituminous coal and lignite.

In accordance with the process, extractable carbonaceous matter present in the pulverized raw coal is digested or dissolved under conditions of elevated temperatures and pressures utilizing a high boiling liquid solvent of high aromaticity thereby forming a solution of such extractable carbonaceous matter (hereinafter referred to as a coal solution). Fusain and the mineral matter or ash are substantially unaffected by the solvent and are suspended in the coal solution.

The coal solution while in a free flowing state is filtered to separate the suspended solids (including undissolved extractable carbonaceous matter) and is thereafter heated to a temperature above incipient coking and passed to a coking unit. Product coke is withdrawn from the coking unit and passed to subsequent processing units including coke handling and calcining facilities. The vaporous products are withdrawn from the coking unit and are introduced into a fractionating unit where they are separated into various fractions, such as, for example: a light gas and gasoline fraction; a medium and heavy middle oil distillate fraction; and a heavy bottoms distillate fraction. A portion or all of the high boiling liquid solvent of high aromaticity utilized for dissolving or digesting the extractable carbonaceous matter present in the raw coal is derived from a distillate fraction recovered from the fractionating unit.

Referring to Figure 2.17, ground or pulverized coal selected from the group consisting of bituminous coal, subbituminous coal and lignite, are collected in a hopper 1 from which it is continuously distributed at a desired rate by a conveying mechanism 2 into a solutizer tank 3 maintained at a pressure of from 1 to 7 to 8 atmospheres. As illustrated, conveying mechanism 2 is a screw type feeder which introduces the coal into solutizer 3 without loss of pressure therein. Any conventional means of mechanical transfer may suffice, providing the means allows for positive transfer of the coal into solutizer 3 without a substantial loss of pressure therein.

The high boiling liquid solvent of high aromaticity is introduced into solutizer 3 through line 4 at a rate so as to provide a ratio of solvent to coal of from 1/2 : 1 to 6 : 1. Normally, a solvent to coal ratio of from 2 : 1 to 3 : 1 is preferred, since effective extraction rates are obtained within this ratio range while minimizing filtration costs. Solutizer 3 is maintained at a temperature of from 600° to 850°F., preferably of from 750° to 825°F. and above the final decomposition temperature of the initial coal whereby a substantial portion of the extractable carbonaceous matter in the raw coal is thermally depolymerized. The products of depolymerization are soluble in the highly aromatic solvent and thereby form, with the solvent, the coal solution. Undissolved and insoluble solids including undissolved extractable carbonaceous matter, and insoluble mineral matter or ash and mineral charcoal of fusain are suspended in the coal solution. An agitator (not shown) may be provided to agitate the coal-solvent mixture during solvation.

Solvation temperatures are maintained in solutizer 3 by withdrawing and circulating a portion of the coal solution and coal-solvent mixture through an external heating system. The withdrawn portion is passed through line 5 by pump 6 under the control of valve 7 to heater 8 and thereafter reintroduced through line 9 into solutizer 3. In this manner, solvation temperatures are maintained within solutizer 3 without the necessity of a high temperature and pressure heating system, which would be the case, if the solvent was preheated to a temperature sufficient to maintain solvation temperatures within the solutizer. A through-put time of the raw coal of from 5 to 120 minutes is normally sufficient to dissolve or digest effectively and efficiently the extractable carbonaceous matter.

Since the solvent may have an initial boiling temperature (converted to one atmosphere) as low as 650°F., whereas solvation temperatures may be as high as 850°F., solutizer 3 is provided with vent line 10 under the control of valve 11 to permit the withdrawal of the lower boiling components of the solvent and any volatile matter vaporized from the raw coal. In this respect, it has been observed that the quantity of volatile matter is practically negligible. A substantially uniform coal solution, where undissolved and insoluble solids are suspended, which include mineral charcoal or fusain and mineral

FIGURE 2.17: PRODUCTION OF ASH-FREE ANODE CARBON

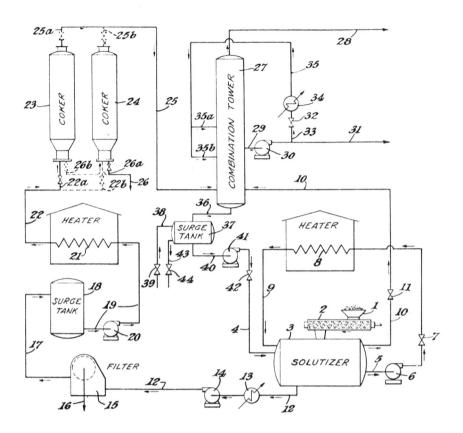

Source: W.J. Bloomer and S.W. Martin; U.S. Patent 3,379,638; April 23, 1968

matter or ash, is withdrawn through the bottom drawoff 12 and is drawn through cooler 13 by pump 14 and passed to a continuous rotary filter 15. The coal solution is cooled to a temperature of from 400° to 700°F. during its passage through cooler 13. Preferably, the rotary filter 15 is precoated with conventional filter aids and is normally operated at a pressure of 40 to 60 psig to effect efficient removal of substantially all of the suspended solids including undissolved carbonaceous matter. The filter cake is washed and dried to recover absorbed solvent and is withdrawn from filter 15 through line 16. The substantially deashed coal solution is passed through line 17 to surge drum 18 from which it is passed through line 19 and pump 20 to heater 21 (a suitable coil heater). The coal solution is heated to a temperature of from 850° to 1050°F. in heater 21 and is passed therefrom through line 22 to a coking unit.

The coking unit, as illustrated, is a delayed coker and is comprised of coke drums 23 and 24. The heated coal solution in line 22 is introduced through line 22a into coker 23 where the charge is decomposed into coke and a vaporous effluent. The coker overhead in line 25a is passed through line 25 to a fractionating unit. While coker 23 is being filled with coke, coker 24 is being decoked with product coke withdrawn through lines 26a and 26 for subsequent processing. In normal operation, cooling and decoking of coker 24 is completed prior to the filling of the coker 23. With decoking completed on coker 24 and having filled coker 23 to a predetermined level, the coker charge is diverted to coker 24 through line 22b, with the vaporous effluent in line 25b being passed to the fractionating unit through line 25. After cooling, coker 23 is decoked, with product coke being passed through lines 26b and 26 for subsequent processing.

The coker overhead in line 25 is introduced into a fractionating or combination tower 27 which is provided with suitable fractionating decks (not shown). Introduction of the effluent into the tower may result in some foaming. This may be effectively inhibited by the addition of a small amount of an antifoam agent, at the point of introduction or at some elevated point in the tower. The hereinbefore mentioned distillate and volatile matter in line 10, which are evolved during solvation, are introduced into the lower portion of the tower 27.

The combination tower overhead products in line 28 comprising condensible and noncondensible components are passed to conventional processing units to separate the condensible components from the noncondensible components. A medium and heavy middle oil is withdrawn from an intermediate point on the tower 27 through line 29 by pump 30 and is passed through line 31 to refining units (not shown). A portion of the middle oil in line 29, under the control of valve 32, is passed through line 33, waste heat boiler 34, and line 35 and is thereafter split into at two portions (lines 35a and 35b) for introduction as reflux into tower 27.

Tower bottoms in line 36 are passed to surge tank 37. By properly controlling the temperature level within tower 27, the distillate fraction in line 36 has an initial boiling temperature (converted to one atmosphere) of from 650° to 850°F. and represents all or a portion of the solvent to be used for dissolving or digesting the extractable carbonaceous matter in the pulverized raw coal feed. As hereinbefore mentioned, when processing bituminous coal, solvent requirements may usually be satisfied by operating the fractionating unit so as to obtain a distillate having an initial boiling temperature (converted to one atmosphere) of about 750°F. If additional solvent is required (over the 750°F. + distillate) the fractionating unit may be operated to provide a distillate having an initial boiling temperature (converted to one atmosphere) as low as 650°F. or if desired, the fractionating unit may be operated to provide the latter distillate, withdrawing excess solvent over solutizer requirements for utilization in other processes.

Example 1: In this process a bituminous coal having the following proximate analysis:

Analysis

	Percent by Weight
Moisture	1.4
Volatile matter	36.6
Fixed carbon	56.6
Ash	5.4

was crushed and ground to a particle size distribution whereby 37.3% was retained on a #100 mesh screen. For comparison purposes, combined sulfur was analyzed as being 1.46 weight percent. The crushed coal and a tar distillate having an initial boiling temperature of 750°F. (converted to one atmosphere) were introduced into the solutizer zone to provide a 3:1 ratio of solvent coal. The mixture was agitated while maintaining a temperature of 800°F. and a pressure of 5 atmospheres. The resulting coal solution was cooled to a temperature of 450°F. and passed through a filter precoated with a standard filter aid. The filtered coal solution represented an 86.3% recovery of extractable carbonaceous matter based on the crushed coal and had the following properties:

Properties

SG (100°/100°F.)	1.2407
Softening point, °F. (B & R)	152
Sulfur (wt. percent)	0.46
Carbon residue (wt. percent):	
Ramsbottom	30.9
Conradson	31.3
CS_2 solubility (wt. percent):	
Bitumen	76.66
Ash	0.02
Difference	23.22

The filtered coal solution was heated to 910°F. and coked to provide a coke which was recovered from the coker having the following properties:

Properties

	Weight Percent
Volatile matter	10.9
Sulfur	0.27
Ash	0.13
Iron	0.036
Silicon	0.009
R_2O_3	0.112
Nickel	0.0073
Titanium	0.013
Vanadium	0.00024
Boron, ppm	–

Example 2:   The following example illustrates that a lower grade coal having a high ash and sulfur content may be effectively deashed to provide a coal solution having an ash content substantially equal to that derived from the high grade coal illustrated in Example 1. A bituminous coal having the following proximate analysis:

Analysis

	Percent by Weight
Moisture	2.69
Volatile matter	37.7
Fixed carbon	38.9
Ash	19.66

was crushed and ground to a particle size distribution whereby substantially all of the crushed coal passed the combined sulfur was analyzed as being 3.72 weight percent. The crushed coal and a tar distillate having an initial boiling temperature (converted to one atmosphere) of 750°F. were introduced into the solutizer zone to provide a 3:1 ratio of solvent to coal. The mixture was agitated while maintaining a temperature of 800°F. and a pressure of 5 atmospheres. The resulting coal solution was cooled to a temperature of 550°F. and passed through a filter precoated with a standard filter aid. The filtered coal solution represented a 67.3% recovery of extractable carbonaceous matter based on the crushed coal and had the following properties:

Properties

SG, (100°/100°F.)	1.2516
Softening point	147
Sulfur (wt. percent)	0.63
Carbon residue (wt. percent):	
Ramsbottom	32.7
CS_2 solubility (wt. percent):	
Bitumen	76.81
Ash	0.06
Difference	23.13

Approximately 89 weight percent of the original sulfur content of the raw coal was separated from the coal solution and was carried in the filter residue as ash in the form of inorganic pyritic and sulfate sulfur. The percent increase in sulfur reduction would appear to be a result of the increased ratio of inorganic pyritic and sulfate sulfur to organic sulfur in low grade coals.

Note that in the above examples, the sulfur and ash content of the filtered coal solutions were substantially the same. This illustrates that the effectiveness of deashing and desulfurizing a coal solution is not restricted to any particular grade or rank of coal selected from the group consisting of bituminous coal, subbituminous coal and lignite.

Deashing of Coal Without Utilizing Hydrogen

W.J. Bloomer; U.S. Patent 3,375,188; March 26, 1968; assigned to The Lummus Company describes a process for producing useful carbonaceous matter from coal and in particular the production of substantially ash-free coke from a coal selected from the group consisting of bituminous coal, subbituminous coal and lignite.

This process provides an improved method for producing ash-free coke from a deashed coal solution utilizing a solvent having a boiling range within cutpoints of from 600° to 900°F., whereby such a solvent is highly refractory and is not adversely effected by coking operations, and is substantially recoverable for reuse.

It is known that the effective solvents for coal are those that have an angular configuration of the rings, like phenanthene and that boil above 300°C. (572°F.). Nonangular, or linear, condensed ring systems, such as anthracene, to the contrary have a greatly reduced selective solvent action on the constituents of coal that act as binding agents for the micellar portion of the coal. It is this removal of the binding material that leads to the complete disintegration of the colloidal nature of the coal, and peptization of the micelles in the solvent. Thus, the angular-ringed phenanthrene (BP 644°F.) has an extraction efficiency for the coal carbonaceous material of about 95% of the ash-free coal, whereas the linear structure of anthracene yields only an approximate 24% recovery on the same basis.

Coal carbonization crude tar fractions, such as "anthracene oil" contain appreciable quantities of both anthracene and phenanthrene and by virtue of the latter components, are good solvents. This aromatic oil might typically boil between 520° and 750°F. However, it had been found by utilization of a solvent having cutpoints (converted to one atmosphere) of from 600° to 900°F. which is derived from a coal tar pitch, that efficient solution is effected through use of the higher boiling alkylated homologues of phenanthrene and similarly high boiling polycyclic condensed aromatic ring compounds of angular structure. It will become apparent that the solvent is comprised of materials boiling within the range of these cutpoints. One important advantage of the solvent is that extraction efficiency increases through repeated use of the solvent, since the refractory nature of the solvent is improved with each pass through the process.

Other refractory polycyclic aromatic solvents obtained from petroleum catalytic and thermal cracking operations can also be utilized in the process and extraction efficiency of such a solvent would similarly increase by improving the refractory nature of the solvent by each pass through of the process until a totally recoverable solvent is obtained, of highest solvency.

According to Figure 2.18, raw coal, selected from the group consisting of bituminous coal, subbituminous coal and lignite, is crushed and ground in conventional crushing and grinding equipment (not shown). The particle size distribution may range up to 10 mm. The ground or pulverized coal is collected in a hopper 1, from which it is continuously distributed at a desired rate by a conveying mechanism 2 into a solutizer tank 3 maintained at a pressure of from 1 to 5 atmospheres. As illustrated, conveying mechanism 2 is a screw type feeder which introduces the coal into solutizer 3 without loss of pressure therein. Any conventional means of mechanical transfer may suffice, providing the means allows for positive transfer of the coal into solutizer 3 without a substantial loss of pressure therein.

The high boiling liquid solvent having cutpoints of from 600° to 900°F. is introduced into solutizer 3 through line 4 at a rate so as to provide a ratio of solvent to coal of from 1/2 : 1 to 6 : 1. Normally, a solvent to coal ratio of from 1 : 1 to 3 : 1 is preferred, since effective extraction rates are obtained within this ratio range while minimizing filtration costs. Solutizer 3 is maintained at a temperature of from 600° to 850°F., preferably of from 750° to 800°F., and at a pressure of about 1 to 10 atmospheres, whereby substantially all of the extractable carbonaceous matter present in the raw coal is thermally depolymerized. The products of depolymerization are soluble in the solvent and thereby form, with the solvent, a homogeneous coal solution. Insoluble solids including mineral matter or ash mineral charcoal or fusain are suspended in the coal solution. An agitator (not shown) may be provided to agitate the coal-solvent mixture during solvation.

FIGURE 2.18:   DEASHING OF COAL WITHOUT UTILIZING HYDROGEN

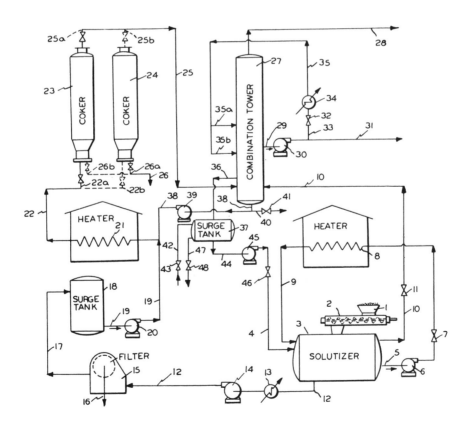

Source: W.J. Bloomer; U.S. Patent 3,375,188; March 26, 1968

Solvation temperatures are maintained in solutizer 3 by withdrawing and circulating a portion of the coal solution and/or coal-solvent mixture through an external heating system. The withdrawn portion is passed through line 5 by pump 6 under the control of valve 7 to heater 8 and thereafter reintroduced through line 9 into solutizer 3. In this manner, solvation temperatures are maintained within solutizer 3 without the necessity of a high pressure heating system which would be the case if the solvent was preheated to a temperature sufficient to maintain solvation temperatures within the solutizer.

A throughput time of the raw coal of from 3 to 120 minutes is normally sufficient to effectively and efficiently dissolve or digest the extractable carbonaceous matter. Since the solvent has an initial cutpoint (converted to one atmosphere) of 600°F., whereas solvation temperatures may be as high as 850°F., solutizer 3 is provided with vent line 10 under the control of valve 11 to permit the withdrawal of the lower boiling components of the solvent and any volatile matter vaporized from the raw coal.

In this respect, it has been observed that the quantity of volatile matter is practically negligible. A substantially uniform coal solution, where undissolved and insoluble solids are suspended, which include mineral charcoal of fusain and mineral matter or ash, is withdrawn through the bottom drawoff 12 and is passed through cooler 13 by pump 14 to a continuous rotary filter 15. Accordingly, it has been recovered in excess of 95% of the extractable carbonaceous matter based on ash-free coal.

The coal solution is cooled to a temperature of from 400° to 700°F. during its passage through cooler 13. Preferably, the rotary filter 15 is precoated with conventional filter aids and is normally operated at a pressure of 40 to 60 psig to effect efficient removal of substantially all of the suspended solids. The filter cake is washed and dried to recover absorbed solvent and is withdrawn from filter 15 through line 16. Precoating the filter substantially improves the separation of undissolved and insoluble particles from the coal solution.

Utilizing a precoated filter, filtered coal solutions where prepared which when analyzed for ash only varied between 0.02 to 0.08 weight percent, irrespective of the ash content of the raw coal which varied from 1 to 20%. This indicated that the efficiency of the deashing by filtration was a function of the size of the ash particle rather than the ash content. Utilizing filter aids having a high carbon content, the filter cake may be charged to a combustion unit to recover the Btu content thereof.

The substantially deashed coal solution is passed through line 17 to surge drum 18 from which it is passed through line 19 and pump 20 to heater 21 (a suitable coil heater). The coal solution is heated to a temperature of from 850° to 1050°F. in heater 21 and is passed therefrom through line 22 to a coking unit maintained at a pressure of 1 to 6 atmospheres. The coking unit, as illustrated, is a delayed coker and is comprised of coke drums 23 and 24. The heated coal solution in line 22 is introduced through line 22a into coker 23 where the charge is decomposed into coke and a vaporous effluent. Introduction of the solution into the coker may result in some foaming. This may be effectively inhibited by the addition of a small amount of an antifoam agent, at the point of introduction or at some elevated point in the coker.

		Example No.				
Coal	I	II Pana		III Illinois	IV Seacoal	V Seacoal
		Raw	De-ashed			
Coal Proximate Analysis, percent by weight:						
Moisture	2.69	Moisture-free Basis		2.75	1.4	1.4
Volatile Matter	37.7	33.6	32.6	38.90	36.6	36.6
Fixed Carbon	38.9	56.6	67.1	53.99	56.6	56.6
Ash	19.66	9.8	0.3	7.11	5.4	5.4
Sulfur	3.72	4.0	1.0	1.18	1.46	1.46
Chlorine		0.15	0.003			
Solvent:						
Boiling range, °F.:						
Initial	About 750	600		600	About 750	600
Final	About 1,050+	900		900	About 1,050+	900
Refractorized	No	Yes		Yes	No	Yes
Solvent to Coal Ratio	3-1	3-1		2-1	2-1	3-1
Solution Temperature,° F.	800	800		785	800	800
Solution Pressure, p.s.i.g.	75	75		75	75	75
Residence Time, min.	20	20		3	20	20
Filtration Temperature	550	625		600	450	600
De-ashed Coal Recovery:						
On crushed coal	67.3	83.6		85.3	67.5	90.0
On ash-free coal	83.8	92.7		91.8	71.3	95.2
Sp. Gravity (100°/100° F.)	1.2516		1.2250		1.2523	1.2140
Softening Point,° F. (B&R)	147.		131.5		212.	
Sulfur, wt. percent	0.63				0.44	0.51
Carbon Residue, wt. percent:						
Ramsbottom	32.7					23.9
Conradson				35.9		
CS_2 Solubility, wt. percent:						
Bitumin.	76.81		78.56		68.35	81.01
Ash	0.06		0.08		0.07	0.05
Difference	23.13		21.36		31.58	18.93

The coker overhead in line 25a is passed through line 25 into a fractionating unit. While coker 23 is being filled with coke, coker 24 is being decoked with product coke withdrawn through lines 26a and 26 for subsequent processing. In normal operation, cooling and decoking of coker 24 is completed prior to the filling of the coker 23. With decoking completed on coker 24 and having filled coker 23 to a predetermined level, the coker charge is diverted to coker 24 through line 22b, with the vaporous effluent in line 25b being passed to the fractionating unit through line 25. After cooling, coker 23 is decoked with product coke being passed through line 26b and 26 for subsequent processing.

The coker overhead in line 25 is introduced into a fractionating or combination tower 27 which is provided with suitable fractionating decks (not shown). The hereinbefore mentioned distillate and volatile matter in line 10, which are evolved during solvation, are introduced into the lower portion of the tower 27. The combination tower overhead products in line 28 comprising condensible and noncondensible components are passed to conventional processing units to separate the condensible components from the noncondensible components. A medium middle oil is withdrawn from an intermediate point on the tower 27 through line 29 by pump 30 and is passed through line 31 to refining units (not shown).

A portion of the middle oil in line 29, under the control of valve 32, is passed through line 33, waste heat boiler 34, and line 35 and is thereafter split into at least two portions (lines 35a and 35b) for introduction as reflux into tower 27. In the table on the previous page, there are provided examples setting forth data relative to the composition of the raw coal, solvent ratios temperatures and pressures of solvation, and analysis of the coal extract solution.

DUAL SOLVENT SYSTEMS

Liquefaction of Coal in a Dual Solvent System

R.S. Corey, F.J. Riedl and D.R. Campbell; U.S. Patent 3,535,224; October 20, 1970; assigned to Universal Oil Products Company discusses a process for liquefying coal utilizing a dual solvent system of a polycyclic aromatic hydrocarbon primary solvent and a halogenated hydrocarbon secondary solvent having 6 to 20 carbons which minimizes ash contamination of the coal extract. Valuable liquid hydrocarbon products are recovered from the resulting coal extract.

This process is predicated on the presence of an ash agglomerating agent in the solvent extraction zone. Such an agent is for convenience purposes herein referred to as a "secondary solvent." It is believed that one of the reasons the process produces such desirable results is that the secondary solvent acts in some way as an initiator for agglomerating the micro-size particles of ash into large solid particles which are then more amenable to separation from the liquid coal extract via centrifugation, decantation, filtration, etc. The ultimate effect of the secondary solvent, in addition to rendering the ash more readily removable is to produce a liquid coal extract of higher quality and in many cases of higher hydrogen content than would otherwise be obtained. Additional benefits may also accrue in this process by utilizing a finely divided hydrogenation catalyst in the solvent extraction zone, as well as hydrogen gas in conjunction with secondary solvent, more fully described hereinafter.

The critical feature of the process is in the use of an ash agglomerating agent in the extraction zone as an adjunct to the primary solvent. It is intended that this process be wide in scope in that any agent which has the ability to agglomerate ash as herein defined from smaller particles into larger particles in a manner sufficient to render such ash more readily separable from the liquid coal extract is to be included within the concept of this method. Particular agglomerating agents include halogenated hydrocarbons having from 6 to 20 carbon atoms per molecule. More particular agglomerating agents include aromatic hydrocarbons, such as mono- and dichloronaphthalene; mono- and dibromonaphthalene; chlorobenzenes; chloro- and bromo-Tetralins and Decalins; and the like.

The operating conditions for the solvent extraction zone include a temperature of from 250° to 500°C., a pressure from 500 to 5,000 psig, a solvent to coal weight ratio from 0.2 to 10, a residence time from 30 seconds to 5 hours, the presence of secondary solvent (previously discussed hereinabove) and, preferably, the presence of hydrogen sufficient to dissolve coal such that a total in excess of 50% by weight of maf coal feed into the solvent extraction zone has been liquefied.

Since the purpose of the extraction zone is to substantially convert coal into liquid coal extract, it may be desirable to add to the extraction zone a catalyst. The catalyst may be conventional, may be homogeneous or heterogeneous and may be introduced into the pulverization zone and/or extraction zone in admixture with either the liquid solvent or with the solid coal.

From a knowledge of the characteristics of the coal, solvent and of the properties desired for the end product, one will know whether or not it may be desirable to use any or all of these features in the solvent extraction zone. If a catalyst is desired, conventional solid hydrogenation catalyst can be satisfactorily utilized, such as nickel-molybdate on an alumina-silica support or a cobalt-molybdate catalyst or any other hydrogenation catalyst known to those skilled in the art and applicable to the solvent-coal system environment maintained in the extraction zone including the use of a slurry-catalyst system.

Hydrogenation in the extraction zone, generally, accomplishes the following functions: transfer of hydrogen directly to coal molecules; transfer of hydrogen to hydrogen-donor molecules; transfer of hydrogen from hydrogen-donor molecules to coal molecules; and various combinations of the above. By way of emphasis, as used herein, the term "extraction zone" is intended to include the pulverization step, the digestion step or combined pulverization-digestion step.

After separation of the gaseous materials, including hydrogen, undissolved coal residue (e.g., ash) and catalyst, if any, from the total effluent of the extraction zone, the liquid coal extract is passed into conventional recovery facilities where valuable liquid hydrocarbons are recovered. Typically, these recovery facilities comprise fractionation columns for the separation therein of the liquid coal extract into products such as normally gaseous hydrocarbons, relatively light hydrocarbons comprising essentially middle oil, relatively heavy hydrocarbons comprising materials suitable for use as a coal solvent and a bottoms fraction comprising residue material which is suitable for fuel.

The secondary solvent may also be separated from the liquid coal extract by conventional means, such as distillation, either before, during or subsequent to the separation of the extract into desired products. In essence, therefore, the valuable liquid hydrocarbons recovered from the liquid coal extract include, for example, gasoline boiling range products and/or chemical, aromatic hydrocarbon-containing fractions, heavy fuel oil fractions, and the like.

Example: A sample of bituminous coal was crushed to 100 mesh size, mixed with Tetralin and colloided on an Eppenbach Colloidal Mill. The particle size after 5 hours of operation was reduced to less than two microns. (95% by weight of the coal was less than two microns with none larger than 100 microns.) This mixture was then subjected to the following conditions:

Temperature, °C.	430
Pressure, psig	2,000
Tetralin/coal ratio, wt.	3:1
Secondary solvent	None
Hydrogen gas rejection (also H_2S)	Yes
Residence time, hours	0.5

A coal extract having the following properties was recovered:

Molecular Weight	503
Weight percent sulfur	1.29
Percent benzene insolubles, weight	12.12
Percent hydrogen, weight	7.18

The solids were filtered from the extract and were analyzed with the following results:

U.S. Sieve Series	Particle Size, weight percent
On No. 4	5.4
On No. 10	16.8
On No. 20	14.4
On No. 50	16.3
On No. 100	21.8
On No. 200	13.5
On No. 270	5.0
Thru 270	6.8

MULTISTAGE SOLVENT EXTRACTION SYSTEMS

Successive Extraction and Fractional Distillation

L. Thibaut; U.S. Patent 2,707,163; April 26, 1955; assigned to Compagnie Francaise des Essences Synthetiques Societe Anonyme, France describes a process for the treatment of solid or liquid carbonaceous materials such as coal, lignite, peat, oil-bearing products, primary tars or tars of a high temperature, lignite tars, heavy or middle oils, bituminous shale or asphaltic limestone oils for transformation into products of high value such as, motor-fuels or substitutes, or for the production of special motor-fuels such as isooctanes and homologues, alcohols, ethers, ketones and the like. This method consists in effecting simultaneously in one and the same space the chemical treatment of the carbonaceous materials, their concomitant fractional distillation and the separation of the various products resulting from this treatment.

In the application of this method the operations can take place in a liquid or in a gaseous medium. It can be advantageous to submit the carbonaceous materials, in the same space, to combined treatments in successive stages in a liquid medium and in a gaseous medium, the treatment in the gaseous medium acting upon the lightened products coming from the treatment in the liquid medium and leading the treated products to the double treatment of the following stage. The sequence of the double treatments in several stages can be combined with a treatment effected only in a liquid medium or in a gaseous medium and either before or after or simultaneously before and after the previous treatments, all these treatments being performed in the same space.

Any additional preheated or nonpreheated materials can be introduced into the different stages or into the different zones of fractional distillation in any desired quantity for directing, promoting or retarding the reactions. These materials can be inert or active, and of the same kind as the materials to be treated or different from them. It is also possible to provide additions of suitable chemical agents for simultaneously insuring an accessory treatment such as a purification, a separation by means of solvents, or a refining operation, for instance. Owing to their temperature and also to their quantity and their kind, they allow of performing all the desired adjustments.

Liquid or gaseous samples can be taken out from any point of the treatment space yielding treated and fractionally distilled or even rectified and refined products in the corresponding stage and doing away with any subsequent operation for making the best of the products. This sampling can be performed either by drawing off, at any suitable point, a gaseous mixture from which the oils are obtained, after the condensation or by effecting a separation inside the treatment apparatus itself and by drawing off the separated oils from the apparatus and directly in a liquid condition.

In this latter case means are provided, at various points of the treatment space and more particularly in all the treatment stages or only in certain stages, which insure the condensation by mixing or the surface condensation of the vapors which pass through the stage. After having been freed from the condensed parts the gaseous products pursue their ascending circulation, while the condensed products are taken off from the treatment space. The separation of the products can also take place in the treatment space through solution in suitable solvents which are introduced and removed at any convenient point.

The products already selected can be immediately collected. They can also be submitted to a rectification or to a farther reaching treatment. More particularly the concomitant treatment and fractional distillation of the carbonaceous materials can be combined with a fractional distillation without treatment performed in the same space above or below the zone of combined treatment and fractional distillation or inserted in the zone. For carrying out the method the treatment space can be formed either of a single treatment chamber or of a plurality of similar chambers united together and arranged in series, in parallel or in series-parallel.

In the case of a single chamber the stages or successive treatment and fractional distillation zones can be connected with one another in order to insure one or a plurality of distinct circulations of the carbonaceous materials to be treated in combination with one or a plurality of circulations of the gaseous mixture. Thus, the treatment stages, although arranged in series on the travel of the gaseous mixture which passes successively through them, can be connected in groups receiving products of the same kind or different products and insuring distinct parallel circulations.

The stages of the various groups, which overlap one another, are connected so that they are arranged in series according to the scale of the temperatures of the treatment space while insuring the treatment and the fractional distillation on different products in distinct circulations. Furthermore, suitable connections between the different stages can permit of the selective passage of the liquid or gaseous fractionally distilled products from one group to another, which insures a selective treatment of the selected products together with the progressive fractional distillation.

In case the treatment space is formed of a plurality of chambers the latter are connected with one another so that they insure one or a plurality of simultaneous or successive circulations for the treated materials through their passage in countercurrent with one or more gaseous circulations, their selective separation in a plurality of stages in a progressive manner and the gradation of the reactions of transformation. These chambers can be arranged in series on the travel of a single gaseous circulation or in parallel on distinct gaseous circulations.

The passage of the materials to be treated from one chamber to another or their travel in one and the same chamber can take place in series or in parallel from a single introduction of the starting materials in a continuous circulation in one of the chambers and parallel circulations derived from products which have been fractionally distilled in the other chambers, all the circulations being submitted to the fractional distillation and to the concomitant chemical treatment.

The preheating of the carbonaceous materials to be treated is not indispensable. In certain cases it is sufficient to introduce the materials at ordinary temperature or slightly preheated into the upper part of the treatment space which renders unnecessary or simplifies the preheating operation which is usual with the other methods and which is often delicate because of the tendency of the carbonaceous materials to coke.

The temperature equilibrium is adjusted through the temperature and the delivered quantity of the materials, i.e., of the starting materials as well as the materials of addition which are introduced into the treatment space and through the choice of their zone of introduction. Sometimes, however, this equilibrium is difficult to obtain and maintain in conditions which are sufficiently precise for insuring a well defined and stable progression of temperatures in the different zones of treatment in order to insure a selective classification of the products. This is more particularly the case when the reaction heat quantities are high. The carbonaceous materials which are introduced even at ordinary temperature cannot absorb the thermal energy which is evolved in the course of the treatment. It is then necessary to supply a refrigerating energy in order to insure the fractional distillation.

Figure 2.18 is a vertical sectional view of a plate column for the fractional splitting up and the simultaneous thermal or catalytic treatment of the materials. According to Figure 2.19, the apparatus for the treatment and the fractional splitting up of carbonaceous materials is formed of a chamber 20 the walls of which are adapted to the conditions of operation (temperature, pressure, chemical action or corrosion) and in which are arranged plates 21 superposed with bubbling caps 22 and downpipes 23.

On the upper plate or any other plate is provided the inlet 24 for the carbonaceous materials to be treated, which may be liquids or solids in suspension in an oil. In the case of solid matter the latter can be introduced in the form of a paste but it is also possible to introduce separately the suspension liquid and the crushed solid material, the mixture taking place inside the column itself on the plate or plates on which the materials are poured.

At the upper end is a pipe 25 for the eduction of the light products. In the lower part is arranged a means for the supply of a hot fluid (flue gases, steam, inert gases, oxidizing or reducing gases, hydrogenating gases, hydrocarbons, and the like), as, for instance, a pipe 27 is the outlet for the removal of the residues if any. The products to be transformed (liquid or suspension of solids) which are preheated or nonpreheated and introduced at 24 move progressively downward either through their own weight or through the action of mechanical means and fall from one plate to another through the downpipes 23, whereby they pass successively through stages in which the physico-chemical conditions are different owing to the variations of the temperatures and possibly to the presence of catalyzers in a liquid or in a gaseous medium.

In the contrary direction the gaseous mixture introduced at 26 passes through the plates 21 successively in an ascending circulation while flowing through the bubbling means 22. By adjusting the quantity of products to be treated which are introduced at 24 at a high temperature and the quantity of the hot gaseous products introduced at 26 and possibly by using other adjusting means it is possible to establish in the column a scale of temperatures which gradually vary from one plate to another.

FIGURE 2.19:   SUCCESSIVE EXTRACTION AND FRACTIONAL DISTILLATION

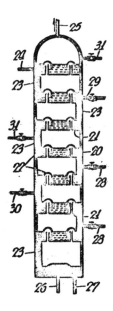

Source: L. Thibaut; U.S. Patent 2,707,163; April 26, 1955

In each stage the liquid products are submitted to a chemical, thermal or catalytic treatment and to a separation of the light products, whether the latter come from the starting materials without any transformation or result from the treatment. In their turn, the so separated products are submitted to the chemical treatment in a gaseous medium before they reach the upper stage while passing through the bubble caps 22.

On the upper plate the heavy products which have been carried along condense and are submitted, as the case may be, to the reaction in a liquid medium, whereafter they are taken into the descending circulation through the tubes 23, while the light products continue their ascending circulation after having been mixed, if necessary, with the light products formed on the plate.

This operation is repeated in the same manner in all the stages as well as on the plates during the descending travel of the products in the liquid state as in the free space between the level of the liquid on a plate and the plate lying immediately thereabove during the ascending travels of the products in the gaseous state. Thus, the carbonaceous materials are submitted to successive treatments, in a plurality of stages at different temperatures which correspond to the compositions of the mixture selected in the treatment, which conditions vary from one stage to another, and they are simultaneously fractionally split up and separated.

In the upper part, at 25, only the light products of the last stage of the selective treatment are collected. The residues of the heavy products, if any, collect in the lower part of the column and are removed at 27. On the different stages the intermediary products can be removed for instance at 28 and 29 in the gaseous or in the liquid state. The products which are obtained at 25, 27, 28 and 29 are condensed, as the case may be, and, if necessary, expanded and separated from the incondensable gases introduced or formed during the successive treatments in the various stages, this being obtained by any usual suitable means.

Instead of introducing at 26 simultaneously heated gases or vapors, it is possible to use any other kind of heating for the column, either an internal or an external heating (not shown). It is also possible to provide, at the upper part or in different stages, inlets for the introduction of liquid or gaseous products, heated or nonheated, as 30 and 31, adapted for adjusting the temperatures, promoting or directing the treatment in the corresponding stage and, if necessary, for playing the part of a catalyzer.

Liquefaction of Coal by a Three-Stage Solvent Extraction Process

J.G. Gatsis; U.S. Patent 3,583,900; June 8, 1971; assigned to Universal Oil Products Company describes a process whereby coal is converted into valuable liquid products utilizing a three-stage solvent extraction process. The coal is first contacted with a conventional coal solvent such as tetrahydronaphthalene, with the resulting liquid coal extract extracted with a first aliphatic solvent to produce an asphaltene free extract with the resultant residue being treated with a light aromatic solvent to further produce a second coal extract. Each of the extract materials are separately refined, and produced are coal products free of solid material without the utilization of intricate filtration principles.

It was found that the dissolved coal components extracted from the coal in conventional solvent extraction processes utilizing conventional coal solvents such as tetrahydronaphthalene (available as Tetralin) and present in admixture with unconverted coal, ash and excess solvent is readily separated from such material into distinct hydrocarbon fractions in a manner which allows complete conversion of the extracted coal materials, in an efficient processing manner to liquid products. This coal extract present after conventional solvent extraction operations contains hydrocarbons of varying hydrogen to carbon atomic ratios with these hydrocarbons existing in relatively distinct hydrogen to carbon atomic ratio ranges.

There exists a hydrogen rich segment which has a hydrogen to carbon atomic ratio of from 1.1:1 to 1.3:1 and referred to herein as the hydrogen rich components. There also exists hydrogen-lean asphaltene components which have a hydrogen to carbon atomic ratio of 0.6:1 to 1.0:1. Within this range of hydrogen-lean asphaltene components, there esists a relatively high-hydrogen to carbon atomic ratio segment having a hydrogen to carbon atomic ratio of 0.8:1 to 1.0:1. This process comprises the following steps of:

(a) contacting coal with a first coal solvent capable of converting coal to liquid products in a coal liquefaction zone, under extraction conditions, and under hydrogen pressure to produce a liquefaction zone product comprising a liquid coal extract of hydrogen-rich components and hydrogen-lean asphaltene components of relatively high and low hydrogen to carbon atomic ratios in admixture with unconverted coal and ash particles;

(b) contacting the liquefaction zone product with a second, light aliphatic solvent, selective for the hydrogen rich coal extract components, in a first extraction zone, at extraction conditions, to provide a first extraction zone effluent comprising a hydrogen-rich, second solvent, liquid phase essentially free of asphaltenes, solid coal and ash particles and a hydrogen-lean, asphaltene coal extract phase containing unconverted coal and ash particles;

(c) separating, from hydrogen-rich phase, at least a portion of the second selective solvent to provide a hydrogen-rich coal extract;

(d) refining, at least a portion of the hydrogen-rich coal extract, under refining conditions in a first refining zone to provide a refined liquid coal product;

(e) contacting hydrogen-lean asphaltene-containing phase with a third selective solvent at extraction conditions in a second extraction zone to provide a second extraction zone effluent comprising a relatively high hydrogen to carbon atomic ratio asphaltene coal extract, third solvent phase and an unconverted coal, ash, and relatively low hydrogen to carbon atomic ratio asphaltene phase;

(f) separating, from high hydrogen to carbon atomic ratio asphaltene phase at least a portion of the third solvent to provide a relatively high hydrogen to carbon atomic ratio asphaltene containing coal extract;

(g) hydrorefining high hydrogen to carbon atomic ratio asphaltene coal extract at hydrorefining conditions in a second refining zone to provide a hydrogen enriched coal product; and

(h) carbonizing at least a portion of low hydrogen to carbon atomic ratio asphaltene phase to provide a coal tar distillate and a solid char material.

The coal preferably utilized in the process is bituminous coal such as Pittsburgh seam coal. More preferably this bituminous coal has a high volatile content and typically greater than about 20% by weight of the moisture and ash free (maf) coal. Preferred solvents for use in the coal liquefaction zone of the process, as a first coal solvent capable of converting coal to liquid products, are those which are of the hydrogen donor type and which are at least partially hydrogenated such as the naphthenic-aromatic hydrocarbons. Preferably, the first coal solvent is one which is in the liquid phase at the hereinafter described temperatures and pressures utilized in the extraction and/or pulverization step of this process. Typically, these solvents are employed as mixtures of hydrocarbons and are derived at least in part from the intermediate or final products obtained from subsequent processing of the liquid coal extract.

Typically these first coal solvents utilized in the coal liquefaction zone boil between 200° and 425°C. Examples of the preferred naphthenic-aromatic liquefaction zone solvents are the di- or tetrahydro derivatives of anthracene and phenanthrene. Also preferred are the aromatic hydro derivatives of naphthalene such as tetrahydronaphthalene (Tetralin). As used herein, naphthenic-aromatic solvents refer to polycyclic compounds where at least one of the rings of the compound is aromatic and at least one of these rings is not aromatic. These compounds are also commonly referred to as polynuclear compounds.

Also suitable for utilization within the process are the completely aromatic polycyclic compounds such as biphenyl, the methyl naphthalenes, the dimethylnaphthalenes, mixtures of phenanthrene and anthracene, etc., as well as their alkyl derivatives. Other types of solvents which may be utilized as a first coal solvent in the coal liquefaction zone include phenolic compounds such as phenols, creosols, xylenols, particularly when utilized in admixture with any of the foregoing solvents, particularly tetrahydronaphthalene. In general, the partially hydrogenated aromatic compounds referred to hereinbefore as naphthenic-aromatic compounds are preferred over the completely aromatic polycyclic hydrocarbons. In any event the solvent suitable for use in the coal liquefaction zone must be a solvent having the capability of depolymerizing particulate coal under extraction conditions as hereinafter defined, and capable of converting the coal to liquid products.

Suitable solvents for use in the first extraction zone of this process where the liquid coal extract produced in the coal liquefaction zone is first extracted with a second selective solvent, belong to the broad class of compounds known as light aliphatic hydrocarbons and include the C_3 to C_9 aliphatic paraffins either as a mixture of such compounds or as an individual species. Preferred solvents include pentane, hexane and heptane, particularly normal heptane. It is to be noted by those skilled in the art that these classes of secondary aliphatic extraction solvents have no substantial effect on the conversion of solid coal to a liquid coal extract. Therefore, it is a requirement of the process that the coal liquefaction zone utilize those solvents which are applicable to the conversion of solid coal particles to the liquid form and the first stage extraction zone solvent be limited to those solvents which serve to separate the hydrogen-rich components from the hydrogen-lean asphaltene components in admixture with undissolved coal, ash, etc., contained in the liquid coal extract produced in the coal liquefaction zone.

In other words, it has been found that light aliphatic solvents such as a C_3 to C_9 alkanes including their various isomeric forms, are selective for the hydrogen-rich components to the substantial rejection of the hydrogen-lean asphaltene components and, as importantly, the undissolved coal and ash residue. The extract choice of a selective second solvent depends on the extraction conditions desired in the first extraction zone. For practical purposes the temperature selected for the first extraction zone should be at least 30°C. below the critical temperature of the first stage extraction zone solvent in order to maintain the components with the proper pressure in primarily the liquid phase. In general the temperatures utilized for the first stage extraction zone should not exceed 300°C. Another second solvent suitable for utilization in the first extraction zone of the process includes an unreformed naphtha hydrocarbon stream, namely a hydrocarbon stream having a boiling range of from 200° to 300°F. and containing less than about 20% by volume aromatic hydrocarbons.

The operating conditions to be utilized in the first stage extraction zone utilizing second light aliphatic solvent such as heptane include a temperature from 50° to 300°C. and more preferably from 50° to 150°C., a hydrogen pressure from 100 to 1,000 psig and more preferably from 350 to 700 psig, a solvent to feed ratio from 0.5 to 5 by weight, a total liquid hourly space velocity from 0.5 to 5 or more, and in the presence of a hydrogen-containing gas in an amount from 500 to 5,000 scf/bbl. of liquid feed present in the first extraction zone. These conditions are sufficient to substantially separate on a selective basis the hydrogen-rich components from the hydrogen-lean asphaltene components, coal, and ash contained in the liquid coal feed passed to the first extraction zone from the coal liquefaction zone.

After the liquid coal extract-solid coal mixture is contacted with the foregoing second light aliphatic solvent a two-phase liquid system results. An upper phase containing the hydrogen-rich liquid coal components (typically 40 to 60% of the liquid coal formed) dissolved in the second light aliphatic solvent and essentially free of undissolved coal, ash etc. (i.e., less than 0.005 weight percent solids) is separated from a lower phase containing the hydrogen-lean liquid coal asphaltene components in admixture with any undissolved coal ash, catalyst (if any) etc. This hydrogen-lean asphaltene phase containing undissolved coal etc. is removed as a slurry from the first extraction zone for further processing and extraction with a third selective solvent in a second extraction zone.

The upper rich solvent phase from the first extraction zone comprising the second light aliphatic solvent having dissolved therein the hydrogen rich components is further processed by such means as fractionation, hydrogenation, hydrocracking, etc. in order to separate and convert the hydrogen rich liquid coal extract into more valuable products such as relatively light hydrocarbons, relatively heavy hydrocarbons, chemicals, fuels, etc. As previously mentioned, a portion of these separated products in the liquid coal extract may be satisfactorily utilized as at least a portion of the first coal solvent utilized in the coal liquefaction zone.

The hydrogen-lean asphaltene containing phase removed from the first extraction zone and containing asphaltene components of relatively high and low hydrogen to carbon atomic ratios in admixture with undissolved coal, ash, etc. is then contacted with a third selective solvent at extraction conditions in a second extraction zone to provide a second extraction zone effluent comprising a relatively high hydrogen to carbon atomic ratio asphaltene coal extract-third solvent phase and an unconverted coal, ash and relatively low hydrogen to carbon atomic ratio asphaltene phase. Suitable solvents for use in this second extraction zone belong to the broad class of compounds known as ketones, monocyclic aromatics, and their naphthenic derivatives.

Examples of ketones which may be used satisfactorily in the second extraction zone of the process include acetone, methyl ethyl ketone, methyl butyl ketone, methyl isobutyl ketone, dibutyl ketone etc. Other solvents applicable, as stated, for use in the second extraction zone include the monocyclic aromatic hydrocarbons such as benzene, toluene, xylenes, etc. and their corresponding naphthenic derivatives such as cyclohexanes. As in the case of the secondary extraction solvents used in the first extraction zone the tertiary solvents utilized in this second extraction zone have no substantial effect on the conversion of the solid coal to a liquid coal extract.

Therefore, it is a requirement of this process, as heretofore stated, that the coal liquefaction zone utilize those solvents which are applicable to the conversion of solid coal particles to the liquid form and that the first stage and second stage extraction zone solvents be limited to those solvents which separate the various components produced during the coal liquefaction step. In other words, it has been found that the ketones, monocyclic aromatics, cyclohexane and alkyl cyclohexanes are selective for those hydrogen-lean asphaltene components having a relatively high hydrogen to carbon atomic ratio when compared to the other hydrogen-lean asphaltene components to the substantial rejection of the relatively low hydrogen to carbon atomic ratio asphaltene components and undissolved coal and ash.

The exact choice of a second selective solvent depends on the extraction conditions desired in the second extraction zone. For practical purposes, the temperature selected for the second extraction zone should be at least 30°C. below the critical temperature of the third selective solvent in order to maintain the components with the proper pressure in primarily the liquid phase. In general the temperatures utilized for the second stage extraction zone should not as in the case of the first stage extraction zone, exceed 300°C.

The operating conditions utilized in the second stage extraction zone utilizing a third selective solvent, namely a ketone, monocyclic aromatic or cyclohexane solvent include conditions similar to those conditions utilized in the first extraction zone utilizing a second selective solvent namely a temperature from 50° to 300°C. and more preferably from 50° to 150°C., a hydrogen pressure from 100 to 1,000 psig and more preferably from 350 to 700 psig, a solvent to feed ratio from 0.5 to 5 by weight, liquid hourly space velocity from 0.5 to 5 and in the presence of a hydrogen containing-gas, in an amount, added from 500 to 5,000 scf/bbl. of liquid feed present in the second extraction zone. These conditions are sufficient to substantially separate on a selective basis those hydrogen-lean asphaltene components having a relatively high hydrogen to carbon atomic ratio from those hydrogen-lean asphaltene components having a relatively low hydrogen to carbon atomic ratio as contained in the liquid feed passed to the second extraction zone from the first extraction zone.

In any event, after the liquid coal extract-solid coal mixture is contacted with the foregoing third selective solvent a two-phase liquid system results. An upper phase containing the asphaltene components with a relatively high hydrogen to carbon atomic ratio (typically 30 to 50% of the liquid coal formed in the coal liquefaction zone and 80 to 95% of the hydrogen-lean asphaltene components present in the effluent from the first extraction zone) and containing very minor amounts of undissolved coal, ash, etc. having an extremely small particle size such as less than 0.01 micron is separated from a lower phase containing the hydrogen lean asphaltene components having a relatively low hydrogen to carbon atomic ratio, in comparison to those components contained in the upper phase, and in admixture with essentially all of the undissolved coal, ash, etc. as present both in the liquefaction zone effluent and extraction zone one effluent. This low hydrogen to carbon atomic ratio asphaltene solid coal slurry is removed from the second extraction zone for further processing.

From the upper phase recovered from the second extraction zone, at least a portion, and preferably all of the third selective solvent is removed to yield a liquid coal product containing the richest in terms of hydrogen content, of the hydrogen-lean asphaltene components. In addition, there is a very minor amount (i.e., less than 0.05 weight percent) of finely divided coal, ash and other solid particulate matter. Further the recovered asphaltenes contain themselves a number of organometallic compounds.

To convert the hydrogen-lean asphaltene components to more valuable hydrocarbon products such as gasoline, these components must be first hydrogenated since hydrocracking or fluid catalytic cracking of these asphaltenes without hydrogenation would result in great amounts of coking and, in general inefficient conversions. Unfortunately, these hydrogen-lean asphaltene compounds cannot be processed in conventional fixed-bed catalytic processes because of the rapid catalyst deactivation caused by the organometallic compounds and the fine particulate matter, such as ash contained therein.

Further, the ash-like material gradually creates deposits in the catalyst bed which eventually cause the catalyst bed to plug and/or have excessively high pressure drops rendering practical hydrocarbon processing unfeasible and subsequent removal of the catalyst difficult. Further, even if such fixed bed operations as utilized in the first refining zone could be utilized in hydrogenate asphaltenes, the hydrogenation of these asphaltenes is best effected separately from the processing of the hydrogen-rich components recovered from the first extraction zone because of the different processing conditions and catalysts required to efficiently hydrogenate and otherwise upgrade each fraction.

Accordingly, the higher hydrogen to carbon atomic ratio asphaltene constituents are to be processed in a nonfixed bed catalytic hydrorefining zone designated herein as a second refining zone such as a slurry process or an ebullating bed process at hydrorefining conditions. As used herein "hydrorefining" includes the myriad of hydrogen consuming reactions such as desulfurization, denitrogenation and hydrocracking as well as hydrogenation, with such reactions often proceeding simultaneously. Suitable catalysts for use in this hydrorefining zone are to contain a catalytically active metallic component possessing both cracking and hydrogenation activity such as the metals of Group V-B, VI-B and VIII of the Periodic Table.

Of these, preferred are vanadium, chromium, iron, cobalt, nickel, niobium, molybdenum, tantalum and/or tungsten. Group VIII noble metals are undesirable only because of economic considerations. While these catalytic metals may be deposited on known porous support materials such as alumina, silica-alumina, zeolitic aluminosilicates, etc., it is preferred to use unsupported versions of these metals since the supported catalysts will readily deactivate and are not readily regenerable.

The effluent from this hydrorefining zone is continuously withdrawn, separating therefrom upgraded hydrocarbons by known means and these hydrocarbons are suitable for further processing, if desired, in the hereinbefore described first refining zone. This converted material withdrawn has an upgraded hydrogen to carbon atomic ratio of 1.1 : 1 to 1.4 : 1 and is free from asphaltenes and finely divided coal and ash. The unconverted material along with solid particulate catalysts, etc., is withdrawn and recycled to form a portion of the feed to the hydrorefining zone with a drag stream withdrawn from this converted material to control the solids level in the zone and to recover and continuously regenerate a portion of the catalyst.

Therefore, the process entails reducing coal to a fine, particulate size either in the presence or absence of a first coal solvent converting the coal in the presence of a first coal solvent to a liquid coal product of hydrogen-rich components and hydrogen-lean asphaltene components; extracting the hydrogen-rich components with a second light aliphatic solvent and refining these components in a first refining zone; extracting from the hydrogen-lean asphaltene components, the components with a relatively high hydrogen to carbon atomic ratio with a third selective aromatic, ketone or naphthene solvent and hydrorefining the resultant extract in a second refining zone; and, carbonizing the lower hydrogen to carbon atomic ratio asphaltene components to produce a coal tar distillate which may be refined in either the first or second refining zone.

Of importance is that this process eliminates the need for any intricate separations heretofore utilized for the separation of unconverted coal from the liquid coal products.

Referring to Figure 2.20, coarse size coal having an average particle diameter generally in excess of 0.08" and less than 2.5" is introduced to liquefaction zone 4 via line 1. A suitable first coal solvent having an enriched hydrogen content such as tetrahydronaphthalene and hydrogen gas enter the liquefaction zone via lines 2 and 3 respectively. As depicted, this liquefaction zone includes a pulverization step and an actual coal liquefaction step. In this pulverization step, the coal in admixture with coal solvent and maintained under hydrogen pressure is pulverized by conventional means under pulverization conditions including a temperature of about 100°C., a hydrogen pressure of 70 psig and a solvent to coal weight ratio of about 2, to reduce the coarse size coal to an average particle diameter between 0.08" to 0.04".

After removal of unpulverized, oversized coal, the resultant coal solvent-coal mixture is passed to a liquefaction step where the coal is actually dissolved and/or extracted by the coal solvent at a temperature of about 500°C. and in the presence of 1,000 to 100,000 scf of hydrogen/bbl. of coal solvent-coal mixture present therein. At the completion of this liquefaction step, excess coal solvent and hydrogen are removed, although not necessary, by conventional distillation means within liquefaction zone 4 and the resultant liquid coal extract–unconverted, finely divided coal and ash mixture is passed via line 5 to extraction zone I 6.

Within extraction zone I 6, the coal liquefaction zone effluent 5 is contacted with a second light aliphatic solvent such as heptane, entering via line 11, under extraction conditions including a temperature of about 150°C., a solvent to extraction zone feed weight ratio of about 3, a pressure of about 500 psig and preferably in the presence of added H2 gas, added by means not shown at a rate of about 100 scf/bbl. of extraction zone I 6 feed.

FIGURE 2.20: LIQUEFACTION OF COAL BY A THREE-STAGE SOLVENT EXTRACTION PROCESS

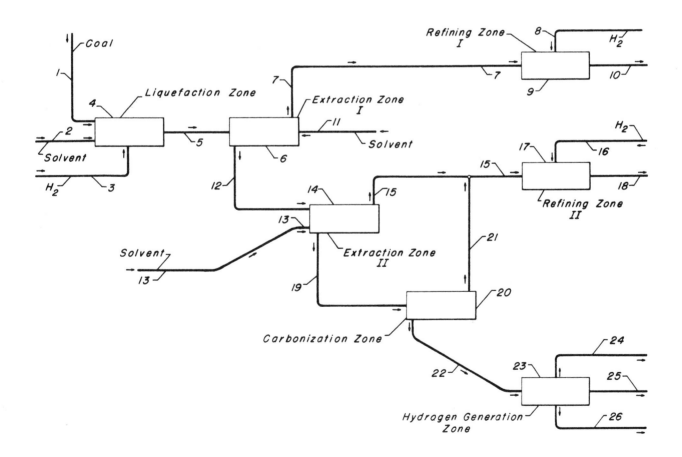

Source: J.G. Gatsis; U.S. Patent 3,583,900; June 8, 1971

Within this zone 6, the second solvent selectively removes the hydrogen-rich liquid coal components and excess coal solvent, if present, from the hydrogen lean asphaltene liquid coal products and undissolved coal, ash, etc. to form a solid and asphaltene free, solvent-hydrogen rich liquid-coal phase which after removal of the excess second solvent is, withdrawn via line 7. This stream is then passed via line 7 to refining zone I 9 where, in the presence of H2 entering line 8, the liquid coal is hydrorefined to more valuable products which are removed via line 10. Preferably this hydrorefining in refining zone I 9 comprises a first stage desulfurization and denitrogenation followed by a second stage hydrocracking, both stages comprising fixed-bed catalytic processes.

A residue stream comprising unconverted coal, ash and other solid particulate matter in admixture with hydrogen-lean asphaltene components having a segment with a relatively high hydrogen to carbon atomic ratio and a segment with relatively low hydrogen to carbon atomic ratio in comparison to each other is withdrawn from extraction zone I 6 via line 12 and passed via line 12 to extraction zone II 14 where this residue is extracted with a third selective solvent entering via line 13. This solvent comprising either ketone, monocyclic aromatic or cyclohexane solvent, preferably a monocyclic aromatic such as benzene, is contacted with extraction zone I residue at extraction conditions including a temperature of about 150°C., a solvent to extraction zone feed ratio of about 3, a pressure of about 500 psig and preferably in the presence of hydrogen gas added by means not shown at a rate of about 100 scf/bbl. of extraction zone II 14 feed.

Within extraction zone II 14, the third selective solvent selectively removes the asphaltene constituents with a relatively higher hydrogen to carbon atomic ratio from the relatively lower hydrogen to carbon atomic ratio constituents to form a solvent-higher hydrogen to carbon atomic ratio asphaltene liquid coal phase relatively free of solid material and containing a very minor amount (0.01 weight percent) of material less than 0.01 micron in size after removal of excess solvent.

This material is removed and passed via line 15 to refining zone II 17 where, in presence of hydrogen added via line 16, the high hydrogen to carbon atomic ratio constituents are hydrorefined, preferably by contacting in an upflow manner with an unsupported vanadium sulfide catalyst at hydrorefining conditions including a temperature of about 425°C., a hydrogen pressure of about 3,000 psig, and a hydrogen to feed ratio of about 15,000 scf/bbl. of feed. Upgraded hydrogenated products are withdrawn via line 18 and may, if desired, be further refined in refining zone I 9.

Extraction zone II 14 residue comprising the low hydrogen to carbon atomic ratio asphaltene constituents in admixture with unconverted coal ash, etc. is removed and passed via line 19 to carbonization zone 20 where, at carbonization conditions including a temperature of 590°C., this material is carbonized to form a liquid coal tar distillate product withdrawn and passed via line 21, and further processed in refining zone II 17. Alternatively, this coal tar distillate may be passed directly to refining zone I 9. A highly carbonaceous char solid residue is withdrawn and passed via line 22 to hydrogen generation zone 23 where by means well-known to the art, the water-gas shift reaction is effected and hydrogen gas suitable for utilization in the hydrogen consuming steps of this process are withdrawn via line 24. Other gaseous materials are removed via line 25 and unreacted char is removed via line 26.

Example: A 1,000 g. sample of Pittsburgh Seam, bituminous coal containing 5.83 weight percent hydrogen and 84.7 weight percent carbon was crushed to 100 mesh and smaller size, mixed with 3,000 g. of tetrahydronaphthalene solvent and placed in an Eppenback Colloid mil for further size reduction of the particulate coal. After 5 hours operation at room conditions a coal-solvent mixture where all of the coal was less than 100 microns in diameter and about 75% less than two microns in diameter was produced.

The resultant colloided coal-solvent mixture was then subjected to the following extraction conditions to convert the coal into liquid coal products: temperature, 430°C.; pressure, 2,000 psig; solvent : coal weight ratio, 3 : 1; hydrogen : coal-solvent mixture (scf/bbl.) ratio, 4,000; coal residence time, 0.5 hour.

The resultant liquid extraction product, after removal of coarse coal particles in excess of 10 microns in diameter and removal of coarse coal particles in excess of 10 microns in diameter and removal by fractionation of excess solvent possessed the following properties:

Molecular weight	503
Percent hydrogen, weight	7.18
Percent carbon, weight	87.70
Percent solids (coal, ash, etc.), weight	0.50

The liquid coal extraction product was then admixed with heptane at a 5 : 1 heptane to liquid coal weight ratio and subjected to an extraction at 150°C. for a period of 0.5 hour. At the completion of this period, the mixture was allowed to cool to room temperature and settle with two phases forming a hydrogen-rich upper (heptane) phase and a hydrogen lean asphaltene lower phase. These phases are separated, with 51% of the original coal extract contained in the upper heptane phase. This liquid coal product, after removal of the heptane solvent is free of solid particulate matter and contains 8.68 weight percent hydrogen, 83.75 weight percent carbon, and has an average molecular weight of about 370. The lower residue-containing phase contains 6.53 weight percent hydrogen, 83.30 weight percent carbon, has an average molecular weight of about 780 and contains all of the solids present in the original, filtered coal-liquid extract product. This lower, residue phase was then admixed with benzene at a 5:1 benzene to residue weight ratio and subjected to extraction at 150°C. for a period of 0.5 hour. At the completion of this period, the mixture is allowed to cool and settle with two phases forming, an upper benzene phase containing the asphaltene components of higher hydrogen to carbon atomic ratio, relatively free of solid particulate matter (i.e., 0.01 weight percent of particles less than 0.01 micron in diameter) and a lower phase containing the lower hydrogen to carbon atomic ratio asphaltene components.

The liquid coal contained in the upper phase was 43% of the original liquid coal extract or 88% of the heptane insoluble residue. This material after benzene removal has an average molecular weight of 680, contains 6.75 weight percent hydrogen and 83.01 weight percent carbon. The insoluble residue, comprising 6% of the original coal extract or 12% of the heptane insolubles has an average molecular weight of 1,550 and contains 5.64 weight percent hydrogen and 86.07 weight percent carbon.

The asphaltenes contained in the benzene phase after removal of the benzene, is processed in a conventional pilot plant for upflow slurry processing in the presence of 6 weight percent vanadium sulfide catalyst, expressed in elemental form, at a pressure of 3,000 psig, a liquid hourly space velocity of 0.5, and a temperature profile from reactor bottom to reactor top of about 380° to 435°C. A hydrogen circulation rate of about 15,000 scf/bbl. is also maintained. Recovered is a product having a weight percent hydrogen of about 9.66 and a weight percent carbon of about 89.80. This product is comparable to the coal product obtained in the heptane extraction and is suitable for further processing if desired in the same manner as this heptane soluble fraction.

The low hydrogen to carbon atomic ratio asphaltene fraction containing undissolved coal, ash, etc. is subjected to a low temperature carbonization at 590°C., recovering therefrom a coal tar distillate having a molecular weight of about 590 containing 84.8 weight percent carbon and 7.9 weight percent hydrogen and suitable for further hydroprocessing in the same manner as either the high hydrogen to carbon atomic ratio asphaltene fraction or the hydrogen-rich heptane soluble fraction.

Not only are the more readily processed hydrogen-rich components separated from the hydrogen-lean asphaltene components with each fraction separately processed to insure maximum utilization of each fraction, but each of these fractions are obtainable essentially free of solid coal and ash particles, thus avoiding the cumbersome filtration type processes requiring complete solid removal heretofore utilized by the art. Similar results are obtained utilizing alternative solvents as hereinbefore described in this specification.

Two-Stage Solvent Extraction System

W.K.T. Gleim, R.S. Corey, F.J. Riedl and G.R. Sunagel; U.S. Patent 3,598,718; August 10, 1971; assigned to Universal Oil Products Company describe a process whereby coal is converted to liquid products utilizing a two-stage solvent extraction process where the liquid coal products are separated from unreacted coal and ash without requiring filtration. The coal is first contacted with conventional coal solvents, such as tetrahydronaphthalene under hydrogen pressure; the solvent is removed via fractionation; and hydrogen-rich coal components produced are recovered free of particulate matter by solvent extraction with a light aromatic or ketone solvent.

It has been found that the higher value, higher hydrogen content liquid coal components present in admixture with undissolved coal particles, ash, etc., at the completion of a conventional solvent extraction process utilizing conventional solvents such as Tetralin are readily separable from the lower value, low hydrogen content components of the liquid coal extract. This dual separation is accomplished by removing at least a portion and preferably the entire solvent from the liquid coal extract by conventional means, such as distillation, and treating the resultant residue with a selective light monocyclic aromatic, a cyclohexane, or ketone solvent. This selective solvent selectively removes the high hydrogen content components from both the low hydrogen content components and the undissolved coal, ash, and solid inorganic materials rendering a solid free, high hydrogen content liquid phase.

This process relates to a method for the conversion of solid, ash-containing coal particles into liquid products which comprises the steps of:

(a) contacting the coal with a first solvent in a first contacting zone under hydrogen pressure and extraction conditions to produce an effluent containing a liquid coal extract comprised of hydrogen-rich components and hydrogen-lean components in admixture with the solvent and unconverted coal and ash particles;

(b) separating from the effluent at least a portion of the first solvent to produce a stream of coal extract in admixture with at least a portion of the unconverted coal and ash particles;

(c) contacting the stream with a second solvent selective for the hydrogen-rich coal extract components in a second contacting zone at extraction conditions to produce a second zone effluent containing a hydrogen-rich liquid phase and a hydrogen-lean liquid phase; and

(d) separating from the second zone effluent a hydrogen-rich liquid phase and a hydrogen-lean liquid phase, the second zone hydrogen-rich liquid phase being essentially free of unconverted coal and ash particles.

Preferred solvents for use in the first stage extraction step of this process are those which are of the hydrogen donor type and which are at least partially hydrogenated such as the naphthenic-aromatic hydrocarbons. Preferably, the first stage solvent is one which is in the liquid phase at the recommended temperature and pressures utilized in the extraction and/or pulverization step of this process. Typically, those solvents are employed in mixtures of hydrocarbons and are derived, at least in part, from the intermediate or final products obtained from subsequent processing.

Typically, these first stage solvent hydrocarbons or mixtures of hydrocarbons boil between 200° and 425°C. Examples of such preferred naphthenic-aromatic first-stage solvents are the di- or tetra-, hydro derivatives of anthracene and phenanthrene. Also preferred are the aromatic hydro derivatives of naphthalene such as tetrahydronaphthalene (Tetralin). As used herein, naphthenic-aromatic solvents refer to polycyclic compounds where at least one of the rings is aromatic and at least one of the rings is not aromatic.

Also applicable within the process are the completely aromatic polycyclic aromatic compounds such as biphenyl, the methylnaphthalenes, the dimethylnaphthalenes, mixtures of phenanthrene and anthracene, etc., as well as their alkyl derivatives. Other types of solvents which may be utilized as first-stage solvents include phenolic compounds such as phenols, cresols and xylenols, particularly when utilized in admixture with any of the foregoing solvents. In general, the partially hydrogenated aromatic compounds are preferred over the completely aromatic polycyclic hydrocarbons. In any event, the solvent suitable for use in the first-stage extraction zone must be a solvent having the ability to depolymerize the pulverized coal during this extraction step.

The amount of solvent to be utilized in the first-stage extraction zone of this process and which includes the pulverization zone, generally will range from 0.2 to 10 lbs. of solvent per pound of coal. Satisfactory results are obtained in utilizing approximately a 1:1 to 3:1 solvent to coal ratio on a weight basis.

The first extraction zone includes pulverization of the large coal to smaller particulate coal in either the presence or absence of solvent as well as a digestion zone where the coal is either initially contacted with solvent if none were present during the pulverization step or, more preferably, where the effluent from the pulverization step where solvent was utilized is allowed to fully extract the coal to form a liquid-coal extract. The operating conditions for the digestion zone include a temperature from about 300° to 500°C., a hydrogen pressure from about atmosphere to 10,000 psig, a solvent to coal weight ratio from 0.2 to 10, and a residence time from 30 seconds to 5 hours, so correlated as to dissolve in excess of 50% by weight of the maf coal and to convert this coal to liquid products.

Since the purpose of the digestion zone is to substantially complete the conversion of solid coal into a liquid-coal extract, it is desirable to add to this digestion zone additional solvent, a hydrogen-containing gas, and/or a hydrogenation catalyst to the digestion zone. If such a catalyst is required or desired, it may be of a conventional hydrogenation type and may be used either homogeneously or heterogeneously. Thus, this catalyst may be introduced into the pulverization zone and/or digestion zone in admixture with the liquid first selective solvent or with the solid particulate coal.

The operating conditions to be utilized in the second stage extraction zone utilizing the ketone, monocyclic aromatic or cyclohexane solvent include a temperature from 50° to 300°C., and more preferably from 50° to 150°C., a H_2 pressure from 100 to 1,000 psig, and more preferably from 350 to 700 psig, a solvent to feed ratio from 0.5 to 5 by weight, a liquid hourly space velocity from 0.5 to 5, and in the presence of a hydrogen-containing gas in an amount from 500 to 5,000 scf/bbl. of liquid feed present in the second extraction zone. These conditions are sufficient to substantially separate, on a selective basis, the hydrogen-rich components from the hydrogen-lean component contained in the liquid feed passed to the second extraction zone from the first extraction zone.

The liquid-coal extract obtained from the first extraction zone will contain compounds of widely varying physical characteristics since the first extraction step is relatively nonselective. However, the liquid coal extract may be characterized as being composed of basically two liquid fractions, namely a hydrogen-rich fraction and a hydrogen-lean fraction. As used herein, the term "hydrogen-lean component" or words of similar import are intended to include those components which are basically insoluble in benzene or cyclohexane.

These hydrogen-lean components typically have an average molecular weight of 1,000 to 5,000 and contain 3 to 5% by weight hydrogen. On the other hand, as used herein, the term "hydrogen-rich components" or other words of similar import are intended to include those components which are basically soluble in benzene or cyclohexane.

These hydrogen-rich components typically have a molecular weight of less than 1,500 and more typically from 300 to 1,000 and have a hydrogen content on a weight basis in excess of 5% and typically have a hydrogen content from 6 to 9% by weight. The above characteristics of the two major fractions contained in the liquid extracted coal are, of course, influenced to some extent by the solvent extraction conditions utilized in the first-stage extraction zone including the depth of extraction employed in this first step. It is to be recognized that the hydrogen-lean components characteristic of the liquid-coal extract will only be influenced slightly by the extraction conditions but will be considerably influenced by the type of coal utilized as a feed to the process.

In any event, after the liquid-coal, extract-solid coal mixture is contacted with the foregoing second selective solvent, a two-phase liquid system results. An upper phase containing the hydrogen-rich liquid coal components (typically 60 to 90% of the liquid coal formed) and essentially free of undissolved coal, ash, etc., (i.e., less than 0.5 weight percent solids) is separated from a lower phase containing the hydrogen-lean, liquid-coal components in admixture with any undissolved coal, ash, etc. This hydrogen-lean, solid coal slurry is removed from the second extraction zone for use as fuel or for the conversion thereof to relatively pure hydrogen by the use of the water-gas reaction. The thus produced hydrogen may then be utilized within the process as hereinbefore described.

The rich solvent from the second extraction zone comprising either the ketone, cyclohexane, or monocyclic aromatic hydrocarbon having dissolved therein the hydrogen-rich components is further processed by means well-known to those skilled in the art such as fractionation, hydrogenation, hydrocracking, etc., in order to separate and convert the liquid-coal extract into more valuable products such as relatively light hydrocarbons, relatively heavy hydrocarbons, chemicals, fuels, etc.

Referring to Figure 2.21, coarse coal having an average particle diameter generally in excess of 0.08" and usually less than 2.5" is introduced into the process via line 1. A suitable selective first solvent with an enriched hydrogen content, such as Tetralin, is introduced via line 2 and admixed with the fresh feed coarse coal entering from line 1. Oversized solid material resulting from incomplete size reduction in the hereinafter described pulverization zone is recycled to the pulverization zone via line 3 and admixed with fresh coal and solvent. This entire admixture of coarse coal and first selective solvent is passed via line 4 into mill 5 which may be of the conventional ball mill type adapted for use in the presence of a liquid according to means well-known to those skilled in the art.

Suitable pulverization conditions such as a temperature of about 100°C., a pressure of about 70 psig, and a solvent to coal weight ratio of about 2.0 are maintained in mill 5 such that the coarse coal is reduced to an average particle diameter between 0.08" and 0.04". The effluent from mill 5 containing Tetralin and undissolved coal of proper small particle size and undissolved, oversized coal is passed via line 6 into first separator 7 which may be of the hydroclone type. Conditions are maintained in separator 7 whereby the oversized coal particles, preferably, in admixture with at least a portion of the liquid material, are removed via line 3 and returned to mill 5 as previously discussed.

The first selective solvent, Tetralin, plus fine, undissolved pulverized coal is removed from first separator 7 via line 8 and is admixed with a hydrogen-containing gas entering from line 10, and the total mixture is passed via line 8 into digestion zone 11 which may be a jacketed, stirred type vessel. Added Tetralin solvent, if any, may be introduced into the system via line 9 in an amount sufficient to maintain the solvent to coal ratio at the desired level and/or to maintain the hydrogen content in digestor 11 at a sufficiently high level. Furthermore, hydrogenation catalyst (from means not shown) may be advantageously used in the digestion step. Makeup hydrogen, if required, is added to the system via line 15. Preferably, the amount of hydrogen present in the digestion zone is from 1,000 to 100,000 scf of hydrogen per barrel of coal-solvent mixture entering digestor 11 via line 8.

The entire effluent from digestion zone 11 is removed via line 12. This effluent consists of undissolved coal particles, ash, solids, etc., in a very finely dispersed state in admixture with Tetralin solvent, liquid-coal extract and hydrogen gas. This effluent is passed via line 12 to a second separator 13. Within separator 13, which may comprise one or more separation vessels including flash and fractionation columns, hydrogen gas is removed via line 14, commingled with makeup hydrogen entering via line 15 and passed to digestion zone 11 as hereinbefore described via line 10. At least a portion and preferably all the first solvent Tetralin is removed via line 16 and is commingled with solvent recovered in the hereinafter described third separation zone 26 entering via line 20 and makeup solvent entering via line 19 and passed via lines 2 and 9 to pulverization zone 5 and digestion zone 11, respectively, as hereinbefore described.

The effluent from second separator 13 containing solvent (i.e., Tetralin) not removed therein, liquid-coal extract containing hydrogen-rich and hydrogen-lean components and undissolved coal, ash, etc., is removed and passed via line 17 to extraction zone 21. If desired, a portion of this material may be withdrawn via line 18, commingled with line 16 for recycle to digestion zone 11 and/or pulverization zone 5.

Within extraction zone 21, a second separator 13 effluent (extraction zone feed) is contacted with either a ketone, monocyclic aromatic, cyclohexane, or alkylcyclohexane, selective solvent entering via line 23 under extraction conditions including a temperature of 150°C., a solvent to extraction zone feed weight ratio of about 3, a pressure of about 500 psig,

FIGURE 2.21: TWO-STAGE SOLVENT EXTRACTION SYSTEM

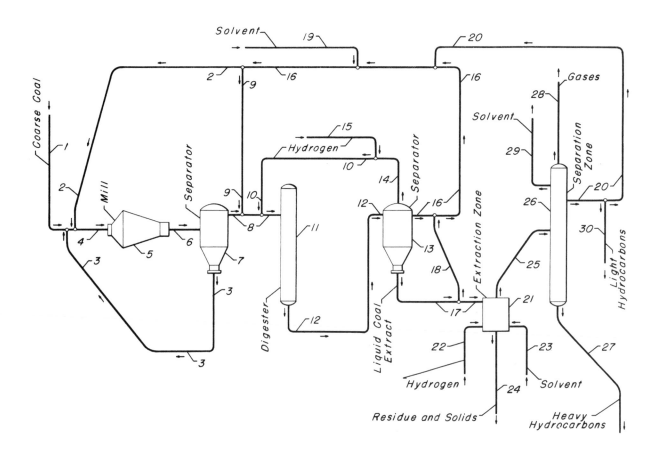

Source: W.K.T. Gleim, R.S. Corey, F.J. Riedl and G.R. Sunagel; U.S. Patent 3,598,718; August 10, 1971

and preferably in the presence of hydrogen gas added via line 22 at a rate of about 100 scf/bbl. of extraction zone 21 feed. Within this zone 21, the selective solvent selectively removes the hydrogen-rich, liquid-coal extraction components from the hydrogen-lean components and undissolved coal, ash, etc., to form a solvent-hydrogen-rich, liquid-coal stream free of solids which is withdrawn via line 25 and passed to second separation zone 26. A residue comprising hydrogen-lean, liquid-coal components and undissolved coal, ash, etc., is withdrawn from extraction zone 21 via line 24 and is disposed of as fuel or source of additional hydrogen through the water gas reaction (means not shown).

Third separation zone 26, comprising a plurality of separation means including fractionation columns, separates the extraction zones solvent from the hydrogen-rich, liquid-coal extract components such as the naphthenic and naphthenic-aromatic hydrocarbons and other gasoline boiling range hydrocarbons. Within zone 26, the selective ketone, monocyclic aromatic, or cyclohexane solvent is withdrawn, via line 29; normally gaseous materials, if any, are withdrawn via line 28; hydrogen-rich aromatic and naphthenic-aromatic, liquid-coal components suitable for use for further processing and/or as a solvent for the pulverization and/or digestion zone are withdrawn via line 20 with the net make of light hydrocarbons removed via line 30; and, the higher molecular weight hydrogen-rich components removed via line 27.

Example: A 100 g. sample of Pittsburgh seam, bituminous coal was crushed to 100 mesh and smaller size, mixed with 300 g. of Tetralin and placed in an Eppenback colloidal mill for further size reduction of the particulate coal. The mill was operated for 5 hours and produced a coal solvent mixture where all of the coal was less than 100 microns in diameter and 95 weight percent of the coal was less than 2 microns in diameter. The resultant colloided coal-Tetralin mixture was then subjected to the following extraction conditions to convert the coal into liquid products.

Temperature, °C.	430	Hydrogen : coal mixture ratio (scf/bbl.)	4,000
Pressure, psig	2,000	Coal residence time, hours	0.5
Tetralin : coal weight ratio	3:1		

The resultant liquid extraction product, after centrifuging and removal of excess Tetralin solvent, possessed the following properties:

Molecular weight	503
Hydrogen, weight percent	7.18
Carbon, weight percent	87.70
Solids (coal, ash, etc.), weight percent	0.50

This extraction product is then admixed with benzene in a 5:1 benzene to extract weight ratio and subjected to a second extraction at 120°C. for a period of 1 hour. At the completion of this period, the mixture is allowed to cool and settle with two phases forming a hydrogen-rich upper (benzene) phase and a hydrogen-lean lower phase. These phases are separated with 78 weight percent of the original coal extract contained in the upper benzene phase.

The "liquid coal" contained in the upper phase contains 7.75 weight percent hydrogen, has an average molecular weight of about 450 and is essentially solid-free (i.e., less than 0.01 weight percent). The lower, residue-containing phase contains 5.52 weight percent hydrogen, has an average molecular weight of about 1,150 and contains essentially all of the solids present in the original extraction products.

Two-Stage Solvent Extraction Utilizing a Solids Filtration System

G.R. Sunagel, R.S. Corey, F.J. Riedl and W.K.T. Gleim; U.S. Patent 3,598,717; August 10, 1971; assigned to Universal Oil Products Company describe a two-stage solvent extraction method for converting solid coal into liquid coal extract. The first-stage uses the conventional solvents, such as polyaromatic hydrocarbons, alkylnaphthalenes, anthracene oil, or partially hydrogenated aromatics as for instance, Tetralin. The liquefied coal stripped of the solvent is then extracted with a ketone to produce a hydrogen-rich extract fraction and a hydrogen-lean extract phase. The hydrogen-rich fraction is recovered and used as a source for valuable chemicals and liquid fuels. The hydrogen-lean fraction may be used for plant fuel and/or as a source for additional hydrogen through conversion by the "water-gas" reaction.

This process provides a method for liquefying solid particulate coal which comprises the steps of: (a) contacting the coal with a selective first solvent under conditions sufficient to convert the coal into liquid coal extract containing hydrogen-rich components and hydrogen-lean components; (b) separating the liquid coal extract from undissolved coal and from at least a portion of the first solvent; (c) contacting the separated liquid coal extract from step (b) under extraction conditions with a second solvent selective for hydrogen-rich components; and, (d) recovering hydrogen-rich components and hydrogen-lean component as separate product streams.

The process is quite similar to the one described previously in U.S. Patent 3,598,718, but differs in the fact that this process includes a filtration apparatus as part of the system. Typically, the first-stage solvent hydrocarbons or mixtures of hydrocarbons boil between 260° and 425°C. Examples of suitable first-stage solvents are tetrahydronaphthalene (Tetralin), Decalin, biphenyl, methylnaphthalene, dimethylnaphthalene, mixtures of phenanthrene and anthracene, etc. Other types of solvents which may be added to the preferred first-stage solvents of this process for special reasons include phenolic compounds, such as phenols, cresols and xylenols. It is also to be recognized that in some cases, it may be desirable during a subsequent separation step, typically, prior to the second stage extraction operation, to add an antisolvent, such as saturated paraffinic hydrocarbons, such as n-hexane, to aid in the precipitation of tarry and solid residue from the liquid coal extract of the process.

Since the purpose of the digestion zone, including the first selective solvent in the pulverization and digestion zones, is to substantially complete the conversion of the solid coal into a liquid coal extract, it may be desirable to add to the digestion zone additional solvent, add a hydrogen-containing gas to the digestion zone, and/or utilize a catalyst in the digestion zone. If a catalyst is required or desired, it may be of the conventional hydrogenation type either homogeneous or heterogenous and may be introduced into the pulverization zone and/or digestion zone in admixture with the liquid first selective solvent or with the solid coal.

Examples of conventional hydrogenation catalyst which may be used in the first extraction zone include a cobalt-molybdate, a nickel molybdate, a nickel tungstate or any other hydrogenation catalyst which can operate in the presence of sulfur-containing charge stocks and is applicable to the solvent-coal system environment maintained in the first extraction zone, including the use of a slurry-catalyst system.

Hydrogenation in the digestion zone, generally, accomplishes the following functions: transfer of hydrogen directly to coal molecules; transfer of hydrogen to hydrogen-donor molecules to coal molecules; and combinations of the above. Homogeneous catalyst may be introduced with the coal or with hydrogen-donor compounds in the pulverization step or in the digestion zone. By way of emphasis, as used herein, the term "first extraction zone" is intended to include the pulverization step, the digestion step or the combined pulverization-digestion step. After separation of the undissolved coal residue of at least a portion of the first selective solvent and catalyst, if any, from the total effluent of the digestion zone, the liquid coal extract is contacted in a second extraction zone.

Suitable preferred solvents for use in the second stage extraction zone are ketones. Examples of ketones which may be used satisfactorily include acetone, methyl ethyl ketone, methyl butyl ketone, dibutyl ketone, etc. Other suitable solvents for use in the second stage extraction include monocyclic aromatic hydrocarbons (e.g., benzene, toluene, xylene, etc.) and naphthenic hydrocarbons (e.g., methylcyclohexane, etc.). It is a requirement of this process that the first stage extraction zone utilize those solvents which are applicable to the conversion of solid coal particles to liquid form and that the second stage extraction zone be strictly limited to a solvent which serves to separate the hydrogen-rich components from the hydrogen-lean components contained in the liquid coal extract produced in the first extraction step.

In other words, it was found that the ketones, as well as the other abovementioned secondary solvents are selective for the hydrogen-rich components to the substantial rejection of the hydrogen-lean components. The choice of selective solvent depends upon the extraction conditions desired in the second extraction zone. The initial boil point of the solvent should be above the temperature selected for the second extraction zone. For practical purposes, the temperature selected for the second extraction zone should be at least 30°C. below the critical boiling point of, for example, the ketone in order to maintain the components in primarily liquid phase. As a rule, the temperature for the second extraction zone should not exceed 450°C.

Referring to Figure 2.22, coarse coal having an average particle diameter generally in excess of 0.08" is introduced into the system via line 10. A suitable selective first solvent enriched in hydrogen content, such as Tetralin, is introduced into admixture with the coarse coal from line 11, the major source of which is more fully discussed hereinafter. As previously mentioned, the oversized solid material from the pulverization zone is also preferably returned to the pulverization zone via line 12. The entire admixture of coarse coal and first selective solvent is passed via line 13 into mill 14 which conventionally may be of the ball mill type adaptable for use in the presence of a liquid according to means well-known to those skilled in the art.

FIGURE 2.22:   TWO-STAGE SOLVENT EXTRACTION UTILIZING A SOLIDS FILTRATION SYSTEM

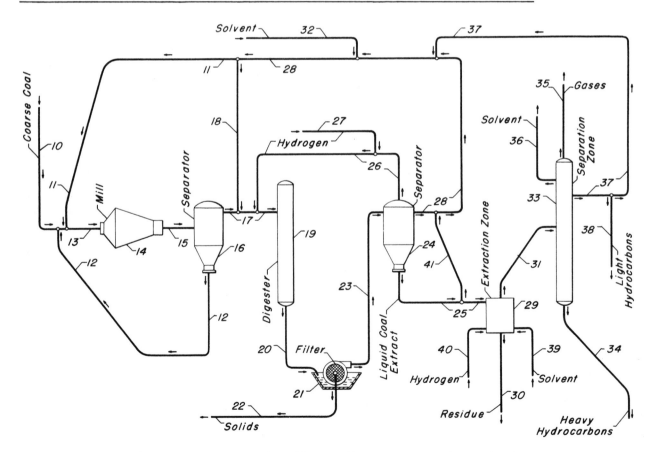

Source: G.R. Sunagel, R.S. Corey, F.J. Riedl and W.K.T. Gleim; U.S. Patent 3,598,717; August 10, 1971

Suitable pulverization conditions include a temperature of about 380°C., a pressure of about 70 psig and a solvent to coal ratio of about 1.0 is maintained in mill 14, such that the coarse coal is reduced to an average particle diameter between 0.08" and 0.04", and at least a portion of the coal, say, about 17% by weight is dissolved into the Tetralin. The effluent from mill 14 containing Tetralin having dissolved therein the liquid coal extract and containing undissolved coal of proper small particle size and undissolved coal of oversize is passed via line 15 into separator 16 which may be of the cyclone type. Conditions are maintained in separator 16 whereby the oversized coal particles, preferably, in admixture with at least a portion of the liquid material is removed via line 12 and returned to mill 14 in a manner previously discussed.

First selective solvent, e.g., Tetralin, having dissolved therein at least a portion of the coal plus undissolved pulverized coal is admixed, preferably, with a hydrogen-containing gas from line 26 and passed via line 17 into digestion zone 19 which may be a jacketed stirred type vessel. Added Tetralin solvent, if any, may be introduced into the system via line 18 in an amount sufficient to maintain the solvent to coal ratio at the desired level and/or to maintain the hydrogen content present in digester 19 at a sufficiently high level. Furthermore, hydrogenation catalyst (from means not shown) advantageously may be used in the digestion step. Makeup hydrogen, if any, may be added to the system via line 27. Preferably, the amount of hydrogen present in the digestion zone is from 1,000 to 100,000 scf/bbl. of coal-solvent mixture entering digester 19 via line 17.

The entire effluent from digestion zone 19 is passed via line 20 into filtration zone 21 where solid residue, including solid hydrogenation catalyst, if any, is separated from the liquid material and removed from the system via line 22. Filtration zone 21, preferably, is a rotary filter device, precoated with conventional filter aids and is, typically, operated at a pressure from 50 to 100 psig, sufficient to effect removal of substantially all of the suspended solid matter including undissolved carbonaceous matter. The filter cake is washed and dried by conventional means to recover absorbed liquid material. The mother liquor, including any gaseous materials, is removed from filtration zone 21 via line 23. The material in line 23 comprises solvent having dissolved therein liquid coal extract comprising both hydrogen-rich components and hydrogen-lean components.

As previously mentioned, if desired, by means not shown, an antisolvent, such as a light hydrocarbon of the hexane type, may be added to filtration zone 21 in an effort to further aid in removing tars and solid materials from the desired solvent and liquid hydrocarbons making up the liquid coal extract. If an antisolvent is used, the material in line 23 will also contain such added light hydrocarbons.

The material from filtration zone 21 is passed through line 23 into separator 24 which may comprise one or more separation vessels, including fractionation columns for the separation of the hydrogen gas and added light hydrocarbons, if any, from the other hydrocarbonaceous material. Although separation zone 24 has been shown in a position following filtration zone 21, it is within the concepts of this process to arrange for the separation of gaseous materials, such as hydrogen gas, prior to filtration zone 21. In other words, another embodiment of this process would include a gaseous (e.g., hydrogen) separation zone, not shown, in line 20 between digester 19 and filter 21. However, for purposes of this illustrative embodiment only, separation zone 24 has been placed between filtration zone 21 and secondary extraction zone 29 more fully discussed hereinbelow.

In keeping with the illustrative embodiment, hydrogen gas is removed from separation zone 24 via line 26 and returned to digester 19. Preferably, that portion of the normally liquid material entering separation zone 24 from line 23 which comprises first selective solvent component (Tetralin) is withdrawn via line 28 and returned to the digestion zone and/or pulverization zone, as previously discussed. Therefore, the liquid coal extract substantially free of solid matter, free of hydrogen gas, and free of normally gaseous hydrocarbons and, preferably, free of first selective solvent components, is removed from separator 24 via line 25.

The material in line 25, comprising liquid coal extract substantially free of solvent (although, it is recognized that a portion of the liquid coal extract may be suitable for use as the first selective solvent more fully developed hereinbelow) is passed into secondary extraction zone 29. If desired, a portion of the material in line 25 may be returned via line 41 into line 28 for recycle to the digestion zone 19 and/or pulverization zone 14.

Extraction zone 29 is maintained under extraction conditions, including the presence of a ketone class solvent which enters the system via line 39 and a temperature of about 150°C., a solvent to extract ratio of about 3, a pressure of about 500 psig and, preferably, having introduced into the zone added hydrogen gas via line 40 in an amount of about 100 scf per barrel of extract entering zone 29. A residue comprising hydrogen-lean components is withdrawn from second extraction zone 29 via line 30 and disposed of as fuel or as a source of additional hydrogen through a water-gas reaction (by means not shown).

The rich solvent comprising ketone having dissolved therein hydrogen-rich components, such as naphthenic and naphthenic aromatic hydrocarbons and gasoline boiling range hydrocarbons is passed via line 31 into separation zone 32 which comprises a plurality of separatory means including fractionation columns. Conditions are maintained in separation zone 33, which are known to those skilled in the art from the teachings herein, sufficient to recover the ketone solvent which is withdrawn via line 36, to recover the normally gaseous materials, if any, which are withdrawn from line 35, to recover and separate naphthenic and naphthenic aromatic type hydrogen-rich components suitable for use as the first selective solvent which is withdrawn via line 37 and returned to digestor 19 and mill 14 in the manner previously discussed, with the net production of light hydrocarbon components being withdrawn from the system via line 38, and to separate and recover the relatively heavy hydrocarbons, also hydrogen-rich, which are withdrawn from the system via line 34. The residual fraction in line 34 comprises basically a heavy fuel oil and is used desirably in a fuel system. Added first selective solvent, such as Tetralin, external of the process may be added to the system via line 32, if desired.

Example: Pulverized bituminous coal was liquefied via solvent extraction using anthracene oil at 430°C. and the presence of hydrogen gas. The solid residue was removed and a liquid coal extract obtained. 100 g. of the liquid coal extract was contacted with boiling methyl ethyl ketone. The resulting ketone-extract product was filtered to remove solid residue and ash. The solvent was distilled off and a final extract obtained (40 g.). The final extract and the liquid coal extract were analyzed for hydrogen with the following results:

	Weight Percent Hydrogen
First-stage, liquid coal extract	5.2
Second-stage, final extract	5.7

It is evident from this data that the second solvent extraction step significantly upgraded the liquefied coal, e.g., the 0.5% increase in hydrogen content.

MICROWAVE AND ULTRASONICS FOR LIQUEFACTION AND EXTRACTION

Utilizing Microwave Energy for the Liquefaction of Coal

R.D. Stone; U.S. Patent 3,503,865; March 31, 1970; assigned to Universal Oil Products Company describes a process for liquefying coal by subjecting bituminous coal particles to microwave energy and recovering valuable liquid hydrocarbon products from the resulting liquid coal extract. According to this process the pulverized coal is subjected to wave energy having a frequency above 1,000 megacycles. Preferably, this wave energy is of microwave frequency.

Apparatus and equipment for generating the wave energy are standard and well-known to those skilled in the art. Typically, for example, such equipment might include an oscillator such as a Magnetron, an amplifier such as a Klystron, and a radiation device for transmitting the wave energy to the material to be treated. Operating conditions during the liquefaction step include a temperature from 100° to 500°C. and a pressure from 1 atmosphere to 10,000 psig sufficient to convert at least 50% by weight maf coal into normally liquid products.

Suitable solvents for use in this process are those of the hydrogen-donor type and are at least partially hydrogenated and include naphthalenic hydrocarbons. Other hydrocarbons, such as naphthalene, methylnaphthalene, etc. may also be used if added hydrogen gas is also used in the extraction zone. Preferably, the solvent is one which is in liquid phase at the recommended temperature and pressure for extraction. Mixtures of the hydrocarbons are generally employed as the solvent and, preferably, are derived from intermediate or final products obtained from subsequent processing following the practice of this process. Typically, the solvent hydrocarbons or mixtures of hydrocarbons boil between 260° and 425°C. Examples of suitable solvents are tetrahydronaphthalene (Tetralin), Decalin, biphenyl, methylnaphthalene, dimethyl-naphthalene, etc.

Other types of solvents which may be added to the preferred solvents of this process for special reasons include phenolic compounds, such as phenols, cresols, and xylenols. It is also to be recognized that in some cases it may be desirable during a subsequent separation step prior to the removal of the solvent from the liquid coal extract to add an antisolvent, such as saturated paraffinic hydrocarbons like hexane, to aid in the precipitation of tarry and solid residue, e.g., ash, from the coal extract.

The optimum conditions for operating this process in the presence of a selective solvent are for the liquefaction step to include a temperature from 200° to 500°C., a pressure from 500 to 5,000 psig, a solvent-to-coal ratio from 0.2 to 10, and a residence time in the liquefaction zone from 30 seconds to 5 hours and, still more preferably, include the presence of hydrogen sufficient to dissolve coal such that a total in excess of 50% by weight of the coal feed into the liquefaction zone has been liquefied into normally liquid products.

Since the purpose of the extraction zone is to substantially convert coal into liquid coal extract, it may be desirable to add to the extraction zone a catalyst. The catalyst may be conventional, may be homogeneous or heterogeneous and may be introduced into the pulverization zone and/or extraction zone in admixture with either the liquid solvent or with the solid coal. From a knowledge of the characteristics of the coal, solvent and of the properties desired for the end product, one will know whether or not it may be desirable to use any or all of these features in the solvent extraction zone.

If a catalyst is desired, conventional solid hydrogenation catalyst can be satisfactorily utilized, such as palladium on an alumina support or a cobalt-molybdate catalyst or any other hydrogenation catalyst known to be applicable to the solvent-coal system environment maintained in the extraction zone including the use of a slurry-catalyst system.

After separation of the gaseous materials, including hydrogen, hydrogen sulfide, undissolved coal residue (e.g., ash) and catalyst, if any, from the total effluent of the extraction zone, the liquid coal extract is passed into conventional recovery facilities where valuable liquid hydrocarbons are recovered. Typically, these recovery facilities comprise fractionation columns for the separation therein of the liquid coal extract into products such as normally gaseous hydrocarbons, relatively light hydrocarbons comprising essentially middle oil, relatively heavy hydrocarbons comprising materials suitable for use as a coal solvent and a bottoms fraction comprising residue material which is suitable for fuel. In essence, therefor, the valuable liquid hydrocarbons recovered from the liquid coal extract include, for example, gasoline boiling range products and/or chemicals, aromatic hydrocarbon-containing fractions, heavy fuel oil fractions, and the like.

Example 1: A Pittsburg Seam Coal is pulverized to an average particle diameter of about −14 Tyler screen size. The crushed coal is mixed with Tetralin on a 1:1 weight basis and passed into a reaction zone maintained under a temperature of 300°C. and a pressure of 1,000 psig. The admixture is then subjected to a microwave energy for a period of about 3 hours. Approximately, 80% by weight of the maf coal is converted to C_6+ hydrocarbonaceous product.

Example 2: The reaction of Example 1 is repeated except that 5,000 scf/bbl. of solvent of hydrogen is introduced into the reaction zone. Approximately, 85% by weight of the maf coal is converted to C_6+ hydrocarbonaceous products in significantly less time than in Example 1, e.g., 2 hours. The experiments are again repeated and similar results are experienced by substituting ultraviolet light for the microwave energy.

Example 3: The reaction of Example 1 was repeated except that no wave energy was imposed on the solvent-coal mixture. In order to convert 80% by weight maf coal to C_6+ products required significantly longer time, e.g., 3+ hours, but also required significantly higher temperature, e.g., 400° to 450°F.

Ultrasonic Treatment as an Aid in the Solvent Extraction and Solubilization of Coal with Quinoline

T. Kessler, A.G. Sharkey, Jr., J. Malli, Jr. and R.A. Friedel; U.S. Patent 3,577,337; May 4, 1971; assigned to the U.S. Secretary of the Interior describe a process in which coal is extracted in quinoline by treatment of a coal-quinoline slurry with ultrasonic irradiation at ambient temperature. The quinoline may then be removed from the solubilized coal fraction by conversion to a water-soluble quinoline salt. The solubilized fraction may be used for production of gasoline, aromatic chemicals, carbon black, electrode carbons, low-sulfur and -ash fuels for power plants, etc.

It has been found, according to this process, that the use of quinoline as solvent, when exposed to ultrasonic irradiation, results in an efficient and economical extraction of coal. Quinoline has previously been used in extraction of carbonaceous fuels; however, the use of high temperatures, i.e., about 300°C., was necessary for efficient extraction. In this process, on the other hand, the extraction may be carried out at ambient temperature. The economics of the process is thereby considerably improved as a result of the reduction or elimination of the required amount of thermal energy.

Quinoline has been found to be unique in exhibiting efficient extraction at ambient temperature. The superiority of this solvent as compared to other conventional solvents is illustrated in the example below. According to this process, a slurry of the coal in quinoline is subjected to ultrasonic irradiation at ambient temperature. The initial slurry suitably consists of 10 to 40 weight percent of coal and is prepared by conventional means such as grinding or pulverizing the coal to a particle size of 595 to 44 microns and introducing the finely divided coal into the quinoline by any conventional means. The process is generally most effective with high-volatile-A bituminous coals; however, other coals such as high-volatile-B, high-volatile-C bituminous, and cannel may also be treated. Pure quinoline is not necessary for efficient extraction, crude quinoline-base fractions (water free) usually being satisfactory.

Ambient temperature, i.e., about 30°C. is generally optimum in the process. However, temperatures in the range of 20° to 40°C. usually result in effective and economical extractions. Atmospheric pressure is satisfactory. The extraction is preferably carried out in an air atmosphere. Inert gases may be used but generally show no advantages.

Irradiation of the coal-quinoline slurry may be carried out in any suitable apparatus such as a tank-type ultrasonic cleaner. Frequency of the radiation will range from 30 to 90 kHz. Optimum power and duration of the irradiation will depend on the frequency employed, the type of coal, particle size of the coal, size and configuration of the reaction vessel, amount of quinoline employed, etc., and are best determined experimentally; however, a power of about 0.5 watt or less per square centimeter of slurry and an irradiation time of 4 to 6 hours is usually satisfactory. The radiation may be supplied by any conventional ultrasonic generator such as Model 040015, Ultrasonic Industries, Inc., cleaner.

Following irradiation, the solubilized coal and excess quinoline are removed from the undissolved coal residue by conventional means such as centrifugation or filtration. The residue is then preferably washed with additional quinoline; the washings are then added to the solubilized coal-quinoline mixture. Quinoline is then recovered from the solubilized coal-quinoline mixture by conversion of the quinoline to a water-soluble salt. This is readily accomplished by addition of water and sufficient acid to give a mixture having a pH of 1.5 to 2.0. The volume of water added is suitably 5 to 10 times the volume of quinoline used to form the original slurry. Concentrated hydrochloric acid is the preferred acid; however, 1:1 HCl may also be used. At a pH in the above range the quinoline is converted to a water-soluble salt, leaving the solubilized coal product suspended in the quinoline-acid-water mixture. The coal product is then separated by filtration or centrifugation and is preferably washed with water to remove any occluded quinoline or acid. The quinoline-acid mixture can then be converted to quinoline by neutralization with sodium hydroxide and the quinoline then reused in the extraction process.

Example: A commercial ultrasonic generator operating at a frequency of 80 kHz with a total output of 80 watts was used to irradiate one-half gram samples of Pittsburgh seam coal (<325 mesh) in 5 ml. of solvent for 4 hours at ambient temperature (30°C.) in an argon atmosphere. In a single experiment with quinoline, the irradiation time was extended to 24 hours. After irradiation, the solvent-extract mixture was removed from the coal residue by centrifugation. The coal residue was then washed with two 5 ml. portions of solvent; the washings were added to the solubilized coal-quinoline mixture. Concentrated hydrochloric acid was added to the solubilized coal-quinoline mixture until a pH of 1.5 was obtained.

75 ml. of distilled water were added to separate the solvated coal from the soluble quinoline hydrochloride. The solvated coal was removed from the mixture by filtration and washed with 500 ml. of distilled water to remove all traces of occluded quinoline hydrochloride. The amount of coal solvated by various solvents is shown in the following table.

Ultrasonic Solvation of Pittsburgh Seam Hvab Coal at Ambient Temperature

Solvent	Weight Percent Coal Solvated
Quinoline	49
Pyridine	19
Formamide	10
N,N-dimethylformamide	<1
1,2,3,4-tetrahydronaphthalene	4

As seen from the above table, approximately half of the coal was solvated after 4 hours of irradiation in quinoline, 2 1/2 times the yield with pyridine. Yields were considerably less with formamide, N,N-dimethylformamide, and the hydroaromatic, 1,2,3,4-tetrahydronaphthalene. 79% of the coal was solubilized in quinoline when the irradiation time was increased from 4 hours to 24 hours. By contrast, mechanical agitation of a coal-quinoline slurry for 24 hours at ambient temperature solubilized only 10% of the coal.

THERMAL LIQUEFACTION OF COAL WITH SOLVENTS

In the process developed by W.H. Seitzer and R.W. Shinn; U.S. Patent 3,594,304; July 20, 1971; assigned to Sun Oil Company a subbituminous coal is liquefied by rapidly heating a slurry of the powdered coal in a hydrogenated solvent at a temperature range of from 440° to 450°C., and a residence time of from 5 to 20 minutes.

A coal liquefaction process for subbituminous coal has been found which is able to achieve solution of 90% or more of the coal and which minimizes gas production. This is accomplished in accord with this process by subjecting a subbituminous coal to solution in a hydrogenated polynuclear solvent under pressure of hydrogen of from 2,000 to 3,000 psig and maintaining the temperature of the process within the narrow range 440° to 450°C. for a period of 5 to 20 minutes residence time. In view of the literature, it is indeed surprising to find that the critical conditions of the process make possible a significant increase in amount of coal dissolved and in minimizing the amount of gaseous products formed. As indicated, the coal used in the process will be a subbituminous coal and this will include lignite coals such as North Dakota lignite, Powder River Subbituminous Coal, and the like.

The solvent used in the process will be a hydrogenated polynuclear solvent frequently known as a hydrogen donor solvent. These donor solvent materials are well-known and comprise aromatic hydrocarbons which are at least partially hydrogenated, generally having one or more of the nuclei saturated or partially saturated. Several examples of such materials are Tetralin, dihydronaphthalene, dihydroalkylnaphthalene, dihydrophenanthrene, dihydroanthracene, dihydrochrysene, tetrahydrochrysene, tetrahydropyrene, tetrahydrofluoranthene and the like. Of particular value in this process as hydrogen donor solvents are the hydrophenanthrenes and hydroanthracenes such as dihydroanthracene.

It will be understood that these materials may be obtained from any source, but are readily available by partially hydrogenating appropriate aromatic products by conventional techniques. Specific preferred examples of such materials are anthracene oil and Tetralin. In the preferred process the solvent used will be a distillate fraction of the dissolved coal which has been hydrogenated by any standard commercial technique. The amount of solvent used in the process may vary, but enough must be used to provide a stirrable slurry. Usually the amount of solvent used will be a weight ratio of oil to coal of about 1:1 to 5:1. The preferred parameters of the process are a temperature of 445° to 450°C., a pressure of 2,500 pounds per square inch gauge, a solvent to coal ratio of about 2:1, and a residence time of 10 to 20 minutes.

In carrying out the process, a slurry of the powdered coal in the hydrogen donor solvent is introduced into a pressure reactor and the reactor is pressured with hydrogen to a pressure of from 1,000 to 1,500 psig. As the contents of the reactor are stirred or agitated, the temperature is raised rapidly to the critical temperature range of 440° to 450°C., and the pressure rises to between 2,000 and 3,000 psig. In raising the temperature care must be exercised to avoid holding the reaction products at temperatures between about 400°C. and reaction temperature for any length of time. No significant solution or changes in the coal will occur below about 400°C., but when the reaction mass reaches the 400°C. range, then the rise in temperature to 440° to 450°C. must be rapid, say within a few minutes, in order to avoid chemical changes in the coal which will reduce its conversion to soluble products.

On the other hand, if the temperature goes above 455°C., recoking of the coal liquid occurs and thus solubility is drastically reduced. As also indicated, the time used for the process is critical and residence time at a temperature of 440° to 450°C. is preferably between 10 and 20 minutes. If a residence time of less than about 5 minutes is used, solubility is again reduced to an impractical amount. On the other hand, if operation is continued for more than about 20 minutes, then the formation of gases such as methane, ethane and propane are so great as to significantly reduce the efficiency and economics of the process. After the solution is completed in accord with the above steps, heating is stopped and the products are filtered hot or, optionally, cooled before filtering.

It is also unexpected that the process must be carried out in a single stage. It would be thought that hydrocarbon gas formation could be kept to a minimum by employing a two-step system, i.e., partial liquefaction at a low temperature (say 425° to 435°C.) and then final and more complete liquefaction at a higher temperature (about 450°C.). However, it is found that such two-stage operation results in coking and much lower solution being obtained. Thus, only the very narrow critical conditions of the process give the high coal solubility necessary for a satisfactory commercial process.

The dissolved coal formed by the process is a valuable product similar in many respects to a crude oil and is subjected to the usual refining operations to produce petroleum products. For use in this manner, the solution is merely filtered to remove the small amount of insoluble products present, and the filtrate treated in accord with conventional refinery techniques. In order to more fully describe this process, the following examples are given.

Liquefaction of coal was carried out in stirred pressure reactors which contained powdered Big Horn Coal and a hydrogenated anthracene oil (BP 500° to 750°F.), the weight ratio of liquid oil to coal being 2:1. The reactor was pressured with hydrogen to about 1,200 psig and the temperature raised rapidly to the desired temperature. The stirred reactor was held on temperature for 20 minutes, cooled and the insoluble material filtered off. The following table shows the results obtained and points up the critical temperature range of 440° to 450°C.

Temp., °C.	Time, mins.	Final Pressure, psig	Percent Organic Dissolved	Hydrocarbon Gases, wt. % of Coal
430	20	2,900	83	2.9
440	20	2,800	92	4.1
450	20	2,800	90	5.3
450	20	3,000	95	5.3
460	20	2,600	80	8.2

Following the experimental details set forth above, the time of reaction was varied. The results are shown in the following table.

Temp., °C.	Time, mins.	Final Pressure, psig	Percent Organic Dissolved	Hydrocarbon Gases, wt. % of Coal
450	5	2,800	88	3.4
450	20	2,800	90	5.3
450	20	3,000	95	5.3
450	60	2,800	92	13.5

As can be seen from the above table, the reaction time is critical to the amount of coal dissolved and to the amount of hydrocarbon gases evolved. Maximum solubility of coal and minimum evolution of gases occurs at about 20 minutes of reaction time within the critical temperature range. When more than about 20 minutes residence time is permitted yield of unwanted hydrocarbon gases increases significantly. The need for a hydrogenated oil in this process is indicated in the table shown on the following page where it is seen that when an unhydrogenated anthracene oil is used the coal solubility dropped to 41%.

Thermal Liquefaction of Coal

Temp., °C.	Time, mins.	Final Pressure, psig	Percent Organic Dissolved	Hydrocarbon Gases, wt. % of Coal
450	20	2,300	41*	3.1
450	20	2,800	90	5.3

*Unhydrogenated anthracene oil

The effect of pressure in the process is observed in the results set forth in the following table. Here it is observed that pressures below about 2,500 psi significantly reduce the amount of coal solution.

Temp., °C.	Time, mins.	Final Pressure, psig	Percent Organic Dissolved	Hydrocarbon Gases, wt. % of Coal
450	20	1,400	83	5.6
450	20	2,800	90	5.3
450	20	3,000	95	5.3

As indicated, the process is also dependent upon use of a single step procedure. Thus, liquefaction at a lower temperature subsequently followed with a higher temperature cause coking and greatly decreases the amount of coal solution to the 75% range. Likewise, the high temperature in the second step causes a large amount of hydrocarbon gases to be formed. These results are seen in the following table.

Thermal Liquefaction of Coal

Temp., °C.	Time, mins.	Final Pressure, psig	Percent Organic Dissolved	Hydrocarbon Gases, wt. % of Coal
445	20			
465	40	2,800	79	11.4
445	20			
465	40	2,700	76	10.8
430	20			
450	40	2,400	82	8.4

SEPARATION OF COAL-OIL SUSPENSIONS

G.W. Hodgson, G.F. Round and J. Kruyer; U.S. Patent 3,505,201; April 7, 1970; assigned to Research Council of Alberta, Canada describe a process for the thermal separation of coal-oil slurries by flash distillation where the slurry is injected into a heated reactor, the oil is flash distilled leaving oil-free coal char particles. The reactor has a fluidized bed of coal char particles and is maintained at a temperature of 600° to 1000°F. The fluidized bed is maintained by drawing off char and injecting fluid gas. The vapors are separated from solids by a cyclone and then fractionated and condensed to form only phases and an overhead gas.

The coal-oil slurries may, for example, be slurries formed as suspensions of pulverized or finely divided coal in crude oil in order to facilitate transportation of coal by pipeline. The pipelined mixture may be moved to points adjacent the market areas of the respective components and processed at those points to recover the coal and oil constituents.

One of the most important problems associated with pumping of a coal-in-oil slurry is the necessity of economically obtaining a clean separation of the two components once the slurry has reached the market locality. Two modes of separation have been investigated, separation by classification in multicyclones and separation by flash vaporization in a heated reactor. Flash vaporization of a mixture of Leduc crude oil and "Edmonton coal," using a hot fluidized solids reactor has yielded a dry char suitable as a fuel for thermal power stations and an oil that had undergone little change. The process is concerned with this thermal separation of a slurry of coal-in-oil.

The particles being fluidized are granular coal char particles, and the fluidizing gas is recycled process gas. As the gas is passed upwards through the bed, there is a certain flow at which the particles are disengaged somewhat from each other. In this condition, the bed behaves as a fluid, hence the name "fluidization." In order to maintain gas flow through the bed a finite pressure gradient is required to overcome friction, and to increase the rate of flow a greater pressure gradient is required. When the pressure drop approaches the weight of the bed over a unit cross-sectional area, the solids begin to move. This condition is known as the "onset of fluidization." A fluidized system may be used to effect a separation of mixtures of substances some of which are essentially volatile, and the other, nonvolatile. The volatile components on being introduced to a hot bed of fluidized particles rapidly absorb the heat of vaporization and join the fluidizing gas stream passing through the bed while the nonvolatile components remain with the fluidizing particles in fluidization reactor. Thus in the case of slurries of coal in oil, the oil components tend to pass out of the reactor while the coal components remain with the coal char particles in the reactor. One of the main features of this process is that at the temperatures required to effect such a separation, the coal char product resulting from the thermal separation process is superior as a fuel to the coal that was present in the original slurry, having picked up nonvolatile components of the oil. The loss of these components from the recovered oil is balanced off by the production of volatile substances from the coal during the process. These become part of the oil product and process gas stream.

The apparatus shown in Figure 2.23a comprises a feed reservoir 1 designed to contain coal-oil slurry which is conveyed to slurry-pump 2 which pumps the slurry into reactor 3 through conduit 4. The crude oil may be augmented with an admixture of heavy crude oil and/or asphalts and petroleum residuums. Initially the entire apparatus is purged with an inert gas such as nitrogen supplied under pressure from source 5, the nitrogen flow being controlled by valve 6. Once the apparatus has been purged the gas used is recycled from the system.

The nitrogen and/or the recycled gas is delivered to the bottom of reactor 1 through preheater 7, and enters the reactor via conduit 8 and maintains the bed of solids in a fluidized state indicated at 9, the bed being supported mechanically by a foraminous metal plate 10 seated immediately above conical section 11 of the reactor. The reactor is heated by means of electrical heaters indicated at 12. It will be noted that the upper section 13 of the reactor is of larger cross section than the lower section 14. The larger cross section at the top of the reactor causes a reduction in gas pressure and velocity in that area which facilitates separation of char and dust from ascending vapors.

Most of the heat necessary for the flash vaporization of the oil and the carbonization of the coal to a char is supplied by heating wires 12 although the temperature of the gas entering the reactor is a factor in controlling the bed temperature. As shown in Figure 2.23b, the reactor may be covered with a layer of asbestos cement 15 in order to reduce heat loss. It is also contemplated as part of the process to rely on the combustion of the products of the reactor, the process gas and the char product, as a source of heat for the reaction. Pressure and temperature in the apparatus is recorded at desired points in the line and at several levels in the reactor, by means of manometers and thermometers, not shown.

Hot oil vapors and quantities of char particles and dust ascend into cyclone 16 mounted in section 13 of the reactor. The particles settle in the cyclone and are removed through cyclone leg or conduit 17 which protrudes through the reactor wall. Quantities of char are removed from the reactor through leg 18, the removal being controlled by solenoid valve 19. The slurries studied comprised a mixture of 70% w./w. Leduc crude oil (38.4° API) and 30% w./w. Edmonton subbituminous coal, while others involved mixtures of Lloydminster crude oil and Canmore coal. These were selected to illustrate the process in relation to the pipelining operations for which the process might be used.

FIGURE 2.23:   SEPARATION OF COAL-OIL SUSPENSIONS

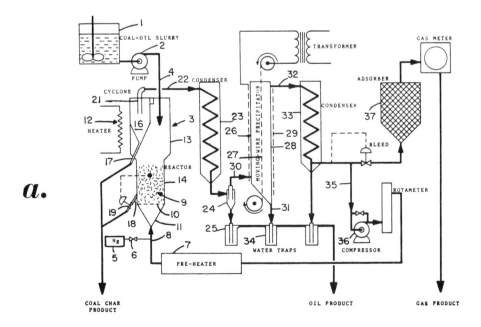

(continued)

FIGURE 2.23: (continued)

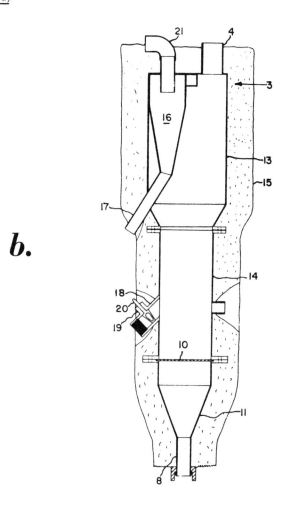

b.

Source: G.W. Hodgson, G.F. Round and J. Kruyer; U.S. Patent 3,505,201; April 7, 1970

The most difficult fluidized-bed separations are those requiring high heat inputs and those marked by high gas velocities in the fluidized bed. Thus, a fairly dilute slurry of coal-in-oil such as the above 30 to 70 mixture, and a slurry containing a heavy crude oil such as the Lloydminster oil represent very difficult operating conditions, and any process suitable for such conditions can be readily operated for more favorable conditions of feed. The preferable range of coal concentration in the slurry is thus 30 to 70 or more weight percent.

The preferred range for the heavy oil component is from zero to an upper value of 80% or more, a value limited largely by the pipeline flow characteristics of the slurry, the greater the heavy oil content, the greater the enrichment of the coal char product. In the laboratory experiments the mixture of coal in oil, which for example might be a slurry of about 100-mesh coal suspended in crude oil, at a concentration of 30 to 40% by weight, is injected into a reactor in which oil is flash vaporized leaving behind the oil-free coal particles in the form of coal char. The slurry is introduced into a fluidized bed of coal char particles, the bed temperature being maintained at about 600° to 1000°F. The vaporized oil is recovered in an overhead stream, and the suspended coal becomes part of the fluidized bed, which is maintained at a predetermined operating inventory level by appropriate withdrawal of the coal particles via leg or char-removal conduit 18.

The temperature of the bed in the experimental studies was varied over a wide range, the operating limits being determined by the failure of the char particles to remain dry and free flowing for the lower limit and by a limited heat input for the upper limit. In the laboratory tests the distillation of oil was incomplete at temperatures below 700°F., with the effect that the coal char particles tended to agglomerate and thereby prevent proper fluidization. The preferred reaction temperatures are in the 900° to 1000°F. range where the gross characteristics of the recovered oil are at least as favorable as those of the oil in the feed slurry, and the heating value of the coal char product approaches a maximum.

Thus there is evident an unexpected result which may be attributed to the particular configuration of the system, as will become more evident below. Slurry to be delivered to the reactor is maintained under vigorous agitation in feed reservoir 1 located above the top of the reactor, falling directly into the fluidizing bed. The preferred type of pump used to transmit the slurry is a "Sigma" pump. The feed is introduced through the top of the reactor rather than the side with the result that a more complete removal of the oil from the char was rendered possible which in turn, enabled the fluidizer to be operated at a lower temperature than would be possible otherwise. At a reactor temperature of 900°F., for example, the percentage of benzene-extractibles was reduced from 1.6 to 0.2% by introduction of the feed at the top of the reactor.

Within the reactor a bed of solids composed principally of coal char particles is kept in a constant state of fluidization by means of fluidizing hot gas delivered to the bottom of the reactor from the preheater, and if desired in addition, by means of a stream of inert gas such as nitrogen. The quantity of solids in the reactor at any given time was indicated by determining the pressure of the bed, and as pointed out above a series of manometers is used for this purpose, the manometers indicating the pressure differential between the top of the reactor and taps (not shown) that may be located on the side of the reactor at appropriate or desired levels.

The first tap may, for example, be placed just above plate 10, the second 3" above the first and the third 6" above the first. Drawoff of char from the bed, to maintain a constant quantity of fluidizing solids, is accomplished by a pressure-sensitive solenoid plug valve 19, the pressure-sensitive switch 20 (see Figure 2.23b) controlling the valve responding to pressure changes in bed height. Entrained dust and char thrown up as "streamers" from the bed are separated by cyclone 16 as explained above and collected as part of the total char product.

There is constant formation of gaseous products in the reactor which results in a continuous increase in the amount of gas within the system which necessitates constant removal to maintain the desired operating pressure. During the startup period the system may be filled with an inert gas such as nitrogen, but after about one hour of operation, however, less than 5% of the original nitrogen remains in the system as part of the recirculating gas.

A stream of the vapor formed in the reactor is constantly being diverted into the cyclone where the treated coal char particles settle out and are removed by gravity at removal point 17. Hot vapors formed from the coal and the oil pass overhead from the cyclone through conduit 21 and are delivered through line 22 to a water-cooled condenser 23. An oil fog and a liquid product result from the initial condensation and are conducted to cyclone 24. The condensed liquid is passed through water trap 25 and the oil portion collected.

The oil fog from the condenser is preferably delivered from cyclone 24 into a moving-wire electrostatic precipitator 26, the moving wire 27 acting as a self-cleaning electrode. Where a stationary wire is used it is found that the electrode becomes coated with asphalt and entrained dust. The outside wall 28 of the precipitator may be painted with silver conducting paint as indicated at 29 the paint acting as the second electrode. As shown in Figure 2.23a fog enters the precipitator at 30, oil is removed at 31 and gas at 32. The precipitator collects between 10 and 50% of the total oil product, depending upon the reactor temperature. For example, at a reactor temperature of 900°F. approximately five times as much "fog" oil is produced as is the case at 700°F.

The overhead gas and vapors from the precipitator 26 are passed into a second water-cooled condenser 33, liquid from this condenser being passed to water trap 34 and the oil collected and combined with the condensed oils from the first condenser and the precipitator as a total oil product. Wet gases leaving the condenser are preferably partially recycled via line 35 to maintain the desired fluidization velocity and pressure within the reactor, the gas to be recycled being compressed in compressor 36. Unrecycled gas is passed through charcoal adsorber 37 where adsorbable components are removed and the dry gas metered and collected. An average recovery of 96% of total feed in the laboratory tests may be accounted for on a mass balance basis, the remainder being accounted for as gas leaks, char dust, and oil in interconnecting lines and vessels.

The gas mass flow rate through the bed was controlled by a compressor and a bypass valve and measured with a rotameter, the rotameter being calibrated for nitrogen at room temperature. Since the fluidizing gas was recirculated constantly, it soon became very rich in hydrocarbon gases, hydrogen, carbon monoxide and carbon dioxide. This continuous buildup of gases within the system necessitated a constant removal of a portion of these in order to maintain the desired operation pressure. After one hour of operation, as has been indicated, less than 5% of the original nitrogen remained as part of the recirculating gas. A rotameter reading was chosen so that the bed was operating well within the turbulent fluidized region. This reading was found by plotting the pressure gradients in the bed versus rotameter readings. Good mixing of the bed was indicated by equal temperatures at various levels in the bed.

A comparison of the products produced by the carbonization of Edmonton coal at 500°C. (932°F.) and fluidization of Edmonton coal with Leduc oil at 910°F. is shown in the table on the following page.

Feed Coal: 11,190 Btu/lb., Dry Basis; Fixed Carbon 68.8%, Volatiles, 36.2% Dry Ash-Free Basis

Fluidization		
(Experiment 1—Slurry: 30% coal w./w.): Total feed = 18.80 lb. Feed rate 3.8 lb./hr.	Pounds	Percent
Products:		
Char	4.04	21.2
Water	0.76	4.0
Oil	12.16	63.9
Gas	2.08	10.9
Total	19.04	100.0
	Feed	Product, Percent
Oil Analysis:		
Sediment	0.45	2.40
C residue	1.45	0.74
Volatiles	98.15	96.86
Total	100.00	100.00
		Percent
Char Analysis:		
Ash		11.9
Volatiles		18.5
Fixed C		69.6
Total		100.0
12,440 B.t.u./lb., dry basis		

Carbonization		
		Percent
Products:		
Char	73.9	73.9
Free Water	3.5	....
Water	7.0	10.5
Tar	3.5	....
Light Oil	1.3	4.8
Gas	10.6	....
H$_2$S	0.2	10.8
Total	100.0	100.0
Char Analysis:		
Ash	12.8	
Volatiles	13.8	
Fixed C	73.4	
Total	100.0	
11,940 B.t.u./lb., dry basis		

The above table shows a comparison of a typical fluidization experiment at 910°F. with a carbonization at a slightly higher temperature, for the same coal. While an overall quantitative comparison is not possible since the systems are not equivalent, e.g., in carbonization there was no contributing oil and the atmosphere was not inert, it is possible to compare the chars formed on a lb./lb. basis. Fluidization gave a char of better heating value and lower ash content, both desirable features. Water and other volatiles were removed from the coal and petroleum coke was deposited on the char. The following table shows the results of several fluidization runs at various temperatures, the analytical results being compared with the oil and coal feed materials.

Run	1	2	3	4	5	Oil Feed
Bed Temperature, ° F.	875	780	750	725	700	....
Total Feed, Lb.	23.4	14.7	17.9	10.2	23.3	....
Feed Rate, Lb./Hr.	4.5	7.3	3.6	3.4	4.4	....
Oil Analysis:						
Gravity, A.P.I.	33.0	35.2	34.0	36.6	34.4	38.4
Viscosity, cst.:						
70°	9.26	6.32	7.37	5.53	8.97	5.07
100° F.	4.46	4.17	4.65	3.66	6.33	3.40
Unsaturates, U, percent	17.6	15.8	11.8	15.4	11.6	10.5
Asphaltenes, percent	0.46	0.20	0.22	0.25	0.14	0.10
Carbon Residue, percent						1.40
Sulfur, percent	0.28	0.18	0.24		0.27	0.24
Sediment, mg./ml.	1.26	4.11	3.70	3.36	2.70	3.61
Distillation, ° F.:						
I.B.P.	218	180	180	164	183	137
5%	269	248	235	221	230	178
10%	303	283	281	254	267	214
20%	371	358	349	317	345	280
30%	442	434	421	387	414	350
40%	503	494	485	469	477	433
50%	569	550	555	514	548	520
60%	679		636	593	611	763
70%			673	676		
80%				708		
90%				712		
Coal Analysis (Char):						
Ash, percent	12.7	11.0	10.1	10.7	10.9	10.0
Benzene Extractibles, percent	0.16	0.33	0.98	1.35	1.94	0.32
Volatiles (dry), percent		18.4	25.9	26.1	28.9	31.7
Heating Value, B.t.u./Lb.:						
(Dry Basis)	12,660	12,400	12,170	11,960	11,860	11,200
(Dry Ash Free Basis)	14,500	13,920	13,550	13,400	13,300	12,600
Gas Produced, S.c.f./Lb. Feed:						
Total	2.04	0.25	2.90	0.65	1.10	....
H$_2$	1.20	0.02	0.52	0.07	0.15	....
CO	0.06	0.06	0.49	0.05	0.06	....
CO$_2$			0.06		0.10	....
CH$_4$	0.20	0.03	1.22	0.24	0.45	....
Other hydrocarbons	0.58	0.14	0.61	0.29	0.34	....

In each instance the oil product compares favorably with the feed and the coal product is markedly improved. It is obvious that this process is more than a simple resolution of a two component mixture. It is even more than a simple distillation of the volatile compounds of each component. Chemical changes are taking place, to the benefit of one or both of the slurry components, as indicated by the nature of the gas production, and by the character of the oil. This may be attributed to the catalytic nature of the surface of the coal char particles at the reaction temperatures involved.

HYDROGENATION PROCESSES

NONCATALYTIC HYDROGENATIONS

Process for the Hydrogenation of Coal

E.F. Pevere, H.V. Hess and G.B. Arnold; U.S. Patent 2,658,861; November 10, 1953; assigned to The Texas Company describe a process for the noncatalytic hydrogenation of coal. In this method coal and oil are admixed to form a liquid at a temperature within the range of 550° to 850°F. and the resulting liquid is atomized into a hydrogenation reactor operated at a temperature within the range of from 750° to 850°F. and a pressure above 1,000 psig. Hydrogen is preferably used as a dispersing medium for atomization of the coal. The coal may be liquefied at a temperature of 550° to 700°F. and the resulting liquid heated to a temperature within the range of from 750° to 850°F. prior to hydrogenation. The process will be more readily understood from the following detailed description and the accompanying drawing (Figure 3.1).

FIGURE 3.1: PROCESS FOR THE HYDROGENATION OF COAL

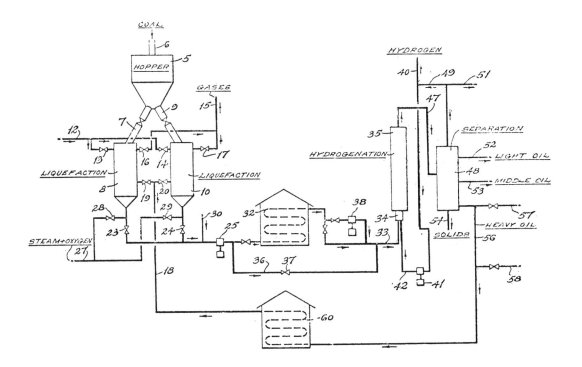

Source: E.F. Pevere, H.V. Hess and G.B. Arnold; U.S. Patent 2,658,861; November 10, 1953

With reference to Figure 3.1 coal of a suitable particle size is supplied to a hopper 5 through a conduit 6. From the hopper the coal may be fed through conduit 7 into liquefaction vessel 8 or through conduit 9 into liquefaction vessel 10. Any number of such vessels may be employed. With two vessels, as illustrated, one of the vessels is charged with coal and oil to prepare a liquefied coal feed stream for hydrogenation while the other is being discharged to the hydrogenation reactor. When a vessel has been filled with coal from the hopper, inert gas from line 12 may be admitted to the vessel to purge it of air.

Valve 13, associated with vessel 8, and valve 14, associated with vessel 10, are provided for this purpose. Air and other gases may be vented from the vessels to line 15. Gases from vessel 8 are vented to line 15 through valve 16; those from vessel 10, through valve 17. Preheated oil from line 18 may be admitted to vessel 8 through valve 19 and to vessel 10 through valve 20. When a vessel is filled with coal and oil the valves are closed and the coal particles at least partially liquefied due to the combined effect of heating and the solvent or plasticizing action of the hot oil. A substantially homogeneous liquid mixture of coal substance and oil is thus obtained. Mechanical mixers, not illustrated, may be supplied to insure complete disintegration of the coal, if desired.

As illustrated in the drawing; the coal is subjected to intimate contact with hot oil without agitation, effecting solution of a part of the coal in the oil and leaving a porous friable residue in the liquefaction vessels 8 and 10. The resulting liquid, comprising liquefied coal and oil, is discharged from vessel 8 through valve 23 and from vessel 10 through valve 24 to a charge pump 25 as feed for the hydrogenation step.

Inert gas from line 12 may be admitted to the vessel during the period of discharge to the feed pump. Gas from line 12 may be supplied under pressure to build up a pressure within the vessel and aid in the removal of liquid from the residual solid. This gas may be heated if desired to an elevated temperature. This porous friable residue remaining in the liquefaction vessel is in a state nearly ideal for gasification. A mixture of steam and oxygen may be supplied to the liquefaction of vessels through line 27. The flow of gas from line 27 is controlled by valves 28 and 29 associated with vessels 8 and 10, respectively. The resulting products of gasification may be discharged into line 15 for further use as desired.

Catalyst may be admitted through line 30 into admixture with the stream of liquefied coal and oil. From the charge pump 25 the liquefied coal and oil stream is passed through a heating coil 32 and charged through line 33 into an atomizer 34 associated with a hydrogenation reactor 35. The coal feed stream may be fed directly from the charge pump 25 to the atomizer 34 through line 36 as controlled by valve 37. Since it is generally desirable to carry out the hydrogenation reaction at a pressure above 1,000 psig and often not desirable to subject the heating coil 32 to excessive pressure, a second charge pump 38 may optionally be provided to increase the pressure of the hot charge stream immediately prior to introduction of the stream to the atomizer 34.

Hydrogen is admitted to the system through line 40. Fresh and recycled hydrogen are pumped by a pump 41 through line 42 into the atomizer 34. In the atomizer 34, which may be of any conventional type, the liquefied coal feed stream is broken up into small droplets and dispersed in the stream of hydrogen from line 42. From the atomizer, the dispersion of liquefied coal and hydrogen is discharged directly into the hydrogenation zone 35. In the dispersed state, the hydrogenation reaction proceeds rather rapidly.

Somewhat more hydrogen is usually required for atomization and dispersion of the atomized coal stream than is required in the conventional liquid phase hydrogenation. This merely results in a higher recycle rate, since hydrogen consumption, for a given percentage conversion, is not appreciably affected. The hydrogenation reaction results in precipitation of ash and the more difficultly hydrogenatable fraction of the coal substance as solids. These solids are entrained in the effluent stream discharged from the hydrogenation zone 35 through line 47. The hydrogenation effluent is passed to a separation system 48 where it is separated into various fractions. Any of several known conventional methods of separation may be employed.

A gaseous fraction is recycled to the hydrogenation reactor through line 49 to pump 41. A portion of the gaseous fraction may be purged from the system through line 51. A light oil fraction is taken from the separation system through line 52 and a middle oil fraction through line 53 for further processing. In accordance with general conventional practice, the middle oil stream is subjected to further hydrogenation in vapor phase to produce motor fuels. Residual solids separated from the oils in the separation system 48 are discharged through line 54.

Heavy oil is discharged from the separation system through line 56 as a recycle stream to the liquefaction vessels 8 and 10. A portion of the heavy oil may be withdrawn for other uses through line 57. Other oils may be supplied if desired to the heavy oil recycle stream through line 58. The heavy oil stream is heated in a heating coil 60 to the desired temperature prior to admission to the liquefaction vessels 8 and 10 through line 18. All of the heat required for the process may be supplied by the hot oil stream.

In a typical operation of a process such as illustrated, Pittsburgh Bed coal containing 2% water, 31% volatile matter, 58% fixed carbon, and 9% ash, as received, is subjected to hydrogenation. The coal is charged to a liquefaction vessel in the form of lumps about 1/2" to 1/4" in average diameter. This coal is mixed with heavy oil obtained from the hydrogenation of coal in an amount approximately equal in weight to the weight of the coal. The oil is preheated to a temperature of 850°F. before admixture with the coal, resulting in a temperature of 750°F. in the liquefaction vessel. About 65% by weight of the coal is liquefied and extracted by the liquid oil without agitation leaving a porous friable carbonaceous residue. The resulting liquid comprising liquefied coal is atomized with hydrogen into a reactor at 750°F. and 1,000 psig.

Partial Hydrogenation of Coal at Elevated Temperatures and Pressures

The process developed by P.C. Keith and F. Ringer; U.S. Patent 2,885,337; May 5, 1959; assigned to Hydrocarbon Research, Inc. relates to a method for hydrogenating coal to yield liquid products, and more particularly to a process for hydrogenating bituminous coal and for cracking the products of hydrogenation in a fluidized bed in the presence of hydrogen. The process comprises pasting powdered bituminous coal with an oil fraction and hydrogenating the coal paste or suspension to convert from 60 to 85% of the carbon content of the coal to liquid and gaseous products.

In general, it is advisable to convert 75% of the carbon content of the coal in this partial hydrogenation step. The conditions for hydrogenating coal while suspended in oil are well known. For instance, a temperature of 600° to 1000°F. and a pressure of 1,000 to 12,000 psig may be used. The reaction time is governed by the chosen conditions under which the coal hydrogenation is conducted but is limited to give the desired conversion in the range of 60 to 85% of the carbon content of the coal.

The cracking operation is conducted at an elevated temperature in the range of 900° to 1400°F., preferably 1200° to 1300°F., and at a pressure in the range of 150 to 800 psig, preferably 250 to 650 psig. It has been found that the suppression of coke formation during cracking is achieved to a material extent when the partial pressure of hydrogen within the cracking zone is at least 35 psi and preferably in the range of 75 to 150 psi. It is curious to note that the maximum benefits from the presence of hydrogen occur at hydrogen partial pressures not exceeding 200 psi so that there is little justification in seeking a hydrogen partial pressure greater than 200 psi. As a preferred mode of operation, the cracking is carried out by injecting the mixture of liquid products and solid residue from the partial hydrogenating step into a fluidized mass of the solid residue from the coal used in the process.

Particulate solids such as bauxite may be added to the fluidized mass in the cracking zone to make the mass more easily fluidizable. With the aid of hydrogen flowing through the cracking zone, the injected hydrogenation mixture is converted to a gasiform effluent and a substantially dry carbonaceous residue. The gasiform effluent, which is readily separable from the dry carbonaceous residue, is removed for recovery of its constituents by conventional methods, such as rectification. The substantially dry carbonaceous residue in admixture with the contact material is withdrawn from the cracking zone and passed to a gasifying or regenerating zone where a regenerating gas consisting of a preponderance of steam and a minor proportion of high-purity oxygen gasifies the carbon under conditions favoring the production of hydrogen and carbon monoxide.

Steam-to-oxygen molar ratios in the range of 1.5:1 to 5:1 are generally satisfactory for maintaining the gasifying temperature in the desirable range of 1600° to 2500°F. Steam-to-oxygen molar ratios of 2:1 to 3:1 and gasifying temperatures of 1700° to 2000°F. are preferred. The gasifying zone operates at substantially the same pressure maintained in the cracking zone. The high-purity oxygen may suitably be the product of air liquefaction and rectification containing at least 90% by volume of oxygen, preferably at least 95%.

Figure 3.2 schematically illustrates an arrangement of apparatus suitable for carrying out the process. Coal from a feed 11, a pasting hydrocarbon oil from line 12 and a catalyst if desired enter mixer 13 where they are intermixed to form a paste which flows through line 14. A pump 15 pressurizes the paste to the operating pressure of the partial hydrogenation step, e.g., 1,000 to 12,000 psig. Pressurized hydrogen from line 17 and paste from line 14 enter hydrogenator 16 where a temperature of 600° to 1000°F. is maintained.

The hydrogenation reaction per se and the equipment necessary for hydrogenation as known to the literature ("Liquid Fuel from Coal", Industrial and Engineering Chemistry, May 1949, volume 41, pages 870 through 885) is carried out in hydrogenator 16 to convert between 60 and 85% of the carbon content of the coal to liquid and gaseous products. A preferred set of hydrogenating conditions is 10,000 psig, 875°F. and 75% conversion. The hydrogenated paste is removed from hydrogenator 16, optionally cooled in heat exchanger 18 and passed to separator 19. Unreacted hydrogen, H_2S, NH_3, water vapor, hydrocarbon gases and low boiling normally liquid organic compounds are removed in vapor phase through line 20.

The normally liquid components of the vapor are condensed out in stripper unit 21 for recovery of gas and liquid products which are withdrawn through lines 22 and 23, respectively. If desired, a hydrogen-containing gas may be separated and recycled from unit 21 to hydrogenator 16. The temperature at which vapors are separated from the hydrogenated paste may vary widely. In general, a separation temperature in the range of 400° to 600°F. is preferred. Separation at below

400°F. will retain more of the lower boiling liquid products in the hydrogenated paste, advantageously increasing its fluidity but also increasing the volume of material which must subsequently pass through the cracking zone.

FIGURE 3.2: PARTIAL HYDROGENATION OF COAL AT ELEVATED TEMPERATURES AND PRESSURES

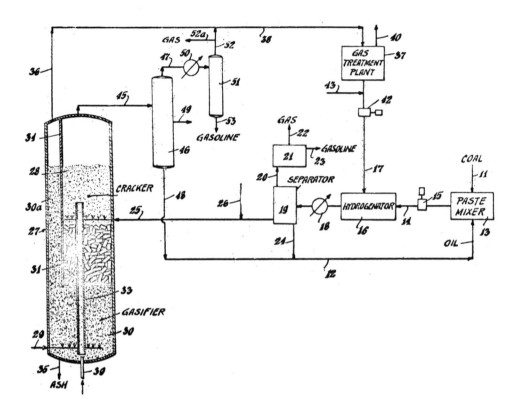

Source: P.C. Keith and F. Ringer; U.S. Patent 2,885,337; May 5, 1959

Separation at above 600°F. will remove substantially all lower boiling liquid products from the hydrogenated paste as well as some of the higher boiling liquid products which should advantageously be converted to lower boiling products in the subsequent cracking step. After the vapors are separated from the hydrogenated paste, the remaining mixture of liquid hydrogenation products and solid residue is charged through line 25 to the cracking zone 28 of vessel 27. A transport gas or oil may be added from line 26 to facilitate the injection of the residual paste into zone 28.

Vessel 27 contains a fluidized bed of finely divided contact material which circulates from freely fluidized cracking zone 28 down through a thermal barrier 31, which suitable may be a section packed with Raschig rings or the like, into freely fluidized gasifying zone 30. A transport gas, such as steam, from line 39 carries contact material through upflow tube 33 back into cracking zone 28. The mixture of liquid hydrogenation products and solid residue entering cracking zone 28 is converted therein to vapors and a substantially dry carbonaceous residue at a temperature in the range of 900° to 1400°F., preferably 1200° to 1300°F., and in the presence of hydrogen-containing regeneration product gas.

The carbonaceous residue becomes part of the fluidized bed of contact material passing down through thermal barrier 31 into gasifying zone 30 where it is gasified at a temperature in the range of 1600° to 2500°F. by oxygen and steam introduced near the bottom of zone 30 from line 29. Ash having a carbon content of a few percent by weight or less is withdrawn through line 35 at a rate which maintains a substantially constant solids inventory in vessel 27. The regeneration product gas consisting predominantly of hydrogen, carbon monoxide and excess steam fluidizes the contact material while passing up from zone 30 through thermal barrier 31 and cracking zone 28, thus providing at the same time the desired hydrogen-containing atmosphere in cracking zone 28. Regeneration product gas and the gasiform products of cracking are withdrawn overhead from cracking zone 28 through line 45 and passed into fractionating tower 46. Tower 46 may be operated to pass overhead through line 47 all gases and liquid products, including gasoline hydrocarbons, boiling up to 400°F. Higher boiling liquids such as diesel oil may be withdrawn by way of line 49 while a heavy bottoms fraction discharged through line 48 is desirably recycled through line 12 to mixer 13 as pasting oil. Advantageously, the pasting oil requirements are made up by taking all the bottoms fraction from tower 46 and supplementing it with sufficient oil drawn from separator 19 by line 24 to provide the necessary balance. It is to be understood, however, that an extraneous pasting hydrocarbon oil may be substituted for either or both of these products of the process. When oil is drawn from separator 19 through line 24, it is preferable to decrease the content of solids suspended therein by settling, centrifuging or like operation; obviously, the portion of oil flowing through line 25 to cracking zone 28 will then have a higher concentration of solids.

The gases and low boiling products removed from tower 46 through line 47 are cooled in heat exchanger 50 and passed into separator 51 from which the condensed liquid products rich in gasoline hydrocarbons are removed through line 53 and the gases through line 52. These gases may be passed through line 38 into gas treatment plant 37 where such components as H_2S, NH_3, CO_2 and CH_4 are separated to leave a residual gas comprising essentially hydrogen and carbon monoxide. By the water-gas shift reaction, the carbon monoxide of the residual gas may be converted to additional hydrogen and carbon dioxide which may be readily eliminated to yield high-purity hydrogen, i.e., at least 90% by volume of hydrogen.

A desirable expedient which allows a more facile recovery of high-purity hydrogen involves removing a side stream of regeneration product gas from gasifying zone 30 without becoming admixed with the cracked products in zone 28. A partition or barrier 34 is placed in the upper portion of vessel 27, extending from the top of vessel 27 to a level below packed section 31. Barrier 34 splits the upflowing regeneration product gas so that part passes into cracking zone 28 to be removed with the products of cracking, while the rest simply passes up through zone 30a and discharges through line 36, substantially undiluted with hydrocarbons. This side stream of regeneration product gas can be passed through line 38 into gas treatment plant 37. Taking off a side stream through line 36 advantageously reduces the load on the effluent recovery system comprising tower 46 and separator 51. Moreover, the treatment of side stream 36 to produce high-purity hydrogen is simpler than the treatment of the gas from line 52 bcause regeneration product gas contains substantially only H_2, CO, CO_2 and H_2O.

In any event, hydrogen of over 90% by volume purity and at substantially the elevated pressure of the cracking operation is recovered from gas treatment plant 37. This hydrogen is further pressurized by compressor 42 and fed by line 17 to hydrogenator 16. Additional hydrogen, for instance, the hydrogen-containing gas in line 22, may be added by way of line 43, with or without any intervening treatment of the gas. While the gas from line 22 may be separately treated, it may be added to the gas in line 38 and passed through treatment plant 37.

Gaseous products of the process may be withdrawn through line 52a and/or recovered as a by-product stream 40 from gas treatment plant 37, as well as from line 22. From these gas streams, an LPG (liquefied petroleum gas) product may be obtained. The gases also contain quantities of H_2S, NH_3 and CO_2 which may be removed to leave a valuable fuel gas of high heating value. The primary liquid product of the process comprises gasoline hydrocarbons (boiling up to 400°F.). A minor portion of this gasoline is produced in the hydrogenation operation and removed from stripper 21 through line 23. The major portion of the gasoline is produced in cracking zone 23, recovered in separator 51 and removed through line 53.

In a typical operation of the process, in which all quantities of materials are given on an hourly basis, 100 tons of coal having 40% by weight of volatile matter and 5% by weight of ash on a moisture-free basis is pasted with 150 tons of hydrocarbon oil in mixer 13. The oil is made up of 26 tons of bottom fraction (line 48) and 124 tons of recycle oil (line 24). An additional 30 tons of solids contained in the recycle oil are returned to mixer 13. The paste is hydrogenated at 10,000 psig and 875°F. and with a residence time of 30 minutes. The hydrogen gas input is 2.25 Mscf (million standard cubic feet) of 91% by volume purity. Approximately 75% of the carbon in the coal is converted to liquid and gaseous hydrogenation products. The hydrogenated paste is cooled to 500°F. and allowed to settle in separator 19, vapors and gases being removed overhead through line 20. The settled paste is split into the recycle stream of 124 tons of pasting oil containing 30 tons of solids and a thicker stream of 75 tons of liquid hydrogenation products containing 29 tons of solids. The gasiform effluent leaving separator 19 by way of a line 20 is cooled and separated into:

6.4 tons gasoline (not including C_3 hydrocarbons)
4.0 tons H_2S and NH_3
10.0 tons water

After condensation of liquid products and removal of H_2S and NH_3, there remains 0.88 Mscf of gas having the following composition (on volume basis):

	Percent
H_2	60
CO	10
CO_2	2
CH_4	19
C_2 hydrocarbons	5
C_3 hydrocarbons	4

The hydrogen actually consumed in the hydrogenation amounts to 1.5 Mscf. The thicker stream (line 25) of hydrogenated paste totaling 104 tons of liquid and solids is fed into cracking zone 28 along with 0.23 Mscf of transport gas. Vessel 27 operates at a pressure of 400 psig and with a temperature of 1200°F. in cracking zone 28. Gasifying zone 30 is supplied with 46.5 tons of oxygen and 52 tons of steam suitably preheated. The temperature in gasifying zone 30 is 1750°F. The total gasiform effluent removed from cracking zone 28 through line 45 is separated into 0.80 Mscf (dry basis) of gas, 23.3 tons of gasoline (91-93 CFRR clear octane number) and 26 tons of hydrocarbons boiling above 400°F. All of the hydrocarbons boiling above 400°F. are recycled to hydrogenator 16 as pasting oil. The approximate composition of the gas product in Mscf is:

H_2	0.21
CO	0.18
CO_2	0.06
CH_4	0.18
C_2H_4	0.06
C_2H_6	0.04
C_3H_6	0.04
C_3H_8	0.01

and minor quantities of N_2, NH_3 and H_2S. By depropanizing the gases leaving separator 51 and stripper 21, an LPG product amounting to 4.3 tons is obtained. A total of 29.7 tons of gasoline is recovered from 100 tons of coal containing 5 tons of ash.

Hydroconversion of Solid Carbonaceous Materials

The process developed by D. Eastman and W.G. Schlinger; U.S. Patent 3,075,912; January 29, 1963; assigned to Texaco Inc. describes a method for the hydroconversion of solid carbonaceous materials. This process relates to the treatment of coal and may be applied to the hydrogenation of anthracite, or bituminous coal or lignite. Referring to Figure 3.3, coal is introduced through line 21 to grinding mechanism 22 where it is pulverized to an average particle size of below –60 mesh.

FIGURE 3.3: HYDROCONVERSION OF SOLID CARBONACEOUS MATERIALS

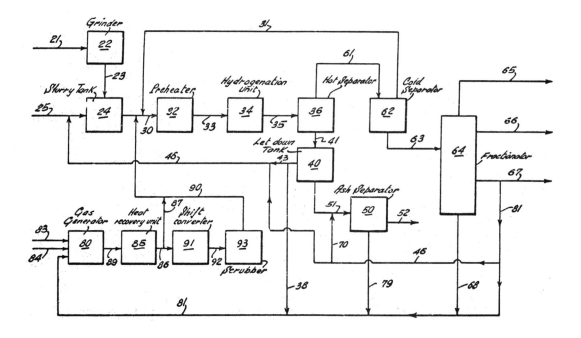

Source: D. Eastman and W.G. Schlinger; U.S. Patent 3,075,912; January 29, 1963

The powder is transferred through line 23 to mixing chamber 24 where it is mixed with oil introduced through line 25. The coal oil slurry is then transferred through line 30 and with hydrogen from line 31 is introduced into preheater 32 where the temperature is raised to 500° to 600°F. The heated slurry and hydrogen are then passed through line 33 to hydrogenation unit 34 where they are subjected to highly turbulent flow. The hydrogenation product is removed from hydrogenation unit 34 through line 35 and introduced into hot separator 36 where gaseous material is separated from the liquid product. The liquid product is transferred to let down tank 40 through line 41.

In let down tank 40, the pressure is reduced and a separation is effected between the heavy oil and the oil saturated residue. The heavy oil is removed from let down tank 40 through line 43 and may be returned to slurry tank 24 through lines 46 and 25 or sent to gas generator 80 by means of lines 43, 38 and 81. The heavy oil saturated ash is sent to ash separator 50 through line 51 where the heavy oil is separated to a large extent from the ash which is removed from ash separator 50 through line 52, the oil being withdrawn through line 79. Ash separator 50 may be either in the form of a centrifuge or in the form of a separating tank containing a lower layer of water. In either case, dilution of the heavy oil with a lighter oil is preferred in the first case to facilitate the removal of the ash and in the second case to minimize the possiblity of the formation of oil-water emulsions.

The overhead from hot separator 36 is withdrawn through line 61 and after cooling in a heat exchanger (not shown) is sent to cold separator 62 from which hydrogen is withdrawn through line 31 and returned to preheater 32 through line 30. The liquid hydrogenation product is removed from cold separator 62 through line 63 and introduced into fractionator 64 where a separation is made of light hydrocarbon gases withdrawn through line 65, a motor fuel fraction withdrawn through line 66, a middle distillate fraction withdrawn through line 67 and a residual fraction withdrawn through line 68. When a portion of the middle distillate is used to dilute the heavy residue withdrawn from let down tank 40 through line 51 it is sent through lines 67, 81, 46, 70 and 51 to ash separator 50 where it facilitates the separation of the heavy oil from the ash. If desired, a portion of the middle distillate from fractionator 64 may be used to form a slurry of the coal feed, in which case it is sent to mixing chamber 24 through lines 67, 81, 46 and 25.

Hydrogen for the process is preferably supplied by partial combustion of the heavy liquid products resulting from the hydrogenation of the coal. Heavy oil from ash separator 50 for the bottoms from fractionator 64 or a portion of the middle distillate from fractionator 64 may be sent to generator 80 through lines 79 and 81, 68 and 81 or 67 and 81 respectively or a mixture thereof may be used as feed to gas generator 80. Steam from line 84 and oxygen from line 85 are also introduced into gas generator 80 where the oil is subjected to partial combustion. The products are removed from generator 80 through line 89 and partially cooled in heat recovery unit 85, which may be, for example, a heat exchanger in which the hot gaseous products are passed in indirect heat exchange with water.

The resulting steam may be used as a source of power for the grinding operation. The product gases then may be sent through to preheater 32 by means of lines 86, 87, 90 and 30 or if a high concentration of hydrogen is desired, may be subjected to a water-gas shift in shift reactor 91 where the partial combustion products are contacted with an iron oxide catalyst in the presence of steam, the carbon monoxide reacting with steam to produce carbon dioxide and additional hydrogen. The shifted gas is transferred through line 92 to scrubber 93 where the gas is contacted with an amine solution for the removal of CO_2 and a gas containing 95% hydrogen is removed and sent to preheater through lines 90 and 30.

Example: A slurry composed of 10 parts by weight of bituminous coal pulverized to a particle size of -60 mesh and 11 parts by weight of a middle distillate, is mixed with 10,000 cubic feet of a gas containing 80% hydrogen per barrel of slurry. The mixture is passed through a tubular reactor at a temperature of 950°F., a pressure of 5,000 psig, a reaction time of 50 seconds and at a turbulence level of 450. The hydrogen containing gas is made up of 7,640 standard cubic feet of recycle gas and 2,360 standard cubic feet of makeup hydrogen having a purity of 95%. After hot and cold separation, let down, centrifuging and fractionating, the products obtained per 100 lbs. of coal feed are as follows.

	Lbs.
Ash and unconverted coal	8.0
H_2S, CO, CO_2	2.5
H_2O	6.0
NH_3	2.0
C_1 to C_4 hydrocarbon gases	12.0
C_5 to 400°F. end point gasoline	37.0
Middle distillate (including 110 lbs. in slurry)	130
Heavy oil	20.5

Hydrogen consumption amounts of 1,400 standard cubic feet per 100 lb. coal feed. Of the 130 lbs. of middle distillate, 110 lbs. is recycled per 100 lbs. of coal feed to make up additional slurry, 10 pounds is withdrawn to storage and the remaining 10 lbs. together with 20.5 lbs. of heavy oil are charged with 15.2 lbs. of steam and 31.5 lbs. of oxygen to a synthesis gas generator. The gas generator is operated at 290 psig and 2400°F. After quenching, the effluent gases are passed to a shift converter and then contacted with an amine scrubber. The product gas amounts to 1,400 standard cubic feet of 98% purity hydrogen which is used as makeup for the hydrogenation unit. The gasoline produced has the following characteristics.

Gravity, °API	59.3
Distillation range, °F.:	
IBP	92
10%	124
50%	252
90%	360
EP	402

This gasoline may be upgraded, by catalytic reforming, to produce a motor fuel having a leaded octane number of 100.

CATALYTIC HYDROGENATIONS

Catalytic Hydrogenation of Carbonized Coal Vapors

R.C. Perry and C.W. Albright; U.S. Patent 3,231,486; January 25, 1966; assigned to Union Carbide Corp. found the amount of tar residue or asphalt obtained upon condensation of the low temperature tar vapors can be materially reduced in some cases to less than 10% of the low temperature tar produced, and the quantity of low molecular weight oils correspondingly increased if the vapors from the carbonization are stabilized by subjecting them to a mild catalytic hydrogenation treatment prior to their condensation. By operating in this way, one can effect the removal, in the vapor phase, of the unsaturated and reactive groups contained by the compounds resulting from the carbonization, making a more stable, lower molecular weight tar which is more amenable to separation.

Catalysts that can be used in the process are those known as hydrogen-treating catalysts. Such catalysts have been used in the past for desulfurization, denitrification, deoxygenation, and hydrogenation of petroleum feed stocks. Typical catalysts of this type are the cobalt molybdate catalysts, which comprise cobalt and molybdenum oxides on a suitable support. These catalysts contain, in general, from 1.0 to 8.1 weight percent of cobalt and from 5 to 17 weight percent of molybdenum, based upon the total catalyst weight, the weight ratio of molybdenum to cobalt being, in general, from 1.6:1 to 4.8:1. These catalysts may also contain other metal oxides, such as nickel oxide and sodium oxide, the metal being present in an amount up to 0.5 weight percent of the total catalyst weight or they may contain only cobalt oxide or molybdenum oxide alone.

The carbonization process is that employing a fluidized bed of the material to be carbonized. When the process is employed in conjunction with such a carbonization process, the hydrogen used in the catalytic treatment can be employed as the fluidizing gas, thus taking advantage of whatever hydrogenation of char occurs during carbonization. The catalytic hydrogenation of this method can be conducted at hydrogen pressures of at least 200 psig. This ability to stabilize the coal tars from the carbonization at such low pressures is the major advantage of this process. The method is not limited to low pressures and can be applied after the process of dry coal hydrogenation at 3,000 psig. The higher pressures result in higher tar yields and accordingly higher yields of the low molecular weight oils produced by this process. It is preferred, however, to conduct the catalytic hydrogenation at pressures of from 200 to 3,000 psig.

Example: The coal employed was Elkol coal, a commercial, strip-mined Wyoming coal classified as a subbituminous B coal. The coal was pulverized to pass a 40 mesh screen and then oven dried at 120°C. in a nitrogen atmosphere prior to use. The analysis of the feed is summarized in Table 1 below.

TABLE 1	Proximate Analysis (Dry Basis)	Weight Percent
	Volatile matter	43.3 ± 0.5
	Ash	2.8 ± 0.3
	Fixed carbon	53.9 ± 1.0
	Ultimate Analysis (Moisture, Ash Free Basis)	
	C	75.6 ± 0.5
	H	4.9 ± 0.1
	N	1.3 ± 0.1
	S	0.9 ± 0.0
	O (by difference)	17.3 ± 0.5

A weighed batch of the dried coal was charged to the feed hopper, the unit was pressurized and the gas flow established. The coal feed from one of the hoppers was set at the desired rate and the coal was mixed with process gas, either nitrogen or hydrogen, that was preheated to 400°C. Since char retention time in the reactor was 15 minutes, the prerun was continued for 15 minutes after equilibrium was established in the system. At the end of the prerun period the liquid and char receivers were drained, the coal flow from the second hopper was started and the run was started. The operating conditions for each run are summarized in Table 2 below.

TABLE 2

Run Number	1	2	*3
Fluidizing Gas	N_2	H_2	H_2
Pressure, p.s.i.g.	400	400	400
Average Hydrogen partial pressure, p.s.i.g.		341	290
Carbonization Temp., °C	515	515	515
Catalyst Temp., °C			435
Time of Run, hr.	7.50	6.50	8.42
Coal Feed Rate, gm./hr.	467	534	409
Catalyst Space Velocity, lb. tar/ lb. catalyst/hr.			0.42
Linear Gas Velocity (in Carbonizer), ft./sec.	0.1	0.5	0.5
Hydrogen Circulation Rate, SCFH	Nil	100	80

*Catalytic Run.

PRODUCTS, WEIGHT PERCENT
[Moisture, ash free basis]

Run Number	1	2	3
Char	75.9	75.3	72.2
Water	6.2	8.7	11.7
Tar	6.4	8.2	7.7
Gas	11.5	7.3	8.8
Hydrogen Reacted		−0.3	−1.0
Unaccounted for	0.0	0.8	0.6
	100.0	100.0	100.0

After completion of a run, the carbonizer and catalyst bed were cooled. The run char was removed from the char receiver and weighed. The liquid product (tar) from the four condensers was drained into a common vessel. The char obtained by the above described procedure is typical of those obtained from low temperature carbonization processes. The gas recycled to the carbonizer was analyzed and these analyses are shown in Table 3 below:

TABLE 3

Run Number	1	2	3
Yield:			
Lb./ton of coal	224	142	170
CF/ton of coal	3,085	1,810	2,550
	Analysis (H_2 and N_2 free basis), Volume Percent		
Component:			
CO	26.5	33.3	32.2
H_2	6.1		
CH_4	27.6	30.6	41.4
C_2H_4			0.6
C_2H_6	5.5	9.0	10.1
C_3H_8		0.7	2.0
CO_2	34.3	26.4	13.7
CO/CO_2 Ratio	0.77	1.26	2.35
Heating Value, B.t.u./ft.³	444	549	700

From Table 3 it can be seen that the heating value of the gas is upgraded by the process which upgrading is due primarily to the increase in the ratio of CO to CO_2 of from 0.77 for the nitrogen run (Run 1) to a value of 2.35 for the catalytic hydrogenation run (Run 3). The liquid product from the condensers, a mixture of tar, water and acetone, was distilled in a small laboratory packed column to a head temperature of 70°C. at a 6:1 reflux ratio. The distillate consisted of acetone with negligible amounts of oil, as determined by gas chromatographic analysis. The distillation was then continued to a head temperature of 110°C. (maximum kettle temperature of 200°C.). The distillate contained light oil and water, which were separated by decantation.

The tar residue remaining in the kettle was extracted with 4 parts by weight of n-hexane to 1 part by weight of residue by warming on a steam bath with stirring for 1 hour. The mixture was cooled to room temperature and the hexane extract was poured off, leaving insoluble asphalt as a residue. The hexane extract was distilled in a small laboratory packed column to a kettle temperature of 200°C., removing the n-hexane, which was shown by gas chromatography analysis to contain a negligible amount of oil. The oil remaining in the kettle was combined with the earlier-obtained oil from the dewatering step. The yields of tar, asphalt and oil obtained in each run are summarized in Table 4 from which can be seen that the process results in an increase in the amount of oil from 66 lbs. per ton of the coal charged for the non-catalytic, nitrogen-fluidized run (Run 1) to 120 lbs. per ton of coal charged for the process (Run 3). There is a corresponding reduction in the amount of asphalt produced from 58 lbs. per ton of coal for the nitrogen runs to 30 lbs. per ton of coal for the catalytic hydrogenation runs.

TABLE 4

Run Number	1	2	3
	Yields, Lb. per Ton of Coal		
Tar	124	158	150
Oil	66	82	120
Asphalt	58	76	30
	Yields, Percent of tar		
Oil	53	52	80
Asphalt	47	48	20

The reduction in the amount of asphalt resulting from the coal carbonization effected by the process is believed to be caused mainly by the reduction of compounds containing hetero atoms, such as nitrogen, sulfur and oxygen, in the tar. The amounts of hetero atoms found in the tar from the various runs are shown in Table 5 below, expressed in wt. % of tar.

TABLE 5

Run Number	1	2	3
Oxygen	10.6	9.3	5.7
Nitrogen	1.0	0.9	0.9
Sulfur	0.7	0.6	0.4
	12.3	10.8	7.0

From Table 5 it can be seen that the process reduces the amount of hetero atoms present in the tar from 12.3 weight percent for the run conducted in nitrogen (Run 1) to 7 weight percent for the catalytic hydrogen-fluidized process (Run 3). The oil obtained from each run was distilled and the fraction boiling at a temperature of from 110° to 260°C. was recovered. This fraction amounted to 44.5 volume percent of the oil recovered from Run 1, 42.5 volume percent of the oil recovered from Run 2 and 46.6 percent of the oil recovered from Run 3. These fractions were then extracted to recover the phenols contained in the oil. The yields are shown in Table 6 below.

TABLE 6

Run Number	1	2	3
Phenols (−260° C.), lb./ton of coal	3.5	8.9	9.7
Percent in C_6–C_8 range	54	46	75
C_6–C_8 Phenols, lb./ton of coal	1.9	4.1	7.3

From Table 6 it can be seen that the process substantially increases the amount of low molecular weight phenols that can be recovered from the tars produced by coal carbonization processes and particularly increases the amount of phenols, cresols and xylenols (C_6 to C_8 phenols) that can be recovered.

Liquid Phase Hydrogenation of Coal

F.B. Sellers; U.S. Patent 2,753,296; July 3, 1956; assigned to Texaco Development Corporation describes a process for the hydrogenation of a solid carbonaceous material. The process is particularly applicable to the treatment of coal and may be applied to hydrogenation of anthracite, bituminous coal, or lignite. It involves the liquid phase hydrogenation of coal. In carrying out the method, an intimate association between finely powdered coal and hydrogenation catalyst is obtained by bringing them together in the heating zone.

Accordingly, a slurry is made up of coal, vaporizable carrier liquid, and catalyst and the resulting slurry passed as a confined stream in turbulent flow through a heating zone where the slurry is heated to at least a temperature sufficient to vaporize substantially all of the carrier liquid. The heating zone preferably comprises an externally heated tubular coil. Vaporization of liquid in the coil results in a considerable increase in volume which, in turn, results in forming a dispersion of the solid particles in vapor moving through the coil at high velocity. Very effective pulverization of the coal results. At the same time, the catalyst is most intimately associated with the pulverized particles of coal.

The catalyst may be added to the slurry in the form of solid particles, suitably having a comparable size range as the coal, or it may be dissolved in the carrier liquid. In either case, the catalyst appears to be more active than when mixed with powdered coal in the usual manner, probably because of the more uniform and more intimate combining of the two by the process. Water and liquid hydrocarbons are preferred as the carrier liquid. When water is used as the carrier liquid, it is separated from the powdered coal mixed with oil in the usual manner to form a paste for hydrogenation. The quantity of liquid admixed with the coal to form the suspension may vary considerably depending upon the process requirements and the type of coal and liquid used in preparation of the suspension. A minimum of 30% oil or 35% water, by weight, is ordinarily required to form a fluid suspension. Preferably at least 40% or 45% water, by weight, is used to form a suspension which may be readily pumped with suitable equipment, for example, with a diaphragm type pump of the type commonly used for handling similar suspensions of solids. The quantity of liquid required to form a fluid slurry is readily determined by trial.

The particle size of the coal fed to the heating step is not of especial importance. Generally, it is permissible to use particles having an effective diameter of less than 1/4 inch. Smaller sizes are even more readily handled. Preferably the bulk of the particles charged have a size range of from 3/32 inch to 200 mesh. The vaporization of liquid in the slurry and the resulting high velocity fluid flow in the coil readily reduces the coal to a particle size substantially all of which are smaller than 200 mesh. Since the heating of the dispersion, under turbulent flow conditions, results in disintegration of coal, costly pulverization by mechanical means is eliminated. It is contemplated that in most applications, the coal will be reduced only to a particle size such that it may be readily handled as a suspension or slurry.

The linear velocity of the liquid suspension at the inlet to the heating coil should be within the range of from 1 to 10 feet per second. The velocity of the gasiform dispersion at the outlet of the coil will vary within the range of from 25 to 3,000 feet per second, depending upon the pressure at which it is discharged. The temperature at the outlet of the heating coil may range from 250° to 1500°F. or higher. The temperature is at least sufficient to insure substantially complete vaporization of the oil present in the dispersion. When a liquid hydrocarbon is used as the carrier fluid, the temperature preferably is at least as high as the temperature at which hydrogenation is initiated, generally 600°F. A temperature within the range of 650° to 1400°F. is generally preferred as the temperature at the outlet of the heating coil. Higher temperatures within practical limits are often advantageous.

Vaporization of the carrier liquid takes place in the first portion of the coil, forming a dispersion of solid particles in vapor flowing at a velocity many times the velocity of the slurry. This vaporous dispersion may be passed through a heated or unheated section of coil to effect further pulverization and, if desired, heating of the solid particles. No distinction is made here between heated and unheated portions of the coil, the entire coil being referred to as the heating zone or heating coil. It will generally be found desirable to employ a tubular heating and grinding coil having an internal diameter within the range of from 1/2 to 2 inches and a length within the range of from 100 to 500 feet.

Pressure, in itself, is not critical in the heating step. The temperature and pressure relationships affecting vaporization are well known. It is desirable to operate the heating step at a relatively low pressure. With oil, a pressure within the range of from 50 to 500 psig at the outlet of the heating coil is generally desirable; this aids in subsequent condensation of the vapor. A considerable reduction in pressure takes place in the heating coil due to resistance to flow. This pressure reduction may be on the order of, for example, 100 to 1,000 psi in order to produce a flow rate of slurry of 1 to 10 feet per second. Liquid phase hydrogenation of coal is a well-known procedure. A mixture of oil and powdered coal is supplied to a reactor operated at elevated temperatures and pressures. Pressures may range from 3,000 to 10,000 psig and temperatures from 600° to 900°F. Generally, the higher pressures and temperatures are preferred. Various metals or metal oxides may be admixed with the coal and oil as hydrogenation catalysts.

Catalysts suitable for the hydrogenation of coal are known. Among the numerous catalysts are various compounds, particularly the oxides, sulfides or nitrides, of titanium, tin, copper, lead, zinc, chromium, cobalt, iron, various alkali metals, and rare earths. Of the many catalysts mentioned in the art, stannous oxalate and ferrous sulfate have shown the most promise for commercial operations. Stannous oxalate is insoluble in water, whereas ferrous sulfate is water-soluble. With reference to Figure 3.4, crushed coal is admixed with oil in a mixer 5 to form a slurry. A catalyst for the hydrogenation of coal is added and admixed with the coal and oil in the slurry. The slurry is forced by pump 6 through line 7 into a heating coil 8 disposed in furnace 9. Hydrogen from line 11 is introduced via line 12 into line 7 in admixture with the slurry prior to its introduction to the heating coil. The gasiform dispersion of powdered coal in oil vapors is discharged from the heating coil through line 13 and passed to a cooler 14 where it is cooled to a temperature sufficient to condense at least a portion of the vapors or the more readily condensible constituents.

Additional oil, or catalysts, or both, may be admitted through line 15. The resulting condensed liquid admixed with solid particles from the coal is separated from the uncondensed vapor in separator 16. The liquid oil and powdered solid are passed as a paste or slurry by pump 17 through line 18 into a hydrogenation zone 19. The vapors may be compressed by a compressor 21 and passed via line 22 into line 18 to the hydrogenation zone 19 or discharged through line 23. The vapors may be passed through line 23 and subjected to vapor phase hydrogenation or used for other purposes. Hydrogen is supplied to the hydrogenation zone from line 11 by line 24. The resulting products from the hydrogenation step, comprising residual carbonaceous solid, or pitch, and heavy oil resulting from the hydrogenation of the coal, is discharged through line 26 to separator 27. Recycle gas, comprising unreacted hydrogen is returned through lines 28 and 24 to the hydrogenation zone 19. Pitch, or residue, is discharged from the system through line 31. The heavy oil is drawn from the separator 27 through line 32 from which it may be passed through line 34 to storage for further processing. Heavy oil may be recycled through line 33 to the mixer 5 for preparation of the feed slurry.

FIGURE 3.4: LIQUID PHASE HYDROGENATION OF COAL

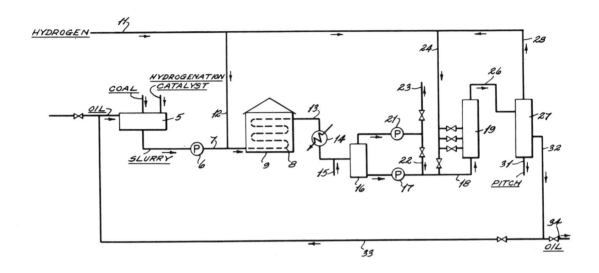

Source: F.B. Sellers; U.S. Patent 2,753,296; July 3, 1956

In a typical operation of the process such as illustrated in Figure 3.4, heavy oil produced by liquid phase hydrogenation of coal is admixed with particles of low ash bituminous coal having a size range of from 3/32" to 200 mesh. Five barrels of oil is admixed with each ton of crushed coal to form a readily pumpable slurry. Ferrous sulfate is admixed with oil and supplied to the slurry at the rate of 4 pounds per ton of coal as catalyst for the hydrogenation reaction. The slurry is pumped at one foot per second into a heating coil at a pressure of 500 psi. Hydrogen is supplied to the heating coil at the rate of 18,000 standard cubic feet per ton of coal.

The temperature of the mixture at the outlet of the heating coil is 1000°F. and the pressure is 300 psi. 95% of the oil is converted to vapor on passing through the heating coil. The temperature of the mixture discharged from the heating coil is reduced to 650°F. at 350 psi. The condensed liquid, powdered coal, and uncondensed vapors are admixed with an additional 18,000 standard cubic feet of hydrogen and passed at a pressure of 10,000 psi into a hydrogenation zone. The effluent of the hydrogenation step is separated without reduction in pressure into a gaseous fraction, predominantly hydrogen, which is recycled, a heavy oil fraction or crude product of the hydrogenation step, and residual solid or pitch. A portion of the heavy oil is returned to the mixing zone for admixture with the fresh coal. The heavy oil products amounts to 1,700 pounds per ton of coal fed to the process.

Efficient Catalytic Hydrogenation of Coal Paste

E.W. Doughty, J.H. Howell and M.A. Eccles; U.S. Patent 2,832,724; April 29, 1958; assigned to Union Carbide Corp. relate a fundamental improvement in the process of coal hydrogenation where the costs of the equipment required are greatly reduced and the efficiency of the method is increased. According to this process, the pulverized coal and the pasting oil are heated separately to a high temperature. By preheating the pasting oil, independently of the coal, no anomalous viscosity effects are obtained and the viscosity of the pasting oil decreases normally with the temperature. Likewise, by heating the pulverized coal in the absence of the pasting oil, coal particles are not surrounded by a viscous oil which would tend to form a gelatinous paste.

Upon mixing the hot pulverized coal and the hot pasting oil a semicolloidal dispersion or partial solution of the coal in the oil occurs leading to pastes sufficiently fluid for pumping. Such pastes may be then pumped under pressure together with the necessary hydrogen directly to the hydrogenation converter without further heating of the paste. In order to achieve the formation of a fluid paste, it is necessary that the coal and the pasting oil be heated to such a degree that the mixed paste will have a minimum temperature above that where excessive viscosities are encountered. Thus, it is necessary that the mixed paste have a minimum temperature of 300°C. and it is preferable that the paste have a temperature in the range of 325° to 400°C. The temperature to which the oil and coal are heated individually need not be a minimum of 300°C., but each may be heated individually to a temperature so that, on mixing, the temperature of the mixture will be at least 300°C. It has been found that the coking reaction is quite slow in this temperature range, so that the pastes may be kept at 325° to 400°C. for the time required for mixing, storage and transport to the hydrogenation converter.

By this method of mixing, coal pastes containing in excess of 50% coal by weight, for example 65 to 75%, may be prepared in a fluid state, wherein the prior practice is limited by the viscosity of the paste to coal concentrations of 40 to 50%. The use of more concentrated coal pastes permits a proportionate reduction in the size of the hydrogenation equipment required for a given throughput of coal. Since the converters must be built to withstand pressures of 10,000 psi or higher at inside temperatures of 480° to 540°C., any reduction in their size represents an important economy. In Figure 3.5, a flow sheet is shown giving the essential elements of a coal hydrogenation process in which the paste is prepared by this method.

FIGURE 3.5: EFFICIENT CATALYTIC HYDROGENATION OF COAL PASTE

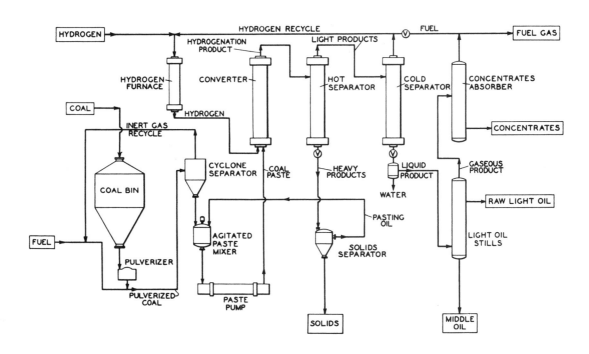

Source: E.W. Doughty, J.H. Howell and M.A. Eccles; U.S. Patent 2,832,724; April 29, 1958

In the flow sheet, coal enters the process and is stored in a bin, from which it passes to a pulverizer. The pulverized coal is picked up in a hot stream of inert gas which is kept at the heating temperature by combustion of the required amount of fuel gas. The powdered coal is heated by this hot stream of gas up to 325° to 400°C. and then passes to a cyclone separator where it is recovered from the inert gas which is recycled. A purge is taken from this recycle to maintain it at an approximately constant volume. The hot coal powder passes from the separator to a paste mixer equipped with an agitator where it is mixed at a temperature of 325° to 400°C. with hot pasting oil. The required pasting oil may be recycled from the separated hydrogenation products. A catalyst, such as a tin compound, is usually incorporated with the paste in the mixer. The mixing of the paste can be carried out in a continuous manner by feeding the hot coal into an agitated mixer, and continuously withdrawing paste from the mixer.

The paste is pumped from the mixer by a paste pump up to reaction pressures of 2,000 to 10,000 psi and passes to the converter. Hydrogen is introduced in the system under reaction pressure and heated above or below reaction temperatures depending on the thermal requirements of the system in a suitable hydrogen furnace from which it passes together with the coal paste to the converter where a known chemical reaction occurs between the coal and the hydrogen at temperatures of 450° to 550°C. Heat released in the reaction may be removed by known practices, but the introduction of a hot paste below the reaction temperature is advantageous. Thus, part of the heat of the reaction will be absorbed in bringing the paste feed up to reaction temperature, particularly if good circulation of the reactants is obtained in the converter.

The hydrogenation product passes to a hot separator where the heavy products, i.e., the heavy pasting oil and solids are removed, and the separated heavy products are treated to separate the solids, as by filtration or centrifuging. The hot pasting oil freed of solids is recycled to the paste mixer. Depending on the yields of the various fractions desired, some of the pasting oil may be withdrawn as a heavy product. The light products pass from the hot separator to the cold separator where the liquids are separated from the hydrogen, methane, and other uncondensed constituents, part of the hydrogen-methane fraction being recycled and part being withdrawn as fuel gas.

The liquid product from the cold separator, after being decanted from water, passes to a light oil still, where it may be fractionated into a gaseous product, a raw light oil and a middle oil. The gaseous products pass to a concentrates absorber where C_2 to C_5 hydrocarbons may be separated as concentrates, and the remainder of the gaseous product withdrawn as fuel gas. The following example illustrates the preparation of coal paste by the improved method.

Example: Pulverized coal was introduced into an electrically heated autoclave equipped with an agitator, and heated. Pasting oil was heated in a separate vessel and blown with nitrogen pressure into the autoclave at a temperature of 350°C. Two runs were made at coal concentrations of 50 to 60% in the pastes respectively. In both cases, a fluid mixture was obtained at the autoclave temperature and there was no visual evidence of coking. Samples of the hot paste when cooled set to a hard, brittle solid similar to hard asphalt. When reheated to approximately 250°C., the solids remelted in a manner similar to asphalt or pitch. The first sample, at 50% concentration, was mixed for 14 hours during which time the temperature fell from 350° to 260°C.; of the total time, only 25 minutes were at a temperature of 300°C. or higher. The second sample, at 60% concentration, was agitated for 2 hours, during which time 45 minutes were occupied in cooling the batch from 350° to 300°C.

Hydrogenation tests in a static bomb were run on both the 50 and 60% coal pastes thus mixed at an initial hydrogen pressure of 2,500 psi for one hour at 480°C. to determine whether any carbonization or other adverse change occurred during the long contact time at elevated temperatures. For comparison, a control run was also made under the same conditions in which a 50% coal paste, prepared from the same coal and oil used in making the hot mixed sample, was charged to the bomb without preheating. In carrying out the test runs, the hot mixed pastes were allowed to cool prior to hydrogenation. In each run, 200 g. of the paste was charged to the bomb which was then filled with hydrogen at 2,500 psi at 50°C. The contents of the bomb were then heated for 1.5 hours until a maximum temperature of 480°C. was reached, at which point the pressure in the bomb was 3,700 psi. The charge was held at this temperature for one hour, at which time the pressure was 2,800 psi. The bomb was then cooled and the products analyzed.

In the control run, the conversion of coal to gaseous and liquid products was 93%, where the conversions to liquid and gaseous products of the 50 and 60% coal pastes which were hot mixed were 92 and 93% respectively. The liquid products of the hydrogenation step contained chemically combined hydrogen; the carbon to hydrogen weight ratio being 12.9 for the control run, and 13.5 and 12.3 respectively for the 50 and 60% coal pastes prepared by hot mixing. These date indicate that preparation of the coal paste by separate heating of the coal and oil, and then mixing, does not impair the effectiveness of the hydrogenation step in converting the coal to liquid and gaseous hydrogenation products.

Catalytic Hydrogenation of Coal with Water Recycle

The hydrogenation of coal is enhanced in both reaction conversion and selectivity by maintaining in the reaction zone from 0.05 to 0.30 pound of water per pound of coal. The process of B.L. Schulman; U.S. Patent 3,488,280; Jan. 6, 1970; assigned to Esso Research and Engineering Co. comprises the introduction and maintenance of water in a catalytic hydrogenation zone where solid coal in a liquid solvent is contacted with a solid catalyst and gaseous hydrogen. Preferably, the water is introduced into the reactor as part of the moisture in the coal but can also be obtained by steam stripping the spent catalyst and the char-ash mixture from the reactor, and recycling the stripping steam, together with hydrocarbon oils removed from the catalyst and char-ash into the reaction zone.

Figure 3.6a is a diagrammatic sketch of a hydrogenation reactor where coal is contacted with a liquid solvent, solid catalyst, and gaseous hydrogen; and Figure 3.6b is a schematic diagram of the combined system including the reactor, spent catalyst stripper, and the char and ash stripped. Referring first to Figure 3.6a, the reactor 100 is seen to include an internal draft tube 102 through which the liquid can be recycled internally. The reactor recycle is accomplished by means of an impeller 104 driven by an electric motor 106. Into the reaction zone 100 are introduced the coal by way of line 108, solvent by way of line 110, and catalyst by way of line 112.

The coal is preferably added in a paste (e.g., 50% solids) of coal and solvent. The catalyst may be added along with the coal or solvent. A hydrogen-rich recycle gas (e.g., 70% or more H_2) is introduced into the reaction zone by way

FIGURE 3.6: CATALYTIC HYDROGENATION OF COAL WITH WATER RECYCLE

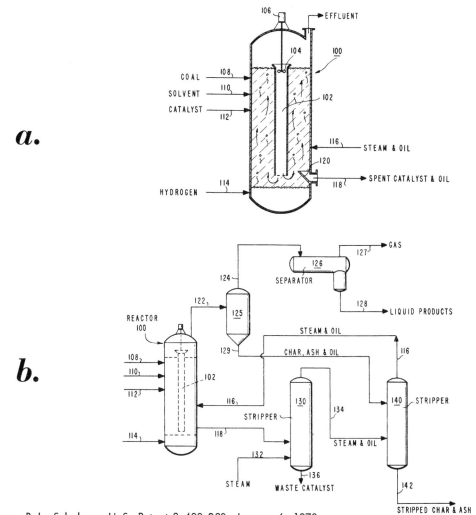

Source: B.L. Schulman; U.S. Patent 3,488,280; January 6, 1970

of line 114 and water, preferably in the form of steam, is introduced by way of line 116. Catalyst is withdrawn by way of line 118 through a drawoff tray 120. Within the reactor 100, the catalyst and coal may be maintained in the form of a liquid-fluidized bed, with the liquid product being withdrawn by way of line 122. The reaction is carried out as a mixed phase; that is, it will contain solid, liquid, and gaseous phase reactants and catalysts.

Referring now to Figure 3.6b where similar reference numerals are used to refer to the elements shown in Figure 3.6a, the reactor 100 is seen to be associated with a steam stripper 130 for spent catalyst and a steam stripper 140 for the char and ash. The coal, solvent, catalyst, water and hydrogen are introduced into the reaction zone as above discussed. The reaction is carried out in the reactor 100, and the liquid products are removed as effluent through line 122 into a hydroclone 125 and then through line 124 into separator 126. Solids are removed from hydroclone 125 by way of line 129 and conducted to stripper 140. From separator 126 a gas product (containing some steam) is withdrawn by way of line 127 and liquid products (containing some dissolved water) are removed by way of line 128. The liquid products in line 128 may be posttreated, for example, by hydrocracking, to produce the desired products.

A liquid stream is intermittently or continuously withdrawn (as shown schematically by way of line 122), and is passed through a thickener 125 (such as a hydroclone) to obtain a char and ash stream (in oil) which is passed into the char and ash stripper 140 where it is contacted with steam and oil from the spent catalyst stripper. A steam plus oil recycle stream is obtained which is carried by way of line 116 for reintroduction into the hydrogenation reaction zone. Spent catalyst and oil are removed by way of the drawoff tray 120 in line 118 and passed into a catalyst stripper 130. Fresh steam (for example, 450 psig steam further compressed as required) is introduced by way of line 132 and contacted with the spent catalyst for the removal of oil. The steam and oil from steam stripping are passed by way of line 134 into the char and ash stripper 140 to serve as the stripping steam. Waste catalyst is removed by way of line 136 for disposal. Stripped char and ash are removed from the char and ash stripper by way of line 142 for disposal.

TABLE 1: OPERATING CONDITIONS

Catalytic Hydrogenation Zone	Min.	Max.	Pref.
H_2O/coal, wt. ratio [1]	0.10	0.50	0.35
Solvent/coal, wt. ratio [1]	0.5	4	1–2
CS_2/catalyst rate, lbs./hr./lb.[2]	0.02	0.10	0.08
H_2/coal rate, M s.c.f./ton [1]	25	75	50
Temp., °F	700	850	800
Pressure, p.s.i.g.	1,000	3,500	2,000
Coal residence time, hrs.	0.25	2	0.5
Catalyst withdrawal rate, lbs./ton coal	0.2	2	1
Catalyst Stripper:			
H_2O/catalyst, wt. ratio	0.1	1	0.5
Temp., °F			
Pressure, p.s.i.g.	Same as reactor		
Char and Ash Stripper:			
H_2O/char and ash, wt. ratio	0.1	1	0.5
Temp., °F			
Pressure, p.s.i.g.	Same as reactor		

[1] Based on moisture-free coal in the reactor (but includes moisture in raw coal feed).
[2] Based on catalyst added to the reactor.

The coal is hydrogenated to form liquid products by contact in the catalytic hydrogenation zone with a solid catalyst, a liquid solvent, and molecular hydrogen. Where the catalyst is a sulfided metal, it may be desirable to maintain a flow of carbon disulfide into the reactor to prevent reduction of the catalyst to the metal. Water is fed into the reaction zone to improve both conversion and selectivity. The coal is preferably crushed before introduction into the reactor, having a maximum particle size less than 0.005" (passing through a 100 mesh size Tyler screen). Suitable coals for use in the process are found in the lignites, subbituminous coal and bituminous coal, etc. Suitable catalysts are cobalt molybdate, $SnS + CH_3I$, $Fe + Fe(SO_4)$, Ni, etc., in the form of 1/32" to 1/16" prills. Cobalt molybdate on alumina is preferred. The solvent which is used in the reaction zone is preferably a hydrogen-donor solvent such as tetralin or partially hydrogenated 3 or 4 ring aromatics (anthracene, etc.). Such a solvent may be obtained by hydrogenation of the hydrocracked liquid products of this reaction. Such a solvent would boil within the range from 450° to 950°F., with the preferred range being 600° to 950°F.

The solvent/coal weight ratio, within the range shown in the above table, is chosen to maintain the coal in a fair dispersion within the reaction zone. The recycle of the solvent and coal mixture, internally or externally, and of hydrogen-containing gas helps to maintain the coal and catalyst in a fine admixture throughout the reaction zone. In the catalytic hydrogenation zone, up to 85 to 95 weight percent of the maf coal feed will be converted into liquid and gaseous products. Of the converted coal, 70 to 75% will be liquid and the remainder gaseous. As it is known, the ratio of hydrogen to carbon decreases with increasing molecular weight, so that the highest consumption of hydrogen would be associated with the production of methane gas (CH_4, which has an H/C atomic ratio of 4). For comparison, the atomic ratio of hydrogen to carbon in octane, C_8H_{18}, is 18/8 (= 2.25).

In aromatic products, such as benzene, C_6H_6, the atomic ratio is 1:1. Thus, it is desirable to obtain as much liquid product as possible, so that the hydrogen consumption can be minimized. In the table shown below there are three batch runs comparing the hydrogenation of subbituminous coal with and without water. The runs were made in a pressure bomb; all reactants were charged into the bomb and then heated to the indicated temperature and pressure. From this table it is seen that the addition of water increases the yield of liquid product and decreases the hydrogen consumption (i.e., better selectivity). It should also be noted that in most cases the conversion of coal has been enhanced where similar operating conditions were chosen.

TABLE 2

Run No.	1SB–1	1SB–2	1SB–3
Operating conditions:			
Catalyst	Cobalt molybdate		
Conversion, wt. percent	89	86	91
Temperature, °F	826	826	861
Pressure (cold), p.s.i.g	800	800	800
Pressure (hot)	2,400	1,950	2,150
Tetralin/coal [1]	2.6	2.6	2.6
Coal/catalyst [1]	1.5	1.5	1.5
CS_2/catalyst	0.08	0.08	0.08
Time, hrs.	1.0	1.0	1.0
H_2O/coal [1]	0.34	0.06	0.06
H_2/coal [1]	0.07	0.07	0.07
H_2 consumption [2]	0.042	0.046	0.056
Yields, wt. percent MAF coal:			
CO_2	6	4	3
H_2O	14	16	17
C_1–C_4	3	4	11
C_5+Liquid	68	65	63
Char	11	14	9

[1] Based on moisture-free coal in the reactor, lbs./lb.
[2] Based on MAF coal, lbs./lb.

Referring to Table 2 and comparing the Runs 1SB-1 and 1SB-2, a subbituminous coal was hydrogenated in a pressure bomb under an initial pressure of 800 psig and a final (hot) pressure of 2,400 lbs. Note that at a temperature of 826°F., the conversion with water (0.34 H_2O/coal) was 89% as compared to 86% in 1SB-2 without water (0.06 H_2O/coal). Note also that the yield of C_5 +liquid in 1SB-1 was 68 weight percent whereas 1SB-2 showed only a 65 weight percent yield of C_5 +liquid. The higher conversion and liquid yield were obtained at a lower consumption of hydrogen, 0.042 for 1SB-1 as compared to 0.046 for 1SB-2. When the temperature was raised to 861°F. (1SB-3), the coal without water showed an increase in conversion to 91%, but this was accomplished by an increase in the yield of C_5 +liquid (to only 63%). Note that hydrogen consumption was increased to 0.056.

Balanced Hydrogenation of Coal

M.G. Pelipetz; U.S. Patent 2,860,101; Nov. 11, 1958; assigned to U.S. Secretary of the Interior describes the hydrogenation of a carbonaceous material to convert it into a useful product with a higher hydrogen to carbon ratio, basically a synthetic liquid or gaseous fuel. By a suitable and critical combination of several variables this process in one hydrogenation step produces a premium grade, stable gasoline from coal or other carbonaceous material. The process is as follows.

1. Powdered coal, impregnated with an active catalyst, is mixed with a distillable oil obtained from the process. Suitable active catalysts which have been utilized are nickelous chloride, stannous chloride, and ammonium molybdate.

2. The resultant paste is introduced into a vessel together with gaseous hydrogen under a pressure of more than 475 atmospheres and a temperature of more than 500°C. While a cylindrical vessel may be used, excellent results have been obtained with a tubular converter consisting of a helical tube of large length to diameter ratio. The residence time of the reactants is kept at from 15 seconds to 15 minutes. The favorable results shown below at 15 seconds strongly suggest that satisfactory conversions might be obtained at even shorter times, say 5 seconds.

3. The products from the reaction, solid and gaseous, are cooled and reduced in pressure. The resulting liquids are distilled to separate a distillate product oil with an end point of less than 200°C. The liquid remaining after the distillation is a distillable oil which may be easily removed from the small amount of unreacted coal by simple distillation, decantation or filtration. This oil is recycled to produce paste for introducing additional coal. The product oil is gasoline with an end point of 200°C. The gasoline meets all specifications for premium grade motor fuel, being highly aromatic in character and showing excellent stability.

Example: A mixture of (1) coal impregnated with ammonium molybdate equivalent to 1 weight percent molybdenum based on coal and (2) 60% distillable oil obtained by the hydrogenation of coal, was continuously pumped, together with hydrogen gas, into a 40 ft. tube maintained at 525°C. and 600 atmospheres pressure at a rate so that the residence time of the coal-oil-hydrogen mixture was 15 seconds. The product obtained in this manner was cooled, reduced in pressure and distilled. A gasoline production of 56.4% by weight of coal was obtained. Sufficient distillable oil was produced to prepare a paste with additional coal. Sufficient hydrocarbon gas was produced to supply all hydrogen requirements of the method. Continuous operation was maintained for more than 8 hours. A light oil prepared under conditions described previously was subjected to detailed analysis. The following important chemicals and their quantities were found.

	Weight Percent
Benzene	18.6
Toluene	31.7
Xylenes and ethyl benzenes	24.5
C_9 aromatics	6.9
Naphthenes	17.1
Paraffins	1.2
	100.0

The large quantity of aromatics present indicate the possibility of using this process to prepare these valuable compounds for which a tremendous demand exists.

Hydrogenation of Coal in the Absence of a Pasting Solvent

The process of W.C. Schroeder, L.G. Stevenson and T.G. Stephenson; U.S. Patent 3,152,063; October 6, 1964; assigned to Fossil Fuels, Inc. provides for the production of liquid and gaseous hydrocarbons by the rapid and direct hydrogenation of dry pulverized coal, lignite or char, in the absence of pasting oil, at relatively low pressures, at temperatures below 600°C. and with very short contact times between the pulverized coal and hydrogen. The reaction conditions are much less severe than previously required for coal hydrogenation processes and the process can be performed with fewer steps and in simplified equipment. Figure 3.7a is a flow sheet illustrating diagrammatically the method. Figure 3.7b is a graph showing the effect of gas residence time upon the conversion of the coal to liquids, gas and tar at a pressure of 2,000 psig and a temperature of 500°C.

FIGURE 3.7: HYDROGENATION OF COAL IN THE ABSENCE OF A PASTING SOLVENT

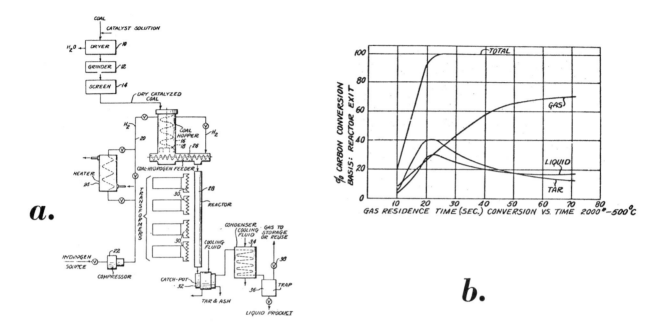

Source: W.C. Schroeder, L.G. Stevenson and T.G. Stephenson; U.S. Patent 3,152,063; October 6, 1964

Referring now to Figure 3.7a, operation of the process is described as follows: coal from any suitable source, preferably ground to approximately 70% through 200 mesh, is catalyzed by slurrying or spraying with an ammonium molybdate solution or with a solution of any other suitable catalyst followed by drying in a dryer 10. The dried catalyzed coal is reground in grinder 12 and is then screened on screen 14 to eliminate lumps. The dry, pulverized and catalyzed coal is then charged to a coal hopper 16 which is capable of being closed and pressurized.

This hopper may be provided with a low-speed agitator (diagrammatically shown at 18) to prevent bridging of the coal. After the hopper has been filled it is closed by suitable means (not shown), and the unit is brought up to full operating pressure by the introduction of hydrogen through line 20 from the compressor 22. The hydrogen may be supplied from any suitable source, e.g., it may be produced in the plant or shipped in by tank truck or other means. If desired, it may be preheated to a temperature below that at which it will react with the coal by passing all or a portion thereof through a suitable heater 24.

The hydrogen line 20 is connected to the coal hopper 16 and also to the end of a feed screw 26, which as shown is an integral part of the bottom of the coal hopper 16. The feed screw feeds coal in a horizontal direction from the bottom of the hopper 16 to the top of a tubular reactor 28. The feed screw is driven by a variable speed transmission (not shown) through a stuffing box at the end of the screw opposite the discharge end. Hydrogen pressure in the coal hopper is equalized with that in the feeder and in the reactor. The hydrogen introduced at the end of the screw feeder 26 sweeps the coal particles from the screw feeder into the top of the reactor 28.

A plurality of hoppers and feeders may be connected to the top of the reactor to provide continuous operation, one being on cycle while another is being filled. It will be understood that the coal-feeding arrangement illustrated is merely one of any number of suitable devices that could be used. An improved device which eliminates the use of mechanical agitators, feed screws and stuffing boxes is disclosed in copending Serial No. 769,380; filed May 11, 1959, entitled "Methods and Apparatus for Feeding Finely Divided Solids". The reactor 28, as illustrated, is in the form of an elongated, vertical tube. Tubular reactors 8 feet long of stainless steel and having inside diameters of 0.625" and 1.116" have been satisfactorily used in extensive test runs. It will be understood, however, that commercial apparatus may employ other types of reactors including those containing a multiplicity of tubes surrounded by a heating medium, and that the flow through the reactor may be either downward or upward, depending upon the design of the particular reactor and the velocity of flow of the suspension of coal and hydrogen therethrough. However, downward flow of coal and hydrogen as shown in Figure 3.7a has been found most satisfactory.

The reactor 28, as shown in Figure 3.7a, may be selectively heated at different zones thereof to any desired temperature up to 800°C. by means of a series of separately controlled electric heaters 30, which receive their power from associated transformers. From the reactor 28 the reaction products enter a catch pot 32 where heavy tars, ash and/or unreacted solids are deposited. The catch pot may be suitably cooled by introduction of cooling fluids such as air or water, into the jacket, as shown.

The tar and ash from the catch pot may be sent to a further hydrogenator, if desired, whereby the tar is converted to light liquid and gaseous products, and catalyst is recovered from the ash. The gaseous products and the lighter uncondensed liquid products pass through the catch pot and into a condenser 34. Light oils condensed at this point are collected in a trap 36 and form one of the products of the hydrogenation reaction. The trap 36 may be cooled by any suitable means. The noncondensable gases pass through a let-down valve 38 into suitable collecting tanks or are passed into other portions of the plant for reuse.

Example: The coal hydrogenation unit feed hopper was charged with 6,810 g. of bituminous coal, which has been ground to allow 70% to pass through a 200 mesh screen and to which 1% by weight of molybdenum had been added as an aqueous ammonium molybdate solution, and which had been dried and rescreened. The reaction zone of the 1.16" ID reactor was heated to 500°C. The system was purged and pressurized with hydrogen to 2,000 psig; and the hydrogen flow rate was adjusted to 3.9 scfm, resulting in a calculated residence time of 29 seconds. The dry, catalyzed coal was fed to the reaction zone at the rate of 418 g./hr. or 18.5 lbs./hr./ft.^{3} of reactor volume for a period of 10 hours.

The reactor temperatures during the operating period were 262°C. at the reactor inlet, 502°C. 1/4 of the way through the reactor, 501°C. 1/2 way through the reactor, 502°C. 3/4 of the way through the reactor, and 501°C. at the reactor exit. A total of 4,267 g. of coal were fed during the 10 hour period. Conversions were calculated on the basis of carbon content of the feed stock and products. On that basis, unhydrogenated material constituted 7.6% of the charge; tars and heavy liquids constituted 26%; light liquid 29%; and gas 37.3%. Gas analysis was as follows (hydrogen-free basis):

	Percent
Methane	50
Ethane	33
Propane	13
n-Butane	3

The light liquid component contained primarily alkyl substituted cyclohexanes, benzene, toluene, xylene and other alkyl substituted benzene compounds. In order to determine the effect of time, a series of such tests were run covering the period from 13 to 71 seconds at 500°C. and 2,000 psig hydrogen pressure; using molybdenum catalyst. The data derived from these tests are plotted in Figure 3.7b.

Hydrogenation of Coal in the Presence of Pasting Media

E.L. Frese, H.M. Schappert and W.E. Simmat; U.S. Patent 2,738,311; March 13, 1956; assigned to Koppers Company, Inc. describe a process for the hydrogenation coal, such as bituminous coal and lignite, where engine fuels, such as gasoline, diesel fuel, jet fuel and the like, are produced together with valuable chemicals, such as phenols and aromatics. Figure 3.8 is a general schematic flow sheet of an entire plant employing the method. One important phase of the overall system (as shown in Figure 3.8) is the liquid phase hydrogenation process.

As shown therein, a portion 80 of the total raw coal 81 needed for the entire plant is dried and ground 82, solid catalyst 83, such as iron salts, for example, iron sulfate, iron ore, tin or molybdenum salts and other catalysts known to the art, being added during the grinding operation to effect uniform admixture through the coal as shown in Figure 3.8. To the dry ground coal and catalyst 84 is added pasting oil 85 (heavy oil recycled from the method) and the oil, coal and catalyst mixed 86, such as by mulling, grinding and equivalent operations, to form a paste 87.

The paste is then hydrogenated in liquid phase 88 in the manner described above. In accordance with this process, the conditions maintained in the liquid phase hydrogenation some are such that the coal fed to the zone is converted into normally liquid products boiling above gasoline which consist principally of heavy oil and contain a minor portion of middle oil, as described more fully below. The slurry 89 from the hot catchpot, which consists of heavy oil, catalyst, unconverted coal, and substantially nonvolatile conversion products of coal, such as asphalt, is directed to a thermal decomposition zone 91, operated as described more fully below, together with portion of the intermediate catchpot liquid product 92.

FIGURE 3.8: HYDROGENATION OF COAL IN THE PRESENCE OF PASTING MEDIA

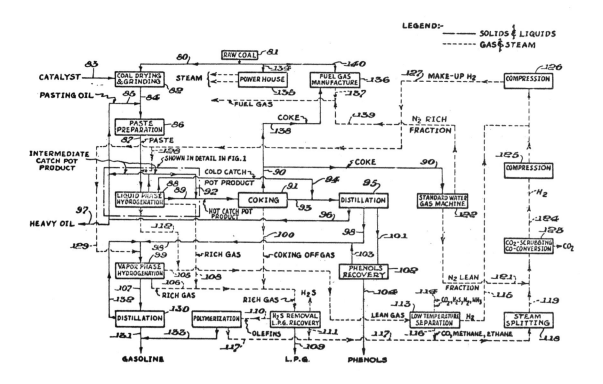

Source: E.L. Frese, H.M. Schappert and W.E. Simmat; U.S. Patent 2,738,311; March 13, 1956

The thermal decomposition zone is preferably a coking zone, such as moving bed of coke particles on or into which the the slurry is sprayed, the coke particles being hot enough to effect vaporization and thermal decomposition of the relatively high boiling hydrocarbons from the coal (a typical thermal coking system of this type is described in an article on Continuous Contact Coking by W.H. Schutte and W.C. Offut, which was published in the July 14, 1949 issue of the Oil and Gas Journal on page 90). Other types of coking known to the art, such as delayed coking or coking on fixed or moving beds of particles of inert refractory heat carriers such as fused inorganic oxides, for example, quartz or alumina, may be employed.

In the conversion zone, e.g., coking zone 91, the heavy oil and any asphalt present are thermally decomposed and/or vaporized, under conditions described more fully below, into vaporous products and solid carbonaceous residue 90. The vaporous products consist principally of middle oil and gasoline 93 formed by either thermal cracking or coking of the heavy oil fed to the coking zone but also include some gas and a substantial minor amount of heavy oil produced by vaporization and/or cracking of any asphalt or other substantially nonvolatile products of hydrogenation present.

Therefore, if desired, the conditions of the thermal cracking can be controlled in such a way that the products obtained contain a certain quantity of olefins for further use. The solid carbonaceous residue consists principally of the coke used as heat carrier and the coke resulting from the conversion of heavy oil into middle oil and gasoline together with the solid catalyst, the ash (metallic constituents) of the coal, and particles of unconverted coal. The vaporous products from the coking zone 91 are condensed and the liquid portion 93 thereof directed, together with the liquid hydrogenation products 94 from the cold catch, to a distillation operation or zone 95. By distillation there is obtained (a) heavy oil fraction 96 which fraction has an initial boiling point of 625°F., such as from 600° to 650°F. and contains all higher boiling volatile oil from the coal, at least a portion of which is recycled 85 to the pasting operation as pasting oil, or

120

sent to storage 97 for sale or other uses, (b) a fraction containing middle oil and gasoline, which fraction has an end boiling point or dew point at atmospheric pressure of 625°F., and which is forwarded 98 to the vapor phase hydrogenation operation or zone 99 and (c) a phenol-containing fraction 101, boiling between about 320° to 450°F. which is forwarded to a phenol recovery operation or zone 102 in which phenols are separated from hydrocarbons, such as by extraction, reaction with caustic or other known methods. The hydrocarbons 103 so separated are added to the charge to the vapor phase hydrogenation 99 while the phenols 104 are sent to storage for sale. The gasoline and middle oil formed in the liquid phase hydrogenation operation and in the coking zone are converted in the vapor phase hydrogenation zone into gasoline.

By a series of catchpots or condensers similar to those described the vapor phase hydrogenation products are separated into lean gas 105, rich gas 106 and normally liquid products 107. The rich gas 106, together with like material from the liquid phase hydrogenation 108 and from coking 100, is treated to remove sulfur-containing compounds, principally hydrogen sulfide, and fractionated, yielding a low pressure gas fraction 109, consisting substantially completely of propane and butane, commonly referred to as LPG, which can be sold as such, low boiling olefins, such as propene and butene 110 and a lower boiling fraction 111 containing methane, ethane, ethylene and some hydrogen and impurities.

The lean gas 105, together with similar material 112 from the liquid phase hydrogenation is subjected to separation 113, by low temperature or in a Hyperscorber system or the like with the production of (a) a fraction 114 containing carbon dioxide, hydrogen sulfide, nitrogen and ammonia, which may be disposed of or further processed, (b) a hydrogen concentrate 115 containing from 95 to 98% of hydrogen and (c) a hydrocarbon fraction 116 containing carbon monoxide, methane and ethane. The hydrocarbon fraction 116, together with similar material remaining after polymerization 117 of olefins in the olefinic fraction 110 of the lean gas, is subjected to steam splitting 118 (i.e., catalytic conversion by known methods of low boiling hydrocarbons to hydrogen and carbon oxides).

The product gas 119, from the steam splitting 118 together with water gas 121 produced in a standard water gas machine 122 from all or a portion of the coke 90 from the coking zone, is forwarded to an operation or zone 123 in which the carbon monoxide, together with steam, is converted, as by known catalytic methods, into hydrogen and carbon dioxide, the latter being scrubbed out of the gas to yield a substantially pure (95 to 98%) hydrogen 124. This hydrogen is then compressed in several stages in two zones (such as to 20 in zone 125 then 700 atmospheres in zone 126) and employed as makeup hydrogen 127 charged 128 to the liquid phase hydrogenation 88 and charged 129 to the vapor phase hydrogenation 99.

The products 107 from the vapor phase hydrogenation 99 are forwarded to a distillation operation or zone 130 where they are separated into gas, gasoline 131 and high boiling products 132, which are recycled in the vapor phase hydrogenation step. The gasoline 131 from vapor phase hydrogenation may be combined with polymer gasoline 133 produced by polymerization of low boiling olefins produced in the system. A portion, generally one-third or less, of the total coal needed for operation of the entire plant or system is used 134 to operate the necessary utilities 135 providing steam at high and low pressures and electricity.

The required fuel gas is manufactured 136 from a portion of the coke from the coking zone 91, from the high nitrogen gases 139 produced in the standard water gas machine 122 and the remainder from coal generally about one tenth to one sixth of the total coal 140. The fuel gas 137 so manufactured is used for firing boilers, preheaters and the like. A portion of the coal needed for fuel gas manufacture is saved by substituting a portion 138 of the coke produced in the coking operation or by augmenting the fuel gas with gas 139 produced in the water gas operation 122.

Contact Catalysis of Vapors from Destructively Distilled Coal

The process described by M.G. Huntington; U.S. Patent 3,244,615; April 5, 1966; assigned to Pyrochem Corporation relates to the vapor phase total hydrogenation, i.e., saturation of olefins and to the removal of oxygen, sulfur and nitrogen as their respective hydrides from the primary vapors initially distilled from solid hydrocarbonaceous substances such as oil shale, asphaltenes, coal, bituminous impregnations; peat, wood and other vegetable matter. In Figure 3.9, there is a diagrammatic flow sheet presentation of this process.

Coal or oil shale (primarily kerogen), or asphaltenes or any other initially solid hydrocarbonaceous material containing carbon, hydrogen, oxygen, sulfur and nitrogen, is introduced schematically at 10 to a suitable distillation means 12. The distillation means may be any suitable type of distillation means. While in the distillation means the initially solid hydrocarbonaceous materials are subjected to thermal exposure to distill volatiles therefrom with a minimum of thermal alteration beyond the initial pyrolysis of the original solid material.

The distilled matter will be in the vapor phase and will include permanent gases and condensable vapors. These primary volatile products of distillation may be withdrawn from the distillation means through line 14. The solids which are products of the distillation may be removed from the distillation means as indicated schematically at 16. The requisite heat for providing the thermal exposure is illustrated diagrammatically at 18 as a heat input to the distillation means. Hydrogen, preferably preheated, is provided from a suitable source 20 and may either be introduced into the distillation means 12 together with the solid carbonaceous materials through line 22 or may be directly introduced into vapor phase output line 14 through line 24. A valve 26 is shown as controlling the path of the hydrogen. If the hydrogen is sufficiently preheated to furnish the thermal input from the thermal exposure in the distillation means, of course, this would replace the source of heat illustrated schematically at 18.

FIGURE 3.9:   CONTACT CATALYSIS OF VAPORS FROM DESTRUCTIVELY DISTILLED COAL

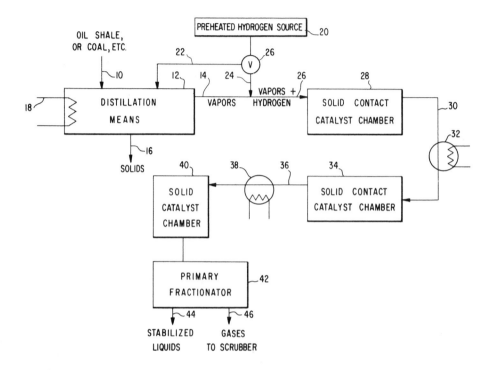

Source: M.G. Huntington; U.S. Patent 3,244,615; April 5, 1966

The vapors from the distillation together with the hydrogen are then passed through line 26 to a solid contact catalyst chamber 28 while still in the initial vapor phase. The initial vapor phase products of the pyrolysis have been thermally split from the large complex molecules having molecular weight in the order of 10,000 into smaller fragments which are molecules having a molecular weight less than 300. However, these smaller molecules are highly reactive for two primary reasons. First, because the unsaturation of the hydrocarbons, i.e., olefins, therein, and second because of the presence of oxygen in organic combustion.

However, by combining the vapor phase products with hydrogen while they are still in the initial vapor phase, and passing them across a solid contact catalyst, the unsaturated hydrocarbons will be saturated, i.e., the olefins will be saturated to paraffins. Also, the oxygen may be removed as water vapor and the tar acids, such as phenol, destroyed. That is, the purpose of the solid contact catalyst chamber 28 is to saturate the olefins and remove organic oxygen as water from the initial vapor phase products of distillation. This effectively prevents interreaction of the compounds in the distillate and the resulting formation of large molecules.

The vapors from the contact catalyst chamber 28 pass out through line 30 where they are subjected to temperature control in heat exchanger 32 and then may pass to a second solid contact catalyst chamber 34. The solid catalyst in chamber 34 is contacted with the vapors for the completion of the removal of oxygen as water and further for partial removal of noncyclic organic nitrogen as NH_3 and partial removal of organic sulfur as H_2S. The vapors from chamber 34 may be taken off line 36 through temperature control 38 and if desired passed to a further solid catalyst chamber 40. Solid catalyst chamber 40 will be used if the system pressure were greater than 100 psia and its purpose is to further accomplish sulfur removal to less than 100 ppm and nitrogen removal excepting hetrocyclic compounds. The vapors from this catalyst chamber, or directly from catalyst chamber 34, may then be passed to a primary fractionator 42 and the condensed products therefrom will be in the form of stabilized liquids from line 44 which may be passed to secondary fractionator with reboiler and gases which are passed via line 46 to conventional gas scrubbers. The contacting of the hydrogen entrained vapor phase volatiles with the solid catalyst while still in a vapor phase prevents polymerization and other subsequent liquid phase intermolecular reactions. The contacting with the catalyst can be accomplished at a sufficiently rapid rate by contacting the hydrogen entrained vapors over solid catalysts such as cobalt molybdate supported on alumina. The size and other parameters of the catalytic treatment including the liquid hourly space velocity and the catalyst contact time are chosen such that the olefins will be saturated and the oxygen in organic combination substantially removed from the particular distillate from the solid hydrocarbonaceous input material. It is important to note that a method is provided by this process where the yield of liquids under mild operating conditions is at least equal to the maximum volume obtainable from low temperature carbonization assay. At the same time, the character of the final distillate is stable and therefore predictable.

Countercurrent Solvent Extraction with Simultaneous Hydrogenation

In the process of E.F. Nelson; U.S. Patent 3,488,278; January 6, 1970; assigned to Universal Oil Products Company coal is liquefied in a continuous countercurrent fashion utilizing a selective solvent which is introduced into the solvent extraction zone through a plurality of spaced points from the lower end of the zone. Added hydrogen and hydrogenation catalyst are used in the extraction zone to further aid in converting crushed coal into liquid hydrocarbonaceous products.

The purpose of an extraction zone, including the addition of hydrogen to the extraction zone, is to substantially complete the conversion of the coal into a liquid coal extract, it may also be desirable to add to the extraction zone a hydrogenation catalyst. The catalyst used may be conventional, may be homogeneous or heterogenous and may be introduced in the pulverization zone and/or extraction zone in admixture with the liquid solvent or with the solid coal or may be introduced as a separate stream into the upper end of the extraction zone.

Conventional solid, particulate hydrogenation catalyst (e.g., finely divided) may be desirable, such as palladium on an alumina support or a cobalt-molybdate catalyst or any other hydrogenation catalyst, and applicable to the solvent-coal system environment maintained in the extraction zone including the use of a slurry-catalyst system. Hydrogenation in the extraction zone generally accomplished the following functions: transfer of hydrogen directly to coal molecules; transfer of hydrogen to hydrogen donor molecules; transfer of hydrogen from hydrogen donor molecules to coal molecules; and combinations of the above. Homogenous catalysts may be introduced with the coal, or hydrogen donor compounds, in the pulverization step prior to the extraction zone. Examples of homogenous catalysts suitable include compounds containing tin, nickel, molybdenum, tungsten, and cobalt.

Referring to Figure 3.10, crushed coal having an average particle diameter of at least -8 Tyler screen size is introduced from hopper 10 into coal liquefier 11 which is maintained under coal liquefying conditions. Lean solvent is introduced into the system via line 12 and is split into spaced introduction points via lines 13, 14 and 15 in an amount sufficient to provide an upward flowing velocity which hinders the settling of the coal particles passing downwardly through liquefier 11. The amount of lean solvent entering the spaced introduction points is in a ratio of 80:15:5, respectively, by volume.

Sufficient hydrogen gas is introduced into liquefier 11 via line 19 and passes in an upwardly flowing direction through the extraction zone. A typical cobalt-molybdate hydrogenation catalyst in solid particulate form is introduced into the upper end of liquefier 11 via line 19. Thus, the lean solvent and hydrogen pass in countercurrent fashion with the coal and catalyst particles. Rich solvent containing dissolved coal together with other gases including hydrogen is removed from liquefier 11 via line 16 and passed into recovery facilities. Conventionally, the hydrogen gas may be separated (by means not shown) from the other materials and recycled to liquefier 11. Similarly, a portion of the liquid coal extract may also be recovered (by means not shown) and returned to liquefier 11 as lean solvent therein. Ash and residue including solid catalyst is removed from the system via line 17 and passed into recovery facilities not shown for the reclaiming of the catalyst and reuse in the extraction zone.

In a manner of operating, the materials in contact at point 23 include solvent which is relatively lean having been introduced via line 13, hydrogen gas, downward passing coal particles and catalyst particles. In many respects the condition of the materials at point 23 may be termed "semiplastic". As the material passes further down the column, the condition at point 22 may be termed a condition of relatively high ash content zone since at that point substantially all of the coal to be extracted has been converted into liquid phase. In addition, the velocity of the materials flowing upwardly at point 23 is greater than the upward flow velocity of materials at point 22. One of the reasons for controlling the conditions in this manner of relative velocity is that at point 23 there are significantly greater numbers of relatively fine coal particles than at point 22.

By similar analogy, the condition at point 21 is one of extremely high ash content with essentially no coal particles to be dissolved. The introduction of the hydrogen into the zone at point 21 creates a condition of relatively high turbulence which aids in the further separation of any remaining coal particles from the undissolved ash, catalyst, the residue which continue down the column. Point 20 defines a settling zone where low Reynolds number liquid flows are maintained so that the ash, residue, and catalyst will have a chance to settle out of the liquid phase and be washed by at least a portion of the lean solvent which enters liquefier <u>11</u> via line <u>15</u> and passes downward as a wash through the settling zone.

FIGURE 3.10: COUNTERCURRENT SOLVENT EXTRACTION WITH SIMULTANEOUS HYDROGENATION

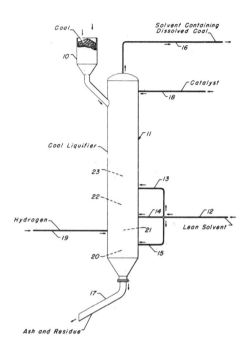

Source: E.F. Nelson; U.S. Patent 3,488,278; January 6, 1970

Rapid Hydrogenation of Coal

<u>W.C. Schroeder; U.S. Patent 3,030,297; April 17, 1962; assigned to Fossil Fuels, Inc</u>. describes a process for the rapid hydrogenation of coal to produce hydrocarbon liquids and gases and particularly, such a process where the liquid fraction produced is predominantly aromatic in nature. The process differs from those known up to the present time for coal hydrogenation in that the reaction between the coal and hydrogen is completed in a period of time of two minutes or less; the hydrogen pressure may be varied over a range from 500 to 6,000 psig with satisfactory results; the conversion of carbonaceous matter in the coal to liquid and gases is substantially complete, it being possible to convert over 90% of the carbonaceous matter of the coal to liquid and gases in less than two minutes reaction time.

The process can be so operated that the liquid product contains about 90% single-ring aromatic compounds, naphthalene and derivatives thereof; the consumption of hydrogen is near the minimum theoretical amount required for production of the liquid compounds; the ratio of gas to liquid fractions in the product can be controlled; the hydrogenation can be carried out in the presence or absence of a catalyst; the products obtained from the process are readily separable from coal ash or any solid material; and the products are of simple composition and are readily separable by distillation or other conventional chemical or petroleum refining processes into commercial chemicals such as benzene, toluene, xylene, naphthalene, gasoline and oils, and hydrocarbon gases.

As an example of the commercial application of this process to produce aromatic oils and hydrocarbon gases from coal, reference is made to Figure 3.11 which illustrates diagrammatically one form of apparatus for carrying out the method. The equipment consists of two closed coal-storage vessels <u>12</u> and <u>12a</u> for the storage and feeding of pulverized coal. These vessels are capable of being maintained under high pressure and are filled with pulverized coal through inlet pipes <u>13—13a</u> and valves <u>14—14a</u>. The coal is fed alternately from either one or the other of the storage vessels <u>12—12a</u> by a screw conveyor <u>16</u> or <u>16a</u> into a pressurized hydrogen stream supplied to a pipe line <u>18</u> from a suitable source. Valves <u>20</u> and <u>20a</u> are provided so that coal may be selectively withdrawn from either vessel <u>12</u> or <u>12a</u>. The combined hydrogen-coal stream in line <u>18</u> passes into a preheater <u>22</u>, which may comprise one or a plurality of tubes <u>22a</u> provided with a jacket <u>23</u> heated by hot gases from furnace <u>24</u>. A pressure return line <u>26</u> connects line <u>18</u> to storage vessels <u>12—12a</u>

through valves 28—28a so as to equalize the pressures while coal is being fed. From the preheater 22 the hydrogen-coal stream passes to a reactor 30, which may comprise one or more tubes 30a provided with a temperature-control jacket 32, so that the temperature of the reactants can be maintained at the desired value. All of the gases, vapors, and solids leaving the reactor 30 pass through pipe 34 into a cyclone 36 where the major amounts of any remaining coal and ash are separated from the gases and vapors.

FIGURE 3.11: RAPID HYDROGENATION OF COAL

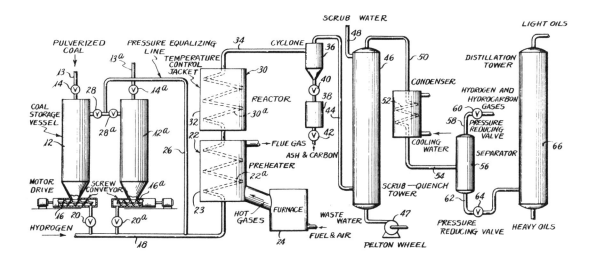

Source: W.C. Schroeder; U.S. Patent 3,030,297; April 17, 1962

The cyclone 36 is equipped with a receiver 38 provided with valves 40 and 42, which allow the intermittent removal of solids from the system without interference from the gas flow. The gases and vapors from the cyclone 36 pass through pipe 44 to a scrub-quench tower 46 where a spray of water is introduced through line 48 to lower the temperature to at least 250°C. The quench tower 46 is positioned as close as possible to the reactor 30 to rapidly lower the temperature of the gases and vapors issuing therefrom, to prevent further hydrogenation which may destroy the valuable liquid products.

The water in tower 46 absorbs acid gases such as hydrogen sulfide and carbon dioxide, and also absorbs any ammonia formed. The water leaving the bottom of tower 46 is dropped in pressure through Pelton wheel 47 and after release of dissolved gases and separation of any oils and tar may be cooled and recycled for further use in tower 46. After the gases and vapors have been quenched in tower 46, they pass through pipe 50 to a condenser 52 where they are further cooled indirectly by heat exchange with water or other cooling fluid to condense out the liquid hydrocarbons. The resulting gas-liquid mixture passes through pipe 54 to a separator 56 from which gases are taken off the top through pipe 58 and pressure-release valve 60, and liquids are drawn off the bottom through line 62. The liquids are then passed through pressure-reducing valve 64 to a distillation tower 66 where they can be fractionated into the desired higher and lower boiling liquid fractions.

In the tests reported in Table 1, the retention time of the products at reaction temperature was dependent on the rate of hydrogen flow as well as upon the time of quenching the reactor, i.e., at the lower rates of hydrogen flow a substantial portion of the liquid reaction products remainder in the reactor for the full period, but with the higher rates of hydrogen flow the liquid as well as the gaseous products were carried out of the reactor as formed. In one minute at 600°C. (Tests 1 and 2) about two-thirds of the coal was converted to hydrocarbon liquids and gases. The liquids formed were 15 to 16% of the maf (moisture- and ash-free) coal, and the hydrocarbon gases 26 to 33%. The remaining material to make up the 66 to 88% converted was CO_2, water, NH_3, H_2S, and minor amounts of other gases.

The hydrogen flow rate during these tests was at the rate of 20 standard cubic feet per hour. About one-third of the liquid produced at 600°C. was distillable and highly aromatic in nature, the remaining fraction being a heavy oil. The next two tests, 3 and 4, show that at 800°C. with 0 and one minute at maximum reaction temperature and with the same hydrogen flow rate the percent of coal converted increased slightly. The percent of liquid hydrocarbons decreased to

125

around 10 to 15% and the hydrocarbon gas increased to 40%. In these tests, however, the oil product was lighter than in tests 1 and 2, one half of the liquid product being distillable and high in aromatic components.

TABLE 1:   RAPID HYDROGENATION OF COAL TO LIQUIDS AND GASES AT 600° AND 800°C.

Test No.	Temp., °C.	Time Above 300° C. (Min.)	Time at Max. Temp. (Min.)	Hydrogen Flow, Standard cu. ft. per/hr.	Based on moisture- and ash-free coal			Nature of oil
					Percent of coal converted	Percent liquid hydrocarbons formed	Percent hydrocarbon gas formed	
1	600	2.9	1.0	20	67.6	15.1	32.6	Heavy.
2	600	2.3	1.0	20	66.1	16.2	26.7	Do.
3	800	2.0	1.0	20	73.1	9.9	37.2	Light.
4	800	3.0	1.0	20	67	13.8	41.2	Do.
5	800	2.5	0.0	50	83	23	¹40	Very Light.
6	800	2.5	0.0	100	90	39	¹40	Do.
7	800	1.7	0.0	100	88.4	48.9	31.8	Do.
8	800	1.8	0.0	100	85.0	38.8	39.6	Do.
9	800	2.5	0.0	228	94	31	¹35	Very Heavy.
10	800	2.5	0.0	228	97	39	¹42	Do.

¹ Estimated.

Test 5 was the same as 4, except that the rate of hydrogen flow was increased from 20 to 50 standard cubic feet per hour, so as to carry products of reaction out of the heated zone at a faster rate, and the time at maximum temperature was decreased from one minute to 0 minute. In spite of the decreased retention time, the percent of coal converted increased to 83% and the liquid hydrocarbons to 23%. Substantially all of the liquid product was a very light oil, distillable under atmospheric pressure and having a high proportion of aromatic constituents. Test 6 was run under the same conditions as 5, except that the hydrogen flow was increased from 50 to 100 standard cubic feet per hour, thereby removing products of reaction from the heated zone at a still faster rate, i.e., further decreasing retention time. The percent of coal converted increased to 90 and the liquid yield to 39. The gas yield remained at 40%. The oil was very light, high in aromatics, and completely distillable.

In tests 7 and 8 the flow rate of hydrogen was again 100 standard cubic feet per hour, thus rapidly removing products of the reaction from the reactor. The total time above 300°C., however, was reduced to 1.7 minutes in test 7 and to 1.8 minutes in test 8. At the hydrogen flow rate of 100 standard cubic feet per hour, the retention time of the products at reaction temperature was about five seconds. With zero time at maximum reaction temperature, the percent total conversion remained high (85 to 90%) and the percentage conversion to liquid products was at a maximum for this series of tests. Moreover, the liquid product was a very light, completely distillable oil, high in aromatic constituents.

Tests 9 and 10 were duplicates and were at the same conditions as 6, except that the hydrogen flow was further increased to 228 standard cubic feet per hour. In these tests total conversion of the coal was well above 90%, hydrocarbon liquids formed were from 31 to 39%, and hydrocarbon gas 35 to 42%. However, the liquid was very heavy, being almost a tar in consistency. It is apparent from tests 9 and 10 that the hydrogen velocity had now become so high that the retention time for the products from the coal hydrogenation in the heated zone was too short to complete the conversion to light oils. At a flow rate of 228 standard cubic feet of hydrogen per hour, the retention time for the gases and liquids in the heated section of the reactor was calculated to be 2.3 seconds. Table 1A below shows the results of tests for the hydrogenation of coal in the absence of all added catalysts. The test conditions, except where otherwise indicated, were the same as in test 6 reported in Table 1.

TABLE 1A: RAPID HYDROGENATION OF COAL TO LIQUIDS AND GASES WITHOUT A CATALYST

Test No.	Time above 300° C. (Minutes)	Time at Temp. (Minutes)	Percent of Coal Converted	Percent Liquid Hydrocarbons	Percent Hydrocarbon Gas Formed
6-a	1.6	0.0	73.4	31.4	38.9
6-b	1.9	0.0	76.3	26.6	46.7

The liquid fraction was in the form of a light oil, high in aromatics. It is apparent from Table 1A that the rapid high temperature hydrogenation process proceeds satisfactorily with or without a catalyst.

TABLE 2: RAPID HYDROGENATION OF COAL TO LIQUIDS AND GASES AT 900° AND 1000°C.

[Sample — 8 g. of Coal (Weight on a Moisture- and Ash-Free Basis)]
(Catalyst — 1% Molybdenum on Basis of Moisture- and Ash-Free Coal)

Test No.	Temp, ° C.	Time Above 300 ° C. (Min.)	Time at Temp. (Min.)	Pressure, p.s.i.g.	Hydrogen flow, s.c.f./ hr.	Based on moisture- and ash-free coal			Nature of oil
						Percent of coal converted	Percent liquid hydrocarbons formed	Percent hydrocarbon gas formed	
11	900	3.2	0	3,000	20	78.3	14.8	40.7	Light.
12	900	4.0	1	3,000	20	83.7	17.4	46.8	Do.
13	900	3.7	0	1,000	20	67.0	21.2	21.3	Do.
14	900	4.6	1	1,000	20	69.9	23.8	24.1	Do.
15	1,000	3.8	0	500	20	66.8	11.8	18.7	Heavy.
16	1,000	5.2	1	500	20	73.0	27.0	29.0	Do.

Table 2 shows the results of tests on the hydrogenation of coal at 900° and 1000°C. for hydrogen pressures between 3,000 and 500 psig in the presence of a catalyst. Tests 11 and 12 at 3,000 psig show 78 to 84% coal conversion, with a 14 to 17% liquid yield and a 40 to 47% gas yield. When the pressure was decreased to 1,000 psig, as in tests 13 and 14, the conversion dropped to 67 to 70%, the liquid yield increased to 21 to 24%, and the yield of hydrocarbon gas was also in the range of 21 to 24%.

In tests 15 and 16 the temperature was increased to 1000°C. and the pressure decreased to 500 psig. Under these conditions conversion was in the range 67 to 73%, liquid hydrocarbon yield from 12 to 27%, and gaseous hydrocarbons from 18 to 29% and oil was fairly heavy. The products resulting from operating under these conditions are similar to those obtained by operating at the other end of the preferred range, i.e., at temperatures around 600°C. and pressure of 6,000 psig. It will be apparent that best results are obtained in the 700° to 900°C. range.

Example: For the purpose of this example it will be assumed that 300 pounds (on a moisture- and ash-free basis) of New Mexico coal will be hydrogenated per minute in the system described in the drawing, at 800°C. and 6,000 psig, to produce 150 pounds of liquid product and 3,600 standard cubic feet of mixed hydrocarbon and hydrogen gases. To operate under the conditions selected for this example, coal storage vessels 12 and 12a are charged from the top with coal pulverized to a suitable size, such as 70% through 200 mesh. Coarser or finer particles can be used if desired, but the maximum size should be such as to freely pass through the preheat and reactor coils.

About 100 mesh or smaller particle size is generally satisfactory. Valves 20 and 28 are opened to connect vessel 12 to the hydrogen line 18 and valve 14 is closed. Vessel 12a is isolated from the hydrogen line 18 by keeping valves 20a and 28a closed. Hydrogen gas is then brought through line 18 and the entire system pressurized to 6,000 psig. With hydrogen flowing through the system at the rate of 21.3 pounds per minute, furnace 24 is started and the hot products of combustion are allowed to flow over preheater 22 until the temperature of the hydrogen gas at the exit of the preheater is between 600° and 700°C. The hydrogen gas continues through reactor 30 and on through the rest of the system.

When even temperature and flow conditions have been established, screw feeder 16·is started and is operated at a rate that feeds 300 lbs. of moisture- and ash-free coal per minute to the hydrogen stream in line 18 (130 lbs. hydrogen per ton of as-received coal). Vessel 12 is of such a size that it will provide coal for at least 15 to 20 minutes. When the coal in this vessel is depleted, vessel 12a is then put in the line to feed coal and vessel 12 is reloaded. Vessels 12 and 12a, used alternately, provide a continuous and controlled coal feed to the process. Pressure equalizing line 26 keeps a balanced pressure on both sides of the feed vessel so that the feed screw does not have to operate against a pressure differential.

The coal-hydrogen stream which now contains 8 lbs. of entrained coal per cubic foot of hydrogen at the operating conditions, passes through preheater 22 to be preheated. The gas velocity in the tubes of preheater 22 is calculated at 15 to 20 feet per second. It will be understood that lower or higher gas velocity may be used, provided the gas velocity is such that the coal particles will move substantially at the same rate as the gas stream. The calculated retention time of the coal particles in preheater 22 is less than a minute, the stream reaching a temperature of 600°C. in this time. The temperature attained in the preheater tube 22 should be at least sufficient to initiate the conversion of the coal to the desired products. From preheater 22 the gas-solid stream flows to reactor 30. As the result of the formation of some methane in reactor 30, the temperature of the gases will rise 150° to 200°C. as they pass through the reactor at five feet per second and the retention time in the reactor also is less than one minute.

The products from the hydrogenation reaction, which consist of a mixture of gases, vaporized liquids, ash and any unreacted coal, then pass from reactor 30 to cyclone 36, where a major portion of the solid material (mainly ash) is separated. This solid is discharged from the pressure system at intervals through valved receiver 38. Gases and vaporized liquids are then quenched in scrub-quench tower 46 by spraying water into the stream to lower the temperature to around 250°C. This will retard further hydrogenation reactions which may destroy valuable aromatic liquid products. The products are then further cooled in condenser 52 to temperatures in the range of 25° to 50°C. to condense the vaporized liquids in the gas stream. From condenser 52 the products, which is now a mixture of gases and liquids, goes to separator 56, which is a vessel in which the liquids separate from the gas. The gases are taken off the top through a pressure-reducing valve 60 at the rate of 3,600 standard cubic feet per minute. The composition of the gas in volume percent is 40% CH_4, 5% C_2H_6, 1% C_3H_8 and 50% H_2, with small amounts of CO, CO_2, N_2 and other impurities. The heating value of the gas is 600 Btu per cubic foot. It can be purified to remove NH_3, CO_2, and H_2S and is then suitable for a wide variety of industrial purposes. Since the gas already contains nearly half hydrogen, it is very useful for the production of hydrogen for making ammonia, methanol, and other chemicals.

The product gas can also be used to furnish the hydrogen for use in the hydrogenation process itself and it is in excess of the actual requirements. Where the gas is to be used for this purpose, it may be mixed with steam and passed through a catalytic reforming unit where the steam and hydrocarbon gases react to form H_2, CO and a small amount of CO_2. Further steam is then added to this product and it is passed over a suitable catalyst to produce a further reaction between the CO and steam to furnish more H_2 and convert the CO to CO_2. After removal of the CO_2 a relatively pure hydrogen stream is available for the coal-hydrogenation process.

Other well-known methods are available for converting the product gases from the coal hydrogenation process to hydrogen, such as by partial oxidation with oxygen, and may be used where the economics at the particular plant so dictate. The liquid products from separator 56, amounting to 21 gallons per minute, are passed through a pressure-reducing valve 64 and may then go directly to the distillation tower. The composition of the liquid product comprises benzene, toluene, xylene, light oils in the gasoline range, naphthalene, heavier oil.

Solvation and Hydrogenation of Coal in Partially Hydrogenated Hydrocarbon Solvents

The process developed by W.M. Leaders and J.W. Roach; U.S. Patent 3,607,718; September 21, 1971; assigned to Kerr-McGee Corporation provides a satisfactory method for simultaneously solubilizing and hydrogenating coal. It further provides a process for hydrogenating coal which does not require a catalyst in the solvation vessel, or the use of extremely high over-pressures of hydrogen. The partial hydrogenation of the solvent is accomplished outside of the coal solvation vessel, and in the absence of substances which would poison or otherwise adversely affect the hydrogenation catalyst. The process provides for solubilizing an unusually high percentage of the coal, and maximizes the production of valuable liquid products and minimizes the production of low molecular weight gases and solid by-products. By this process it is possible to obtain a higher yield of the more valuable constituents of the coal, and a lower percentage is lost in processing.

The key feature of this process is the partially hydrogenated solvent which may be a by-product stream produced in normal petroleum refinery operations having a boiling range of 430° to 1000°F., e.g., a catalytic cracker recycle stock such as light recycle catalytic cracker oil, heavy recycle catalytic cracker oil and clarified catalytic cracker slurry oil, thermally cracked petroleum stocks, and lubricating oil aromatic extracts such as bright stock phenol extract. The boiling range of the by-product petroleum stream is preferably between 600° and 1000°F., and should be 700° to 900°F. for better results in most instances. Refractory highly aromatic streams where the aromatic constituents contain two or more fused benzene rings per molecule and make up at least 50% by weight of the solvent are preferred, and for better results the aromatic constituents should be present in an amount of at least 80 to 95% by weight. Clarified catalytic cracker slurry oil is an excellent solvent.

The amount of hydrogen that is added to the solvent during the partial hydrogenation step should be sufficient to hydrogenate a substantial number of the fused benzene rings in the polycyclic hydrocarbon content, but insufficient to hydrogenate all of the fused benzene rings. For instance, when the polycyclic hydrocarbons have 2 to 4 condensed benzene rings before partial hydrogenation, at least one of the benzene rings is retained in the molecule and 1 to 3 benzene rings may be hydrogenated to produce naphthenic rings during the partial hydrogenation step.

As a general rule, approximately 100 to 1,000, and preferably 200 to 700 standard cubic feet of hydrogen per barrel of solvent added, but smaller or larger amounts of hydrogen may be added depending on the desired degree of hydrogenation and the number of fused benzene rings which are present. In instances where the solvent is clarified catalytic cracker slurry oil, it is usually preferred that approximately 400 to 500 standard cubic feet of hydrogen per barrel of slurry oil be added during the partial hydrogenation step.

Referring to Figure 3.12a and 3.12b a partially hydrogenated hydrocarbon solvent to be defined more fully hereinafter is passed from storage vessel 10 to mixer 11 via conduit 12 at a rate controlled by valve 14. Finely divided coal in storage vessel 15 is also passed to mixer 11 via conduit 16 at a rate determined by meter 17. The relative feed rates of solvent and coal are controlled so that the weight ratio of solvent to coal in mixer 11 is between 1:1 and 20:1, and preferably 2:1 and 5:1. Therefore, the best results are usually obtained when the weight ratio of solvent to coal is approximately 3:1. The coal and solvent in mixer 11 are agitated with a motor driven agitator 18, and the slurry thus prepared is passed to pump 19 via conduit 13, and then via conduit 20 to gas-fired heaters 21. The slurry flowing in coil 22 is heated to an elevated temperature which preferably closely approximates the desired initial temperature of solvation, and the heated slurry is then withdrawn via conduit 23 and is passed to solutizer 24. While it is not essential when using partially hydrogenated solvents, it is usually preferred to carry out the solvation in the presence of added gaseous hydrogen. When gaseous hydrogen is added, it may be passed into the slurry flowing in conduit 20 upon opening valve 25 in conduit 26.

FIGURE 3.12: SOLVATION AND HYDROGENATION OF COAL IN PARTIALLY HYDROGENATED HYDROCARBON SOLVENTS

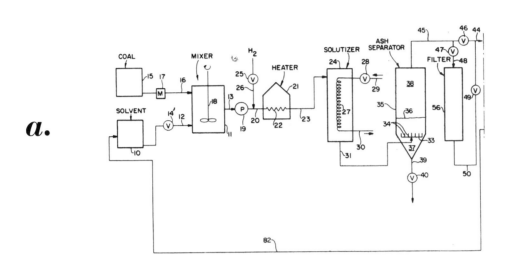

a.

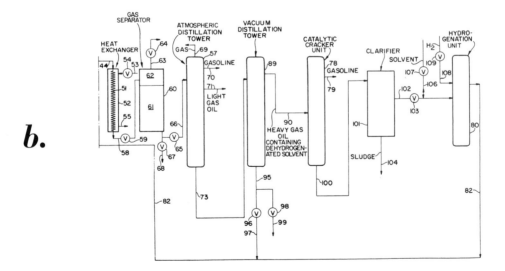

b.

Source: W.M. Leaders and J.W. Roach; U.S. Patent 3,607,718; September 21, 1971

The solutizer 24 preferably operates under a superatmospheric pressure which is determined by the overpressure of gaseous hydrogen when present, the vapor pressure of the solvent at the operating temperature, and/or the hydraulic pressure applied by pump 19. The solvation temperature is determined by the initial temperatures of the slurry in conduit 23 and by the temperature control fluid supplied to coil 27 at a rate controlled by valve 28 in conduit 29 and withdrawn via conduit 30. The solvent is contacted with the coal under the temperature and pressure conditions existing in solutizer 24 for a sufficient period of time to solubilize and hydrogenate a substantial amount of extractable carbonaceous material and to produce a solution which contains finely divided fusain, mineral ash, and other insoluble constituents.

The coal solution containing the insoluble constituents is withdrawn from solutizer 24 via conduit 31 and is passed to header 33 which is provided with a plurality of space outlets 34. The header 33 is positioned in ash separator 35 a substantial distance beneath the interface 36 between the relatively heavy sludge layer 37 and the lighter clarified coal solution 38. The sludge layer 37 contains mineral ash, fusain and other insoluble material, and it is withdrawn via conduit 39 at a rate controlled by valve 40. The sludge 37 is withdrawn at a rate to maintain the interface 36 substantially above the outlets 34 on header 33.

Inasmuch as the coal solution flowing in conduit 31 is at an elevated temperature and has a low viscosity, the heavier insoluble material tends to settle out rapidly when it is passed into ash separator 35. While the mechanism is not fully understood at the present time, it is believed that injecting the solution into the heavy sludge layer 37 tends to agglomerate the micron size solid particles of insoluble material and larger particles are formed which settle even more rapidly. As a result, the lighter clarified phase 38 is substantially free of insoluble material and often it does not require filtering, and especially in instances where the entire deashed coal solution is to be used as a fuel.

The clarified coal solution 38 is withdrawn from the top of ash separator 35 via conduit 45 and, upon opening valve 46 and closing valves 47 and 49, it is passed via conduit 44 to coil 51 in heat exchanger 52. A coolant such as water is supplied to heat exchanger 52 via conduit 53 at a rate controlled by valve 54, and it is withdrawn therefrom via conduit 55. In instances where it is desired to filter the clarified coal solution for the purpose of removing additional insoluble material, valve 46 is closed and valves 47 and 49 are opened, and the clarified coal solution 38 is passed via conduits 45 and 48 to filter 56. The clarified and filtered coal solution is withdrawn via conduit 50 and is passed to conduit 44, and then to coil 51 in heat exchanger 52.

The coal solution may be cooled in heat exchanger 52 to any suitable desired temperature such as 75° to 200°F. or higher, or to a temperature which is suitable for feeding to atmospheric distillation tower 57. The solution is withdrawn via conduit 58 at a rate controlled by reducing valve 59 and is passed into gas separator 60. The gas separator 60 is partially filled with a liquid coal solution phase 61 which has a vapor space 62 thereabove. The coal solution flowing in conduit 58 contains excess hydrogen, hydrogen sulfide produced by desulfurization of the coal during the solvation step, hydrocarbon gases, and other gases which are released into the vapor space 62 upon reducing the pressure on the solution as it passes through reducing valve 59.

The pressure existing within vapor space 62 may be, for example, from substantially atmospheric pressure to 1 or 2 atmospheres. The gases in vapor space 62 are withdrawn via conduit 63 at a rate controlled by valve 64. If desired, the gases may be passed to a sour gas processing step, the sulfur content recovered, and the hydrogen content recycled to conduit 26. In instances where one or more light liquid fractions are not recovered from the coal solution, it may be withdrawn from gas separator 60 via conduit 68 upon closing valve 65 in conduit 66 and opening valve 67. The deashed, degassed and desulfurized coal solution withdrawn via conduit 68 is very useful as a fuel. Inasmuch as it is normally liquid at room temperature, it may be readily pumped and transported by pipeline.

In most instances, it is desirable to recover at least the gasoline fraction and the light gas oil fraction from the coal solution as these are valuable liquid products of commerce, and also a dehydrogenated solvent fraction for recycle in the process. This may be conveniently accomplished by closing valve 67 in conduit 68, opening valve 65 in conduit 66, and passing the deashed and degassed coal solution to atmospherical distillation tower 57. As will be recognized by those skilled in the art, it is not necessary that ash separator 35, filter 56, and heat exchanger 52 be operated at approximately the same pressure as exists in solutizer 24. For example, pressure-reducing valve 59 may be relocated in conduit 31 and gas separator 60 relocated immediately after the valve 59, and in such instances the ash separator 35, filter 56 and heat exchanger 52 may be operated at approximately the same pressure as gas separator 60.

Atmospheric distillation tower 57 may be of a prior art type used in petroleum refining for producing a plurality of hydrocarbon streams from crude oil. The construction and operation of such combination atmospheric distillation towers is well-known, and does not constitute a part of this process. Distillation tower 57 may be operated, for example, to produce a stream of normally gaseous hydrocarbons which is withdrawn via conduit 69, a gasoline stream having a boiling point up to 430°F. which is withdrawn via conduit 70, a light gas oil stream having a boiling range of 430° to 700°F. which is withdrawn via conduit 71 for further refinery processing, and a residue or bottoms stream which is withdrawn via conduit 73. The gases withdrawn via conduit 69 may be used to fire heater 21 or for other fuel purposes; and the gasoline stream withdrawn via conduit 70 may be used for internal combustion engine fuel. The bottoms fraction withdrawn via conduit

73 is passed to vacuum distillation tower 89. In that tower, a heavy gas oil fraction containing dehydrogenated solvent and having a boiling range of, for example, 560° to 950°F. is withdrawn and passed via conduit 90 to catalytic cracker unit 78 where it is cracked and fractionated into lighter products including, for example, a gasoline fraction which is withdrawn via conduit 79, as well as other conventional catalytic cracker products which are not shown. The bottoms stream withdrawn from vacuum distillation tower 89 via conduit 95 may be recycled in the process via conduits 97 and 82 for further thermal cracking and hydrogenation to produce lighter liquid products upon opening valve 96 and closing valve 98. It also may be withdrawn via conduit 99 upon closing valve 96 and opening valve 98 and used as a low sulfur fuel.

The bottoms product withdrawn via conduit 100 from catalytic cracker unit 78 and having a boiling range of from 700° to 900°F. consists of slurry oil produced in the catalytic cracker unit and dehydrogenated recycle solvent. The bottoms product is passed to clarifier 101, from which sludge is removed via conduit 104, and then passed via conduit 102 at a rate controlled by valve 103 to hydrogenation unit 80. If required, makeup solvent may be introduced via conduit 106 into conduit 102 at a rate controlled by valve 107. Such makeup solvent as is required is usually a small percentage of that flowing through the system such as 1 to 10%, and is usually approximately 5 to 6%. Hydrogen is fed via conduit 108 at a rate controlled by valve 109 into hydrogenation unit 80. The partially hydrogenated solvent is then withdrawn via conduit 82 and is passed to solvent storage 10 for reuse in the process.

Example: This example illustrates the preparation of a partially hydrogenated hydrocarbon solvent for use in practicing the process. The feedstock was a clarified catalytic cracker slurry oil produced in normal petroleum refinery operations. The slurry oil had a distillation range of 700° to 1000°F. and an API gravity of 2.1. The slurry oil was partially hydrogenated in a laboratory rocking autoclave at a temperature of 600°F. and under a hydrogen pressure of 500 psig in the presence of a mixed nickel-molybdenum hydrogenation catalyst. The hydrogenation was continued until hydrogen was consumed in an amount equivalent to 600 standard cubic feet per barrel of the slurry oil charge stock. The hydrogenation was terminated, the partially hydrogenated slurry oil was recovered and analyzed, and the analysis was compared with that of the charge stock. The following data was obtained.

Material	Clarified Slurry Oil Feedstock	Partially Hydrogenated Slurry Oil Product
Carbon, wt. %	91.6	91.1
Hydrogen, wt. %	8.1	8.9
Sulfur, wt. %	0.3	Less than 0.1
Gravity, °API	2.1	6.1

Liquid Phase Hydrogenation of Pulverized Coal

F.B. Sellers; U.S. Patent 2,572,061; October 23, 1951; assigned to Texaco Development Corporation describes a process for the hydrogenation of solid carbonaceous material. The process is particularly applicable to the treatment of coal and may be applied to hydrogenation of anthracite, bituminous coal, or lignite. Particles of coal are admixed with a sufficient quantity of oil to form a fluid suspension of the coal particles. This suspension is passed under conditions of turbulent flow through a tubular heating zone where it is heated to a temperature at least sufficient to vaporize a substantial portion of the oil.

Preferably substantially all of the oil is vaporized in the heating zone. Hydrogen is added to the suspension prior to its introduction to the heating zone. Heated powdered coal is discharged from the heating zone in admixture with oil vapors and any residual unvaporized oil. Oil vapors are condensed forming a paste or slurry of powdered coal in oil. The paste or slurry is then passed to a liquid phase hydrogenation step where the coal is reacted with hydrogen at an elevated temperature and pressure. Oil produced as a result of the hydrogenation step is suitable as the source of oil used in making up the dispersion of coal fed to the heating zone.

Referring to Figure 3.13 crushed coal is admixed with oil in a mixer 5 to form a slurry. A catalyst for the hydrogenation of coal is added and admixed with the coal and oil in the slurry. The slurry is forced by pump 6 through line 7 into a heating coil 8 disposed in furnace 9. Hydrogen from line 11 is introduced via line 12 into line 7 in admixture with the slurry prior to its introduction to the heating coil. The gasiform dispersion of powdered coal in oil vapors is discharged from the heating coil through line 13 and passed to a cooler 14 where it is cooled to a temperature sufficient to condense at least a portion of the vapors or the more readily condensible constituents.

Additional oil, or catalyst, or both, may be admitted through line 15. The resulting condensed liquid admixed with solid particles from the coal is separated from the uncondensed vapor in separator 16. The liquid oil and powdered solid are passed as a paste or slurry by pump 17 through line 18 into a hydrogenation zone 19. The vapors may be compressed by a compressor 21 and passed via line 22 into line 18 to the hydrogenation zone 19 or discharged through line 23. The vapors may be passed through line 23 and subjected to vapor phase hydrogenation or used for other purposes. Hydrogen is supplied to the hydrogenation zone from line 11 by line 24. The resulting products from the hydrogenation step, comprising residual carbonaceous solid, or pitch, and heavy oil resulting from the hydrogenation of the coal is discharged through line 26 to separator 27. Recycle gas, comprising unreacted hydrogen is returned through lines 28 and 24 to the hydrogenation zone 19. Pitch, or residue, is discharged from the system through line 31. The heavy oil is drawn from the separator 21 through line 32 from which it may be passed through line 34 to storage for further processing. Heavy oil may be recycled through line 33 to the mixer 5 for preparation of the feed slurry.

FIGURE 3.13: LIQUID PHASE HYDROGENATION OF PULVERIZED COAL

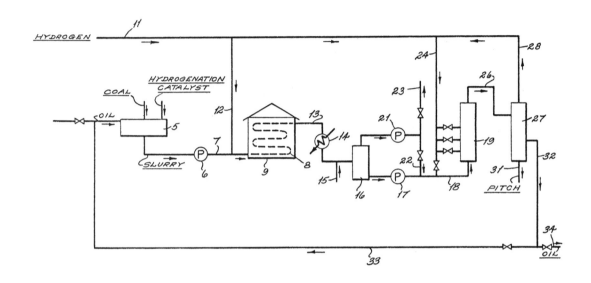

Source: F.B. Sellers; U.S. Patent 2,572,061; October 23, 1951

In a typical operation of the process, heavy oil produced by liquid phase hydrogenation of coal is admixed with particles of low ash bituminous coal having a size range of from 3/32 inch to 200 mesh. Five barrels of oil is admixed with each ton of crushed coal to form a readily pumpable slurry. Ferrous sulfate is admixed with oil and supplied to the slurry at the rate of 4 pounds per ton of coal as catalyst for the hydrogenation reaction. The slurry is pumped at 1 foot per second into a heating coil at a pressure of 500 psi. Hydrogen is supplied to the heating coil at the rate of 18,000 standard cubic feet per ton of coal. The temperature of the mixture at the outlet of the heating coil is 1000°F. and the pressure is 350 psi. Approximately 95% of the oil is converted to vapor on passing through the heating coil.

The temperature of the mixture discharged from the heating coil is reduced to 650°F. at 350 psi. The condensed liquid, powdered coal, and uncondensed vapors are admixed with an additional 18,000 standard cubic feet of hydrogen and passed at a pressure of 10,000 psi into a hydrogenation zone. The effluent of the hydrogenation step is separated without reduction in pressure into a gaseous fraction, predominantly hydrogen, which is recycled, a heavy oil fraction or crude product of the hydrogenation step, and residual solid or pitch. A portion of the heavy oil is returned to the mixing zone for admixture with the fresh coal. The heavy oil product amounts to 1,700 pounds per ton of coal fed to the process.

Cyclic Process for Converting Coal into Liquid Products by the Use of Fixed Catalytic Beds

E.L. Wilson, Jr. and E.F. Wadley; U.S. Patent 3,514,394; May 26, 1970; assigned to Esso Research and Engineering Co. states that conversion of coal extracts obtained by hydrogen-donor solvation of coal is preferably carried out in a fixed bed reactor so that the benefits of plug flow through the reactor can be obtained. Although a downflow reactor is preferred for this service, an upflow reactor would be suitable. However, the pressure drop across a fixed bed reactor of this sort will increase and the activity of the catalyst will decrease with respect to time.

Contained in the extract feed to the reactor are minute particles of solid impurities which deposit in the bed. Also the extract feed contains very heavy hydrocarbonaceous type molecules which will deposit on the surface of the catalyst and with time will begin to foul the surface of the catalyst. When the pressure drop and catalyst activity becomes limiting, the bed must be treated so as to increase catalyst activity and reduce pressure drop. This process accomplishes this by using the deactivated catalyst beds for the hydrogenation of hydrogen-depleted solvent, which (assuming downflow service for extract hydrogenation) is passed through the bed under hydrogenation conditions in an upflow direction at a linear upward velocity sufficient to cause the particles of impurities to be carried with the solvent, thereby removing the deposits from the surface of the catalyst particles and allowing them to be carried from the reactor with the reactor product.

An important advantage of this process is that the catalyst is cleaned and pressure drop across the bed is decreased while the catalyst is being used for a commercial purpose, that is, the hydrogenation of hydrogen-depleted donor solvent. When two or more reactors are used, the solvent may be passed upwardly through the beds of one or more reactors while extract is being passed downwardly through the catalyst bed of one or more other reactors. Thus, a unique cyclic process is presented which will optimize the use of equipment in the hydrogen-donor extraction of coal. The rejuvenation of the catalyst bed is accomplished by using the same deactivated catalyst for the hydrogenation of hydrogen-depleted solvent from the extraction zone. The hydrogen-depleted solvent is passed through the bed in an upflow direction, in contact with molecular hydrogen, under hydrogenation conditions as set forth in the table below.

Solvent Hydrogenation Conditions

	Minimum	Maximum	Preferred
Temperature, ° F.	700	900	750
Pressure, p.s.i.g.	400	2,000	1,500
Hydrogen feed, s.c.f./b.	1,000	9,000	2,500
Space velocity, LHSV	0.2	2.0	1.0

Referring to Figure 3.14, it is seen that a crushed coal feed hopper 100 is provided with a coal such as Illinois No. 6 seam, having been crushed to a particle size that will pass through an 8 mesh screen, is passed through line 102 into a mixing vessel 104, where it is contacted with a hydrogen-donor solvent (obtained as hereinafter discussed) which is introduced by way of line 106.

FIGURE 3.14: CYCLIC PROCESS FOR CONVERTING COAL INTO LIQUID PRODUCTS BY THE USE OF FIXED CATALYTIC BEDS

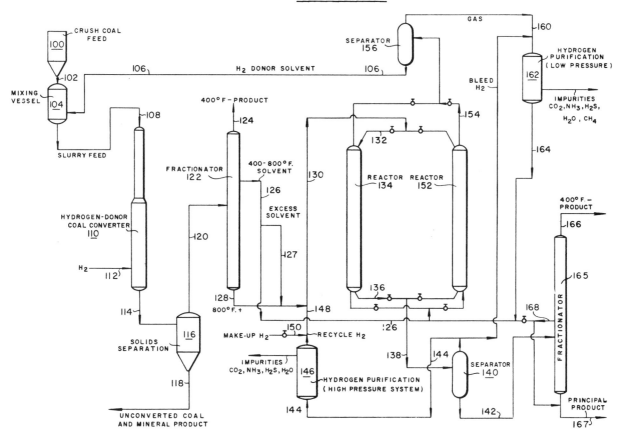

Source: E.L. Wilson, Jr. and E.F. Wadley; U.S. Patent 3,514,394; May 26, 1970

The ratio of solvent to coal is 2 to 1, on a weight basis. The resulting slurry is passed by way of line 108 into a hydrogen-donor coal converter 110, where molecular hydrogen may be admitted if desired by way of line 112; preferably, the hydrogen is not admitted. In the hydrogenation zone, preferred conditions will include a temperature of 750°F., a pressure of 300 psig, a hydrogen feed rate of 2,000 standard cubic feet per ton of maf coal, a space velocity of 1 LHSV and a solvent-to-coal weight ratio of 2. The residence time for the coal in the extraction zone is 1 hour, and the residence time for the solvent in the extraction zone is 1 hour.

A total product is removed from the extraction zone by way of line 114 and is passed through a solid separation zone 116, which preferably is a centrifuge, and a residue stream 118 comprising unconverted coal char and mineral matter is removed while a liquid stream 120 comprising the hydrogen-depleted solvent and coal extract is passed into a fractionator 122. In the fractionator 122 a light product boiling at 400°F. and less is removed overhead by way of line 124. This product comprises about 5% of the total liquids fed into the fractionator. A solvent side stream, boiling within the range of 400° to 800°F., is withdrawn by way of line 126, and a bottoms stream, the material boiling higher than 800°F., is withdrawn by way of line 128.

The bottom stream, which is heavy coal extract, is passed by lines 128, 130 and 132 into a first reactor 134, in a downflow direction, and is withdrawn from the bottom of the reactor by way of line 136 and line 138 for separation in vessel 140, the liquid being passed by way of line 142 and the gases, including unreacted hydrogen, being passed by way of line 144 through a hydrogen purification system 146, including a compressor, and being recycled by way of line 148 into admixture with the extract feed into the reactor. Makeup hydrogen may be added through the line 150.

Concurrently, the hydrogen-depleted donor oil is passed by way of line 126 and line 150 into a second reactor 152 which had been used in the downflow hydrogenation of coal extract until the bed became deactivated and pressure drop became limiting. The hydrogen-depleted solvent is contacted with hydrogen in the reactor 152 under preferred conditions including a temperature of 750°F., a pressure of 1,500 psig, a space velocity of 1 LHSV, and a hydrogen feed rate of about 2,500 scf/b., and is passed from the reactor 152 through line 154 into separator 156, where the hydrogen is separated from the liquid products. The hydrogen gas is passed by way of line 160 into a hydrogen purification system 162 and is recycled into contact with the solvent feed by way of 164. The liquid product, which is a hydrogen-replenished donor solvent is passed from the separator 156 by way of line 106 into the slurrying vessel as described above.

If excess solvent is produced, it may be passed by way of line 127 into line 128 for treatment with the coal extract. The ultimate extract product, which is removed from the separator 140 by way of line 142, is passed into a fractionator 165, where a low-boiling stream is removed by way of line 166 overhead, a bottoms stream is removed by way of line 168 if desired. Optionally, a portion of the side stream 168 may be passed back into the feed stream to the solvent hydrogenation reactor, if this amount of solvent is needed or if the amount of hydrogenation in the reaction zone 152 is insufficient. When the bed in reactor 134 becomes deactivated, the reactor services are switched through the unnumbered lines which are shown, so that reactor 134 is used for the upflow hydrogenation of hydrogenation-depleted donor oil and the reactor 152 is used for the downflow hydrogenation of coal extract.

Effect of Asphaltene Formation During the Hydrogenation of Coal

It has been found by R.W. Rieve and H. Shalit; U.S. Patent 3,619,404; November 9, 1971; assigned to Atlantic Richfield Company that the quantity of asphaltenes present in coal liquefaction products is substantially reduced when the hydrogenation operation is carried out using certain solid catalysts in the absence of slurry medium and certain catalyst/coal weight ratios. This process provides a method for carrying out a coal hydrogenation process. It provides a way for reducing the amount of asphaltenes contained in products from a coal liquefaction operation and for liquefying coal without a slurry medium.

The coal hydrogenation operation is carried out in the presence of an effective catalytic amount of a supported, solid hydrogenation catalyst. Suitable hydrogenation catalysts include the metals, preferably in subdivided form such as powders, of iron, cobalt, nickel, vanadium, molybdenum, or tungsten, or compounds of these metals such as the halides, oxides, sulfides, molybdates, sulfates, or oxalates. Exemplary materials that have heretofore been employed as hydrogenation catalysts include the chlorides of nickel, iron, and cobalt. The catalyst is supported on a carrier material such as alumina, magnesia, silica, titania, zirconia, fullers earth, kieselghur and other commonly used catalyst supports. Each support material can be employed alone or in combination with other support materials and is used in an amount which supports substantially all of the catalyst present.

Example: Two identical hydrogenation runs were carried out with the only difference between the two being that one employed an externally supplied hydrocarbonaceous liquid slurry medium while the other employed no such added slurry medium. In each run a commercially available hydrogenation catalyst was used which contained 3.4 weight percent CoO, 13.2 weight percent MoO_3, 83.4 weight percent Al_2O_3, and 4.1 weight percent sulfur based on the total weight of the catalyst and which was subdivided to be in the particle size range of -100 and +200 mesh (U.S. sieve). The catalyst was employed in the amount of 100 weight percent based on the total weight of the coal. The catalyst was mixed with Pittsburgh 08 coal subdivided to be in the same particle size range as the catalyst. The catalyst/coal weight ratio was 1/1. In both runs the coal-catalyst mixture was exposed to molecular hydrogen at a total pressure of 3,000 psig, a temperature of 800°F. and for 30 minutes. In run No. 1 there was also present 100 weight percent, based on the total weight of coal, of hydrocarbonaceous coal oil having a boiling range of from 675° to 775°F. which had been previously obtained from the hydrogenation of the same type of coal under the same hydrogenation conditions as set forth above. In run No. 2 no coal oil or other externally supplied slurry medium was employed and the dry mixture of solid coal and solid catalyst was exposed to the hydrogen. The gaseous and liquid products were analyzed and the results, reported in weight percent based upon maf coal charged, were as follows.

Products	Run 1 (With slurry medium)	Run 2 (Invention, no slurry medium
Gas	4	7.2
Light Hydrocarbonaceous liquid (boiling range under 500° F.)	3	12.2
Heavy hydrocarbonaceous liquid (boiling range greater than 500° F.)	49.3	40.9
Asphaltenes	20.3	3.8
Water	5.1	10.9
Percent Conversion	70.1	73.8

It can be seen from the above data that the asphaltenes content was substantially reduced, while the overall conversion and the amount of gas and light coal oil were all increased.

USE OF HYDROCONVERSION CATALYSTS

Spherical Catalysts in Coal Extract Hydrogenation

According to F.B. Sprow and G.W. Harris; U.S. Patent 3,575,847; April 20, 1971; assigned to Esso Research and Engineering Company coal extracts containing suspended solids are hydrotreated in a fixed bed downflow reactor. Bed plugging is minimized by using substantially spherical catalyst granules having a minimum diameter at least ten times as great as the maximum dimensions of the suspended solids and maintaining a flow rate above the minimum at which occlusion of the bed results.

In this process it has been found that the deposition of solids within the catalyst bed can be substantially reduced and the efficiency of the bed thereby substantially increased by utilizing catalyst granules which are substantially in the form of spheres, so that the areas of contact between granules are substantially reduced and the positions at which the solids could be occluded and settle out are likewise reduced. It has also been found that by maintaining a minimum rate of flow through the bed, the steady-state condition at which the solid particles are carried through without deposition is reached without undue plugging of flow channels and the efficiency of the bed is thereby increased.

The catalyst to be used is substantially spherical, with a minimum diameter at least ten times as great as the average maximum dimension of the largest 5% of the solid particles carried in the clarified oil. The catalyst may have only a hydrogenation activity or it may have both hydrogenation and cracking activity. Where the catalyst has only a hydrogenating activity, thermal cracking will cause the reduction in average molecular weight, and the catalyst will assist in hydrogenating the fragments. Suitable catalysts are cobalt molybdate, nickel molybdate, nickel, tungsten, and palladium.

Various substrates can be used such as kieselguhr, alumina, silica, faujasites, etc. The cobalt molybdate catalyst is preferred, and may have 3.4 weight percent cobalt oxide, 12.8 weight percent molybdenum oxide, and 83 weight percent alumina. The catalyst may range from 2 to 5 weight percent cobalt oxide and from 10 to 15 molybdenum oxide. Generally, the size of the spheres will range from 1/16" to 1/4". The minimum size is determined by the particles which are being carried in the clarified oil, and generally may also be determined by the ease with which the spheres can be formed. For example, spherical catalyst of 1/8" to 3/16" in diameter would be preferred both from the standpoint of the size of the particles in the clarified liquid and the ease of manufacture and handling of the resulting catalyst. Smaller spheres would tend to increase the pressure drop across the catalyst bed, even though there is an increase in the exposed catalyst area per unit volume.

The substantially spherical catalyst particles can be manufactured in a number of ways: spray-forming, tumbling, molding, etc. Preferably, the particles will be obtained by spraying the molten substrate into a cooling fluid (gas or liquid) so that it will solidify in substantially spherical shape. When this method is used, the particles will not be of uniform size but the product will contain particles of different diameters. If desired, the particles can be separated by sieving so that a fairly uniform final product is obtained. Further, the individual particles, although avoiding the flat spots, sharp edges and straight sides of cylindrical extrudates, are not all actually perfect spheres but will include ovoid or ellipsoid shapes as well as spheres. This is acceptable so long as the bulk of the catalyst particles (e.g., at least 90%) do not have an eccentricity of more than 100% (i.e., the ratio of the maximum particle diameter to minimum particle diameter should not exceed 2:1). It is obvious that crushed particles (which have sharp edges that promote tight packing and resultant occlusion) are not suitable, even though the diameter ratio might be said to be within the above range.

The operation of this process can be visualized by referring to Figures 3.15b and 3.15c which schematically illustrate the manner in which extruded catalyst and spherical catalysts would appear after a solids-containing fluid stream had been passed over the catalyst for an appreciable period of time. In Figure 3.5b it is seen that the large number of relatively horizontal areas which exist in the extruded cylindrical catalyst promote the deposition and collection of solid material which ultimately leads to a blocking of certain flow paths, so that the catalyst area exposed in the blocked flow paths becomes useless insofar as promoting the reaction is concerned.

FIGURE 3.15: SPHERICAL CATALYSTS IN COAL EXTRACT HYDROGENATION

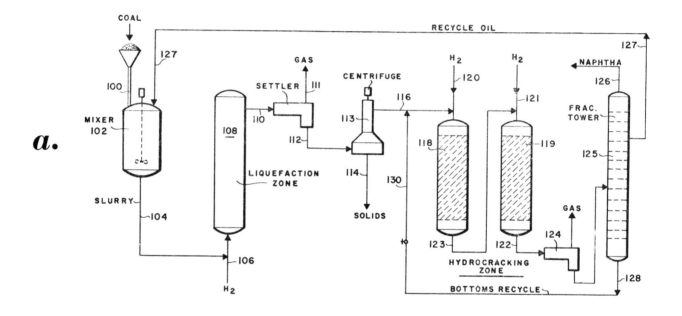

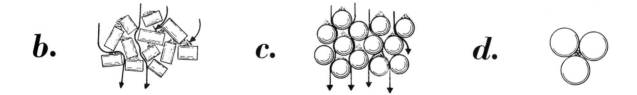

Source: F.B. Sprow and G.W. Harris; U.S. Patent 3,575,847; April 20, 1971

Both the flat ends of the cylinders and the relatively horizontal sides of the cylinders which are horizontally disposed would tend to encourage the deposition and collection of the suspended solids. Referring to Figure 3.15c, by contrast, it is seen that only the upper portion of the sphere would allow the fines to collect, and as to the sloping surfaces other than the upper portion, the fines would be washed off by the flowing liquid before bridging could occur. Further, by reason of the spherical shape of the catalyst, the points of contact between the catalyst granules would be limited to a very small area in the case of spherical catalysts as opposed to the possibility of long lines of contact where cylindrical catalysts may be involved (for example, where two granules are parallel and side by side). In Figure 3.15c, the points of contact are not shown, in order to illustrate schematically the fact that no flow paths are blocked, but it is to be understood that the catalyst particles will be in contact in the bed.

Referring now to Figure 3.15d, it is seen that the diameter of the suspended solids is a material factor in determining the diameter of spherical catalysts which would be suitable for use. As is seen in the diagrammatic representation of Figure 3.15d, when the solid particles have a diameter of one-tenth of that of the spherical catalyst, bridging can occur at the area of most constriction, and therefore, the diameter relationship should be at least 10 to 1 and preferably greater than 10 to 1. Although the entrained solid particles are shown as being spherical in Figure 3.15d, it is to be understood that in the coal extract the particles are irregular in shape and would be less likely to bridge than would spherical particles of the same maximum dimension. Therefore, the relationship of 10 to 1 appears to be a satisfactory and workable ratio.

Coal extract is obtained by the hydrogen-donor extraction process using hydrogenated creosote oil or a similar fraction recovered from coal extraction and hydrocracking. The overall process where the feedstock is obtained can be better understood by reference to Figure 3.15a of the drawings where raw coal is seen to be fed by way of line 100 into a mixer 102 where a slurry is created and withdrawn by way of line 104. Any suitable coal-like material can be used, for example, subbituminous coal, bituminous coal, lignite and asphalt. The coal is generally ground to a particle size of 8 to 300 mesh, and may be dried before it is fed into the mixer 102.

The slurry may be mixed with hydrogen (introduced by way of line 106) and introduced into a liquefaction reactor 108. Within the liquefication reactor, the coal is allowed to dissolve under conditions of high temperature and pressure, such as a temperature within the range from 650° to 850°F. and a pressure from 350 to 2,500 psig. The hydrogen treat rate (if hydrogen is used) may be fairly low, and may suitably range from 100 to 1,000 scf/b. of total slurry charge. In the liquefaction reactor, the coal is depolymerized and partially thermally cracked, and a product is withdrawn by way of line 110 which comprises the coal extract, depleted hydrogen-donor solvent and undissolved solids.

The hydrogen and noncondensable gases are separated from the liquid and solid components and are removed by way of line 111 while the slurry is carried by line 112 to a solids-liquid separation unit such as the centrifuge 113. Solids are removed from the centrifuge by way of line 114, and the clarified liquid is passed by way of line 116 into a hydrocracking zone, suitably comprising two reactors, 118 and 119. In the hydrocracking zone, the clarified oil is contacted with hydrogen introduced by way of lines 120 and 121 and is passed sequentially (via line 123) in downflow across stationary beds of spherical catalyst granules in the reactors 118 and 119.

The clarified oil is preferably in the liquid phase, but may be in the mixed liquid-and-vapor phase, while the hydrogen obviously will be maintained in the gas phase and dissolved in the liquid phase. The catalyst within the hydrocracking reactor is substantially spherical, and is at least ten times larger in minimum diameter than the largest dimension of the particles being entrained in the clarified liquid. The products of the hydrocracking reactor are removed by way of line 122, the hydrogen separated therefrom by means 124, and the liquid is fractionated in tower 125 to obtain a naphtha stream which is removed by way of line 126 for further treatment, a recycle oil which is removed by way of line 127 and a bottoms products which is removed by way of line 128. The bottoms stream is preferably recycled to extinction by way of line 130.

The recycle oil in line 127 has received hydrogen by reaction in the hydrocracking reactors 118 and 119 and is therefore suitable for use as a hydrogen donor solvent. This material, boiling within the range from 350° to 750°F. is recycled and admitted into the mixer 102 as a slurrying oil for the coal 100, as well as providing the donor hydrogen for the liquefaction reaction. The feedstock into the hydrocracking reactor is the material with which the process is particularly concerned. This feedstock, the clarified oil obtained as a coal extract, contains both the dissolved coal and the hydrogen-depleted solvent.

This material also contains suspended particles which were not removed in the centrifuge 112. The material may contain from 0.5 to 15 weight percent solids (usually about 1.0 weight percent) having a particle size from a minimum of 1 micron to as large as 200 microns. Generally, in choosing the size of the catalyst spheres, the largest 5% of the particles will provide a good guide in determining the critical dimension of suspended particles. The largest 5% generally will have a maximum dimension (average) of 150 microns.

Example: An experimental fixed bed was set up that consisted of a 2 inch diameter Lucite column fitted with tapping at both ends for pressure measurements. The column, 36 inches high and packed with 1/8 inch cylindrical extrudate, was operated at ambient temperature and pressure. All of the runs were carried out with a 10 weight percent talc powder suspension in methanol, and methanol saturated nitrogen gas. Methanol was selected as the solvent because its surface tension and viscosity are similar to those at operating conditions of the clarified oil which will be treated in the hydrocracking reactor. The talc particle sizes, ranging from 2 to 17 microns, and with an average size of 8 microns, are comparable to the particle sizes of coal fines and ash expected in the centrifuge overflow. The liquid mass velocity ranged from 1,000 to 3,500 pounds per hour per square foot, and the nitrogen gas/liquid rate varied from 5:1 to 27:1 acf (actual cubic feet) gas/acf liquid. These are typical rates for use in the hydrocracking reactor.

The liquid suspension together with solvent saturated nitrogen entered at constant rates through the top of the column and flowed downward. The runs were continued until the column reached the equilibrium state, that is, no further increase in pressure drop was seen. After each run all solids deposited in the column were collected by washing and packing with clean methanol and the weight of solids obtained by evaporating the methanol. The pressure drop generally rose to an equilibrium value and then remained constant thereafter. At a rate of 1,000 pounds per hour per square foot and a gas/liquids ratio of 5:1, the pressure drop increased in 8 hours to an equilibrium value about 70% higher than the initial value. At a liquid rate of 3,500 pounds per hour per square foot, the equilibrium pressure drop was only 10% higher than the initial value. However, the lower pressure drop is due to the channeling of the reactants past the catalyst without contacting all of the exposed area. The results of the various runs are shown below.

Bed type	Liquid rate /hour/ft.^{2}	gas/ liquid volume ratio	Solid collected from bed, grams
1/8″ Extrudate	[1] 1,000	10/1	77
Do	[1] 2,000	10/1	40
Do	[1] 4,600	10/1	17
3/16″ Spheres	[2] 1,500	10/1	43
Do	[2] 3,000	10/1	16
Do	[2] 4,600	10/1	7
Do	[2] 3,000	10/1	30

[1] 10 weight percent of 8 micron talc.
[2] 2 weight percent of 20 micron talc.

Hydrocracking of Coal Employing a Dual Function Catalytic Adsorbent

R.L. Hodgson; U.S. Patent 3,527,691; September 8, 1970; assigned to Shell Oil Company describes a process for hydrocracking coal with solid, particulate, sorbent catalyst by grinding coal to have a smaller particle size than the catalyst, slurrying the coal in oil, subjecting the slurry to hydrocracking conditions while in contact with the catalyst, separating gas and liquid products from the solids, subjecting the solids to size separation to remove noncatalyst solids from catalyst solids, and returning catalyst solids into contact with fresh slurry. This process involves the following steps.

(1) Grinding coal to a certain maximum particle size.

(2) Decomposition of coal at elevated temperatures in the presence of hydrogen and a solid adsorbent, which immediately adsorbs the decomposition intermediates, is carried out in the absence of a continuous liquid phase, and thus prevents secondary reactions.

(3) Hydrogenation and hydrogenative cracking of the intermediates adsorbed on the solid adsorbent products which desorb from the solid adsorbent.

(4) Separation of the desorbed products from the solid adsorbent.

(5) Separation of ash and char from the adsorbent/catalyst, a separation made especially easy because of the efficiency of conversion of the process and previous adjustment of the particle size of the coal and the adsorbent/catalyst. The coal is ground and classified to a maximum particle size while the catalyst/adsorbent is prepared to have a minimum particle size not smaller than the maximum particle size of the coal. Thereby, the catalyst/adsorbent in the total dry particulate solid phase resulting from the process can be separated from the char and ash in the particulate solid phase by separating the dry particulate solid phase into a fraction consisting of particles smaller than the minimum catalyst particle size, and a larger particle fraction, the former fraction being char and ash and the latter fraction being catalyst/adsorbent.

(6) Recycle of the adsorbent/catalyst together with adsorbed material to step (2) in a continuous circulating-catalyst process.

(7) Introduction of coal into the high-pressure process as a slurry in oil.

Referring to Figure 3.16, raw coal is introduced via line 1 with enough oil introduced through line 4 to produce a pumpable slurry and hydrogen introduced through line 2. This mixture is blended with adsorbent/catalyst and passed to decomposition/adsorption zone 10 where, at elevated temperature and pressure, the coal is thermally decomposed to inter-mediate products which are immediately adsorbed on the solid. Prior to introduction, the coal was ground to a particle size substantially smaller than the size of the particles of adsorbent/catalyst that were used.

FIGURE 3.16: HYDROCRACKING OF COAL EMPLOYING A DUAL FUNCTION CATALYTIC ADSORBENT

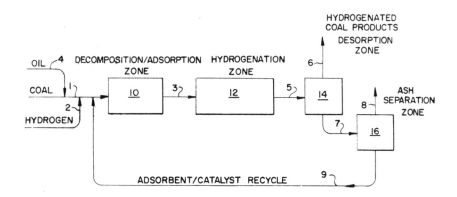

Source: R.L. Hodgson; U.S. Patent 3,527,691; September 8, 1970

From zone 10 adsorbent, with intermediate products adsorbed thereon, together with any desorbed products and unad-sorbed ash and char pass via line 3 to hydrogenation zone 12. Separation of desorbed products may be effected between zone 10 and zone 12. In zone 12 the adsorbed intermediates are cracked and stabilized by hydrogenation. The hydro-genated intermediate products, adsorbent/catalyst, ash and char pass via line 5 to separation zone 14 where the hydro-genated coal products are desorbed to an equilibrium level and removed via line 6 for further processing.

In this specification equilibrium level means an amount which, at a given set of conditions, does not change substan-tially on continued recycle of adsorbent. The solid particulate phase including adsorbent/catalyst recycle, ash and char pass to separation zone 16 via line 7 where the ash is easily removed by suitable means such as elutriation, centri-fugal classification, or screening since the sizing of coal particles initially precludes the presence of ash or char par-ticles in the product from being as large as the catalyst particles. Ash and char are removed via line 8 and the adsor-bent/catalyst solid, now relieved of nonequilibrium adsorbed products is recirculated via line 9 to the beginning of the process where it again contacts a fresh charge of coal.

The following experiments demonstrate the initial decomposition and adsorption of the decomposition products and serve to illustrate the practicality of this step in the process. Dried Illinois No. 6 coal ground to pass through a 200 mesh screen was reacted in a fixed-bed tubular reactor with a charge of adsorbent/catalyst comprising cobalt and molybdenum impregnated on alumina and sized to pass a 42 mesh screen and be held on a 100 mesh screen.

Hydrogen was passed through the bed of coal and adsorbent/catalyst which was maintained at 1,500 psig pressure. The sizing of the coal and catalyst provided easy separation of char and ash from the solid by screening. Successive charges of fresh coal were used with the same adsorbent/catalyst. Each charge of coal (10 g. fed in four 2.5 g. portions) was contacted with 10.3 g. of solid, the solid being recovered and used with a succeeding charge. The results are shown below.

Temperature: 400° to 450°C.[a]; H_2 Flow: 400 cc/min. at 1,500 psi

Coal Charge No.	Run period, min.[b]	Products, percent wt. MAF			Conversion, percent wt. MAF
		Liquid	Residue[c]	Char[d]	
1.................	4 x 15	36	12	31	69
2.................	4 x 15	53	1	24	76
3.................	4 x 15	58	3	15	85
4.................	4 x 15	59	4	11	89
5.................	4 x 15	60	−2	17	83
6.................	4 x 15	66	7	9	91
7.................	4 x 15 }	68	0	4	91
8.................	4 x 20 }				

[a] 450° C. maximum, time counted when reactor reached 400° C.
[b] The 10.3 g. charge introduced in four portions and reacted for 15 minutes each.
[c] Residual material remaining on adsorbent.
[d] Removed with ash.

Hydrogenation and Liquefaction of Coal in the Presence of a Solid Adsorbent

R.L. Hodgson; U.S. Patent 3,549,512; December 22, 1970; assigned to Shell Oil Company describes a process for lique-fication/hydrogenation of raw coal in which reactive decomposition intermediates are immediately adsorbed on a solid adsorbent, hydrogenated and desorbed in a moving bed process. Also disclosed is a complete process providing recycle of adsorbent, recycle of reaction products and separation of ash and char from the adsorbent and products.

The decomposition/adsorption step can be carried out over a wide range of conditions of temperature and pressure. Temperatures in the range of 200° to 600°C. and pressures in the range of 500 to 3,000 psig can be used. Generally, temperatures in the range of 350° to 450°C. and pressures in the range of 1,000 to 2,000 psig are suitable. These relatively mild conditions, in themselves, point up a significant advantage of this process over those previously proposed. While both higher temperatures and pressures may be used, the practical problems of rapidly achieving higher temperatures and the economic detriment of higher pressures limit these variables to the ranges given.

Numerous materials are known to possess the adsorptive capabilities required to accomplish the purposes of this process. For example, naturally occurring or synthetic adsorbent inorganic metal oxides such as montmorillonite clays, kieselguhr, silica, alumina, magnesia, boria, titania, zirconia, beryllia and mixtures thereof. Particularly desirable are the high surface area porous oxide such as cogels or coprecipitates of amorphous silica or alumina and crystalline alumino-silicate zeolites, etc.

While many of the adsorbent solids will have some inherent hydrogenative activity, in general such activity is not suffi-cient to accomplish the desired degree of hydrogenation necessary in this process. Therefore, catalytic hydrogenation activity is supplied by compositing with the adsorbent a hydrogenation component, preferably a metal hydrogenation com-ponent. Suitable for this purpose are the various hydrogenation metals, and metal compounds, such as the oxides and sulfides, known to the art for their hydrogenation ability. Of course, it is highly desirable that the adsorbent have a por-ous structure and high surface area and that the hydrogenation component be distributed in a finely divided or molecular state substantially over the effective adsorptive surface of the solid. Especially preferred hydrogenation components for the adsorbent/catalyst solid of the process are metals and metal compounds, oxides and sulfides, of metals selected from Groups VB, VIB, VIIB, and VIII of the Periodic Table of Elements and mixtures thereof.

Referring to Figure 3.17, raw coal is introduced via line 1 together with an adsorbent/catalyst solid (line 9) to a decom-position/adsorption zone 10 where, at elevated temperature and pressure, the coal is thermally decomposed to intermediate products which are immediately adsorbed on the solid. Hydrogen enters the reaction scheme via line 2. From zone 10 adsorbent, with intermediate products adsorbed thereon, together with any desorbed products and unadsorbed ash and char pass via line 3 to hydrogenation zone 12. In this zone 12 the adsorbed intermediates are cracked and stabilized by hydro-genation. The hydrogenated intermediate products, adsorbent/catalyst, ash and char pass via line 5 to separation zone 14 where the hydrogenated coal products are desorbed to an equilibrium level and removed via line 6 for further processing.

By equilibrium level is meant an amount which, at a given set of conditions, does not change substantially on continued recycle of adsorbent. The solid adsorbent/catalyst recycle, ash and char pass to separation zone 16 via line 7 where the ash is removed by suitable means such as elutriation or screening. Ash is removed via line 8 and the adsorbent/catalyst solid, now relieved of nonequilibrium adsorbed products is recirculated via line 9 to the beginning of the process where it again contacts a fresh charge of coal.

FIGURE 3.17: HYDROGENATION AND LIQUEFACTION OF COAL IN THE PRESENCE OF A SOLID ADSORBENT

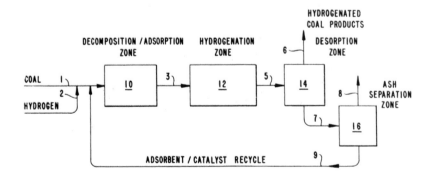

Source: R.L. Hodgson; U.S. Patent 3,549,512; December 22, 1970

Dried Illinois No. 6 coal (through 200 mesh) was reacted in a fixed bed tubular reactor with a charge of adsorbent/catalyst comprising cobalt and molybdenum impregnated on alumina (42 to 100 mesh). Hydrogen was passed through the bed of coal and adsorbent/catalyst which was maintained at about 1,500 psig pressure. The coal and catalyst were sized so that separation of residual char and ash from the solid could be effected by screening. Successive charges of fresh coal were used with the same adsorbent/catalyst. Each charge of coal (10 g. fed in four 2.5 g. portions) was contacted with 10.3 g. of solid, the solid being recovered and used with a succeeding charge. The results of this experiment and the pertinent operating conditions are given in the table below.

Temperature: 400–450° C.[a]
H₂ Flow: 400 cc./min. at 1,500 p.s.i.

	Run period (min.)[b]	Products (percent w. m.a.f.)				Conversion (percent w. m.a.f.)
		CH₄ to C₃H₈	Liquid	Res.[c]	Char[d]	
Coal charge No.:						
1	4×15	4.1	36	12	31	69
2	4×15	5.0	53	1	24	76
3	4×15	5.3	58	3	15	85
4	4×15	5.6	59	4	11	89
5	4×15	5.2	60	−2	17	83
6	4×15	5.6	66	7	9	91
Combined 7–8		6.2	68	0	9	91

[a] 450° C. maximum, time counted when reactor reached 400° C.
[b] The 10.3 g. charge introduced in four portions and reacted for 15 minutes each.
[c] Residual material remaining on adsorbent.
[d] Removed with ash.

Hydroconversion of Coal with a Combination of Catalysts

R.L. Hodgson; U.S. Patent 3,532,617; October 6, 1970; assigned to Shell Oil Company describes a process for hydroconversion of coal to refinable liquid products in which the coal is hydrogenated in the presence of at least two catalysts, one being impregnated on the coal, to obtain both increased conversion and improved selectivity to gasoline and gas oil components.

According to this process, coal is first impregnated with a catalyst, the impregnate solvent or vehicle optionally removed and the resulting catalyst-impregnated coal contacted with a second particulate hydrogenation catalyst (preferably a hydrogenation metal or metal compound supported on a solid carrier) in the presence of hydrogen at elevated temperature and pressure. In the first step, e.g., catalyst impregnation, coal is slurried with a catalyst which is dissolved or dispersed in a liquid vehicle. Thus efficient dispersion of the catalysts, necessarily used in small amounts, with the coal is accomplished. Catalysts which are effective include metal compounds, particularly metal halides and metal sulfides. Another class of catalysts are metal naphthenates. Naphthenates have the advantage of being soluble in hydrocarbons allowing the use of a hydrocarbon or organic impregnation vehicle and thus better contact and dispersion.

Referring to Figure 3.18, coal enters the process via line 11 to a crusher pulverizer 1 where it is reduced in size for efficient impregnation. The crushed coal is transferred to an impregnation vessel 2 where it is mixed with a catalyst such as, for example, ammonium molybdate, in aqueous solution. The catalyst slurry or solution is introduced via line 21. Sufficient solution is added to give the desired amount of catalyst on the coal.

Any hydrogenation metal salt which can be converted to metal sulfides and/or naphthenates are suitable for the practice of the process. Nickel, tin, molybdenum, cobalt, iron and vanadium salts are especially preferred. Any suitable solvent may be used as a carrier for the impregnate, water being of course a logical choice in many instances. However, a lower boiling solvent which can be easily recovered is desirable in some applications. The requirements are solubility of the impregnate in the solvent and nonreactivity or at least limited reactivity of the solvent with the coal. For example, ether has proved a particularly suitable solvent for impregnation of such salts as molybdenum chloride. The concentration of the impregnate in the solvent is not critical. It should be as high as possible to minimize solvent requirements and recovery but not so high as to impair the dispersion or to render the physical properties of the solution unmanageable.

When a metal salt catalyst is used, the amount should be in the range of about 0.01 to 5.0% by weight, an amount between 0.05 and 1.0% weight being preferred.

From the impregnation step the coal and impregnating solution is transferred via line 13 to a drying vessel 3 where solvent is removed. This may be done in various ways well-known in the art, as for example, by passing a hot inert gas through a fluidized bed of coal. Solvent is removed via line 31 and the coal containing the intimately mixed catalytic metal or salt passes via line 14 to vessel 4 where the metal salt is converted to the catalytically active form. Sulfiding is optional but is preferred for use with many metal catalysts used in this process.

When the catalyst is converted, in situ, to the sulfide, any sulfur compound which gives the sulfide compound, i.e., which reacts with the impregnated metal salt is suitable. Hydrogen sulfide is preferred. Again, concentration is not critical and any available hydrogen sulfide-containing gas may be used as, for example, hydrogen sulfide off-gas from refinery streams is appropriate. Relatively pure hydrogen sulfide may, of course, be used. Elevated temperatures are desirable

FIGURE 3.18:   HYDROCONVERSION OF COAL WITH A COMBINATION OF CATALYSTS

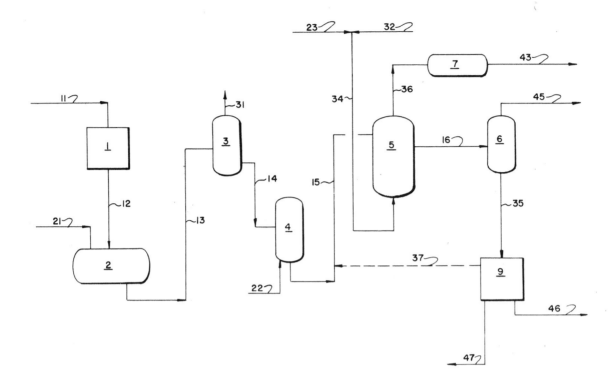

Source: R.L. Hodgson; U.S. Patent 3,532,617; October 6, 1970

for sulfiding, for example, temperatures in the range of 200° to 500°C. In general, sufficient sulfur should be added to convert substantially all the metal to the sulfide form.

Sulfur compound gas enters the sulfiding reactor through line 22. From unit 4, if sulfiding is used, or vessel 3 if sulfiding is not practiced, the impregnated coal enters a hydrogenation zone 5 via line 15. In the hydrogenation zone it is preferred that an ebullating bed of heterogeneous catalyst be used as explained hereinbefore. Hydrogen-containing gas enters the zone via line 34, gaseous products leave the zone via line 36 and liquid product, suspended char and ash and catalyst fines, if any, are removed via line 16.

In the hydrogenation zone, temperatures in the range of 350° to 450°C. and hydrogen pressures in the range of 1,000 to 2,000 psi are preferred conditions which allow maximum advantage to be taken of the dual catalyst system. Of course, higher temperatures and/or pressures may be used if desired. Gaseous products and any excess hydrogen and/or gases used in the hydrogenation zone are removed via line 36 where they pass to separator 7. Hydrogen gas which is separated in separator 7 may be recycled via line 32, mixed with incoming fresh hydrogenation gas from line 23 and returned to the hydrogenation zone 5. Recycle of hydrogenation gas is optional and should not be practiced if the product gas contains excessive poisons which would reduce the effectiveness of the hydrogenative catalysts in the hydrogenation zone. Of course, where undesirable components are present, the gas may be purified before recycling.

Fresh hydrogenation gas, preferably a concentrated hydrogen stream, enters the system via line 23. It is not necessary to employ pure hydrogen-containing gas, for example, off-gases from the catalytic reforming of naphthas being suitable and expedient. Other hydrogen-containing gases from processes which produce hydrogen from hydrocarbons are also suitable.

In an ebullating bed reaction system, a substantial portion of the converted coal is removed as a liquid via line 16. In this process, this stream will be somewhat lower boiling than in previously proposed schemes due to the increased gasoline make resulting from the use of two catalysts. The liquid fraction will contain not only converted coal, but also ash, char, and a minor amount of catalyst fines. One advantage of the ebullating bed operation is the attrition of catalyst which tends to keep fresh catalyst surface available. This mixed stream passes via line 16 to separation zone 6 where distillable oil is taken overhead as the major product. This fraction, which contains primarily gasoline and gas oil boiling range liquids, may be further refined by conventional petroleum refining means.

The residue is discharged via line 35. The residue contains unconverted coal, if any, tar, heavy residual liquids, and ash which was introduced with the coal, and the impregnated catalyst. The tary, heavy residual liquids and unconverted coal can be separated from the ash and if desired recycled via line 37 to hydrogenation zone 5. Alternatively, it may be used to impregnate fresh coal with catalyst contained in a residual stream or as a parting liquid from the impregnated coal. The quantity of this material is less with this process than is known processes. The hydrocarbon residue can be coked to recover additional refinable products and coke, or total hydrocarbon residue or char gasified to produce hydrogen. Recovery and reuse of catalysts will depend upon the total economics of the particular system. If small quantities of in-expensive catalyst are used, recovery may not be justified. Catalyst reuse is not considered a vital part of this process, but the possibility of reuse in some cases is a definite advantage. For example, catalyst contained in the recycle residual liquid may be used to impregnate fresh coal.

Example: A series of experiments were made on the hydrogenation-liquefaction of Illinois No. 6 coal. Representative analysis of this coal is shown in Table 1.

TABLE 1: ILLINOIS NO. 6 COAL

Elemental analysis (percent by weight)*	
Carbon	78.9
Hydrogen	5.4
Nitrogen	1.5
Sulfur	4.3
Oxygen	9.9
H/C (atomic ratio)	0.82
Moisture (percent by weight)	10.9
Ash (percent by weight)	13.3

* Analysis on a maf basis.

The use of combinations of catalysts was examined using powdered palladium on Y-zeolite catalyst (obtained from Linde Co. and designated as SK-100) mixed with powdered impregnated Illinois No. 6 coal. The mixed solids were treated with a 200 cc/min. flow of hydrogen at 1,500 psi for 5 hours at 425°C. The results are summarized in Table 2. For comparison purposes, SiO$_2$ which has no catalytic hydrogenation activity was used instead of the zeolite with untreated raw coal, sulfided coal, and molybdenum impregnated and sulfided coal. Sulfiding the coal had little effect in the absence of an impregnated catalyst. Impregnating with ~0.1 to 0.2% by weight molybdenum and then sulfiding increased both conver-sions and yield of liquid products.

The use of palladium on Y-zeolite in place of the SiO$_2$ did not affect the conversion appreciably but did alter the distrib-ution of products so that almost all the recovered products boiled below about 200°C. With palladium on Y-zeolite as the heterogeneous catalyst, sulfiding the coal or impregnating with molybdenum increased conversion while still giving good product selectivity. When the coal was impregnated with molybdenum, sulfided, and then used with palladium on Y-zeolite, the best results were obtained: 57% by weight basis maf coal liquid product in the gasoline range (C$_4$, 200°C.) at a coal conversion of ~85% by weight (maf). In these experiments, the molybdenum was impregnated to a level of ~0.1 to 0.2% by weight from an ether solution of MoCl$_5$. Similar impregnation to ~0.01% by weight Mo was less effec-tive; however, impregnation with aqueous ammonium molybdate at 0.6% by weight Mo was equally effective. Nickel chloride impregnated and sulfided was also effective when used with the palladium on Y-zeolite heterogeneous catalyst.

TABLE 2

Heterogeneous catalyst [a]	Coal treatment [b]	Products (percent w. MAF)			Conversion (percent w. MAF)
		C←200° C.	200–400° C.[e]	Char	
SiO$_2$	None	14	23	33	67
SiO$_2$	Sulfided	15	26	38	62
SiO$_2$	MoCl$_5$ [d] (I) (S)	22	37	22	78
Pd/Y	None	31	0	41	59
Pd/Y	Sulfided	44	1	27	73
Pd/Y	MoCl$_5$ [d] (I)	46	7	9	91
Pd/Y	MoCl$_5$ [d] (I) (S)	57	3	14	86
Pd/Y	MoCl$_5$ [e] (I) (S)	45	4	22	78
Pd/Y	(NH$_4$)$_6$Mo$_7$O$_{24}$ [f] (I) (S)	57	1	15	85
Pd/Y	NiCl$_2$ [g] (I) (S)	45	11	15	85

a Calcined and sulfided (~10 g.) (<100 mesh), SiO$_2$ not calcined or sulfided.
b Illinois No. 6 (~10 g.) (100–200 mesh), (I) Impregnated; (S) Sulfided.
e Material recovered from 200° C. lines and traps.
d ~0.1% w. Mo.
e ~0.01% w. Mo.
f ~0.6% w. Mo.
g ~0.5% w. Ni.

Catalytic Treatment of Carbonaceous Materials

The process described by B.S. Greensfelder and W.A. Bailey, Jr.; U.S. Patent 2,392,588; January 8, 1946; assigned to Shell Development Company relates to the treatment of carbonaceous materials at elevated temperatures under substantial hydrogen pressure in the presence of catalysts to produce lower boiling products having an enhanced ratio of hydrogen to carbon.

According to this process, hydrocarbons are produced by treating higher boiling carbonaceous materials with hydrogen at pressures above about 200 atmospheres in the presence of a catalyst comprising essentially alumina and boric oxide. Mixtures of alumina with silica and other difficultly reducible oxides have been proposed as carriers for a wide variety of hydrogenation catalysts and it has also been suggested in some cases that small amounts of boric acid may or may not be incorporated in the mixtures used to prepare such carriers. However, these catalysts are essentially different from such hydrogenation catalysts and are believed to be equally or more advantageous for the reactions under consideration than those heretofore used.

The desired properties of the catalysts can be obtained only by the use of alumina in the proper form. Either crystalline or gel aluminas may be employed. Thus the alumina may be a porous alpha or beta alumina trihydrate, alpha alumina monohydrate or gamma alumina.

Suitable crystalline aluminas may be obtained, for example, by the slow crystallization of alpha alumina trihydrate or beta alumina trihydrate from alkali aluminate solutions followed by partial dehydration of the trihydrate to a water content between about 4 and 12%. The aluminas so prepared, unless acid washed, contain appreciable concentrations of alkali, for example sodium. For operation in the absence of steam this is not a disadvantage in the process, and suitable aluminas may contain up to 0.5 to 1.0% sodium. This is in marked contrast to catalysts containing 20% or more silica in which sodium is detrimental and should be avoided.

Suitable alumina gels may be prepared by several different methods. One convenient way is to precipitate an alumina gel from a solution of a soluble aluminum salt such as the nitrate, sulfate or chloride with a base such as ammonium hydroxide or sodium hydroxide. Instead of aluminum salts, a metal aluminate or aluminum amalgam may be used in preparing the alumina gel. Whatever the method of precipitation used, it may be desirable to remove the precipitant from the alumina prior to incorporation of the boric oxide. Excessive amounts of alkali metal salts reduce the activity of the catalyst and may be removed by water washing the gel. The properties of the final catalyst may be improved by peptization of Al_2O_3 in the hydrogel, xerogel, or crystalline state by treatment with acetic acid, for example.

The boric oxide may be incorporated into the alumina in a number of different ways. When alumina in gel form is used, the desired amount of boria may be incorporated by homogenizing the wet hydrous gel with boric acid or by impregnating the hydrous or dried gel with a boric acid solution. In the case of impregnation of xerogel or crystalline Al_2O_3 with H_3BO_3, a temperature preferably greater than 75°C. should be employed to yield a high B_2O_3 content. The mixture is then calcined at about 200° to 600°C. to convert the boric acid to boric oxide. Other boron compounds which may be decomposed to the oxide by heating in this range or at lower temperatures may be used instead of boric acid. For both gel and crystalline aluminas the boric oxide may be applied in solution in an alcoholic solvent.

Alternatively, the alumina may be impregnated by exposure to water vapor carrying hydrated boric oxide, or to vapors of an alkyl borate which will leave a residue of B_2O_3 when decomposed by heating. It is sometimes advantageous when using gel forms of alumina to incorporate the chosen compound in the alumina during the precipitation step. In such cases it is of course not feasible to wash the precipitated gel or to subject it to any other subsequent treatment which would remove the added boron compound. Consequently, more careful control of the precipitation is necessary in order to avoid inclusion of undesirable constituents in the finished catalyst.

In this process, the catalyst used is prepared by depositing boric acid on a synthetic alumina gel and suitably calcining to convert the boric acid to boric oxide. It has the following illustrative characteristics:

Alumina (substantially gamma form)	75%
Boria	10%
Loss on ignition	9%
Surface area	300 sq. m./g.
Bulk density	0.85
Iron	0.2% max.

Using a catalyst of this type a yield of 0.5 kg./l./hr. of gasoline hydrocarbons boiling below 180°C. and having an octane number of 75/76 should be obtained.

Hydrogenation Processes

Catalyst for the Hydrogenation of Hydrocarbon Materials

The process of C.L. Thomas; U.S. Patent 2,377,728; June 5, 1945; assigned to Universal Oil Products Company relates to the production of valuable liquid products including high antiknock motor fuel from coal or mixtures of coal in oil. It concerns improved catalytic agents for these reactions whereby the quality of the products is substantially improved.

The catalysts comprise essentially a mixture of a major portion of a hydrogenating catalyst such as an oxide or sulfide of molybdenum, tin, cobalt, nickel, etc., either alone or disposed on a relatively inert carrier such as silica, diatomaceous earth, alumina, bauxite and the like, in admixture with or impregnated in cracking catalyst composites such as silica-alumina, silica, zirconia, silica-titania, silica-magnesia, silica-alumina-zirconia, silica-alumina-titania, silica-alumina-boric oxide, boric oxide-alumina, boric oxide-zirconia, boric oxide titania, etc., or mixtures of these compounds with one another.

The process is carried out by mixing a slurry of coal in oil with a finely divided powdered catalyst, heating the mixture to a temperature within the approximate range of 300° to 550°C. and preferably about 400° to 500°C., at a pressure of 1,000 to 5,000 pounds per square inch and passing the mixture together with hydrogen or hydrogen-containing gas into a reaction zone wherein substantial conversion occurs.

The hydrogenating component of this catalytic material is selected from known hydrogenating compounds such as the oxides or sulfides of molybdenum, tin, iron, cobalt, nickel, zinc, etc., which may be used alone or supported on relatively inert carriers such as alumina, silica, bentonite and the like. The materials, either singly or in mixtures, may be composited with a second catalytic agent which in itself is not a particularly active hydrogenating catalyst, but which in combination with the hydrogenating component serves to direct and promote the desired reactions.

These materials consist of a type known broadly as silica-alumina, silica-zirconia, silica-alumina-zirconia, etc., and have been enumerated more fully above. They may be prepared by the separate or simultaneous precipitation of the components followed by washing and drying steps whereby alkali metal compounds are substantially eliminated. The composites so formed may be admixed with the oxides or sulfides of the hydrogenating component under conditions such that an intimate mixture of very fine particle size is obtained. The hydrogenating component as a rule is the major component and may make up from approximately 50 to 80% of the finished catalyst composite.

Example: A suitable catalyst comprises silica-alumina having deposited thereon an oxide of molybdenum at approximately equal amounts by weight. Approximately 12% by weight of the catalytic composite is added to a coal in oil slurry which is then treated in the presence of hydrogen at a temperature of 470°C. and a pressure of 2,500 psi resulting in the production of a liquid product consisting of approximately 48% by volume of 78 octane number olefin-free gasoline, and approximately 52% by volume of a higher boiling oil which may be converted by catalytic cracking into additional yields of high antiknock gasoline. When using molybdenum oxide in the absence of the silica-alumina mass, the octane number of the gasoline produced is of the order of 70 and approximately 40% of gasoline is contained in the product. The catalyst powder may be filtered from the product and reactivated by treatment with an oxygen containing gas. Since it is mixed with ash from the coal it is necessary to remove a part of it and replace it with fresh catalyst.

Highly Porous Catalysts

F. Stoewener, E. Keunecke, and F. Becke; U.S. Patent 2,337,944; December 28, 1943 have found that, in practicing catalytic reactions with carbonaceous materials, especially in the refining, aromatizing or destructive hydrogenation of coals, tars and mineral oils, in particular also of middle oils obtained by destructive hydrogenation or from carbon monoxide and hydrogen, excellent yields are obtained, if such porous catalysts or carrier masses be used in which at least 30%, preferably at least 50% and most advantageously from 60 to 85%, of the active pore volume consists of pores of a diameter of between 0 and 2 millionths of a micron. Particularly good results are obtained if at least 15%, preferably at least 25% and most advantageously from 30 to 60%, of the active pore volume consist of pores of a diameter of between 0 and one-millionth of a micron.

It is a great advantage if only the carrier mass of the catalyst, i.e., the skeleton left after dissolving out therefrom any additional catalytic materials, for example metal oxides, satisfies the above conditions. Even better results are usually obtained if the finished catalyst, i.e., the carrier inclusive of the catalytic substance, satisfies the conditions.

Example: 100 grams of a fine pored silica gel obtained by allowing a homogeneous sol (pH 3 to 4.5) to solidify, washing the jelly so obtained until a pH of between 3 and 5 has been reached and drying the jelly at from 200° to 300°C., the active pore volume of which gel consists of 35% of pores with a diameter of between 0 and 1 millionth of a micron, of 35% of pores with a diameter of between 1 and 2 millionths of a micron and of 30% of pores with a diameter of between 2 and 43 millionths of a micron, i.e., of 70% of pores with a diameter of between 0 and 2 millionths of a micron, is saturated with water vapor, gradually soaked with a solution of 8 grams of aluminum nitrate [Al(NO3)3·9H2O] in 50 cc of water and dried at from 120° to 180°C. The dry gel is then impregnated with an aqueous solution of ammonium thiotungstate of 10% strength which contains an excess of ammonium sulfide.

The mass is then dried in the absence of air and put into a reaction tube and heated up to 400°C. while passing through hydrogen. The catalyst which then consists of silica-alumina gel containing 10% of tungsten sulfide is then used in the destructive hydrogenation of a paraffin base gas oil boiling between 210° and 350°C. under a hydrogen pressure of 200 atmospheres at 400°C. with a throughput of 2 kg. per liter of catalyst and per hour. The product obtained contains 62% of gasoline with an octane number of 75.

Nickel Carbonyl Catalyst

In the process described by B.J. Mayland; U.S. Patent 2,756,194; July 24, 1956; assigned to Phillips Petroleum Company oil containing dissolved nickel carbonyl is sprayed into a combustion chamber together with steam and oxygen. At the temperature of combustion the nickel carbonyl is decomposed to elemental nickel which is finely dispersed throughout the products of initial combustion and acts as a catalyst for reforming residual hydrocarbons. The reaction products are cooled by quenching to a point where nickel carbonyl reforms and then it is scrubbed from the gases by the fresh liquid hydrocarbon and reused.

In the hydrogenation of coal part of the pasting oil containing dissolved nickel carbonyl may be diverted to a hydrogenation step wherein a mild hydrogenation of coal or of other carbonaceous materials may be accomplished. The coal is mixed with pasting oil containing nickel carbonyl and the mixture preheated wherein the nickel carbonyl is decomposed to elemental nickel. The slurry is then contacted with hydrogen at an elevated pressure in the hydrogenation zone. A portion of the coal is liquefied and the sulfur in the coal is converted to hydrogen sulfide. The hydrogenated coal and catalyst slurry is passed to a separation zone to remove hydrogen sulfide and liquid product. The residual slurry together with nickel catalyst is taken through a gasification process.

Because the sulfur content of coals may be as high as 10% by weight or more, fuel gas or synthesis gas made by conventional coal gasification processes is in many cases high in sulfur, which is undesirable for various reasons such as corrosion, catalyst poisoning, gum formation, etc. Sulfur compounds may be removed from the gas by many methods including physical absorption and chemical reaction but because of the volume of the gas stream and the presence of high carbon dioxide content, the methods are expensive. The removal of sulfur before gasification in this process overcomes the difficulties just mentioned.

Referring to Figure 3.19, a residual hydrocarbon oil is introduced through a line 32 containing valve 36 to the scrubber 30. Nickel carbonyl contained in a gas mixture formed in the process is admitted to the scrubber 30 from line 37 and is dissolved in the oil. The residual hydrocarbon oil containing usually less than 1.0% by weight of nickel carbonyl based on the feed stock, and preferably between 0.1 and 0.5% by weight, is passed through line 31 and line 26. This mixture is sprayed into the gasification chamber 29 together with oxygen from line 27 and steam from line 28. At the temperature of combustion the nickel carbonyl is decomposed to elemental nickel which is finely dispersed throughout the products of initial combustion and acts as a catalyst for reforming residual hydrocarbons. Typical operating conditions for the gasification process are as follows.

	Broad Range	Preferred Range
Temperature, °F.	1400 to 3000	1800 to 2000
Pressure, atmospheres	1 to 20	2 to 7
Contact time, seconds	0.1 to 10	1 to 5

The reaction products are: methane, water, carbon dioxide, carbon monoxide and hydrogen. A typical analysis may be as follows.

	Mol Percent
Methane	1.0 or less
Water	6 to 8
Carbon dioxide	3 to 4
Carbon monoxide	25 to 35
Hydrogen	65 to 52

The reaction products are cooled, for example by water quenching, to a point where nickel carbonyl reforms and then it is scrubbed from the gases in the scrubber 30 by the fresh liquid hydrocarbon feed from line 32 and reused in the gasification step by recycling through line 31. The nickel is converted to nickel carbonyl in the presence of carbon monoxide at temperatures of 200° to 300°F. in a suitable reaction chamber prior to removal of ash. A cyclone separator (not shown) is placed in line 37 after the water quench to remove the ash through line 39.

Carbon monoxide and hydrogen-containing gas are withdrawn from the scrubber 30 through line 33 to outside utilization through line 34 containing valve 38, or a portion of this gas may be conducted to a water gas shift reaction step 35 to

FIGURE 3.19: NICKEL CARBONYL CATALYST

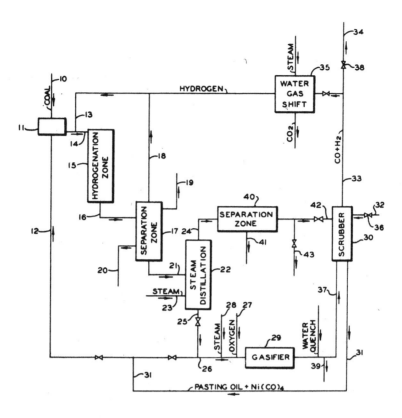

Source: B.J. Mayland; U.S. Patent 2,756,194; July 24, 1956

produce a high hydrogen content gas. The high hydrogen content gas is conducted through line 13 and line 14 to the hydrogenation step 15 to be described subsequently.

A mild hydrogenation of coal may be accomplished using nickel as a catalyst obtained by the decomposition of nickel carbonyl. The process is described with respect to coal but it can be readily modified for other carbon-containing materials such as ground oil shale, shale oil, refinery residuums, etc. In preparing the coal or other carbonaceous material for hydrogenation, it is desirable to pulverize to a relatively fine state of subdivision, preferably such that it will pass through a standard Tyler screen of about 80 mesh. The powdered coal is treated by conventional mechanical separation methods to remove inorganic sulfur.

After being pulverized, the coal is conducted through feed line 10 to chamber 11. In chamber 11, the coal is admixed with a pasting oil from line 12 containing usually less than 1.0% by weight of nickel carbonyl based on the carbonaceous material. This pasting oil is a recycle oil produced in the process as will be described. In general from one to three parts of pasting oil per part of coal provides a suitable fluid consistency for reaction. Normally about 0.01 to 1.0% by weight of the nickel catalyst based on the carbonaceous material is a sufficient amount.

The mixture of coal and pasting oil containing nickel carbonyl is pumped along with hydrogen from line 13 through line 14 and through a preheater (not shown) into the hydrogenation zone 15. Typical operating conditions for the mild hydrogenation of coal are as follows.

	Broad Range	Preferred Range
Temperature, °F.	750 to 1000	800 to 900
Pressure, atmospheres	70 to 700	350 to 550
Contact time, hours	0.25 to 8	1 to 3
Hydrogen, ft.^{3}/lb. of charge	5 to 25	10 to 15

The nickel carbonyl is decomposed to elemental nickel in the preheater, and the elemental nickel acts as the catalyst in the hydrogenation zone 15.

The hydrogenated coal and the catalyst slurry is withdrawn from the hydrogenation zone 15, and passed through line 16 to a separation zone 17. Hydrogen-rich gas is taken off through line 18, and recycled to the hydrogenation step. Light gases and hydrogen sulfide are taken off through line 19. The gasoline fraction boiling below 400° to 430°F. is separated from the remaining heavy-oil slurry. The gasoline fraction is taken off through line 20. The heavy-oil slurry boiling above 400° to 430°F. is withdrawn from the separation zone 17 and passed through line 21 to a steam distillation unit 22, with steam being admitted through line 23. The heavy-oil slurry is steam distilled to obtain a pasting oil fraction taken off through line 24 and a residual slurry taken off through line 25. The pasting oil fraction is passed through line 24 to a separation zone 40 where water is taken off through line 41. The pasting oil is withdrawn from the separation zone 40 through line 42 and passed to a scrubber 30. Excess pasting oil not required for the process can be withdrawn through line 43.

The residual slurry containing the nickel catalyst from the steam distillation unit 22 is taken off through line 25 and passed to line 26. Part of the pasting oil containing dissolved nickel carbonyl from line 31 may be diverted into line 26 and there admixed with the residual slurry in order to obtain a fluid consistency suitable for spraying into the gasification chamber.

Catalytic Hydroprocessing of Coal with Metal Sulfides and Naphthenates

R.L. Hodgson; U.S. Patent 3,502,564; March 24, 1970; assigned to Shell Oil Company describes a process which indicates that the in situ preparation of a hydrogenation-liquefication catalyst impregnated on the coal results in significant improvement in catalytic activity. Metal naphthenates and sulfides are particularly appropriate catalysts for in situ preparation.

It has been discovered that the effectiveness of a metal sulfide or naphthenate catalyst is greatly increased if the coal is first impregnated with a metal salt which is subsequently converted, in its dispersed state, to the corresponding sulfide or naphthenate. Particularly impressive are some of the in situ prepared sulfided metal naphthenate catalysts. The effectiveness significantly surpasses that of a single step impregnation of the catalytic compound itself.

In this process powdered coal is impregnated with a suitable solution of a metallic salt of the hydrogenative metal, e.g., molybdenum chloride, the solvent removed and the salt then sulfided by an appropriate sulfur compound which either reacts with, or decomposes to a form which can react with the metal salt dispersed on the catalyst. Hydrogen sulfide is a convenient and especially suitable sulfiding medium. This embodiment has the additional advantage of allowing impregnation of catalytic compound such as metal sulfides which because of their insolubility cannot be impregnated directly on the catalyst. Heretofore insoluble compounds could only be incorporated by suspension.

When the catalyst is converted, in situ, to the sulfide, any sulfur compound which gives the sulfide compound, i.e., which reacts with the impregnated metal salt is suitable. Hydrogen sulfide is preferred. Again concentration is not critical and any available hydrogen sulfide containing gas may be used, as, for example, hydrogen sulfide off-gas from refinery streams are appropriate. Relatively pure hydrogen sulfide may, of course, be used. Elevated temperatures are desirable for sulfiding, for example, temperatures in the range of 200° to 500°C. are suitable. In general, sufficient sulfur should be added to convert substantially all the metal to the sulfide form.

Sulfiding may be conducted in the same reactor vessel as the hydrogenation reaction or in a separate sulfiding reactor. In one aspect of the process the catalyst can be impregnated with a metal salt, as for example, molybdenum chlorides, the solvent removed and the impregnated coal passed to a suitable reactor capable of high pressure operation where it is sulfided and subsequently hydrogenated. Sulfiding and hydrogenation can be carried out in separate zones of the same continuous reactor, sulfiding preceding hydrogenation.

Metal naphthenates are known to be very effective hydrogenation catalysts. These are conventionally incorporated with the coal, by impregnation of the preformed metal naphthenate, e.g., cobalt naphthenate. In the process significant catalytic enhancement results if the metal naphthenate is formed on the coal by impregnation of the coal either with the metal ion or the naphthenate ion followed by conversion of the impregnated species to the metal naphthenate. For example cobalt naphthenate can be prepared by impregnation of powdered coal with naphthenic acid and then contacted with a cobalt halide salt to form cobalt naphthenate. It is especially preferred to further react the metal naphthenate with a sulfur compound such as H_2S.

Example: A series of experiments were made on the hydrogenation-liquefication of Illinois No. 6 coal. Representative analysis of this coal is shown in Table 1 on the following page.

TABLE 1: ANALYSIS OF ILLINOIS NO. 6 COAL

Elemental analysis (percent by weight)*	
Carbon	78.9
Hydrogen	5.4
Nitrogen	1.5
Sulfur	4.3
Oxygen	9.9
H/C (atomic ratio)	0.82
Moisture (percent by weight)	10.9
Ash (percent by weight)	13.3

* Analysis on a maf basis.

To illustrate the effectiveness of the in situ preparation of metal sulfide catalyst according to this process, samples of powdered coal were impregnated with $MoCl_5$ which was converted to the sulfide form. The powdered coal was impregnated from an ether solution of the $MoCl_5$, the ether being subsequently removed by evaporation. One sample was simply mixed with MoS for comparison. MoS could not be impregnated in the conventional means because of its insolubility. The coal with incorporated catalyst was placed in an autoclave reactor at 400°C. for one hour under hydrogen pressure maintained at 1,400 to 1,500 psig.

After hydrogenation the products were first collected by venting the reactor at 200°C. to obtain gases, liquids boiling up to 200°C., and water. Next the residue was extracted for one-half hour with each of three portions of refluxing benzene and water followed by a 24 hour Soxhlet extraction with methyl ethyl ketone. The extent of reaction was determined both from the recovered products and from the loss in weight of the coal and is reported on a maf basis in terms of solubilization and conversion, defined as follows. The results are shown in Table 2.

$$\text{Solubilization (percent by weight maf)} = \frac{\text{Extractable products}}{\text{Coal fed}}$$

$$\text{Conversion (percent by weight maf)} = \frac{\text{Coal fed} - \text{Recovered residue}}{\text{Coal fed}}$$

TABLE 2

Run No.	Catalyst	Solubilization, percent by weight maf	Conversion, percent by weight maf
A-1 *	2% MoS	32	34
A-2 **	2% $MoCl_5$	59	64
A-3	2% $MoCl_5$, sulfided	79	68
A-4	1% $MoCl_5$	60	65
A-5	1% $MoCl_5$, sulfided	76	82
A-6	0.1% $MoCl_5$	36	47
A-7	0.1% $MoCl_5$, sulfided	52	54

* MoS mixed with powdered coal.
** $MoCl_5$ was impregnated from an ether solution.

These results clearly show the effect of in situ preparation of sulfide catalysts. In every case the solubilization and conversion was markedly increased by in situ sulfiding. It should be noted that the conditions are very mild by conventional standards. While a number of catalysts give greater solubilization conversion at 500°C. and 3,000 psi H_2 pressure than these results, the severe conditions are serious detriments to the commercial feasibility of the process and the increased conversion at the mild conditions used is a significant achievement.

Hydrogenation of Coal Tar in the Presence of Iodine

The process described by L.D. Friedman and R.T. Eddinger; U.S. Patent 3,453,202; July 1, 1969; assigned to FMC Corporation relates to improvements in the visbreaking of coal tar by hydrogenation in the presence of elemental iodine as the hydrogenation catalyst. It has also been discovered that elemental iodine retains its high catalytic efficiency even though the hydrogenating atmosphere contains relatively large amounts of other gases.

In fact, it has been ascertained that a hydrogen concentration as low as 25 mol percent does not significantly retard the catalytic action of iodine. As a consequence many waste and by-product gases which contain hydrogen can be used as a hydrogenation gas in the iodine-catalyzed visbreaking of coal tar. Normally, hydrogenation catalysts lose effectiveness when the hydrogen concentration falls below 70 mol percent; some even lose efficiency when the hydrogen content drops below 90 mol percent. By contrast a 50/50 mixture of hydrogen and diluent gas using iodine as the catalyst is as effective as 100% hydrogen when employing such typical catalysts as cobalt molybdate or nickel tungsten sulfide. This singular catalytic activity of elemental iodine is not readily explainable, but possibly the iodine and hydrogen exist in equilibrium with hydrogen iodide which may constitute the active catalyst.

Although an independent and separate process, this process can be operated in conjunction with a two-stage coal tar hydrogenation. In fact the two-stage operation is desirable in those instances where the coal tar refinery and the oil refinery are located in close proximity to one another. In this combined operation, which is illustrated by the block diagram in Figure 3.20, a mixture of coal tar, hydrogen-containing gas, and iodine is introduced into a coal tar hydrogenator, and hydrogenation is carried out under reaction conditions as above defined. The resulting visbroken tar which is now a flowable, oily liquid is conveyed from the hydrogenator to a separator station where off-gases are removed and aqueous waste liquors separated out and discarded. The oil is next piped to a hydrogenator where the second-stage hydrogenation is carried out with other catalysts, e.g., nickel tungsten sulfide, cobalt molybdate or the like.

The second-stage hydrogenation removes residual nitrogen as ammonia, oxygen as water, sulfur as hydrogen sulfide and any iodine which may be present in the form of an organic iodide. The products from the oil hydrogenator are conducted to a receiver from which the contaminant free oil is removed. Off-gases from the receiver and the visbreaker are led to a scrubber where carbon dioxide and iodine are removed. From the scrubber the off-gas is led to an absorber station where high Btu and LP gases are taken off, while the purified hydrogen passes into the char stripper. The charge to the stripper is composed of bottoms from the visbreaker.

Example: 100 grams of low temperature tar, obtained from the pyrolysis of a Wyoming subbituminous B coal in a fluidized bed, was charged to a 300 cc autoclave along with 2.0 grams of sublimed iodine. The autoclave was pressurized to 3,200 psi with a gas mixture consisting of 50 mol percent hydrogen and 50 mol percent carbon monoxide, and was heated rapidly to 740°F. This temperature was maintained for three hours, during which time the maximum pressure in the bomb reached 4,500 psi but dropped gradually to 4,000 psi. At the end of the heating period, the reactor was cooled, depressurized and emptied.

FIGURE 3.20: HYDROGENATION OF COAL TAR IN THE PRESENCE OF IODINE

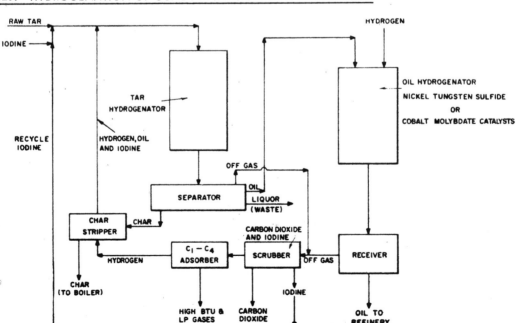

Source: L.D. Friedman and R.T. Eddinger; U.S. Patent 3,453,202; July 1, 1969

The reactor products were filtered and 87 weight percent of oil, based on the dry, solids-free tar, were recovered along with 3.7 weight percent of solids including the catalyst. The viscosity of the oil was lowered from about 100,000 to less than 100 centipoises. The yield of hydrogenated oil was as high as that obtained when this same tar was hydrogenated with iodine or cobalt molybdate catalyst and 100% hydrogen.

Hydrogenation of Coal Employing Zinc Catalysts

The process described by H.H. Storch and M.G. Pelipetz; U.S. Patent 2,606,142; August 5, 1952; assigned to the U.S. Secretary of the Interior relates to the liquefaction of coal and its conversion by means of hydrogenation in the presence of catalysts. It is known that when coal is heated to such high temperatures as 450°C. in the presence of active catalysts under high hydrogen pressures such as 1,000 pounds or higher that in the process hydrogen is consumed; and gaseous, liquid and solid products result.

The process relates to methods for effecting the liquefaction of coal by high temperature hydrogenation wherein finely divided alloys of zinc or certain mixtures of finely divided zinc with other metals are employed as catalysts. Alloys of zinc, comparing favorably in the high order of liquefaction with tin are: zinc-tin, zinc-antimony, and zinc-arsenic. Likewise, powdered mixtures of zinc with tin, zinc with antimony, and zinc with arsenic give high percentages of liquefaction. In order to further illustrate this process, the examples below are given. Example 1 has been included for comparative purposes, that the order of coal liquefaction, wherein the standard tin catalyst has been used, may function as a basis for comparison.

Example 1: A typical Pittsburgh-bed (Bruceton) coal is finely ground and made into a paste with an equal part by weight of tetralin. 1% of tin is added to this paste and the mixture autoclaved with hydrogen under about 1,000 psi initial hydrogen pressure at the conditions shown in the following table.

Duration of Reaction, hours	Temp., °C.	Percent of Coal Liquefied	Percent of Asphalt Formed
1/2	400	80.0	67.2
1	400	81.6	44.7
3	400	89.2	39.0
1/2	415	83.4	49.3
1	415	85.9	23.0
3	415	86.9	19.0

In this and the two succeeding examples, the reaction pressure becomes about 2,000 psi, varying somewhat with the temperature. For that reason, it seems best to specify the initial pressure, which in each example was 1,000 psi hydrogen pressure.

Example 2: When a similar mixture of coal and Tetralin is hydrogenated under the same conditions but with 1% of a powdered zinc-antimony alloy added as the catalyst to this paste, the extent of coal liquefaction is slightly lower than in the above example, but yet good at the corresponding higher temperature after 1 to 3 hours' duration.

Duration of Reaction, hours	Temp., °C.	Percent of Coal Liquefied	Percent of Asphalt Formed
1/2	400	47.9	34.0
1	400	49.2	24.2
3	400	56.3	22.2
1/2	415	58.0	20.8
1	415	67.4	22.6
3	415	74.6	26.6

Example 3: When a similar mixture of ground coal and Tetralin, containing 0.5% tin and 0.5% of zinc-antimony alloy as the catalyst is autoclaved with hydrogen under 1,000 psi initial hydrogen pressure, the following results are obtained.

Duration of Reaction, hours	Temp., °C.	Percent of Coal Liquefied	Percent of Asphalt Formed
1/2	400	70.1	36.5
1	400	84.2	26.3
3	400	87.9	13.0
1/2	415	84.5	27.4
1	415	86.5	17.1
3	415	88.4	9.0

That the satisfactory yield in percent of liquefaction of coal and also the effectiveness of this process' catalysts, as compared with tin may stand out distinctly, a table is presented below wherein the conditions of operation, that is, initial hydrogen pressure, reaction temperature, time of duration, are analogous: initial hydrogen pressure, 1,000 psig,; reaction temperature, 450°C.; duration, 60 minutes. Runs were made both in the absence and in the presence of a hydrocarbon liquid pasting oil which proves that the latter is not necessary. Table 1 summarizes the results of a number of experimental runs.

TABLE 1

| Run No. | Charge, in grams | | | Percent of Liquefaction | Percent of Asphalt Formed |
	Coal	Vehicle	Catalyst		
922	50	-	0.5 Sn + 0.275 NH_4Cl	86.6	26.9
663	50	-	1.25 Zn + 1.88 NH_4Cl	83.1	21.9
1000	50	50 tetralin	0.5 Sn + 0.27 NH_4Cl	89.8	27.9
1011 *	50	50 tetralin	0.25 Sn + 0.25 Zn-Sb + 0.25 NH_4Cl	90.45	37.9
666	50	-	0.5 Zn + 0.05 Sn + 1.13 NH_4Cl	86.2	26.4
274 *	50	-	0.5 Zn-Sn + 0.275 NH_4Cl	85.5	29.2

    * In runs 1011 and 274 supra which embody the process in the use of zinc-antimony and zinc-tin alloy, respectively, the analysis of the alloy components was 50% Zn, 50% Sb, and 50% Zn, 50% Sn, respectively.

Hydrogasification of Carbonaceous Material with Aluminum Chloride

R.W. Hiteshue and W. Kawa; U.S. Patent 3,556,978; January 19, 1971; assigned to the U.S. Secretary of the Interior state that hydrogasification of carbonaceous material at temperatures of about 450°C. or below is accomplished by the use of relatively large amounts of aluminum chloride to catalyze the reaction.

It has been found that carbonaceous materials such as coals, tars, petroleum residues, oils, chars, etc., may be effectively converted to hydrocarbon gases in the C_1 to C_3 molecular weight range at temperatures of about 350° to 450°C. by employing relatively large amounts of aluminum chloride as catalyst. These temperatures permit the use of reactors employing much less expensive materials of construction. In addition, the process produces almost exclusively low molecular weight hydrocarbons, with essentially no liquid products. The following examples will serve to more particularly illustrate the process.

Experiments were made with high volatile A bituminous coal from the Pittsburgh seam, high volatile C bituminous coal from Rock Springs, Wyoming, a Pennsylvania anthracite, a Texas lignite, untopped high temperature tar produced in a commercial slot-type oven, tar from low temperature fluidized carbonization of a Texas lignite, and distillation residue from a Venezuelan crude oil. Coal samples were pulverized to -60 mesh (U.S. Sieve) and dried in air at 70°C. for about 20 hours. Powdered anhydrous aluminum chloride of 99% purity was used as catalyst. Charges of coal and aluminum chloride were premixed in the glass liner by rotating the liner and charge end-over-end for two hours. Hydrogen was obtained from commercial cylinders.

Gases were depressurized through scrubbers that removed water vapor and acid gases (CO_2, H_2S, and HCl formed by reactions of $AlCl_3$). The remaining gases were metered, collected in a holder, sampled, and analyzed by mass spectrometry. Light oil and water were removed by vacuum distillation to about 110°C and 2 to 3 mm. of Hg. Solid and heavy liquid products remaining in the autoclave were washed with water to remove aluminum chloride. Material insoluble in water was separated into benzene-insoluble and benzene-soluble fractions, and the ash content of the benzene insolubles was determined. When about 2 grams or more of benzene-soluble product was formed, it was separated into n-pentane-insoluble (asphaltene) and n-pentane-soluble (heavy oil) fractions.

Yields are expressed as percentages by weight of maf charge. Organic benzene insolubles are defined as total benzene insolubles minus ash. Benzene-soluble oil is the sum of the asphaltene, heavy oil, and light oil. Coal conversion is given on a percentage basis and is defined as 100 minus the percent of organic benzene insolubles. Results are shown in Tables 1, 2 and 3.

The effect of temperature on the distribution of products from HVAB coal is shown in Table 2. Experiments were made with equal weights of coal and aluminum chloride at temperatures of 250° to 450°C. for one hour. In the presence of aluminum chloride, appreciable amounts of benzene-soluble oil and hydrocarbon gases were produced at 250°C. Oil yields decreased and hydrocarbon gas yields increased as temperature was increased. Conversion of coal increased between 250° and 300°C., but there was no significant trend in conversion between 300° and 450°C. At 300°C., increasing the reaction time to two hours resulted in no significant change in product distribution.

TABLE 1: EFFECT OF TEMPERATURE ON THE DISTRIBUTION OF PRODUCTS FROM HVAB COAL AT 4,000 PSI

(50 Grams of Coal, 50 Grams of AlCl₃)

	Time at temp., hrs.	Conversion, weight percent	Yields, weight-percent of MAF coal				
			Organic benzene insols.	Benzene-soluble oil	Hydrocarbon gases	Net water	Acid gases
Temp., ° C.							
250	1	60	40	19	27	1	8
300	1	76	24	15	42	0	16
300	2	70	30	19	41	<1	20
350	1	81	19	3	59	0	-----
450	1	74	26	<1	68	0	16

The effect of aluminum chloride concentration on the distribution of products from HVAB coal was determined at 300°C. Time at temperature was one hour. The amount of aluminum chloride charged was varied between 12.5 and 100 grams. As can be seen in Table 2, very little reaction occurred with 12.5 grams of aluminum chloride in the charge. Hydrocarbon gas yields increased sharply as the amount of aluminum chloride was increased to 50 grams but remained essentially unchanged with a further increase to 100 grams.

TABLE 2: EFFECT OF AlCl₃ CONCENTRATION ON THE DISTRIBUTION OF PRODUCTS FROM HVAB COAL AT 300°C.

(50 Grams of Coal, 4,000 psi, 1 Hour at Temperature)

AlCl₃ charged, grams	Conversion, weight percent	Yields, weight-percent of MAF coal				
		Organic benzene insols.	Benzene-soluble oil	Hydrocarbon gases	Net water	Acid gases
12.5	4	96	4	1	<1	5
25.0	11	89	6	5	<1	9
37.5	25	75	11	11	1	11
50.0	76	24	15	42	0	16
100.0	73	27	16	40	0	

The results shown in Table 3 indicate that the conversion of carbonaceous material to hydrogasification catalyzed by aluminum chloride increases with increasing hydrogen content and with decreasing oxygen content of the material. The least suitable material for hydrocarbon gas production was the lignite which contained the most oxygen. Much of the oxygen in coals is normally removed as water during hydrogenation. Reaction of water with aluminum chloride would produce hydrochloric acid and decrease the aluminum chloride concentration. The yields of acid gases shown in Table 3 provide evidence that reaction with water did occur. Acid gas yields increased nearly linearly with increasing oxygen content of the feed. Yields of hydrogen sulfide and carbon dioxide obtained from coals would amount to only a few percent. In the experiments in which yields of acid gases were high, most of the gas would therefore be hydrochloric acid.

TABLE 3: DISTRIBUTION OF HYDROGENATION PRODUCTS FROM VARIOUS FEED MATERIALS

(50 Grams of Feed, 50 Grams of AlCl₃, 4,000 psi, 1 Hour at Temperature)

Feed material	Temp., °C.	Yields, weight-percent of MAF charge			
		Organic benzene insols.	Benzene-soluble oil	Hydrocarbon gases	Acid gases
Anthracite	450	80	<1	24	6
HVAB coal	300	24	15	42	16
Do	450	26	<1	68	16
HVCB coal	300	74	5	10	26
Do	450	55	3	21	34
Lignite	300	78	<1	8	35
Do	450	33	15	13	44
High-temp. tar	315	25	47	21	1
Do	450	26	4	81	1
Low-temp. tar	300	3	8	74	9
Do	450	4	<1	71	10
Petroleum residue	450	3	1	91	-----

Utilization of Friedel-Crafts Catalysts

In the process described by M.M. Wald; U.S. Patent 3,543,665; November 24, 1970; assigned to Shell Oil Company coal is converted to liquid hydrocarbon products by passing it through a continuous phase catalyst system selected from antimony trichloride, tribromide or triiodide; bismuth trichloride or tribromide; or arsenic triiodide; maintained at a temperature between 200° and 550°C. and under hydrogen partial pressure of at least 250 psi, whereby the catalyst system performs the functions of acting as a hydrogenation catalyst, acting as a cracking catalyst, and providing a medium for maintaining the reactants in suitable relationship to promote reactions and obtain optimum product distribution.

These catalysts have extremely high catalytic activity and therefore give high conversion of the coal at moderate temperatures and pressures. Under the reaction conditions of this process, it is possible to obtain a much more favorable product selectivity. Much less than the usual amount of propane and lighter hydrocarbons are formed thereby greatly saving on the amount of the costly hydrogen gas required for the coal conversion. Because of the high and selective cracking activity of the catalyst, a much larger part of the liquid product than usual boils within the range normally used for gasoline, and therefore less further processing is required. Moreover, the gasoline-range portion of the liquid product contains a high percentage of desirable isoparaffin hydrocarbons, which are high octane components, and of cycloparaffin hydrocarbons which are excellent feeds for catalytic reforming. The catalysts are insensitive to the amounts of water and hydrogen sulfide formed which often are catalyst poisons and their effectiveness is not diminished by the presence of normal amounts of solids such as ash and char.

In Figure 3.21 a vessel 1 is supplied with ground coal via line 2, liquid hydrocarbon recycled from the process as hereinafter described through line 3 and, if desired, a heavy oil, such as a residual fraction from a petroleum refining operation, or a coal extract supplied through line 5. In vessel 1 a slurry is formed between the liquid and solid phases. The slurry contains sufficient liquid to be pumpable and it passes through line 6 into the suction side of pump 7. In pump 7 the pressure of the slurry is raised to reaction pressures, preferably about 1,800 psi, and it passes through line 8 into the lower portion of reactor 9.

In reactor 9 a large pool of catalyst, preferably antimony tribromide, is maintained in sufficient quantity to be a continuous phase during the reaction process. The slurry, introduced beneath the body of liquid antimony tribromide passes upwardly through it, preferably distributed as fine droplets and particles. Hydrogen gas is also introduced beneath the catalyst liquid level through line 10, the hydrogen gas being partly recycle gas recovered from the product and partly fresh hydrogen gas introduced into the system through line 11.

Within reactor 9, which is maintained at 350°C. preferably by adjusting the temperature of the slurry before it enters the reactor, the cracking and hydrogenation reactions occur within the liquid catalyst medium and a product of normally liquid hydrocarbons, which are in vapor phase at reaction conditions, discharge from reactor 9 through line 12. The material in line 12 is cooled and flashed in phase separator 13 to remove a recycle hydrogen stream and the resultant liquid product from the process passes through line 15 into fractionation column 16. In fractionation column 16, light products are passed overhead through line 17 while the heavier materials are returned through the beforementioned line 3 as a liquid medium for slurrying incoming coal.

FIGURE 3.21: UTILIZATION OF FRIEDEL-CRAFTS CATALYSTS

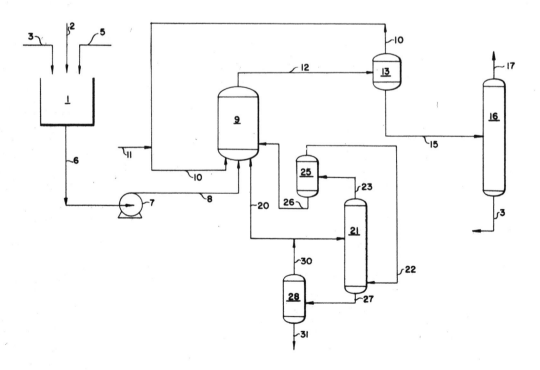

Source: M.M. Wald; U.S. Patent 3,542,665; November 24, 1970

In order to maintain the catalyst at an equilibrium level of activity and cleanliness, a slip stream is removed through line 20 and it passes into extraction zone 21. In extraction zone 21 the liquid catalyst is countercurrently contacted with the solvent entering the lower portion of extraction zone 21 through line 22 and as a result of the countercurrent contact an exact stream consisting of solvent, antimony bromide, and hydrocarbon passes through line 23 into flashing zone 25 which is maintained at lower pressure. In flashing zone 25 solvent is separated from the extract stream and passes overhead through line 22 through which it is returned to the lower portion of extractor 21. The remainder of the extract stream is passed from the bottom of flashing zone 25 through line 26 and returned to the main body of catalyst. The material in line 26 consists almost entirely of the antimony tribromide and hydrocarbon that was removed in the slip stream passing through line 20.

The raffinate phase from extractor 21 consists of ash, char, and ammonia-antimony-bromide complex formed in the reaction zone 9. This material is introduced into regenerator 28 wherein it is subjected to high enough temperature to decompose the complex to form antimony bromide and ammonium bromide. If necessary, hydrogen bromide or bromine is also added to regenerator 28 so that regeneration may be better effected. The regenerated antimony bromide is returned to reactor 9 through line 30, either directly or by being added to the stream in line 20, while the residual material including ash and char is removed through line 31 and subjected to appropriate further treatment.

Example 1: Illinois No. 6 coal ground to between 60 to 200 mesh was employed as the charge. The experiment described herein was an autoclave experiment and it employed 150 grams of antimony tribromide as the continuous liquid phase catalyst and 30 grams of coal. Hydrogen pressure of about 1,800 psi was employed, and the reaction was carried out for 30 minutes at a temperature of 350°C. The hydrocarbon product from the process was as follows:

	Percent by Weight
Propane and lighter	2.1
Butanes	4.8
Pentanes and hexanes	7.3
Cyclo-C_6H_{12}	6.8
$C_7 + C_8$ hydrocarbons	14.8
Hydrocarbon boiling above C_8 and below 250°C.	19.5
Liquid boiling above 250°C.	29.5
Char (insoluble carbonaceous material)	4.2
Water	11.1
Hydrogen sulfide	4.5
Ammonia	1.8
Total	106.4

The hydrogen charged to the process amounted to 6.4% by weight of the coal charge and this amount should be subtracted from the total yield to make a weight balance of 100%.

To complete the above analysis, it should be brought out that the liquid product boiling below 250°C. was examined for hetero-atom content and the analysis indicated that 115 parts per million of organic sulfur still remained in the product, 0.09% weight organic oxygen still remained in the product, and that no organic nitrogen could be detected. The foregoing example establishes that of the carbon and hydrogen in the coal charged to the process, all of it was converted to useable hydrocarbon except 4.2% that remained as char. The example also establishes that the liquid product from the process is highly suitable for use as hydrocarbon fuel or for charging to a petroleum conversion process in that it is substantially free of oxygen, sulfur, and nitrogen which are troublesome ingredients in processing of petroleum.

Example 2: Although antimony tribromide is the preferred catalyst of this process, antimony trichloride, antimony triiodide, bismuth trichloride, bismuth tribromide and arsenic triiodide may be employed when different processing conditions or product distributions are desired. In evaluating the metal halides useful for this process, a series of tests was run under indicated conditions. In each test, 20 grams of coal was employed with enough molten catalyst to produce a continuous phase in an autoclave maintained at 1,800 psi hydrogen pressure. All analyses are based on maf coal, or in other words, on conversion of material that it is possible to convert. The products from the various tests are recorded in the table below.

Catalyst	$SbCl_3$	SbI_3	$BiCl_3$	$BiBr_3$	AsI_3
Temperature, °C.	350	350	325	265	325
Products, g./100 g. MAF coal:					
C_1+C_2	1.2	1.7	1.8	0.4	1.3
C_3	2.8	1.6	8.1	1.6	0.6
C_4	7.7	3.9	16.5	6.0	0.8
C_5	5.2	3.0	8.9	3.7	0.9
C_6	9.6	8.3	9.1	7.4	5.6
C_7+C_8	14.1	12.4	11.5	12.5	8.0
C_9-250° C.	10.9	25.2	7.4	16.3	15.6
Hydrogen consumed, g./100g. MAF coal	5.5	5.9	7.8	5.4	5.0

The data in the preceding table indicate that all of the claimed catalysts have good activity for converting coal to liquid products. The total conversions in every case were 90% or higher on an máf basis.

EBULLATING BED PROCESSES

Gas-Liquid Contacting Process

The process developed by E.S. Johanson; U.S. Patent Reissue 25,770; April 27, 1965; assigned to Hydrocarbon Research, Inc. provides an improved method of effecting contact between liquid and gasiform materials. It provides a method of chemically reacting liquid and gasiform materials in the presence of a mass of solid particles of contact material whereby a decreased pressure drop in the particulate mass, improved contact between the reactants and the contact material, and a decrease in the rate of formation of deposits in the reactor may be accomplished.

This is attained by concurrently flowing streams of the liquid and gasiform material upwardly through a vessel containing a mass of solid particles of a contact material, the mass of solid particles being maintained in random motion within the vessel by the upflowing streams. A mass of solid particles in this state of random motion in a liquid medium may be described as "ebullated". An ebullated mass of solid particles has a gross volume that is larger than that of the same mass when it is stationary. The benefits of this process are obtained when this expansion is at least 10% of the volume of the stationary mass. The contact material is in the form of beads, pellets, lumps, chips or like particles usually having an average dimension of approximately at least 1/32 inch, and more frequently in the range of 1/16 to 1/4 inch. The size and shape of the particles used in any specific process will depend on the particular conditions of that process, e.g., the density, viscosity and velocity of the liquid involved in that process.

It is a relatively simple matter to determine for any ebullated process the range of throughput rates of upflowing liquid which will cause the mass of solid particles to become expanded while the particles are maintained in random motion. The gross volume of the mass of contact material expands when ebullated without, however, any substantial quantity of the particles being carried away by the upflowing liquid and, therefore, a fairly well defined upper level of randomly moving particles establishes itself in the upflowing liquid. This upper level above which few, if any, particles ascend will hereinafter be called the upper level of ebullation. In contrast to processes in which fluid streams flow downwardly or upwardly through a fixed mass of particles, the spaces between the particles of an ebullated mass are large with the result that the pressure drop of the liquid flowing through the ebullated mass is small and remains substantially constant as the fluid throughput rate is increased.

It should be noted that the random motion of particles in an ebullated mass causes these particles to rub against each other and against the walls of the vessel so that the formation of deposits thereon is impeded or minimized. This scouring action helps to prevent agglomeration of the particles and plugging up of the vessel. This effect is particularly important where catalyst particles are employed and maximum contact between fluid reactants and the catalytic surfaces is desired, since such surfaces are then exposed to the reactants for a greater period of time before becoming fouled or inactivated by foreign deposits. For this reason, the process is particularly useful in carrying out various chemical reactions between liquid and gasiform materials in the presence of a solid catalyst.

FIGURE 3.22: GAS-LIQUID CONTACTING PROCESS

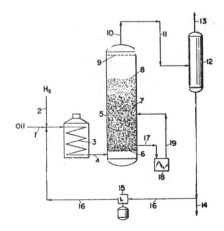

Source: E.S. Johanson; U.S. Patent Reissue 25,770; April 27, 1965

Referring to Figure 3.22, charge stock from line 1 is combined with recycle oil from line 16 and hydrogen-containing gas from line 2 is added to the combined oil, all of the fluid reactants flowing through heater 3. The preheated gas-liquid mixture is then transferred by line 4 to the bottom of reactor 5 which contains a mass of solid particles of hydrogenation catalyst supported on screen or perforated plate 6. When the process is not in operation, the catalyst mass has a stationary bed level 7. When, however, the process is being carried out, the particles are in constant motion with respect to each other and the gross mass expands so that its upper boundary or upper level of ebullation is at 8. The reactor may contain a second screen or perforated plate 9 near its top to prevent stray particles of contact material from leaving reactor 5 with the reaction effluent. It should be noted that screen 9 is near reactor outlet 10, well above upper level of ebullation 8.

The reaction effluent discharging through outlet 10 flows through line 11 into separator 12 wherein it is separated into gasiform and liquid phases. A gasiform stream which comprises unreacted hydrogen and both gaseous and vaporized hydrocarbons is drawn off by line 13 and conventionally treated to recover hydrogen, hydrocarbon gases, gasoline, etc. The separated hydrogen may, of course, be used as part of the hydrogen feed to the system. Part of the liquid drawn from separator 12 through line 14 is sent to product recovery for further treatment to obtain valuable products, e.g., by fractional distillation, catalytic cracking, lubricating oil refining, etc. The remainder of the liquid is circulated by pump 15 through line 16 for recycling to reactor 6 after being combined with fresh feed and hydrogen.

The above description illustrates a process which operates batch-wise as far as the contact material is concerned. When a process is relatively clean, i.e., little or no foreign deposits are formed on the contact particles, the process may be operated in this fashion for a considerable period without interruption. However, when a process causes substantial fouling deposits to be formed on the contact particles, particularly those depending upon high catalytic activity to promote reaction, it is necessary to interrupt the process at intervals and replace the fouled contact material with fresh or regenerated material, although these intervals are lengthened because of the scouring effect produced by ebullation, as already mentioned. When it is desired to operate the process in a completely continuous manner, contact material may be continuously withdrawn from reactor 6 through line 17 as a slurry and sent to catalyst regeneration plant 18. Therein the catalyst particles are separated from the liquid, regenerated, reslurried in the liquid and sent back to reactor 6 by way of line 19.

Example: A residual hydrocarbon oil having a gravity of 8.3°API, a sulfur content of 5.3% by weight and a Ramsbottom carbon residue of 17.2% by weight was hydrogenated by a process as illustrated in the drawing using a cobalt molybdate hydrogenation catalyst of 12 to 16 mesh particle size, a pressure of 3,000 psig and a temperature of 830°F. Hydrogen-rich gas was supplied to provide 1,000 standard cubic feet of hydrogen for each barrel of charge stock entering the reactor. Treated oil was recycled to the reactor at the rate of 27 volumes per volume of charge stock and hydrogen recovered from the reaction effluent was also recycled to the reactor so that the total hydrogen flowing through the reactor was 7,000 standard cubic feet for each barrel of charge stock.

During the first 800 hours of operation, the charge stock together with recycled oil had a total upflow rate of 30 gallons per minute per square foot of horizontal cross-section of the reactor. At this liquid flow rate, the mass of catalyst particles was mildly ebullated and its volume was expanded about 15% over that of the same mass when in a settled state. While the charge stock was essentially a residuum of hydrocarbons boiling above 900°F., the total liquid product recovered from the hydrogenation process comprised approximately 70% by volume of hydrocarbons boiling at temperatures not exceeding 900°F. Accordingly, the operation is said to effect about 70% conversion of the charge stock. The sulfur content of the total liquid product increased from 0.4 to 1.0% by weight during the first 300 hours of operation which represented the usual high initial deactivation of fresh catalyst, but only from 1.0 to 1.4% by weight during the 300 to 800 hour period.

The treated oil recycle rate was then reduced to yield a liquid flow rate of 20 gallons per minute per square foot of horizontal cross-section of the reactor during the 800 to 1,000 hour period at which rate substantially no ebullation or expansion of the catalyst mass occurred. Under these conditions, the sulfur content of the total liquid product increased from 1.4 to 1.7% by weight, indicating a considerable rise in the deactivation rate of the catalyst over that obtained during the 300 to 800 hour period when the mass was in an ebullated state. During the period from 1,000 to 1,230 hours, the oil recycle rate was increased to yield a total liquid flow rate of 40 gallons per minute per square foot and at this rate the catalyst mass was again in an ebullated state and its volume expanded to about 20 to 25% over that of the mass in a settled state.

In this latter period, there was substantially no increase in sulfur content of the liquid product. The lower rate of decline of catalytic activity obtained during the 300 to 800 and 1,000 to 1,230 hour periods as represented by rise in sulfur content of the liquid product as compared with the higher rate of decline of catalytic activity obtained in the 800 to 1,000 hour period when the catalyst mass was stationary indicates that the rate of catalyst deactivation is substantially less when the process is run with the catalyst mass in an ebullated state than when a conventional fixed bed is used.

Comparing the results obtained when the process was operated with the catalyst particles in an ebullated state with the results of a hydrogenation process conducted under similar conditions but with liquid downflow through a fixed bed of catalyst particles, it was found that each pound of ebullated catalyst was as effective as approximately two pounds of catalyst in a fixed bed. Specifically, it was observed in this example that the charge stock was hydrogenated at the rate of 0.14 barrel per day per pound of ebullated catalyst in the reactor. This rate is indicative of a higher space velocity than can be achieved with fixed catalyst particles if comparable products are to be obtained.

Catalytic Hydrogenation of Coal in an Ebullating Bed

S.C. Schuman, R.H. Wolk and M.C. Chervenak; U.S. Patent 3,321,393; May 23, 1967; assigned to Hydrocarbon Research, Inc. disclose an improved process of treating coal with hydrogen in the presence of a catalyst and oils derived from coal.

Hydrogen treatment of coal, while desirable economically, has been beset with many formidable problems. One of these has been the necessity of carrying out reactions in a system where the coal, catalyst, hydrogen and liquid product are in intimate contact. A second problem has been the necessity of maintaining a stable and satisfactory reaction temperature when the reactions which occur are highly exothermic.

A gas-liquid contacting process has been described in U.S. Patent Reissue 25,770 which completely eliminates high pressure drop or plugging difficulties usually found in standard fixed bed processes. In this process, Johanson contacts gases, liquids and solids under conditions so that the solids are in an expanded state and occupy at least 10% greater volume than the settled state of the mass and are in random motion in the gas-liquid system. Such a mass of solid particles in this state of random motion in a liquid or gas-liquid medium may be described as ebullated.

It should be noted that in an ebullated catalyst bed, there is a sharp and finite level of the catalytic solid, below which the catalytic solid exists at a concentration in excess of 5 pounds per cubic foot, and above which it has a concentration of less than 0.10 pound per cubic foot. It is obvious that the ebullated bed completely eliminates difficulties due to the plugging heretofore experienced in conventional fixed bed reaction systems. A collateral benefit of the ebullated bed is that it permits the use of very active catalyst particles of relatively small particle size, which otherwise would be essentially inoperable in a fixed bed system due to excessive pressure drop.

However, the use of an ebullated bed does not eliminate the heat release problems encountered in hydrogenation reactions. In general, it can be said that such problems become severe in a hydrogenation system when hydrogen consumption is obtained corresponding to more than 2,000 standard cubic feet per ton of coal fed. Experience has shown that in hydrogenation, hydrodesulfurization, and hydrocracking reactions, the consumption of 1 cubic foot of hydrogen is accompanied by a heat release from about 50 to 75 Btu. From this, it can be readily calculated that the consumption of 5,000 cubic feet of hydrogen per ton of coal charged will produce a temperature rise across the bed of from 60° to 90°F. if no means of cooling is provided. Obviously, such temperature rises can become much more severe; for example, in cases where hydrogen consumption is 10,000 standard cubic feet per barrel of feed oil charged, temperature rises of 120° to 180°F. will be experienced unless some method of temperature control is utilized. Such high temperature gradients across the bed pose many problems, the principal one being that at least part of the catalyst will be contacted at temperature conditions at which it will be severely deteriorated and degraded due to excessive coke formation.

This process provides an effective hydrogenation system for coal in which catalysts of relatively fine particle size can be employed in an ebullated bed at conditions in which hydrogen consumption is at least 10,000 standard cubic feet per ton of coal charged.

As shown in Figure 3.23, a liquid feed from line 1, consisting of coal ground to a fineness of at least 80 mesh (Tyler) slurried in an oil generated in the process with from 1.5 to 6.0 parts of oil per part of coal, together with hydrogen-containing gas from line 2, both suitably preheated, are passed upwardly into the reactor 3. Entering the reactor the stream passes through a distribution device such as that schematically illustrated as 4. The reactor contains a mass of solid particles of hydrogenation catalyst; when the process is not in operation the catalyst has a stationary bed level 5. However, when the process is carried out as described herein, the catalyst particles are in constant random motion with respect to each other as the gross mass is expanded so that its upper boundary or upper level of ebullation is at 6. Not far above this point, at the zone shown in the drawing at 7, a phase which contains essentially no catalyst is obtained.

The level 6 can be established by the use of a gamma ray instrument by which the mass within the reactor can be established at any reactor height. Gamma rays from the source 8 are absorbed to a varying extent by the mass of material they "see" in passing to the sensing element 9. When the gamma rays must pass through the high density catalyst-containing phase, a much lower reading is obtained on the sensing element than when no catalyst is present. Thus, if the instrument is suitably mounted (such as on a vertical trolley for example), and suitably calibrated, it can establish level 6 with virtual certainty, and furthermore establish the catalyst density which exists at level 6 with high accuracy.

In the example shown, the reaction products leave the reactor 3 through line 10 without separation. However, as is well-known to those skilled in the art, suitable devices may be installed within the reactor to remove the liquid and gaseous streams separately as by a trap-tray.

FIGURE 3.23: CATALYTIC HYDROGENATION OF COAL IN AN EBULLATING BED

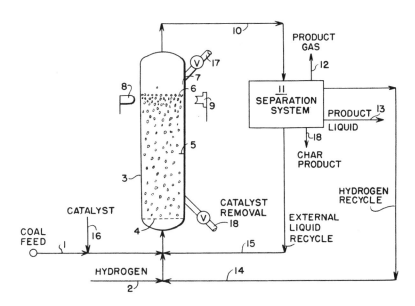

Source: S.C. Schuman, R.H. Wolk and M.C. Chervenak; U.S. Patent 3,321,393; May 23, 1967

The product stream passes into the separation system 11, in which the usual product and recycle streams are obtained by conventional procedures. Schematically illustrated in the drawing are product gas and product liquid streams 12 and 13, and hydrogen recycle stream 14. In the process an external liquid recycle stream is seldom employed, since single pass conversion is generally high; however, the possibility of such a stream is indicated by the line 15. The char is removed through line 18.

Using an ebullated bed as described herein, fresh catalyst may be continuously or semicontinuously added to the reactor system with the feed as shown in line 16, or by a conventional lock-hopper system as in 17. Similarly spent catalyst may be withdrawn through 18.

Example: A coal, such as Illinois No. 6 (bituminous) from the Belleville area, was ground to a fineness all of which passed a 270 mesh (Tyler) screen and was slurried with oil formed in the process. The reactor was operated at a total pressure of 2,700 psig and at an average temperature of about 850°F. The catalyst was cobalt molybdate extended on alumina. The hydrogen throughput was 43 standard cubic feet of hydrogen per pound of coal and the coal throughput was approximately 0.2 pound of coal per pound of slurry. The conversion, on a maf basis to liquid and gas was in excess of 80% with a yield in excess of two and one-half barrels per ton of oil boiling below 900°F. The liquid to gas ratio was 0.08 and the temperature gradient was 9°F.

As noted, the coal is preferably ground to pass an 80 mesh screen and in such case the catalysts, to be three diameters larger, would be in the general size range of 30 to 40 mesh. If the coal is largely smaller than 200 mesh, the catalyst size can be in the 50 to 70 mesh size and if the coal is generally smaller than 300 mesh, the catalyst may be in the 100 to 120 mesh range. It is desirable to have a liquid-gas throughput sufficient to ebullate the catalyst bed without carryover of catalyst but with removal of the residual coal particles (ash). The bed expansion should be at least 10% based on its settled state.

With a utilization of hydrogen in excess of 10,000 scf/ton of coal, conversion ratios in excess of 85% are obtained. Coal throughput can be in the range of 18 to 30 pounds per cubic foot of the reactor.

Production of Low Sulfur Fuel Oil from Coal

The process developed by H.H. Stotler, M. Calderon and C.A. Johnson; U.S. Patent 3,617,474; November 2, 1971; assigned to Hydrocarbon Research, Inc. is primarily adapted to make an inexpensive, low cost, fuel substitute of low gravity which may be used either as ground-up solids or as a liquid if maintained at a temperature above the melting point. The low sulfur characteristic is especially beneficial for reduction of pollution.

FIGURE 3.24:   PRODUCTION OF LOW SULFUR FUEL OIL FROM COAL

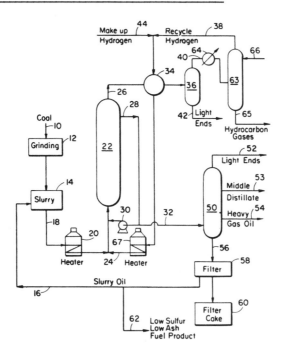

Source: H.H. Stotler, M. Calderon and C.A. Johnson; U.S. Patent 3,617,474; November 2, 1971

Referring to Figure 3.24, coal at 10, appropriately ground at 12 (and not necessarily dried), is mixed at 14 with recycle slurry oil 16 to form a coal-oil slurry. This slurry is passed by line 18 through heater 20 into the lower part of reactor 22. Hydrogen is added at 24. Liquid oil and hydrogen pass upwardly through a bed of catalyst or activated alumina at sufficient velocity to maintain an ebullated bed of catalyst or inert solids such as disclosed in the Schuman U.S. Patent 3,281,393. A gaseous phase is removed overhead at 26 and a liquid stream is removed at 28. The liquid stream is in part recycled through pump 30 to maintain the desired liquid velocity and a net liquid stream is removed at 32.

Preferably the coal is initially ground to all pass 20 mesh and not more than about 10% passing 325 mesh (Tyler). The slurry at 18 is a pumpable slurry with at least equal parts of oil and coal but, if for operating reasons, it is desirable to recycle an additional amount of slurry oil, slurries of one part coal and up to 10 parts oil may be used. A temperature of 800° to 900°F., preferably about 850°F., and a hydrogen partial pressure of 800 to 2,500 psi, and preferably about 1,890 psi, is maintained in the reactor.

The vapors 26 leaving the upper part of the reactor are cooled at 34. Condensed light ends are separated in drum 36 and removed at 42. Vapors leaving drum 36 at 40 are cooled in exchanger 64 and scrubbed with an absorber oil in column 63 to remove light hydrocarbon gases at 65 and hydrogen leaving at 38 is recycled. The recycle hydrogen stream 38 plus makeup hydrogen at 44 also passes through heat exchanger 34, through heater 67 and becomes the hydrogen feed line 24. The liquid leaving the reactor at 32 is separated in one or more fractionation columns 50 into a light ends stream 52, a middle distillate at 53, a heavy gas oil at 54 and a heavy ends at 56.

The heavy ends at 56 contain a substantial amount of solids which are sent to a filter 58. The filter cake is recovered at 60. The filter cake comprises a char and ash product and may contain up to 20% of oil which can be recovered thermally. A centrifuge could also be used. The filtrate leaving filter 58 provides the slurry oil recycle stream 16 and the fuel oil product, 62.

The low sulfur fuel oil product 62 will have an API gravity of about -14° with a Btu value in excess of 16,600 Btu/lb. Normally this product has a boiling point not less than 400°F. and must be kept hot in order to permit pumpability or distillates can be removed to give a product boiling at 900°F. and higher. Alternatively, the fuel oil product can be cooled, solidified and ground and used as a solid combustible fuel low in ash and sulfur, especially when free of distillates.

The reactor 22 may be operated under varying conditions depending upon the maximum sulfur desired in the fuel oil product. The following table illustrates experimental results from the operations. Approximately three barrels of fuel oil with a sulfur content of less than 0.5 weight percent sulfur and 0.56 barrels of naphtha have been produced per ton of Illinois

No. 6 coal. Treatment of coal from the Pittsburgh No. 8 seam has yielded 3.48 barrels of fuel oil per ton and 0.21 barrels per ton of naphtha. In this case the fuel oil product contained approximately 1% sulfur.

The versatility of the reactor is indicated in the table below in which, in one case, 93 pounds of Illinois No. 6 coal per hour per cubic foot was the coal feed rate utilizing a cobalt molybdate on alumina catalyst. In such case the hydrogen consumption was approximately 3.75 scf/lb. The Pittsburgh No. 8 coal was operated at a throughput rate of 187 pounds of coal per hour per cubic foot with activated alumina and only 2 scf/lb. of hydrogen was consumed.

Example of Typical Coal Analyses

(percent by weight)

	Illinois No. 6	Pittsburgh No. 8
Carbon	70.51	74.29
Hydrogen	5.14	5.49
Nitrogen	1.28	1.49
Sulfur	3.39	4.03
Oxygen	8.08	6.40
Ash	11.60	8.30
Volatile matter (maf)	44.56	46.46
Organic sulfur	1.24	2.10

Reactor Conditions

	Illinois No. 6	Pittsburgh No. 8
Pressure, total, psig	2,250	2,250
Temperature, °F.	850	850
Hydrogen consumption, scf/lb.	3.75	2
Catalyst	CoMo on alumina	Alumina
Throughput, lbs./hr./cu. ft.	93	187

Examples of Yields

(pounds per 100 pounds of dry coal)

	Illinois No. 6	Pittsburgh No. 8
CO_2	0.92	1.0
CO	0.31	-
C_1	1.66	4.81
C_2	0.80	-
C_3	1.28	-
C_4 to 400°F.	7.71	2.85
400° to 650°F.	18.19	3.83
650° to 975°F.	9.19	16.41
Residuum (975°F. plus)	35.31	53.15
Coal residue	7.34	6.90
Ash	11.60	8.30
H_2S	1.75	1.80
NH_3	0.72	0.20
H_2O	5.27	1.80

Yield Summary		
Fuel oil (400°F. plus) barrels per ton	3.06	3.48
Naphtha, barrels per ton	0.56	0.21
Sulfur (product), % by weight	0.46	1.02

Hydrogen Donor Solvents in Coal Hydrogenation Processes

M.C. Kirk, Jr. and W.H. Seitzer; U.S. Patent 3,594,303; July 20, 1971; assigned to Sun Oil Company describe a process for hydrogenation of coal where a slurry of pulverized coal in a hydrogen donor solvent is hydrogenated in the liquid phase in the absence of catalyst, vapors from this first hydrogenation are then subjected to a vapor phase hydrogenation in the presence of a sulfided catalyst and thereafter the products of the reaction are separated.

A critical feature of this process is that the pulverized coal to be liquefied is slurried with a hydrogen donor solvent. These donor solvent materials are well-known and comprise aromatic hydrocarbons which are partially hydrogenated, generally having one or more of the nuclei at least partially saturated. Several examples of such materials are Tetralin, dihydro-naphthalene, dihydroalkylnaphthalenes, dihydrophenanthrene, dihydroanthracene, dihydrochrysenes, tetrahydropyrenes, tetrahydrochrysenes, tetrahydrofluoranthenes and the like. Of particular value in this process as hydrogen donor solvents are the hydrophenanthrenes and hydroanthracenes such as dihydroanthracene. It will be understood that these materials may be obtained from any source, but are readily available from the process by separating hydrocarbon fractions formed in the process to obtain the aromatics which have been at least partially hydrogenated, or they may be obtained by partially hydrogenating specific aromatic products by conventional techniques. In order to further describe the process, reference is made to Figure 3.25.

Pulverized coal together with the hydrogen donor solvent which may be from any source (but is preferably obtained from the reaction process itself by hydrogenation of the coal and subsequently separated) is fed into slurry tank 1 where the slurry is taken through line 2 to the liquid phase thermal coal liquefaction zone (bottom section) of reactor 3. Hydrogen is also introduced to this reactor through line 4 and comprises fresh and recycle gas as shown as line 8 and 8a. Reaction conditions in this liquid phase zone are temperatures of about 750° to 840°F. and pressures on the order of 2,500 psig. No catalyst is present in this phase of the process.

Hydrogenation proceeds and vapors of the hydrogen donor solvent and reaction products pass upwardly through reactor 3 into the vapor phase catalytic hydrogenation zone (top section). It will be understood, of course, that although both the liquid phase thermal liquefaction zone and vapor phase catalytic hydrogenation zone are shown in the drawing in a single reactor, this process is equally operable by separating these two stages and using separate reactors for each stage. In the catalytic hydrogenation zone, which contains a supported catalyst as described above, reaction temperatures of about 700° to 800°F. and pressures of about 2,500 psig are maintained.

Ash-containing residue which remains in the first liquid phase thermal coal liquefaction zone is not able to enter the vapor phase catalytic hydrogenation zone and thus has no adverse effect on the catalyst. As ash builds up in the liquid phase zone, it may be removed through line 5 for further processing if desired, as for example, for carbonization or for hydrogen manufacture.

FIGURE 3.25: HYDROGEN DONOR SOLVENTS IN COAL HYDROGENATION PROCESSES

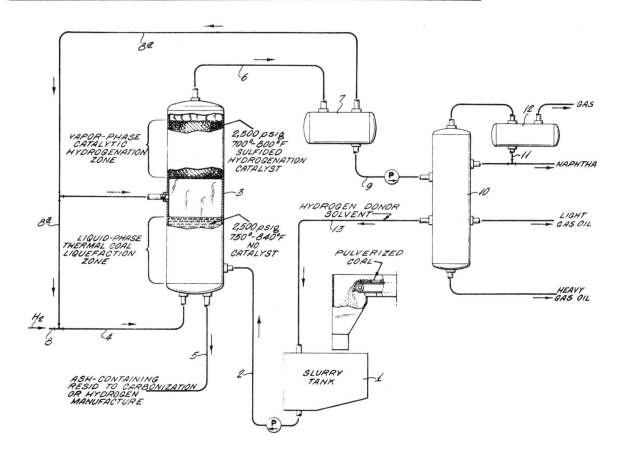

Source: M.C. Kirk, Jr. and W.H. Seitzer; U.S. Patent 3,594,303; July 20, 1971

The volatile products resulting from the catalytic hydrogenation zone are taken off through line 6 into a separator 7 and hydrogen is recycled through line 8a to the reactor. The heavier products are fed to line 9 into a fractionator 10 to produce fractions of naphtha, light gas oil and heavy gas oil. The naphtha may, of course, be separated into a lighter gas fraction by passing part of the naphtha through line 11 into separator 12 to remove the more volatile gas. One of the fractions from fractionator 10 will be the hydrogen donor solvent which is taken through line 13 back to the original slurry tank 1 for mixing with the pulverized coal.

Ebullating Bed Coal Hydrogenation

The process developed by P.C. Keith, E.S. Johanson, R.H. Wolk, S.B. Alpert and S.C. Schuman; U.S. Patent 3,519,555; July 7, 1970; assigned to Hydrocarbon Research, Inc. describes a coal hydrogenation process employing an expanded catalyst bed and producing better than 80% conversion of coal to gas and liquid petroleum products. These products appear to be competitive or superior in cost and quality to available fuels. One can develop a nearly inexhaustible fuel source and industrially make available, commercial competitive fuels. It is also possible with this process to provide either a high or low Btu fuel gas such as methane and hydrogen-carbon monoxide mixture respectively or a natural gas substitute of about 1,000 Btu, which can be placed in pipelines compatible in burning, flow, and metering characteristics with the usual natural gas.

As shown in Figure 3.26, a coal such as bituminous, semibituminous, sub-bituminous or lignite, or a similar material such as shale, entering the system at 10 is first passed through a preparation unit generally indicated at 12. In such a unit it is desirable to dry the coal of all surface moisture and to grind the coal to a desired mesh and then to screen it for uniformity. For the purposes of this process, it is preferable that the coal has a fineness of about 100 mesh and is preferably of relatively close sizing, i.e., all passing 50 mesh and not less than 80% retained on 200 mesh. However, it will be observed that the preciseness of size may vary between different types of coal, lignite and shale.

FIGURE 3.26: EBULLATING BED COAL HYDROGENATION

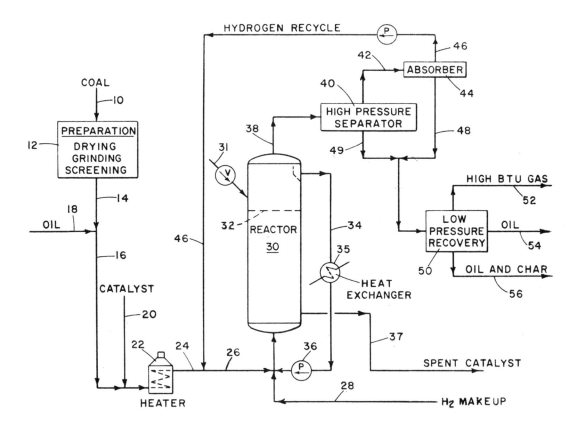

Source: P.C. Keith, E.S. Johanson, R.H. Wolk, S.B. Alpert and S.C. Schuman; U.S. Patent 3,519,555;
July 7, 1970

The coal fines discharge at 14 into the transfer line 16 where the coal is blended with a carrying oil indicated at 18 which, as hereinafter pointed out, is conveniently made in the system. To establish an effective transportable slurry, it is found that the ground coal should be mixed with at least about an equal weight of carrying oil. In addition, a hydrogenation catalyst, if desired, may be added to 20 in the ratio of about 0.01 to 0.20 pound of catalyst per ton of coal. Such a catalyst would be from the class of cobalt, molybdenum, nickel, tin, iron and the like deposited on a base of the class of alumina, magnesia, silica, and the like. It is to be noted that the catalyst need not be added continuously nor is it required that it be in fine admixture with the coal.

The coal-oil slurry is then passed through the heater 22 to bring the slurry up to a temperature in the order of 750° to 950°F., or 800° to 900°F., such heated slurry then discharging at 24 into the reactor feed line 26 wherein it is supplied with makeup hydrogen from the line 28 as well as recycle hydrogen in line 46. The entire mixture of hydrogen and coal-oil slurry then enters one or more reactors 30 passing upwardly from the bottom at a rate and under pressure and at a temperature to accomplish the desired hydrogenation.

Preferred reactor operating conditions are in the range of 750° to 950°F. and less than 3,000 psig. Coal throughput is at the rate of 15 to 150 pounds per hour per cubic foot of reactor space so that the yield of unreacted coal as char is between 5 and 25% of the quantity of moisture- and ash-free coal feed. The relative size of the coal and catalyst particles and condition of ebullation are such that the catalyst is retained in the reactor while the unreacted char is carried out with the reaction products and the slurry oil solid.

The degree of hydrogenation in reactor 30 can be limited to that which will leave sufficient unreacted coal to make hydrogen in a subsequent gasification stage. This hydrogen could then be recycled for use in the hydrogenation step. This type of process would be advantageous in areas where hydrogen is difficult to obtain. However, with gasification, the amount of conversion would be significantly reduced. The effluent stream 38 passing to separator 40 includes a stream that contains gaseous fractions, is virtually free of solid particles of contact material although it may contain char in the liquid. From the separator 40 a gas stream is removed at 42 and then passed to absorber 44. A hydrogen recycle in line 46 removed from absorber 44 may be returned to the reactor 30 to supplement the hydrogen requirements. A liquid stream from the absorber 44 will be removed at 48 and this is joined with the liquid stream 49 from the high pressure separator 40. The joint liquid is then passed to a low pressure recovery system 50.

The low pressure separator 50 permits removal of a high Btu gaseous product at 52 and a solids-free liquid at 54. A separate liquid stream containing char is removed at 56. A portion of the liquid from line 54 may be used to prepare the initial slurry.

Example: Coal having 42% by weight of volatile matter and 10.6% by weight of ash on a maf basis was pulverized to pass through a 100 mesh screen and then admixed with hydrocarbon oil in the weight ratio of 3.3 parts of oil per part of coal. The coal-oil suspension was passed upwardly through a reactor 30 together with hydrogen. The reactor contained a mass of cobalt molybdate on alumina hydrogenation catalyst particles of uniform cylindrical size about 0.025 inch in diameter and 1/8 inch in length. The coal-oil suspension flowed upward through the reactor at the rate of 20 gallons per minute per square foot of horizontal cross-section of the reactor thereby effecting ebullation of the catalyst particles with approximately 50% expansion of the settled volume of the catalyst mass to fill about 80% of the reactor space when in the expanded state.

Hydrogen-rich gas was supplied to the bottom of the reactor at the rate of 80,000 standard cubic feet for each ton of coal entering the reactor. The hydrogenation was conducted at a temperature of 830°F. and a pressure of 2,750 pounds per square inch gauge. The reaction effluent comprising coal-oil suspension of partially hydrogenated coal particles was recycled directly to the reactor at a rate of about 12 volumes per volume of slurry feed to maintain the aforesaid flow rate of 20 gallons per minute per square foot. The conversion of maf coal to liquid and gaseous products amounted to 82% of the weight of maf coal feed.

Coal Hydrogenation in a Catalytic Ebullating Bed Reactor

E.S. Johanson, S.C. Schuman, H.H. Stotler and R.H. Wolk; U.S. Patent 3,519,553; July 7, 1970; assigned to Hydrocarbon Research, Inc. describe a process for the catalytic hydrocracking of solid carbonaceous feed materials by passing an oil slurry of the particulated feed with hydrogen upwardly through a catalytic reaction zone such that the catalyst bed is in the ebullated state and removing gaseous and liquid products from the reaction zone along with solids. The liquid products are fractionated into light distillates, middle oils, recycle and slurry oils and a residuum and solids containing bottoms material. A wash liquid is then mixed with the bottoms material after which the combined wash liquid and bottoms material are subjected to a separation step whereby the residuum and other valuable hydrocarbons in the bottoms material which were retained by the solids are preferentially attracted by the wash liquid. The solids are then separated from the wash liquid solution and the residuum and hydrocarbon products may be easily recovered from the wash liquid.

FIGURE 3.27: COAL HYDROGENATION IN A CATALYTIC EBULLATING BED REACTOR

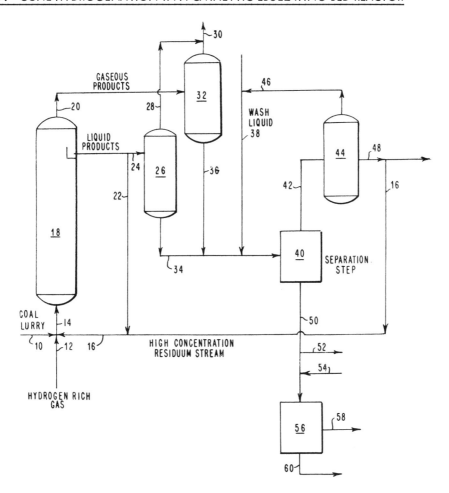

Source: E.S. Johanson, S.C. Schuman, H.H. Stotler and R.H. Wolk; U.S. Patent 3,519,553; July 7, 1970

As shown in Figure 3.27, a carbonaceous fuel material such as bituminous or sub-bituminous coal, lignite or peat, which has been pulverized and dried is introduced at line 10, along with a hydrogen-rich gas at 12 and a high concentration residuum stream from the process at 16 through line 14 into the reaction zone 18. The slurry is normally about a 1:1 mixture of solids and oils. As described heretofore, the reaction zone contains a particulate catalyst which is in an ebullated state due to the velocity of the gas and liquid feed materials, upwardly through it. Gaseous products are removed through line 20 and proceed into separator 32, wherein they are flashed at a pressure somewhat lower than the reaction pressure to produce a light vapor product in line 30 and a liquid in line 36. The liquid products from the reaction zone are removed through line 24. A portion of the liquid products may be recycled to the reactor through line 22, if desired.

The liquid products proceed to separation step 26 wherein they are separated to produce a vapor overhead in line 28, which is combined with the vapor products overhead from separator 32 in line 30. The liquid from separation or flash stage 26 is removed through line 34 and combined with the liquid from flash step 32 in line 36. Separation stage 26 may consist of any number of combination of flash steps, fractionation steps and physical separation steps known to the processing art. For example, the liquid product in line 24 may first be flashed and the liquid and solids from the flash introduced to a liquid cyclone or solids separation unit. Most of the liquids with minimal amounts of the solids are separated and may be utilized as the recycle stream. This stream would consist essentially of residuum and heavy and middle gas oils.

The remaining solids and retained residuum and oil may then be introduced to the process as shown and would be represented by stream 34. If desired, however, the solids and retained residuum material and oil may be put through an additional fractionation step. The bottoms from this step would then constitute stream 34. Regardless, however, of the series or combination of steps employed, one will always end up with a stream containing most of the solids and retained products. Thus, this process is directed basically towards a method for recovering those retained products. The final result, however, of this increased recovery is an overall increase in the yield of distillate products from the coal conversion.

This liquid product now consists essentially of two components. The first component is a combination of light and middle hydrocarbon products and a residuum material, i.e., materials boiling above 975°F. The second component is a solids material which consists essentially of ash and unconverted coal. A wash liquid is added to the liquid product through line 38 and the mixture of the wash liquid and the liquid product proceeds to separation step 40.

	Run		
	A	B	C
	No resid recycle	Resid recycle	Resid recycle
Operating conditions:			
Reactor temperature, ° F		853	
Dry coal feed, lb./hr./ft.³ reactor		18.7	
Distillate recycle, lb./lb. coal	1.00	1.0	1.0
Reactor slurry:			
Residuum, wt. percent	15.0	39.0	43.0
Solids, wt. percent	9.9	10.4	10.6
Pressure, p.s.i.a.	2,250	2,250	2,250
Percent H₂ in vent gas	95.1	95	95
Percent ash in feed	4.6	4.6	4.6
Yields of liquids, wt. percent dry coal:			
Total C₄+liquid	62.3	63.9	64.7
C₄–400° F	22.4	23.4	25.0
400–650° F	15.9	16.8	18.1
650–975° F	1.2	11.7	12.4
975° F.+residuum	22.8	12.0	9.2
Unconverted ash-free coal	10.2	4.5	3.0
C₄+liquids after residuum pyrolysis	48.0	55.0	58.6
C₁–C₃ gas	14.6	16.3	17.0
Wash liquid	None	None	(¹)

¹ Mixture of light aliphatic and aromatic hydrocarbons.

The table above illustrates the improvement that is obtained by use of this process with respect to increased coal conversion and distillate yields. The operating conditions for each run were the same except that in run A, the recycle stream contained only distillate materials, i.e., low residuum concentration, while in run B, the separation step designated 40 was carried out without the wash liquid modification of the process and the amount of residuum recycled was only that recovered from this step. Run C showed the same process as run B except that additional residuum has been recovered as a result of using the wash liquid modification of the process. As shown, not only is the distillate yield and coal conversion increased by use of this process, but also recovery of liquids from the residuum pyrolysis or coking step is increased.

A bottoms material from the centrifugal force device is removed through line 50. This consists essentially of the second component solids material with some retained wash liquid. If it is desired, the entire bottoms material may be removed in line 52 for further downstream treatment, e.g., a coking step. Alternately, the bottoms may be treated in an intermediate separation stage 56 which may consist of either thermal treatment, e.g., atmospheric or vacuum fractionation steps or solvent extraction. It is possible, of course, to use both thermal treatment and extraction procedures in combination.

The type solvent extraction step used depends on the nature of the wash liquid. If the wash liquid is acetone, the bottoms in line 50 would be mixed with water introduced through line 54, and this admixture would then proceed to an intermediate separation stage 56, wherein the water and bottoms are contacted for a sufficient length of time and in such a manner whereby the acetone will be preferentially absorbed in the water. Such contacting procedures are well-known in the art. The water-acetone fraction is then removed through line 58 and the acetone-free solids with a small amount of water are removed through line 60. The acetone-water mixture in line 58 is then fractionated and the acetone is recovered and reused as wash liquid.

Catalytic Hydrogenation in a Series of Ebullating Bed Reactors

M.C. Kirk, Jr.; U.S. Patent 3,594,305; July 20, 1971; assigned to Sun Oil Company describes a process of obtaining hydrocarbons from coal by treating a hydrocarbon oil-coal slurry with hydrogen under catalytic conditions in an ebullated bed system where the reaction involves a series of reactors, each reactor increasing in temperature and pressure, oxygen and sulfur removal occurring in the first series of reactors and finally passing the oil-coal slurry through one or more final reactors which contain catalyst different from the upstream reactors to remove nitrogen compounds and complete hydrogenation, whereby an effluent is obtained suitable for hydrocracking to fuels and other useful petroleum-like products.

Referring to Figure 3.28, oil and finely ground coal particles are slurried in a mixer 1 and the slurry pumped through line 2 to a first ebullated bed reactor 3 which contains the particulate catalyst. Recycle hydrogen gas from the reactor next downstream is also fed through line 4 to the first reactor with the oil-coal slurry, the rate of feed of these materials being sufficient to maintain an ebullated bed. The catalyst in the first reactor will be a cobalt-molybdenum, nickel-molybdenum, nickel-tungsten, or like catalyst supported on a base such as alumina or silica and reaction condition within reactor 3 will be from about 700° to 750°F., and about 2,000 psig. The products of reaction within this reactor are led through line 5 to a gas-liquid separator 6 where H₂S and hydrogen are removed from the oil-coal slurry process stream. H₂S is separated from the hydrogen which is recycled to either reactor 3, reactor 11, or both. The liquid slurry is then led to a still 7 where flash distillation of water and hydrocarbons boiling below about 400°F. (naphthas) are removed. Water is separated and removed and the naphtha is taken through line 8 to storage.

FIGURE 3.28: CATALYTIC HYDROGENATION IN A SERIES OF EBULLATING BED REACTORS

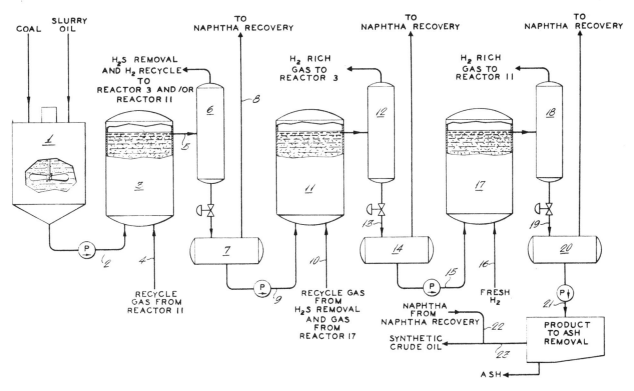

Source: M.C. Kirk, Jr.; U.S. Patent 3,594,305; July 20, 1971

The coal slurry process stream proceeds through line 9 to a second reactor 11 and recycle gas from the next downstream reactor is passed upwardly through line 10 into reactor 11 which contains an ebullated bed of the same catalyst as in the first reactor 3. In this reactor, the reaction temperature and pressure are each somewhat higher than in the first reactor 3. Where, as shown in the drawing, the first series of reactors comprise two reactors, the temperature within the second reactor is on the order of 725° to 775°F. and reaction pressure will be about 2,500 psig. As before, the reaction products are separated in the gas-liquid separator 12, and the hydrogen gas recovered and recycled back to reactor 3. The oil-coal slurry then proceeds through line 13 to still 14 where naphtha and water are removed as before, and the slurry proceeds through line 15 together with fresh hydrogen being introduced at line 16 into a final stage reactor 17 which contains a noble metal catalyst supported on alumina. Where a single final stage reactor is used as shown in the drawing, reaction conditions are on the order of 750° to 800°F. and 3,000 psig.

However, it will be understood that more than one final stage reactor may be used and that temperature and pressure conditions will preferably be such that they will be somewhat higher as the product stream passes through each of the downstream reactors. It is in the final stage reactors that significant hydrogenation occurs with removal of nitrogen compounds. The products pass into the liquid-gas separator 18 where the hydrogen-rich gas is separated and returned to reactor 11 upstream. The oil-coal slurry process stream passes through line 19 into still 20 where hydrocarbons boiling below 400°F. and water are removed and the product process stream is taken to line 21 for removal of ash by filtration or other separation means. The hydrocarbon products from the naphtha recovery systems are fed through line 22 together with product from the process stream in line 23 and comprise the synthetic crude oil of the process which is a crude distillate and can be converted to gasoline by conventional refining processes.

Low Pressure Hydrogenation of Coal in an Ebullating Bed

C.A. Johnson; U.S. Patent 3,607,719; September 21, 1971; assigned to Hydrocarbon Research, Inc. describes a process for the hydroconversion of coal to benzene-soluble hydrocarbon products. It is accomplished at conversion pressures with a hydrogen partial pressure of less than about 1,000 psi in the presence of a hydrogen donor oil and a particulate contact material. Under these operating conditions, the particulate contact material is maintained in random motion. Hydrogen partial pressures as low as 350 psi are practical and economical. From the resulting liquid effluent, a distillate fraction is recovered and it is further hydrogenated to produce an effective hydrogen donor oil.

It has been found in this process that the hydrogenation of coal can take place efficiently at low pressures with the use of ebullated bed technique. The description of the ebullated bed concept and technique is set forth in U.S. Patent Reissue 25,770. A specific characteristic of the ebullated bed is the random motion which is imparted to the solid particles in the reaction zone. Figure 3.29 is a drawing giving a schematic view of the principal elements of this process for the low pressure hydrogenation of coal.

Coal which has been ground so that it all passes through at least 20 mesh (U.S. standard) is fed from line 1 to slurry-mixing zone 4. The coal and suitable oil from the system, hereinafter described are mixed to form a slurry of 1 part coal per 1 to 10 parts oil. The mixing zone 4 is usually maintained at atmospheric or low pressure.

The slurry mixture in line 3 is pumped via pump 6 through preheating zone 8 wherein the temperature of the slurry is raised to between about 400° and 700°F. Hydrogen in line 2 can be fed to the preheater as it exerts an inhibiting effect on coke formation. The heated slurry then enters reaction zone 12 via line 5 and preferably has an upward velocity of between about 0.05 and 0.15 feet per second in the reaction zone. At the same time, gaseous hydrogen enters reaction zone 12 via line 7 at an upward velocity of between about 0.05 and 0.3 feet per second. It is preferred that the combined upward flows of coal slurry and hydrogen be between about 0.2 and 0.4 feet per second. It is not necessary that the slurry temperature be the same as that of reaction zone 12 inasmuch as the hydroconversion reaction is exothermic. When the process is being carried out, the contact particles can enter the system at 22 and are in constant random motion in the reaction zone 12 with respect to each other and the gross mass expands so that its upper boundary or upper level of ebullation is at 18. There is substantially no carryover of contact particles while the finer coal solids are carried out of reaction zone 12 in the liquid effluent.

A recycle of liquid from above the dense phase catalyst zone permits the recycle of essentially solids-free liquid to below the solids-containing bed to assist in keeping the particles in random motion. As shown, this is accomplished by an internal draft tube 14 and pump 10, but as described in U.S. Patent Reissue 25,770, this can also be accomplished externally. The recycle rate is dependent upon slurry feed rate, hydrogen feed rate, reactor size, contact particle size and other system variables affecting ebullation.

FIGURE 3.29:   LOW PRESSURE HYDROGENATION OF COAL IN AN EBULLATING BED

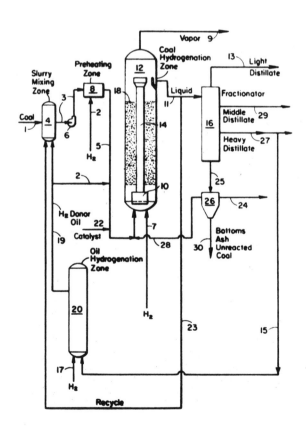

Source: C.A. Johnson; U.S. Patent 3,607,719; September 21, 1971

In reaction zone 12 there is a simultaneous consumption of gaseous hydrogen and transfer of hydrogen from the slurry oil to the coal. The coal conversion consumes an amount of hydrogen equivalent to 2 to 4% of the weight of the coal present. The gaseous hydrogen passing through the reaction zone accounts for about 25 to 75% of the hydrogen consumed and the balance of the reacted hydrogen is provided by the hydrogen donor oil. A vapor effluent leaves reaction zone 12 through line 9. This effluent is suitable for use in hydrogen recovery, hydrogen manufacture and petroleum refining as it contains excess hydrogen, normal gaseous hydrocarbons and naphtha range and middle distillate range hydrocarbons. The liquid effluent leaving reaction zone 12 through line 11 is fractionated at 16 into light and middle distillates, heavy gas oil distillates, residuum boiling range oils, unconverted coal and ash.

The bottoms in line 25 from fractionator 16 pass through separation zone 26 and a portion of the essentially solids-free liquid bottoms pass by line 28 to reaction zone 12 to provide additional recycle as well as undergoing further hydrogenation to lower boiling liquids. Separation zone 26 is preferably a cyclone separator. The remainder of the materials entering separation zone 26 through line 25 leaves in lines 24 and 30 and is suitable for coking, fuel or as a raw material for hydrogen manufacture. In addition, the effluent in line 24 can be subjected to further hydroconversion to low-boiling liquids. Part of the effluent in line 11 may be drawn off before fractionating through line 23 for use in mixing zone 4. The advantage to be found in using either of the recycle streams 23 and 28 is that the recycle helps to maintain the level of residuum boiling range liquids in the reactor which in turn helps to achieve the greatest conversion of coal to low-boiling liquids. It is preferable to recycle the portion of the bottoms in line 28 to reaction zone 12 for the above mentioned maintenance of residuum level in the reactor.

The effluent in line 11 enters fractionation zone 16 wherein a light distillate fraction is removed through line 13, a middle distillate fraction is removed through line 29, a heavy distillate is removed through line 27 and a bottoms fraction is removed through line 25. The required quantity of distillate having a boiling range between about 500° and 1000°F., is recycled via line 15 for hydrogenation for use as the hydrogen donor oil and the net production of this distillate is removed through line 27.

The distillate in line 15 enters oil hydrogenation zone 20 for supplemental hydrogenation. Hydrogen enters zone 20 through line 17. Zone 20 is operated at a hydrogen partial pressure between about 750 and 3,000 psi, at a temperature between about 600° and 800°F., with a hydrogen rate of between about 1,000 and 5,000 scf of hydrogen per barrel, but preferably at 1,000 to 2,000 psi, 700° to 800°F., and with 1,500 scf of hydrogen per barrel. A catalyst suitable for reaction zone 20 is nickel molybdate or cobalt molybdate on alumina and the like. The hydrogen donor oil passes via line 19 to mixing zone 4 to form the slurry with the coal or by line 2 to the reactor 12. The examples shown in the following table are illustrative of the process.

Contact Particles	Cobalt-Molybdate on Alumina			Alumina	
Coal feed, lb./hr./ft.^{3} of reactor	94	31	31	31	31
Pressure, psi	2,250	2,250	500	500	2,250
Slurry oil, lb. oil/lb. coal	4	4	4	4	4
Temperature, °F.	850	850	850	850	850
			(Yield % of Coal)		
Gaseous hydrocarbons	3.4	8.1	5.4	6.6	4.5
C_4 to 400°F. liquid	4	12	12	12	4
400° to 975°F. liquid	40	29	25	14	27
975°F. oil soluble in C_6H_6	12	3	10	17	12
Unconverted coal	9	6	6	7	6
Ash, H_2O, H_2S, NH_3, CO_2	14	16	15	14	12

The above table shows for comparative purposes the results of hydrogenating coal under different conditions of temperature, pressure and contact material. It will thus be observed that using a hydrogen donor oil and operating the coal conversion at 500 psi results in conversions that are substantially equivalent to prior operations at 2,250 psi. Operation at the low pressure materially reduces the costs involved in the reactor construction and the cost of compressing the hydrogen. The slurry oil used in the experiments of the above table was anthracene oil of a 500° to 900°F. boiling range which had been hydrogenated so as to increase its hydrogen content from 5.9 to 7.5 weight percent.

Coal Hydrogenation Process Utilizing an Expanded Particulate Solids Bed

R.H. Wolk; E.S. Johanson and S.B. Alpert; U.S. Patent 3,617,465; November 2, 1971; assigned to Hydrocarbon Research, Inc. describe a coal hydrogenation process which employs an expanded particulate solids bed where the solids are derived from the coal which is placed in random motion by the upflow of a slurry of coal, hydrocarbon liquid and hydrogen to produce better than 80% conversion of coal to gas and liquid synthetic petroleum products.

In this process it has been discovered that the solid ash particles remaining after the hydroconversion of the coal are suitable contact material for use in the reaction zone. One of the important features distinguishing the ash-containing conversion system from a catalyst-containing conversion system is the lower investment required by the former. The ebullating pumps, some high pressure piping, and the catalyst addition with withdrawal systems are all eliminated. Furthermore, the substantial cost of the initial catalyst charge and the cost of continuous catalyst replacements are totally eliminated. Figure 3.30 is a diagrammatic view of the process.

A coal such as bituminous, semibituminous, or sub-bituminous coal or lignite, or a similar solid carbonaceous material such as shale, entering the system at 10 is first passed through a preparation unit generally indicated at 12. It is desirable to dry the coal of all surface moisture and to grind the coal to a desired mesh and then to screen it for uniformity. In accordance with this process the coal should have a fineness of about 100 mesh and is preferably of relatively close sizing, i.e., all passing 50 mesh and not less than 80% retained on 200 mesh. However, it will be observed that the preciseness of size may vary between different types of coals, lignite and shale.

The coal fines discharge at 14 into the slurry-mixing tank 16 where the coal is blended with a slurry oil indicated at 18 which, as hereinafter pointed out, is preferably made in the system. To establish an effective transportable slurry, the ground coal should be mixed with about an equal weight of oil but amounts of up to 10 parts of oil per part of coal can be desirable.

The coal-oil slurry at 20 is then pumped at 21 through the heater 22 to bring the slurry up to a temperature between about 600° and 950°F., and the desired pressure, such heated slurry then discharging at 24 into the reactor feed line 26. Make-up hydrogen is introduced from line 28 and mixed with recycle hydrogen in line 42, and introduced into reactor feed line 26. In a separate embodiment, makeup hydrogen can also be injected into the slurry oil steam before heater 22. The combined hydrogen and coal-oil slurry then enters one or more reactors 30, passing upwardly from the bottom at a rate and under pressure and at a temperature to accomplish the desired hydrogenation.

FIGURE 3.30:   COAL HYDROGENATION PROCESS USING AN EXPANDED PARTICULATE SOLIDS BED

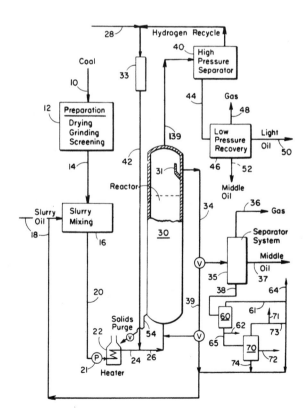

Source: R.H. Wolk, E.S. Johanson and S.B. Alpert; U.S. Patent 3,617,465; November 2, 1971

By concurrently flowing streams of liquid and gasiform materials upwardly through a vessel containing solid particles, the solid particles are placed in random motion within the vessel by the upflowing streams. A mass of solid particles in this state of random motion in a liquid medium and also in contact with a gaseous medium is described as ebullated. The dense ash resulting from coal decomposition reaches an equilibrium level in the reactor. At this level of equilibrium, the rate at which the particulate solids are formed from the conversion of the coal equals the rate at which the particulate solids are carried out of the reaction zone.

It is a relatively simple matter to determine for any ebullated process the range of throughput rates of upflowing liquid which will cause the mass of solid particles to become expanded while at the same time placing them in random motion. However, when fine particles such as ash comprise the bed, a concentration gradient exists along the length of the reactor with the highest concentration existing in the lower two-thirds of the vessel and the lowest concentration at the outlet.

Preferred reactor operating conditions are in the range of 750° to 950°F. and between 500 and 3,000 psig. Coal throughput is at the rate of 15 to 300 pounds per hour per cubic foot of reactor space with the yield of unreacted coal as char less than 10% of the quantity of maf coal feed. Under these conditions the liquid velocity is on the order of 1 to 30 gallons per minute per square foot of horizontal cross section of the reaction zone.

The degree of hydrogenation from a single pass in reactor 30 is such that there is some ash and unconverted coal solids in the liquid stream 34. Stream 34 passes to a low pressure flash system 35. From such a system, it is appropriate to remove gaseous products at 36, a middle oil at 37 and a bottoms at 38. As hereinafter described, some, or all, of this bottoms is recycled to the reactor 30.

The overhead effluent stream 139 passing to high pressure separator 40 is primarily gaseous and is virtually free of solid particles of contact material. From the separator 40 a gas stream 42, largely hydrogen, is removed and after purification and heating at 33 can be returned to the reactor 30 to supplement the hydrogen requirements. A liquid stream 44 from the separator 40 passes to the low pressure recovery system 46. The low pressure separator 46 permits removal of a high Btu gaseous product at 48 and a solids-free light oil at 50. A middle oil stream is moved at 52. A portion of the liquid from line 52 may be used to prepare the initial coal slurry at 16. If desired, solids may be purged from reactor 30 at 54.

The flashed reactor liquid from vessel 35 passes through line 38 to vessel 60 which is a solids separation system. A high solids concentration stream is rejected from the system through line 62. The low solids concentration stream, in line 61, is recycled via 18 to provide slurry oil. Part of this stream can be taken as product through line 64. There are instances where in order to control the velocity in the reactor to a desired level, part of the reactor liquid in 34 can be recycled through line 39 back to the reactor or injected into line 18 to be used as slurry oil.

Another mode of operation utilizes vacuum distillation of the high solids concentration stream 65 in vacuum still 70 to provide a vacuum gas oil in 73, part of which may be recycled as part of the slurry oil in line 18 and part withdrawn as product in line 71. Vacuum still bottoms are withdrawn through line 74 and can either be recycled via 18 or withdrawn as product in 72. Having described the process in general terms, reference is made to a specific example.

Example: Pittsburgh Seam coal as described in Table 1, is processed by passing the coal through a reactor operating at 850°F. and 2,250 psig hydrogen partial pressure. The operating conditions and results are summarized in Table 2 along with a comparison of results obtained in the same reactor with 1/16 inch cobalt molybdate extrudates on alumina. Reactor liquid containing ash and unconverted coal is recycled along with heavy gas oil obtained by vacuum distillation of the reactor liquid stream. The ash concentration in the reactor is found to be about 5.1%.

The yields show a slightly lower yield of liquid products and lower hydrogen consumption of the noncatalytic case. The lower hydrogen consumption is reflected in the quality of the light products. This deficiency is rectified by further downstream treatment advantageously in that more selective catalysts and operating conditions can be used.

TABLE 1: PITTSBURGH SEAM COAL

	As received	Dry basis
Proximate analysis, percent:		
Moisture	1.71	....
Ash	8.19	8.33
Volatile	41.89	42.62
Fixed carbon	48.21	49.05
Total	100.00	100.00
Ultimate analysis, percent:		
Moisture	1.71	....
Carbon	73.00	74.26
Hydrogen	5.40	5.49
Nitrogen	1.46	1.49
Sulfur	3.96	4.03
Ash	8.19	8.33
Oxygen by difference	6.28	6.40
Total	....	109.00

TABLE 2: RECYCLE STREAMS — VACUUM GAS OIL AND REACTOR LIQUID

	Ash containing reactor	Cobalt molybdate containing reactor
Operating conditions:		
Temperature (° F.)	850	850
Pressure (p.s.i.g.)	2,250	2,250
Coal feed rate (lbs./hr./ft.³ reactor)	31.2	31.2
Ash concentration in reactor liquid (weight percent)	5.1	5.1
Recycle rate (lbs./lb. coal):		
Vacuum gas oil	0.83	1.00
Reactor liquid	4.30	4.18
Product distribution weight percent of dry coal:		
C_1–C_3 gas	9.4	11.2
C_4–400° F. liquids	12.6	17.2
400–975° F.	22.6	21.0
975° F. plus residuum oil benzene soluble	28.3	25.6
Benzene insoluble oil plus unconverted coal	13.0	13.2
Ash	8.5	8.5
Water	4.7	4.8
CO plus CO_2	0.6	0.3
H_2S	2.7	1.7
NH_3	0.5	0.7
Total (100 plus H_2 reacted)	102.9	104.5

H-Coal Process: Slurry Oil System

The H-Coal process described by R.H. Wolk and E.S. Johanson; U.S. Patent 3,540,995; November 17, 1970; assigned to the U.S. Secretary of the Interior and Hydrocarbon Research, Inc. converts coal to a light crude distillate by hydrogenation in an ebullated catalyst bed reactor. The process is related to improvements in the H-Coal process directed at increasing the conversion of coal into valuable hydrocarbons by utilizing recycle of slurry oil, composition control, recycle rate and solids content of recycle liquid to the ebullated bed reactor. It has been found that a major factor effecting the conversion of coal to distillate products by hydrogenation in an ebullated bed is the concentration residuum in the reactor zone. A greater amount of residuum in the reactor liquid results in a liquid product having a higher proportion of distillate material and less residuum than heretofore obtained.

It has been normal, in the past, to increase residuum concentration in the reactor by recycling a bottoms portion from the initial liquid effluent flash to the reactor. This bottoms portion however includes a high concentration of unconverted processed solids in the form of ash and unconverted coal. This type of solids buildup in the reactor can destroy the operability of the system with respect to proper temperature control and fluidization of the catalyst bed. Consequently, if an attempt is made to increase the residuum concentration of the reactor liquid, and thereby increase coal conversion, by such a recycle, the operability of the system rapidly decreases due to buildup of unconverted processed solids in the reactor. Figure 3.31 is a flow plan of an ebullated bed coal hydrogenation process where clarified residue is recycled to the reactor according to this process.

Referring now to Figure 3.31, there is shown a simplified flow diagram of an ebullated bed coal hydrogenation where 10 represents a stream of coal feed which is usually ground to a particulate size of from about 30 to 325 mesh. Coal stream 10 is slurried with a combination of liquid hydrocarbon from streams 12, 14 and 16 and then mixed with hydrogen from stream 18. The combined mixture is introduced through line 20 into an ebullated bed reactor 22. Reactor 22 contains a feed zone 24, a catalyst containing zone 26, a liquid product zone 28 and a gaseous product zone 30. The feed slurry passed from the feed zone 24 to the catalyst-containing zone 26 through distributors 32. Any conventional hydrogenation catalyst may be used in zone 26 however, cobalt-molybdate compositions are preferred.

The temperature within reactor 22 should be kept in the range of from about 425° to 475°C. At these temperatures, hydrogenation of the coal produces liquid and gaseous hydrocarbons which, because of their lower densities form zones 28 and 30, respectively, within reactor 22. A portion of the liquid within zone 28 is brought back through the catalyst bed 26 by internal recycle through collector 34, and line 36. Gaseous hydrocarbons are withdrawn from reactor 22 through line 38 and are separated in an atmospheric still 40 into a light distillate product 42 and a heavy distillate product 44. A portion 12 of the heavy distillate may be recycled to slurry the coal feed. Liquid hydrocarbons are withdrawn from reactor 22 through line 46 and are separated in flash drum 48 into a light portion and a residue portion. The light portion is conveyed through line 50 to line 38 for introduction into still 40 whereas the residue portion containing heavy liquid hydrocarbons and solids is passed via line 52 to a vacuum still 54 where further distillate portions 56 and 58 are recovered as overhead.

The bottoms stream 60 from still 54 consists primarily of residuum and unconverted processed solids. This stream is then passed to a liquid-solid separating apparatus such as the liquid cyclone 62 shown in the drawing. Cyclone 62 produces a liquid residue stream 16 for recycle and a solids-containing stream 64. Stream 64 may be further processed as in tower 66 to remove additional liquid residue 14 for recycle while converting the solid portion to char 68.

FIGURE 3.31: H-COAL PROCESS: SLURRY OIL SYSTEM

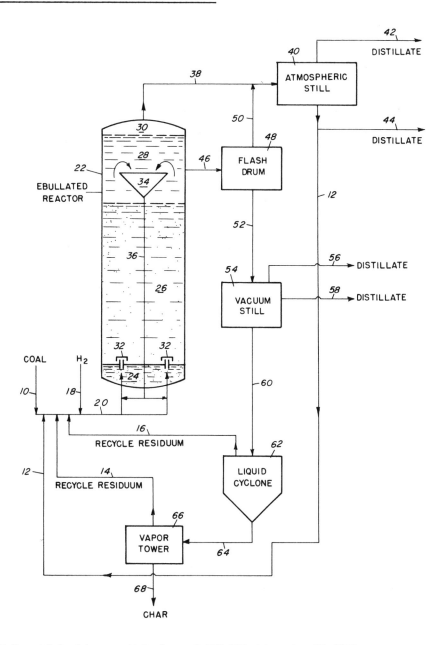

Source: R.H. Wolk and E.S. Johanson; U.S. Patent 3,540,995; November 17, 1970

The improvement obtained by this process is brought about by controlling the amount and composition of the slurry entering the ebullated bed reactor. It has been found that optimum results are obtained by maintaining a residuum concentration in the reactor liquid of from 30 to 45 weight percent while maintaining the concentrate of unconverted processed solids in the reactor liquid at from about 10 to 25 weight percent, and preferably in the range of from 10 to 20 weight percent.

These reactor conditions can be met by recycle of liquid residuum hydrogenation products having reduced solids content. In practice, solids can be removed to a desired level by passing a liquid residuum containing solids such as stream 60 through a liquid cyclone such as 62. The solids leaving a cyclone such as 62 can be further treated as in tower 66 to remove further liquid residuum for recycle.

HYDROCRACKING OF POLYNUCLEAR AROMATICS IN THE PRESENCE OF A ZINC HALIDE

This process by E. Gorin, R.T. Struck and C.W. Zielke; U.S. Patent 3,355,376; November 28, 1967; assigned to the U.S. Secretary of the Interior and Consolidation Coal Company relates to the catalytic hydrocracking of predominantly polynuclear aromatic hydrocarbonaceous materials, and to the conversion to gasoline of substantially nondistillable high molecular weight predominantly polynuclear aromatic hydrocarbonaceous feedstocks which may contain appreciable quantities of nitrogen, oxygen and sulfur compounds, as well as unfilterable ash contaminants.

In this process polynuclear aromatic materials are hydrocracked by contacting a feedstock which is heavier than gasoline with hydrogen and a zinc halide salt at elevated temperatures. In this process zinc oxide acts as an acceptor for removing hydrogen chloride from the system. Figure 3.32 is a diagrammatic view of the process. In the description of the process, $ZnCl_2$ is used as illustrative of the catalyst, and coal extract as illustrative of a sulfur- and nitrogen-containing polynuclear hydrocarbon. Numeral 10 designates a suitable hydrocracking zone to which coal extract and hydrogen are fed through conduits 12 and 14, respectively. Regenerated molten zinc chloride is introduced through conduit 16 into the hydrocracking zone 10 from a regeneration zone 18. The operating conditions maintained in the hydrocracking zone 10 are as follows.

Temperature	500° to 875°F.
Pressure	500 to 10,000 psig
Liquid hourly space velocity	0.25 to 4.20
H_2 feedstock ratio	5 to 50 scf/lb.
$ZnCl_2$ catalyst	At least 15 weight percent of hydrocarbon inventory in the hydrocracking zone

The hydrocracked products, i.e., low-boiling hydrocarbons, are withdrawn through a conduit 20. Spent catalyst is conducted to the regeneration zone 18 via a conduit 22. Normally, the reactions occurring in the hydrocracking zone are as follows.

$$(1) \qquad ZnCl_2 + H_2S = ZnS + 2HCl$$
$$(2) \qquad ZnCl_2 + NH_3 = ZnCl_2 \cdot NH_3$$
$$(3) \qquad ZnCl_2 \cdot NH_3 + HCl = ZnCl_2 \cdot NH_4Cl$$

In this process, it has been found that zinc oxide is extremely useful in the hydrocracking zone as an acceptor, as set forth in the following equation.

$$(4) \qquad ZnO + 2HCl = ZnCl_2 + H_2O$$

By virtue of the use of zinc oxide, loss of HCl from the system is minimized, and corrosion by HCl is controlled. The use of zinc oxide also effectively eliminates the reaction expressed in equation (3) above, thus making it unnecessary to regenerate $ZnCl_2$ from $ZnCl_2 \cdot NH_4Cl$.

The amount of zinc oxide in the hydrocracking zone must be carefully regulated, since the catalytic effectiveness of the latter is seriously inhibited by excessive amounts. We have found that the zinc oxide concentration must be kept lower than a $ZnO/ZnCl_2$ mol ratio of 0.10, and preferably below 0.05. The table shown on the following page shows the effect of different molar ratio of ZnO to $ZnCl_2$ on the conversion of nondistillable coal extract to distillate and also on the yield of low-boiling gasoline stock, i.e., the $C_5 \times 200°C$. portion of the distillate product.

FIGURE 3.32: HYDROCRACKING IN THE PRESENCE OF ZINC HALIDE

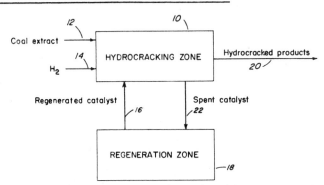

Source: E. Gorin, R.T. Struck and C.W. Zielke; U.S. Patent 3,355,376; November 28, 1967

Hydrogenation Processes

Run No.	26	23	36	68	67
Temperature, °C	427	427	427	399	399
Total Hot Pressure, P.s.i.g	4,200	4,200	4,200	3,000	3,000
Residence Time, Min	60	60	60	60	60
Feed Gm.:					
Extract	50.0	50.0	50.0	50.0	50.0
ZnCl₂	50.0	50.0	50.0	50.0	100.0
ZnO	0	25.0	2.50	2.50	2.50
ZnCl₂/Extract, Wt. Ratio	1.0	1.0	1.0	1.0	2.0
ZnO/ZnCl₂, Mol Ratio	0	0.84	0.084	0.084	0.042
Yields, Wt. Percent MAF Feed:					
(C₁–C₃)	13.0	4.6	10.2	3.4	5.9
i-C₄H₁₀	9.6	1.5	6.3	1.4	5.9
n-C₄H₁₀	1.6	0.5	1.1	0.2	0.9
C₅×200° C. Distillate	60.4	25.5	42.5	39.4	61.0
200×400° C. Distillate	3.1	23.5	23.4	21.0	4.5
Hydrogen Consumed, Wt. Percent MAF Feed	8.7	5.0	7.6	5.6	7.4
Conversion, Wt. Percent MAF Feed	89.8	58.8	84.2	69.0	79.8

The following conclusions are evident from the data in the above table.

(1) High concentrations of ZnO severely inhibit the hydrocracking activity of ZnCl₂, not only with regard to total conversion, but also with regard to cracking to gasoline (see Run No. 23).

(2) A ZnO/ZnCl₂ mol ratio lower than 0.10, e.g., 0.084, is required to get a high conversion to distillate (see Run No. 36); and a ZnO/ZnCl₂ mol ratio lower than 0.05, e.g., 0.042 is required to get a high yield of gasoline, i.e., C₅ × 200°C. distillate (see Run No. 67).

QUADRI-PHASE LOW PRESSURE HYDROGENATION FOR PARTIAL LIQUEFACTION OF COAL

M.G. Huntington; U.S. Patent 3,247,092; April 19, 1966; assigned to Pyrochem Corporation describes a process related to the quadri-phase method for the recovery of the more readily liquefiable petrographic constituents of coal under relatively low pressure hydrogenating conditions and to apparatus for carrying out this method.

This process relates to continuous drying, destructive hydrodistillation and hydrocarbonization of coal and other solid hydrocarbonaceous material. The process concerns a continuous multistage pressurized coal hydrodistillation system in a vertical vessel. The system includes the functions of coal drying, preheating, destructive distillation with coincidental mild hydrogenation and immediate vapor phase catalytic hydrorefining and hydrodealkylating of the condensable volatiles, and coincidental redistilling, hydrorefining and hydrodealkylating of recycled heavy bottoms and selected fractions with whatever entrained solids, partial combustion of char to furnish heat to the system, and thermal cracking of recycled methane to produce elemental hydrogen.

Quadri-phase method refers to the fact that during the free fall of particles of ground coal against the rising stream of hot, pressurized hydrogen in addition to the solid phase, liquid, vapor and gaseous fluid phases all exist simultaneously in or near each particle as it changes from dry coal to nonreacting char.

(1) The Solid Phase — The coal enters the system dry and without liquid vehicle and exits from the system as dry, low volatile, low sulfur char.

(2) The Liquid Phase — A molten liquid phase is formed primarily by the melting of the outer surface of each coal particle. Liquefaction is promoted by the rapid surface adsorption of hydrogen, some of which becomes chemically combined, reducing both the melting temperature and the boiling temperature of the liquefiable coal constituents.

(3) The Vapor Phase — As the liquid surface film rises in temperature to its boiling point at system pressure, it is continuously distilled as a vapor into the thermal carrier stream of hydrogen until nothing but the unreactive char remains with its original ash and nonvolatile catalyst.

(4) The Gaseous Phase — Hydrogen is the thermal carrier and the principal reacting fluid.

The operation of the coal still and the process are described as follows. The input coal is ground but not sized and may be coated either with a catalyst or a recycled hydrogen transfer agent such as phenanthrene either sprayed on while liquid or crushed and mixed with the coal.

With reference to Figure 3.33, the pretreated ground coal is dumped into measuring bin 20 and then into charging lock 22 by opening valve 24. Charging lock 22 is brought up to system pressure by closing valve 26 and opening valve 28. Upon attaining system pressure in charging lock 22, bell valve 34 in the bottom thereof may be opened so that the crushed coal from charging lock 22 is dumped upon the system gyratory shelf feeder unit 12. After the crushed coal has been discharged through bell valve 34, the charging lock 22 may be depressurized by closing bell valves 24 and 34, closing valve

FIGURE 3.33: QUADRI-PHASE LOW PRESSURE HYDROGENATION

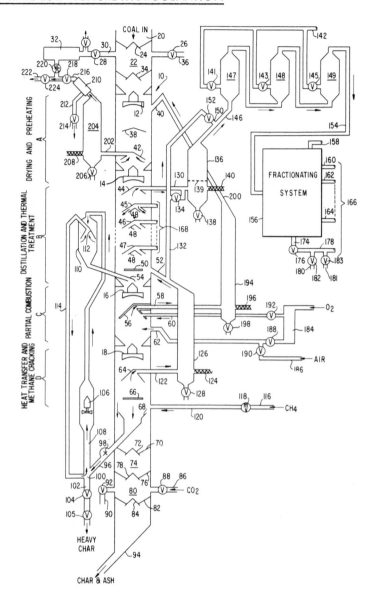

Source: M.G. Huntington; U.S. Patent 3,247,092; April 19, 1966

28 and opening valve 26 which discharges the contained flue gases through line 36 to the atmosphere. The charging lock may be then reloaded as before.

The rate at which the crushed coal is fed off the system gyratory shelf feeder unit 12 or any of the other gyratory feeder shelves is a function of the amplitude and rate of gyration of each gyratory shelf feeder unit.

In the drying deoxidizing and preheating zone A, the crushed coal and hot drying flue gas admitted at 40 mingle in concurrent downward flow. In drying deoxidizing and preheating ground coal, two primary functions are effected at precisely limited temperatures. First is the removal of superficial moisture at steam saturation temperature at system pressure. For example, at a system pressure of about 20 atmospheres (300 psi) the steam saturation temperature is 417°F. A large amount of heat may be rapidly transferred to cold moist coal from a very high temperature gas without thermal destruction of fine coal particles. If, for example, the drying gas enters the zone A through line 40 at about 2800°F., the saturation temperature of steam at system pressure cannot be exceeded until practically all of the superficial moisture has evaporated. At that same time, the coal particles must have also risen in temperature to the saturation temperature of 418°F. At this point, some three-quarters of the available heat has been transferred from the drying gas to the coal and to the surroundings and the temperature of the drying gas has dropped from about 2800°F. to 1200°F. Therefore, in flowing concurrently the very hot drying flue gas can at no time have sufficient thermal heat to destroy even the finest coal fragments.

The other function performed in this zone A is the removal of oxygen from lower ranked coals as carbon oxides and as water vapor, and this occurs primarily between the temperatures of 400° and 650°F. without significant evolution of hydrogen or of hydrocarbons. In this temperature range many oxygenated compounds break down to form water, carbon monoxide and carbon dioxide. However, it is important that the temperature of the coal in zone A is not raised above 650°F. at which point distillation of hydrocarbon begins because any hydrocarbon evolution in zone A must represent a net loss to the system.

The elimination of the carbon oxide gases and water vapor before the distillation and producing the hydrocarbon volatiles is a very important advantage and improves the operation for two principal reasons. First of all, the available hydrogen to carbon ratio of the coal is markedly improved and the significance of this increases with the lower ranks of the coal. Secondly, whatever carbon oxide gases appear in the volatile stream must be scrubbed from any recycle of gases because their diluent effect is cumulative. Moreover, any recycled carbon dioxide in thermal carrier hydrogen becomes, to some extent, a reactive oxidizing agent at system temperatures and interferes with the production of neutral oil. Therefore, coal enters zone A at system pressure and at a relatively cool temperature. The coal is preheated by incoming flue gas coming in about 2800°F. and exiting at a temperature of about 700°F. so that the coal is dried and preheated to about 650°F. as it lies on gyratory shelf 14 and this temperature is just below its temperature range at which evolution of hydrocarbon gases begins to any important extent. Also, the freed carbon oxides and water vapor will be expelled from the system through offtake 202 and after being cooled, the steam condensated will drain off through line 212.

The dried, deoxidized, and preheated coal is then fed off the periphery of gyratory feeder unit 14 into the distillation and thermal treatment zone B. In zone B, a thermal carrier fluid which consists principally of hydrogen is passed countercurrently through the annular cascade of descending coal to drive off the primary volatile matter through offtake cone 44 and flue 130.

Most bituminous coals melt and many actually become liquid between 700° and 900°F. However, the plastic condition usually encompasses a temperature range of no more than 100°F. The fact that some coals soften to the extent of actually becoming fluid, greatly complicates the mechanics of handling coal while it is in the intumescent stage or temperature range. Sticky coal in the 700° to 900°F. temperature range adheres to practically all surfaces cooler than 900°F. with which it comes in contact. Equally serious is the fact that caking coals agglomerate in passing through the plastic range. In the worst situation, if heated en masse without movement, strongly caking coals will actually form a chunk of solid coke the size and shape of the containing vessel. Even those coals which are not considered strongly caking will tend to melt in an atmosphere of hydrogen which is the thermal carrier fluid in this process. However, even sticky coal will not adhere to surfaces which are maintained above the thermal setting temperature of about 900°F. Furthermore, when dispersed and freely falling, agglomeration is negligible.

After being dried and preheated and deoxidized in zone A wherein about half the total heat requirement of the system is supplied, the coal being fed off gyratory shelf 14 falls evenly and freely as an annular cascade into a rising column of pressurized hot hydrogen admitted through line 52, the hydrogen having sufficient heat capacity per unit time so that all of the coal must pass through its intumescent range and become thermally set before arriving at a pile in the bottom of the chamber including the flash carbonization zone B. At the same time, in order to scale off any scabs which may occasionally adhere to the sides of the apparatus, large chunks of refractory firebrick may occasionally be cycled through the system.

It is also important that high sulfur coal can be used in the system and the resultant char will be substantially desulfurized. If coal is heated rapidly in a stream of diluting hot hydrogen as it is in this process in zone B and if the organic molecules of volatile matter which contain sulfur are immediately removed from the solid carbon as they are in this process through offtake cone 44 and line 130, the resultant char will be desulfurized to the extent that a large part of the organic sulfur and half of the pyritic sulfur (but none of the sulfate sulfur) is removed with the stream of volatiles. Much of the remaining portion of pyritic sulfur (FeS) is removed as SO_2 and COS during partial combustion of char at temperatures in the order of 2500° to 3000°F. in combustion zone C. The resulting char exiting from hopper 94 at the bottom of the vessel after also being contacted with hot hydrogen in zone D would contain only a small part of the original sulfur of a high sulfur coal and this, of course, is a desirable characteristic of the char for steam raising, metallurgical use and the like.

Falling coal in zone B, ground to pass through a 30 mesh screen can be heated from 650°F. through its plastic range in less than half a second during a free fall of less than 5 feet against rising hydrogen at 1500°F. It is important to note that the coal particles with a terminal velocity in hydrogen less than the superficial velocity of the hydrogen and which are therefore entrained, may be recycled with the recycled heavy bottoms entering through inlet cone 46 in zone B and sprayed against descending solids.

The coal entering zone B is preferably of such a fineness that its terminal velocity in hydrogen at system pressure may lie between 2 and 12 feet per second. For optimum liquefaction, a catalyst and/or hydrogen transfer agent (phenanthrene) may be coated on the coal particles in a manner most suitable to distribute the catalyst on the surface of each particle of coal. The coal, of course, is dried and preheated in zone A as described above and is dropped into the rising stream of hot thermal carrier hydrogen which partial pressure is from ten to twenty times the partial pressure of the desirable oils in order that they may freely evaporate at system temperature and pressure.

As the coal particles drop countercurrently in zone B through the thermal carrier hydrogen, there is established a reaction zone whose upper limit is defined by the initial melting point of the coal and the formation of a liquid film on the surface of the coal particles. The lower limit of the reaction zone is that horizon in which all the liquid surface film has been completely distilled from the particles and only char and catalyst remain. The vertical extent of the coal melting and hydrogenation reaction zone is principally a function of four controllable parameters of the system including the inlet temperature of the preheated coal particles, the size and size range of the coal particles, the volumetric heat content of the thermal carrier hydrogen per unit time, and the partial pressure of the condensable volatiles.

The contact coking of recycled bottoms and mixed solids may also be accomplished in zone B. By introducing the bottoms into the lower part of zone B for some thermal treatment secondary distillation up to 1800°F. is accomplished and redistillation and contact coking of selected recycled fractions with whatever entrained solids may be therein, is also accomplished. Furthermore, the tars from the various knockout drums can be admitted to line 178 for recycling through inlet 46 with the heavy bottoms and in addition, finely ground coal may be mixed with the heavy bottoms after being admitted through inlet 180.

Thus, as the falling char reaches gyratory shelf 16, it has been heated to a temperature of at least 1600°F. and the volatile matter has been distilled off so that it contains only about 2% of volatile matter. The coal at this point is joined by recycled char from char inlet 54 to provide the necessary heat capacity for the system, as is explained above.

The stream of hydrogen thermal carrier gas and primary volatiles is withdrawn through conduit 130 and is introduced into knockout and tar removal drum 136 at about 900°F. with the vapor pressure of the highest boiling components about 1/10 to 1/20 of system pressure. Next, the combined gas stream is subjected to vapor phase hydrogenation in sequential catalytic chambers 147, 148 and 149. Additional hot hydrogen may be diverted from the main stream of thermal carrier gas through line 132 to conduits 130 and 150 for combination with the mixed gas stream. This further addition of hot hydrogen maintains the gas stream at the desired high temperature of about 1000°F. and prevents any undesired condensation of valuable hydrocarbons, by increasing the temperature and at the same time decreasing the partial pressure and thereby lowering the boiling point of the condensables.

COAL LIQUEFACTION BY LOW PRESSURE HYDROGENATION

H.H. Storch and L.L. Hirst; U.S. Patent 2,464,271; March 15, 1949; assigned to the U.S. Secretary of the Interior describe a process for the destructive hydrogenation of solid carbonaceous materials. In particular, this process relates to a low pressure process for the production of liquid hydrocarbons from coals, such as bituminous coal, lignite and the like, as well as catalysts for carrying out the process.

In the process wherein a solid carbonaceous material susceptible to destructive hydrogenation is admixed with a liquid vehicle and a dispersed catalyst, the mixture is heated to a temperature of at least 300°C., introduced together with excess hydrogen into a closed reaction zone maintained under an elevated pressure of not more than 90 atmospheres. The mixture is then advanced through the reaction zone while the temperature of the reaction mixture is progressively elevated as the mixture is advanced, and the reaction mixture is discharged from the reaction zone at a final temperature of not more than 475°C. Repolymerization and reprecipitation of the normally solid carbonaceous material being destructively hydrogenated can be prevented by maintaining a controlled progressively increasing reaction temperature as the destructive hydrogenation is carried out.

By beginning the destructive hydrogenation at a relatively low temperature, and progressively increasing the temperature in the reaction mixture as the reaction progresses, the deposition of coke and other residues in the equipment is substantially completely inhibited. The initial temperature of reaction is at least 300°C., and preferably within the more restricted range of from 350° to 400°C. Thereafter the temperature within the reaction zone is progressively elevated, as the reaction proceeds, to a maximum temperature of not more than 475°C. Preferably, the final reaction temperature is maintained within the more restricted range of from 425° to 450°C.

Catalysts for carrying out the low pressure hydrogenation are dispersed catalysts comprising stanniferous substances in intimate admixture with halogenous substances. Suitable stanniferous substances include metallic tin, and tin compounds such as tin sulfide, oxide, oxalate, or other tin compound soluble in strong mineral acids. In general, about 0.05% to 0.5% by weight and preferably between 0.1 and 0.3% by weight of the stanniferous substance based on maf solid carbonaceous material is a sufficient amount. The halogenous substance employed in the dispersed catalyst can be molecular chlorine, bromine, or iodine, and the like, but it is preferably in the form of an alkyl halide, or other volatile halogen compound. Iodoform constitutes a preferred halogenous substance and in general, iodine or iodine compounds are superior to other halogenous substances. Usually from 0.02 to 0.2% by weight, based on maf coal or other solid carbonaceous material susceptible to destructive hydrogenation, is a sufficiently large amount of iodoform or other halogenous catalytic substance. The following example illustrates how the process may be carried out.

Example: One part bituminous coal from the Black Creek Bed in Walker County, Alabama, is pulverized to −80 mesh (standard Tyler screen), and admixed with two parts of liquid vehicle, 0.001 part tin sulfide and 0.0005 part iodoform. (The liquid vehicle is prepared by hydrogenation of topped coke-oven tar at from 415° to 435°C. under a pressure of 65 to 70 atmospheres for 3 hours, in the presence of 0.001 part tin sulfide and 0.0005 part iodoform.) The mixture of coal, liquid vehicle, and dispersed catalyst is passed through a tubular preheater made of stainless steel. The preheater is provided with heating and cooling means, and the temperature of the coal-oil paste is elevated therein to 120°C. A second preheater, similarly provided with heating and cooling means, is arranged in series with the first one, wherein the coal-oil paste is further preheated to 370°C.

Thereafter, gaseous hydrogen, separately preheated also to 370°C., is admixed with the coal-oil paste containing dispersed catalyst, and the gas-paste-catalyst mixture is introduced into an elongated stainless steel converter provided with suitable heating and cooling means, and having a length to internal diameter ratio of 20 to 1. An excess of hydrogen is preferably employed, the rate of hydrogen input being maintained between 5 and 25 cubic feet per pound of coal-oil paste although only 0.063 part hydrogen per part coal is consumed. The pressure within the converter is maintained at 65 to 70 atmospheres by suitable valves and pumps, and the reaction temperature within the converter is gradually elevated by heating to 390°C. Over 3 1/2 hours reaction time, the temperature is gradually elevated to 415°C., after which the pressure is released, the product cooled, and an additional 0.001 part tin sulfide and 0.0005 part iodoform is added.

A successive hydrogenation of the primary product is carried out in a similar converter under similar conditions, but the initial conversion temperature is adjusted to 415°C., the final temperature to 435°C., and the reaction time is 3 hours. The reaction mixture is cooled, the pressure let down to atmospheric and the reaction mixture centrifuged to remove ash and a small amount of residue. The yield of oil produced, based on the weight of coal consumed, is 53.4%. 80% of the oil produced is recycled to serve as liquid vehicle for another batch, and 20% is a final product. After extended operating periods, no coke is found in the equipment. The oil produced has the following characteristics.

Specific gravity at 26°C.	1.118
Btu/lb.	16,892
Btu/gal.	157,600
Ash content, percent	0.02
Viscosity, furol, seconds at 122°F.	44.6
Flash point, °F.	225
Distillation (Topping, American Wood Preservers Association Method), volume percent to 350°C.	35
Insoluble (Bureau of Mines Tetralin-Cresol Method), percent	5.7

About 1 to 2.5 volume percent of the oil boils below 235°C., and the oil contains about 1 to 2% oxygen, in the form of tar acids, removable by washing with aqueous alkali solution.

RESIDUUM RECOVERY FROM COAL CONVERSION PROCESSES

H.H. Stotler and M. Calderon; U.S. Patent 3,519,554; July 7, 1970; assigned to Hydrocarbon Research, Inc. describe a process for the catalytic hydrocracking of a solid carbonaceous feed material by passing an oil slurry of the particulated feed with hydrogen upwardly through a catalytic reaction zone at high temperatures and pressures, such that the catalyst bed is in the ebullated state, and removing gaseous and liquid products from the reaction zone along with solids. The liquid products are separated into light distillates, middle oils, recycle and slurry oils and a residuum stream which is recycled to the reaction zone and solids-containing bottoms material which contains both residuum and heavy hydrocarbon oils. A wash liquid in which the residuum and oils have a high solubility, but which has a high volatility relative to the residuum and which is readily condensible with water at about atmospheric pressure is mixed with the bottoms material.

The mixture is then separated into a first portion containing substantial amounts of wash liquid and oil and residuum and a second portion which contains essentially all of the solids along with small amounts of wash liquid and oil and residuum. The first portion is thermally and steam fractionated into pure wash liquid which is returned into the process and oil and residuum which is subjected to further downstream treatment. The second portion is mixed with water at about 180°F. and is then fractionated at reduced pressures such that the water contained in the mixture vaporizes and steam strips the wash liquid from the mixture. This results in a solids water slurry and a water-wash liquid mixture from which the wash liquid may easily be recovered and reused in the process. Figure 3.34 is a schematic flow diagram of this coal conversion process.

A slurry of oil and a carbonaceous solid fuel material, such as bituminous or sub-bituminous coal, lignite or peat, which has been pulverized and dried at 10, hydrogen-rich gas at 12 and a high concentration residuum stream at 15 is introduced to reactor 16 through line 14. The coal slurry used is normally about a 1:1 mixture of solids and oil.

The reaction zone contains a particulate hydrogenation catalyst which is in an ebullated state due to the velocity of the gas and liquid feed materials upwardly through it. Gaseous products are removed through 18 and introduced to separation tank 26, wherein any liquid materials are separated from the vapor products. The vapor products are removed through line 30 and the liquid products are removed through line 34. The liquid effluent from the reactor is removed through line 20 to separation tank 24, wherein a separated vapor product is removed in line 28 and combined with those contained in line 30. The separated liquid products are then removed in line 32. If desired, a portion of the liquid effluent in line 20 may be used as a recycle stream in line 22 back to the reactor, usually for the purposes of providing additional liquid velocity to maintain the ebullated state of the catalyst. The liquid effluent in line 32 consists essentially of solids, residuum and heavy and middle gas oils. This effluent is separated in separator 35 (usually a liquid cyclone) into an overhead, 15, consisting of most of the residuum and oils in the effluent and a minimal amount of solids. Overhead 15 is recycled to the reactor. The bottoms, 37, from separator 35, are introduced to fractionation step 36.

Fractionation step 36 may consist either of single or multiple stage distillation units at both atmospheric and subatmospheric conditions. Products are removed through line 38, the products consisting of middle oils including kerosene, gas oils, etc., and heavier materials boiling up to about 975°F. These products may be further treated downstream using the usual type of refining processes. The bottoms material in line 40 is composed of a first component consisting essentially of residuum and heavier hydrocarbon oils and a second component consisting essentially of solids, including unconverted coal and ash. This solids oil and residuum stream is pumped by pump 42 through line 44 to heat exchangers 46 and 48, wherefrom it exists at a temperature in the range from about 400° to 500°F. and a pressure in the range of from about 150 to 180 psig.

FIGURE 3.34: RESIDUUM RECOVERY FROM COAL CONVERSION PROCESSES

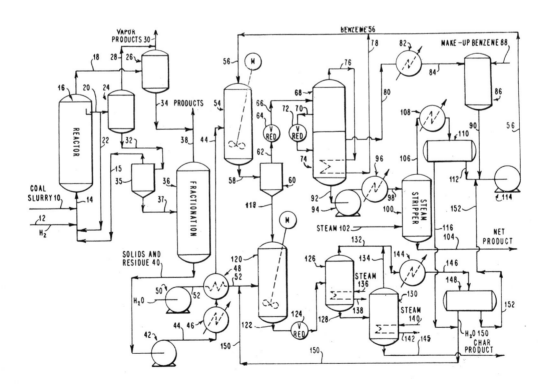

Source: H.H. Stotler and M. Calderon; U.S. Patent 3,519,554; July 7, 1970

The stream in line 44 is then introduced to tank 54, and mixed with hydrocarbon wash liquid at a temperature from about 120° to 200°F. from line 56. The wash liquid may be any suitable hydrocarbon material which has a high solvent power with respect to the oil and residuum, but which also has a high volatility relative to the residuum and is readily condensible with water in the range about atmospheric pressure. Such hydrocarbon materials would be those boiling in the range from about 150° to 300°F. at atmospheric pressure. Typical examples of such compounds are linear and branched aliphatic compounds containing between 6 and 9 carbon atoms, cyclic aliphatic compounds containing between 6 and 8 carbon atoms and aromatic compounds, such as benzene, toluene, ortho, meta and para-xylene and ethyl benzene or combinations thereof. While the choice of the wash liquid depends on the particular economic considerations of the process, the case herein described uses benzene as the wash liquid.

Benzene is added to tank 54 at a rate between one to two volumes of benzene per volume of first component. After allowing sufficient residence time for the benzene to penetrate the pores of the solid, the mixture is removed through line 58 to separation device 60. This device may be any one of a number of liquid solid separation methods known to the art, preferably a hydro-cyclone or liquid centrifuge. A first portion composed of at least about 90% of the benzene and oil and residuum is removed through overhead line 62. After pressure reduction in valve 64, the material is introduced through line 66 to fractionator 68. The temperature in this fractionator is in the range from about 290° to 330°F. and approximately 20 to 30% of the original benzene added is removed as vapor overhead through line 76. The remainder of the material in fractionator 68 is removed through line 70, pressure reduced through valve 72 and introduced to fractionator 74 at a temperature in the range from about 220° to 260°F. and a pressure in the range from about atmospheric to about 30 psig.

The heat for the fractionation in fractionator 74 is supplied by heat exchange with the condensing benzene vapor at about 300°F. from fractionator 68 in line 76. This benzene liquid is then removed in line 78 at a somewhat decreased pressure and introduced to line 56 for reuse as wash liquid. An overhead benzene stream from fractionator 74 is removed as vapor in line 80. It represents about 50 to 60% of the original benzene added. It is then condensed in cooler 82 and mixed with makeup benzene from line 88 in tank 86. The combined benzene streams are then introduced through line 90 to pump 114 which exits the stream into line 56 for reintroduction to the process as wash liquid.

The bottoms from fractionator 74 now consist essentially of the first component residuum and oil material with some benzene. This is removed through line 92, is pumped by pump 94 and passed in heat exchange with 300 psig steam in exchanger 96. The heated oil, residuum and benzene is then introduced through line 98 to steam stripper 100. Steam at 300 psig is introduced to stripper 100 through line 102. An overhead water vapor-benzene mixture is removed through line 106, cooled in cooler 108 and introduced to separation drum 110. The amount of benzene in this overhead constitutes between about 10 to 15% of the original benzene added. Water-free benzene is removed through line 112 where it is combined with benzene from line 90 and introduced to pump 114. The separated water is removed through line 116. The separated water is removed through line 116. The bottoms from steam stripper 100 consists essentially of all the first component which can be recovered, i.e., at least 85%, plus traces of benzene. The recovery of this first component represents one of the major advantages of this process.

The bottoms material from separator 60 consists of about 80% solids material, which is all of the solid material which had been contained in line 58. The remaining 20% is a mixture of oil and residuum material and benzene. This slurry is introduced through line 118 to tank 120, wherein it is mixed with approximately an equal amount by weight of water which is obtained through pump 50 and line 52, after heat exchange with the solids and residuum material in exchanger 48 and water recycled in line 150. This water is at a temperature of about 180°F.

After sufficient mixing time, the slurry is removed through line 122 and pressure reduced in reducing valve 124. It is then introduced to thermal fractionator 126. Heat is supplied to the fractionator by introducing 50 psig steam in line 136 and removing it through line 138. A benzene-water vapor mixture is removed at overhead through line 132 and the solids, remaining residuum, oil, benzene and water are removed as bottoms through line 128 and introduced to a second thermal fractionation unit 130. Heat is supplied to unit 130 by introducing 50 pounds steam through line 140 and withdrawing it through 142. Unit 130, as a result of its series relationship with unit 126, is operated at a somewhat lower pressure. Therefore, the overhead water vapor and the benzene stream in line 134 has a somewhat high proportion of water than the mixture contained in line 132. The stream in line 134 is combined with that in line 132. The bottoms material from unit 130 contains essentially all of the second component solids and water along with traces of benzene and is removed through line 145 as the char product from the plant. If desired, it may be subjected to an additional thermal fractionation similar to those carried out in units 126 and 130.

It is understood that the number of thermal fractionating units is dependent solely on the design parameters of the system, and it is a relatively simple chemical engineering calculation to determine the number of such units required to optimize the process. Normally, if two or three such units are used in series, the temperature of each unit would be in the range from about 200° to 250°F. with each unit operating at successively lower pressures within the range from about atmospheric to 40 psig.

The combined benzene-water vapor overhead fractions from the thermal fractionation units contain between about 5 to 15% of the original benzene added. The overhead is cooled in cooler 144 and then introduced through line 146 to separation drum 148. Water-free benzene is removed from drum 148 through line 152 and introduced to the benzene obtained from the makeup drum 86 and separation tank 110, for reuse in the system. Water is removed from separation drum 148 through line 150, is combined with that water removed from separation drum 110 in line 116, and is then recycled through line 150 back to line 52 for reuse in the system.

Benzene Wash Liquid Recovery

Conditions	Line	Material recovery		
		Percent of initial benzene	Percent of initial solids	Percent of initial oil and residuum
160 p.s.i.g., 350° F	58	100	100	100
110 p.s.i.g., 350° F	62	90		90
Fractionator 68, 60 p.s.i.g., 310° F	76	26		
5 p.s.i.g., 245° F	80	53		
	92	12		90
5 p.s.i.g., 330° F	106	12		
	104	[1] 0.02		90
Drum 110, 2 p.s.i.g., 165° F	112	12		
	116	0.01		
Tank 120, 110 p.s.i.g., 230° F	118	10	100	10
3 thermal units, 33 p.s.i.g., 12 p.s.i.g., 8 p.s.i.g., all at 230° F	146	10		
	145	[1] 0.1	100	10
Drum 148, 2 p.s.i.g., 165° F	152	10	100	10
	150	0.01		
Total lost		0.12		10

[1] Lost

The above table shows a detailed summary of the step by step recovery of benzene, solids, oil and residuum and water for the process as described above. It also outlines the particular temperature and pressure conditions used at various stages throughout the process. The data shown applies to processes using a benzene to heavy oil ratio of both 1:1 and 2:1. The process differences between the use of these two ratios are very slight, requiring only minor changes in heat exchange requirements. Based on the above data, for a 100,000 bpsd refinery using Illinois coal, the material obtained as bottoms in line 40 would consist of about 500,000 pounds per hour each of solids and of oil and residuum component. Using a 1:1 ratio of benzene to oil, 500,000 pounds per hour of benzene would be added in tank 54 as wash liquid. Thus, it is seen that in such a commercial process, only about 600 pounds per hour of benzene would be lost and the recovery of residuum and oil would be at least 400,000 pounds per hour. It is known that if such residuum were processed directly in a fluid coking plant, as opposed to this process, only about a 30% recovery could be expected.

REFINING OF COAL HYDROGENATION PRODUCTS

D.C. Overholt, G.D. Roy and R.R. Warren; U.S. Patent 3,084,118; April 2, 1963; assigned to Union Carbide Corporation describe a chemical process for the refining of liquid coal hydrogenation products. This refining process is one in which ash, unreacted carbon residues and water are all removed from coal hydrogenation liquid product without the disadvantages of the conventional methods. According to this process, there is added to the liquid coal hydrogenation product a liquid hydrocarbon precipitant and as a coagulant, sulfuric acid. This results in the coagulation of a soft plastic-like sludge. Substantially all of the ash and carbon residues are in the sludge while the supernatant liquid is ash-free liquid product plus the precipitant. The sludge and supernatant liquid are readily separated as by decanting the liquid. The supernatant liquid is advantageously water-washed to remove residual sulfuric acid. The precipitant can then be removed from the liquid product in any convenient manner, as by distillation.

The precipitant employed may be aromatic hydrocarbons or aliphatic hydrocarbons or a mixture of both. As the percentage of aliphatics increases the amount of pitch precipitated in the sludge will increase. As it is ordinarily desirable to leave as much pitch as possible in the supernatant liquid a highly aromatic liquid precipitant is desirable, such as benzene, toluene, xylene or mixtures of such aromatics. Benzene is particularly preferred because its low boiling point permits its ready removal from the supernatant liquid by distillation. Also quite useful are crude commercial mixtures of aromatic hydrocarbons, particularly those from which substantially all of the unsaturated aliphatics have been removed. A precipitant such as heptane can be used if a liquid product free of medium pitch is desired. Heptane will precipitate both medium and heavy pitch.

It is to be understood that while the precipitants employed in the process are nominally hydrocarbons, the use of the term hydrocarbons does not exclude the presence of small quantities of compounds containing other elements, as are commonly found associated with hydrocarbons. The quantity of precipitant employed will ordinarily be from 50 to 100 parts by weight of diluent per 100 parts by weight of coal hydrogenation liquid product, with about 70 parts by weight of precipitant ordinarily preferred. The larger proportions are employed with higher viscosity liquid product.

The preferred acid is concentrated sulfuric acid, from 90 to 100% acid, although aminosulfonic acid, NH_2SO_3H, may also be used. The quantity of acid used will ordinarily be between about 2 and 5 pounds of sulfuric acid (on a 98% acid basis) per 100 pounds of liquid coal hydrogenation product. At least 2 pounds of acid, if not more, will be required to precipitate all the ash, while more than 5 pounds will precipitate more sludge than is desirable.

Example: The material to be refined was a liquid coal hydrogenation product having a viscosity of 108 centipoises at a temperature of 55°C. and containing, by weight, 15.38% light oil, 21.25% middle oil, 29.01% pasting oil, 11.64% light pitch, 2.69% medium pitch, 0.06% heavy pitch, 2.95% carbon residues, 8.12% ash and 6.52% water. To 100 lbs. of this liquid product in a tank type reaction vessel was added 70 pounds of benzene. The mixture was agitated vigorously while 4.5 lbs. of concentrated (98%) sulfuric acid was added over a 5 minute period. The agitation was then continued for an additional 5 minutes, after which the mixture was allowed to settle for about 5 minutes. A soft, plastic-like sludge rapidly settled to the bottom of the reaction vessel, resulting in two sharply defined phases, a liquid phase and a sludge phase.

The supernatant liquid phase was decanted, leaving the sludge phase in the vessel. After water-washing to remove traces of sulfuric acid, the supernatant liquid contained 66.0 lbs. of benzene, 8.1 lbs. of light oil, 20.7 lbs. of middle oil, 2.35 lbs. of pasting oil, 10.1 lbs. of light pitch, 2.9 lbs. of medium pitch, no heavy pitch and 0.03 lb. of ash. The sludge phase weighed 42 lbs. 13 lbs. of acetone were added to the sludge and this mixture was agitated vigorously for about 5 minutes and was then allowed to settle for about 5 minutes, after which the supernatant liquid was decanted. The sludge remaining was again washed with 13 lbs. of acetone in the same manner.

The sludge was then dried at a temperature of about 110°C. to remove residual acetone and there remained 15 lbs. of dried coke, which contained no light pitch, 0.3 lb. of medium pitch, 1.6 lbs. of heavy pitch, 5.5 lbs. of carbon residues, 7.4 lbs. of ash and 0.2 lb. of sulfuric acid. The combined acetone supernatant liquid contained 0.5 lb. of light oil, 3.0 lbs. of middle oil, 3.8 lbs. of pasting oil and pitch, 0.9 lb. of sulfuric acid and no ash.

JET FUEL PRODUCTION FROM BLENDED CONVERSION PRODUCTS

A.M. Leas; U.S. Patent 3,533,938; October 13, 1970; assigned to Ashland Oil & Refining Company describes a process by which a high density jet fuel is prepared by hydrocracking a heavy hydrocarbon liquid, preferably coal liquids, separating the hydrocracked portion into a light fraction and a heavy fraction, reforming the light fraction and catalytically cracking the heavy fraction, separating the catalytic cracking product into a light and a heavy fraction, thermally cracking the heavy fraction, solvent extracting the light catalytic product and the reformate to recover aromatics therefrom, alkylating the aromatics, and thereafter hydrogenating the aromatics to produce alkyl naphthenes, dehydrogenating paraffin gases, polymerizing the dehydrogenation product, and hydrogenating the polymer to produce isoparaffin. The isoparaffins and alkyl naphthenes are blended in specified proportions to produce the jet fuel.

UNDERGROUND LIQUEFACTION OF COAL

E.F. Pevere and G.B. Arnold; U.S. Patent 2,595,979; May 6, 1952; assigned to The Texas Company describe a process for the recovery of coal substance from underground deposits in the form of a liquid. This process relates to the underground liquefaction of a liquefiable fraction of a coal deposit by hydrogenation to produce a liquid extract suitable for use in the production of motor fuels.

In carrying out the process, a well bore is drilled into the coal seam through which the hydrogenating agent may be admitted and the resulting liquid product withdrawn. The hydrogenating agent is forced under pressure through the well bore into direct contact with the virgin coal in the underground seam. Gaseous hydrogen is preferable as the hydrogenating agent. The hydrogen permeates the residue relatively thoroughly and produces by reaction with the coal an oil which is an excellent solvent and hydrogen transfer agent. The heavy oil or liquefied coal substance obtained by hydrogenation is one of the best hydrogen carriers known. The hydrogen diffuses upwardly into the coal seam, liquefying the more readily liquefiable coal substance. This liquid then drains down over the less readily liquefiable portion of the coal, thus acting as a hydrogen carrier to facilitate the liquefaction.

The reaction is initiated by raising the temperature at the coal face to the reaction temperature. Any means of supplying heat may be used; preferable are those involving liberation of heat near the face of the coal seam by chemical means. An electrical heater may be placed in the well bore to preheat the reactants. Superheated vapors of a hydroaromatic may thus be supplied to the coal whereupon heat is transferred to the coal upon condensation of the vapors to supplement the heat liberated by the reaction. Once initiated, the exothermic heat of reaction and the heat transfer between the reactants and reaction products serve to maintain the reaction temperature.

The well bore is preferably drilled into a low portion of the coal seam to permit the liquid product to drain down to the well bore for removal. The process is well adapted to working those seams which are inclined at an angle too steep for conventional mining. The process is particularly adapted to working those coal seams which are overlain by a relatively impervious stratum. Generally, the coal seams are overlain with a layer of clay and shale which is relatively impervious and is a good heat insulator.

The loss of hydrogen into pervious adjacent formations may often be largely eliminated by operating at high temperatures for a period of time such that some of the fusible metal salts in the formations are melted or some of the volatile metal salts associated with the coal are vaporized, thus plugging the walls of the adjacent formation. The temperature may be increased by operating at very high pressure to increase the rate of reaction and hence the rate of heat at which heat is liberated by the exothermic heat of reaction. Volatile metals may be supplied to the coal seam in the form of a concentrated solution of a soluble salt of one of the metals during the course of reaction. Halides of zinc and lead, for example, are suitable for this purpose.

A typical product obtainable by underground hydrogenation comprises 60 to 70% liquid hydrocarbons and 10 to 30% gaseous hydrocarbons. About 3 1/2 to 4 barrels of oil are obtained from each ton of coal reacted. Approximately 27% of the liquid hydrocarbon fraction has a boiling range within the gasoline range that is up to 392°F., 50% between 392° and 572°F. and 23% above 572°F. Figure 3.35 diagrammatically illustrates the process.

FIGURE 3.35: UNDERGROUND LIQUEFACTION OF COAL

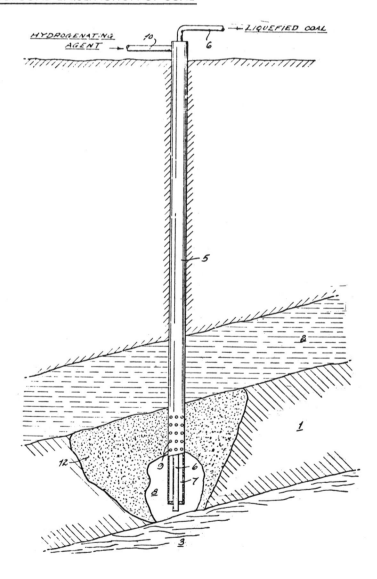

Source: E.F. Pevere and G.B. Arnold; U.S. Patent 2,595,979; May 6, 1952

With reference to the drawing, the numeral 1 designates an underground seam of coal above which is a relatively impervious stratum 2, generally of clay and shale, and below which is another relatively impervious stratum 3, e.g., a layer of clay. A well bore is drilled from the surface of the earth 4 to a low point in the coal seam adjacent the underlying stratum 3. Separate conduits 5 and 6 extend through the well bore into the coal seam. These conduits may be placed in any convenient manner analogous to the placement of tubing and casing in oil wells. As illustrated in the drawing, conduit 6 is placed within conduit 5 leaving an annular passageway 7 therebetween.

An enlarged cavity 8 may be formed at the terminus of the well bore to serve as a collection chamber for liquefied coal. The conduit 5 preferably is closed at its lower end and provided with a number of perforations 9 adjacent the coal stratum as outlets for the hydrogenating agent. The hydrogenating agent is admitted to conduit 5 through pipe 10, flowing through the annular passageway 7 and the perforations 9 into the coal stratum. The liquefied coal or liquid hydrogenation product is withdrawin through pipe 6.

As the hydrogenation progresses, a porous, honeycomb-like residue 12 is left in place in the formation. The liquid resulting from the liquefaction drains away from the residue, collects in the cavity 8 and flows through pipe 6 to the surface where it may be subjected to appropriate refining methods.

CARBONIZATION PROCESSES

THERMAL CRACKING OF COAL

Production of Motor Fuels by Carbonization of Lignite in the Presence of Alkali

The process by H.M. Noel; U.S. Patent 2,676,908; April 27, 1954; assigned to Standard Oil Development Company relates to a method for the efficient utilization of low grade carbonaceous solid material, such as lignite, peat, and the like, and specifically for converting such materials into more valuable products, including motor fuels, aromatic hydrocarbons, fuel gases and the like.

Heretofore and prior to the process it has been found that the production of undesirable phenolic distillation products may be to a large degree minimized and the yield of oil substantially increased by applying the so-called methylation technique to lignite distillation. Thus it has been found in laboratory operations that by adding minor quantities of calcium acetate, sodium carbonate, and iron filings, relatively high yields of oil containing a high proportion of aromatic constituents and very low in phenolic content are obtained.

It is postulated that the reagents convert the phenolic material in situ into the corresponding methylated aromatic compound. Thus phenol is converted into toluene, cresols are converted into xylenes, xylenols into mesitylene, etc., and since the aromatic hydrocarbons distill at substantially lower temperatures than the phenols from which they are derived, valuable high octane gasoline blending material is thus obtained.

Referring to Figure 4.1, numeral 1 denotes the crusher and mixer which is employed to reduce a solid low grade carbonaceous fuel, such as lignite or peat, to a finely divided form, for example, preferably of the order of below 50 mesh, or even less than 100 mesh, although even small lumps, say 1/4 to 1/2 inch size may be employed. Through line 2 are added the chemicals employed in conjunction with the methylation process. Though the quantities employed may vary within fairly wide limits depending upon the nature of the lignite or peat, generally about 2 to 6% of calcium acetate, 1 to 4% of sodium carbonate, and up to 2% of powdered iron or iron filings may be employed, based on the quality of lignite to be treated.

However, under certain circumstances, iron filings are not required for the reaction. As disclosed more fully below, the amount of sodium carbonate added may in accordance with the process be progressively decreased. The salts may be added either in the dry form or in aqueous solutions, but however they may be added, it is highly desirable that they be mixed with the crushed carbonaceous material into as intimate a mixture as possible. If desired, the powdered iron may be substituted in whole or in part by iron oxide and in certain cases iron is not required at all.

The finely ground mixture of carbonaceous solids and chemicals is passed from mixer 1 and line 3 to line 4 wherein it is thoroughly dispersed in a stream of aeration gas which is preferably light hydrocarbon gases from the process, as disclosed more fully hereinafter. The powdered feed in the dispersion is said to be in fluidized form because in this form it is capable of flowing through pipes, valves, ducts, etc., much like a liquid, showing both static and dynamic heads. The fluidized stream is passed through line 4 into the lower portion of carbonization chamber 5 which is in the form of a vertical cylinder.

A grid or screen 7 is located in the lower portion of chamber 5 to support a fluidized bed and to afford good distribution of the upflowing fluidizing gases. Also fed to carbonizer 5 through lines 8 and 4 is a stream of hot combustion residue from the gasification stage, as will be made clear hereinafter. These finely divided solids, having a temperature of from about 1400° to 2000°F., and fluidized if required, by slow currents of fuel gases admitted through aeration taps 9, are passed into contact with cold feed stock and thence into carbonizer 5 at such a rate as to maintain the desired temperature level therein, as described on the following page.

186

The mixture of lignite or peat, combustion residue, and aeration gas comprising light ends from the subsequent distillation is discharged into the bottom of carbonizer 5, the suspension entering below screen or grid 7 and then passing upwardly. Due to the superficial velocity of the gas stream, which is maintained within the limits of about 0.2 to 5 feet per second, the carbonaceous material and the reagent chemicals are formed into a turbulent ebullient mass, resembling a boiling liquid, having a well defined upper level.

The temperature in this zone is capable of very careful regulation and control, and heat is distributed rapidly through the fluidized mass in the carbonization chamber because of the high degree of agitation maintained therein. The temperature is maintained in the range of about 800° to 1100°F. preferably between 850° to 900°F., and the heat required for the carbonization is furnished substantially by the heat of the hot residue recycled from the subsequent gasification combustion zone, which is operated preferably at temperatures substantially above the temperature of the carbonization zone.

FIGURE 4.1:   PRODUCTION OF MOTOR FUELS BY CARBONIZATION OF LIGNITE IN THE PRESENCE OF ALKALI

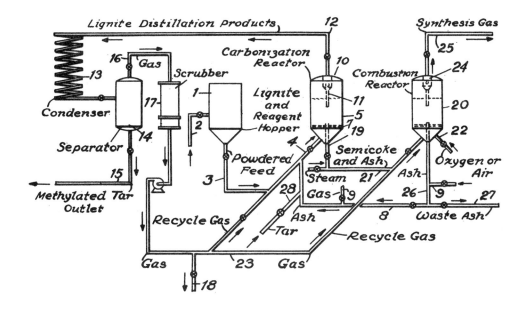

Source: H.M. Noel; U.S. Patent 2,676,908; April 27, 1954

As a result of the carbonization of lignite in chamber 5 in the presence of the reagent chemicals, substantial quantities of aromatic hydrocarbons boiling in the naphtha range are formed, with only minor quantities of phenolic compounds. As a result of the excellent heat transfer and control characteristics of the operation, the temperature of the bed of lignite undergoing distillation is uniform, and cracking and decomposition is substantially minimized, as opposed to prior experiences in fixed or moving bed commercial carbonization processes with the reagent chemicals.

The gaseous products are continuously withdrawn from carbonizer 5 through a dust separator 10 such as a cyclone, which has a dip pipe 11 extending below the upper level of the fluidized bed for returning separated dust. The volatile products are passed through line 12 and cooler 13 to separator 14, where means are provided for segregating tar, light oils, aromatic hydrocarbons, ammonia and gas. Thus condensate comprising aromatics as xylene, toluene, benzene, mesitylene, etc., and alos heavier distillation products such as tar and middle oil may be withdrawn from separator 14, through line 15 and passed to the products recovery system (not shown) where the aromatic hydrocarbons boiling in the naphtha range may be separated from higher boiling materials by fractional distillation.

The lignite gas may be withdrawn overhead from separator 14 through line 16. It is preferably scrubbed free of aromatic material in a conventional oil scrubber 17 or charcoal absorber. The gas comprising low molecular weight hydrocarbons, hydrogen, carbon monoxide, etc., is compressed and passed in part to line 4 to fluidize the powdered feed to the carbonization stage, and the balance may if desired, be passed to the combustion-gasification stage as disclosed more fully on the following page. Also, the gas may be freed from H_2S by any known process of desulfurization prior to its subsequent use, and if desired, some of the gas may be withdrawn through line 18, carbon dioxide removed by scrubbing with alkali or amino alcohols, and a very high calorific fuel gas is thus obtained. Returning now to carbonizer 5, an elongated vertical pipe 19, opening into a pocket below the distillation zone is provided to carry a fluidized stream of solids from the carbonization chamber 5. Semicoke and the solid products of the lignite distillation and chemical reaction are passed through standpipe 19 to line 21 where they are dispersed and suspended in a stream of superheated steam.

The fluidized stream is passed into the lower portion of a gas generator 20, which is of essentially the same type as the carbonizer 5 and is fitted at its lower end with an inlet line 22 for admitting oxidizing gas, such as air or preferably oxygen. The oxidizing gas may also be added to the fluidized stream in line 21. Also admitted to zone 20 may be gas from the lignite distillation, which is admitted through line 23.

The fluidized semicoke in generator 20 is in the form of a turbulent mass fluidized by the upward flowing gases and superheated steam. The gasification of the carbon by the oxygen and steam proceeds rapidly to form carbon monoxide and hydrogen. The heat required for the endothermic gasification reaction is supplied in part by the limited combustion of part of the carbonaceous solids in reactor 20 by the oxygen admitted through line 22, and also by limited combustion of the lignite distillation gas by oxygen from the same source. The total supply of oxygen is carefully controlled to produce synthesis gas and also to generate sufficient heat by combustion to satisfy the heat requirements of the carbonization step.

Thus as a result of the concomitant gasification of carbon and controlled combustion of normally gaseous hydrocarbons, a gas rich in H_2 and CO is produced suitable for a high calorific fuel gas or for the catalytic production of high octane hydrocarbons by the hydrocarbon synthesis reaction. The temperature maintained in reaction zone 20 is in the range of about 1200° to 2000°F., preferably about 1700° to 1900°F. The gasification products are withdrawn through dust separator 24, such as a cyclone and line 25 and may go to product storage, purification for sulfur removal and to the hydrocarbon synthesis plant, or combined with the product withdrawn through line 18 for use as high calorific fuel.

A fluidized stream of hot solids comprising ash and the products resulting from the high temperature treatment of the reagent chemicals, principally calcium oxide, sodium carbonate and minor proportions of iron oxide, is continuously withdrawn from gas generator 20 through pipe 26 at a rate determined by the heat requirements in the carbonization zone. Waste ash may be passed through heat exchangers before being discharged from the system. The balance of the ash withdrawn from generator 20 is passed through aerated lines 8 and 4 back to carbonizer 5 to supply the heat requirements therein.

Fluidized Process for the Further Carbonization of Carbonaceous Solids

The process by W.W. Odell; U.S. Patent 2,557,680; June 19, 1951; assigned to Standard Oil Development Company is concerned with reacting carbonaceous materials, particularly solid carbonaceous materials, by contact with fluidized hot solids and for the production of steam from water by contacting it with hot solids. The solids are heated while passing the same in a stream continuously down through a packed column in contact with a rising stream of hot gases which are products of combustion. The heated solids are removed and circulated along with materials to be cracked, volatilized or otherwise heat-treated into a reactor wherein the heated solids are retained in a fluidized state. Vaporous products are removed from the reactor and separated from the solids after the solids have given up some sensible heat to the material. The solids are then recycled to the column.

Figure 4.2 is a semidiagrammatic illustration of the process. Referring specifically to Figure 4.2, the material to be treated is introduced into reaction zone 10 by means of feed line 1. The feed material together with fluidized solids which are introduced into line 1 by means of line 2 flow upwardly through zone 10 under conditions to maintain a fluidized ebullient bed within zone 10, the upper level of which is at point A. The gasiform products are withdrawn overhead from zone 10 by means of line 3 and handled in any manner desirable.

The products pass through cyclone or equivalent separation means 4 wherein entrained solids are removed from the gases. Solid particles removed in cyclone separator 4 are returned to the fluidized bed in zone 10 by means of line 5. Although fluidized solids may be withdrawn from zone 10 by means of lines 6 and 7, it is preferable to handle the fluidized solids as hereinafter described.

The fluidized solids, for example, solids containing carbon, are removed from zone 10 by means of line 28 and introduced into the upper area X of regeneration zone 20. These fluidized solids are maintained in a fluidized ebullient state in zone 20, the upper level of which is at point B. During the predetermined residence time the fluidized solids in area X are heated by contact with hot upflowing combustion gases which gases are removed from zone 20 by means of line 18, passed through a waste heat boiler 9 and withdrawn from the system by means of line 11.

After the fluidized solids have reached a predetermined temperature as determined by the residence time of the solids in area X the solids flow downwardly between the interstices of solid nonfluidized packing material maintained in an intermediate area Y of regeneration zone 20. The fluidized solids then enter combustion area Z of zone 20 wherein the solids are treated with oxygen-containing gases under combustion conditions.

FIGURE 4.2: FLUIDIZED PROCESS FOR THE FURTHER CARBONIZATION OF CARBONACEOUS SOLIDS

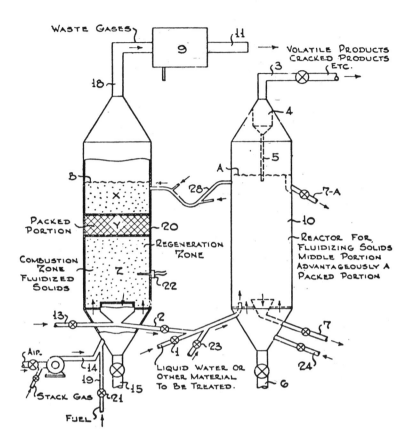

Source: W.W. Odell; U.S. Patent 2,557,680; June 19, 1951

The treated solids are withdrawn from area Z of zone 20 by means of line 2 and handled as hereinbefore described. Fresh fluidized solids or catalyst may be introduced into the system by means of line 13. Air or oxygen-containing gas or hot stack gas may be introduced into zone 20 by means of line 14. If desired a portion of the fluidized solids may be withdrawn from zone 20 by means of line or conduit 15 and handled in any manner desirable. This process can be understood better by the following example which illustrates the carbonization of finely divided coal.

Example: A bed of finely divided coke is fluidized in portion Z of 20 by introducing air at a linear velocity of approximately 1.5 to 2.5 feet per second, through supply conduit 14 passing the air stream out through 18, 9 and 11. The coke is ignited and the air blasting continued for the purpose of heating the coke particles in 20. The bed is built up by supplying an additional amount of coke through valve 13 until the bed level in 20 is about as shown at B. The velocity of the gases flowing through the bed is maintained sufficient to keep the coke in a substantially fluidized state in the areas X, Y and Z. This velocity for coke particles in the range 20 to 100 mesh is approximately 2.0 to 0.6 feet per second.

As soon as the temperature indicated by use of thermocouple 22 in area Z is approximately 1800°F. in this example, the circulation of solids (coke) from 20 through 2 to reaction zone 10 is promoted. Meanwhile finely divided coal is introduced through valve 1 into 10 along with the hot coke and a bed of fluidized solids is built up to a level A in 10. This bed comprises largely particles of finely divided coke along with particles of finely divided coal in various stages of carbonization. The relative amounts of hot coke introduced through 2 and the finely divided coal introduced through 1 are proportioned so that the coal in process reaches the desired maximum temperature in 10. Normally it is desirable to employ about three to six volumes of coke circulated through 2 to one volume of coal circulated through 1. The temperature of the hot coke in area Z may be at any chosen level above the ignition temperature up to or approaching that of the ash softening point of the coke.

It is selected with reference to the desired degree of carbonization of the coal admitted through 1 and will vary for a given coal according to the moisture content of the coal as introduced through 1. The volatile matter, gases and vapors evolved in the carbonization process in 10, are passed out through 4 and 3 and are recovered whereas the carbonized residue is withdrawn through 7 or through 7-A as desired. The particles of carbonized coal are removed from 10 through 8 preferably continuously and conducted back to 20 in an upper area X thereof to be reheated in 20 and recirculated down through Y and Z and back to zone 10 as a heat transfer medium for the carbonization of additional amounts of coal.

It has been found possible to treat a coal so that the volatile content of the coke residue can be controlled at will from a very low volatile content to substantially that of the coal initially introduced. This is done by adjusting the amount of combustion promoted in area Z of 20 and by regulating the amount of recirculation of the hot coke particles through 2 and the relative amount of coal fed through 1.

When employing relatively low temperatures in 20 or when circulating a relatively small amount of hot coke particles through 2, it is sometimes necessary to circulate some stack gases or other inert fluid along with the air supplied through 14 to zone 20 in order that the temperature in area Z be not too high and in order simultaneously to maintain the coke particles in a fluidized state in 20. In treating coal as described in the foregoing it is possible to recover maximum yields of tar and gas with a minimum amount of inert dilution.

Fractional Carbonization of Coal

R.T. Eddinger, L. Seglin and J.F. Jones, Jr.; U.S. Patent 3,574,065; April 6, 1971; assigned FMC Corporation describe a process for pyrolyzing coal by heating it in a first stage fluidized bed in the absence of added oxygen and vapors from coal pyrolysis containing material condensable as oily liquid, at a temperature below the fusion temperature, but sufficiently high to remove some volatiles from the dry coal until about 1 to 10% of the dry coal are removed overhead as volatiles and in at least a second devolatilizing stage, passing the thus treated coal into at least one other fluidized bed at a temperature above that of the first bed and below the fusion point of the solids fed to that stage, in the absence of oxygen for a time sufficient to nearly remove all of the volatiles from the coal condensable to oily liquids.

The process is continued by dividing the nearly devolatilized char into a product stream, a recycle stream and a combustion stream; completely burning the combustion stream, entraining the recycle stream in the hot gases from the combustion stream, separating the entrained recycle char from the hot gases and recirculating the heated recycle stream into the final devolatilizing stage and recovering the condensables from the overheads from the first stage and all of the devolatilizing stages.

Figure 4.3 is a flow sheet of the process as applied to high volatile bituminous B coal without char recycle. Referring to Figure 4.3, coal is fed to a first fluidized bed after first being crushed to a size desirable for fluidization, generally minus 14 mesh. As indicated on the flow sheet, the coal is heated in this first bed by recycle gas to about 600° to 650°F. For high volatile B bituminous coal, about 1 to 10% of the dry coal is removed overhead during a residence time of from about 1 to 30 minutes; of this overhead, about half represents material condensable to oily hydrocarbon liquids.

The dried preheated coal is then fed into the second stage in which the first pyrolysis occurs. In this stage, it is immediately heated to a higher temperature, but below its raised fusion point, to start driving off the bulk of the volatiles. The fluidizing medium is the overhead from the third stage, and consists of gas plus condensable from that stage. Residence time is about 1 to 30 minutes, temperature about 800° to 900°F., and preferably from 830° to 860°F. The stage overhead includes all of the gas and condensables from the coal, excluding that which comes out of the drying-preheating stage. In general, there is enough condensable hydrocarbon to yield about 25% total of oily liquid by weight of the original dry coal.

The partially devolatilized char from stage two goes into a third stage in a fluidized bed where further pyrolysis is carried out at temperatures in the range of 950° to 1050°F. The fluidizing medium is recycle or inert gas. After 1 to 30 minutes in this stage, the char contains about 1% of volatiles which could be recovered as liquid condensate. The overhead from the stage, it will be noted, goes into the second stage.

The char from this stage is divided into three streams, one going to product, one going into a combustion chamber, and one going into the line which carries the combustion product from the combustion chamber into a cyclone. The portion of the char which goes into the combustion chamber, which may be a fluidized bed or not, as desired, is completely burned there with air to produce a hot gas stream which entrains the portion of the char in the entraining line into the cyclone. Here the hot char is separated from the gas which may be exhausted via a heat exchanger to recover its sensible heat, and the hot char is recycled back to the second carbonizing stage to provide the heat necessary for the process. The process may be utilized with additional recycle to reduce the number of stages in the case of high volatile A bituminous coal for example. In such an operation, char from the carbonization stages is recycled back to other carbonization stages to permit higher temperatures than could be obtained without the char recycle due to fusion of the bed.

FIGURE 4.3: FRACTIONAL CARBONIZATION OF COAL

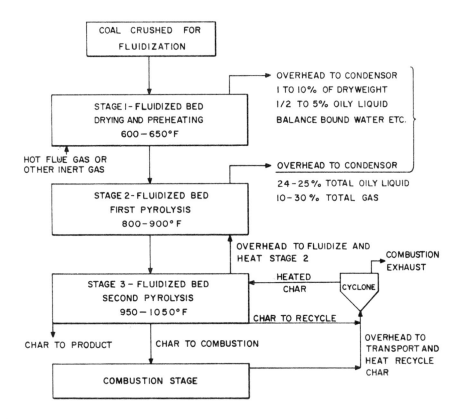

TYPICAL FLOW SHEET

HIGH VOLATILE B BITUMINOUS COAL

Source: R.T. Eddinger, L. Seglin and J.F. Jones, Jr.; U.S. Patent 3,574,065; April 6, 1971

Conversion of Carbonaceous Solids into Volatile Products

The process by F.R. Russell; U.S. Patent 2,741,549; April 10, 1956; assigned to Esso Research and Engineering Company relates to the conversion of carbonaceous materials including solids such as all types of coal, lignite, peat, oil shale, tar sands, coke, oil coke, cellulosic materials, lignin and hydrocarbonaceous liquids such as residual oils, into volatile products such as light oils, tars, coal gases, producer gas, gases containing CO and H_2, or the like, by coking carbonization and/or gasification in a fluidized solids process.

In accordance with the process, a subdivided noncombustible solid is added to a heat generating combustion zone wherein subdivided carbonaceous solids are subjected to combustion, carbon-containing solids as a heat carrier are returned from the combustion zone to an endothermic conversion of fluidized carbonaceous solids and the added noncombustible solids are separated from the carbon-containing solids used as heat carrier, prior to introduction of the latter into the conversion zone. The added noncombustible solids may be an inert low-cost material, such as sand, clay, furnace ash, ash from the carbonaceous charge and the like. Figure 4.4 is a semidiagrammatic illustration of a system suitable for carrying out this process. The system shown therein essentially comprises a coker 10, a water gas generator 30 and a heater 50 whose functions and cooperation will be forthwith explained. It should be understood, however, that either zone 10 or 50 or both may serve different purposes, such as preheating, drying, the production of producer gas or any other

FIGURE 4.4:   CONVERSION OF CARBONACEOUS SOLIDS INTO VOLATILE PRODUCTS

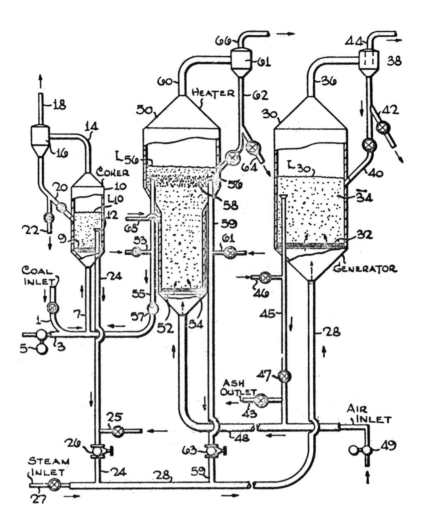

Source: F.R. Russell; U.S. Patent 2,741,549; April 10, 1956

endothermic treatment of carbonaceous solids. While coal will be referred to hereinafter as the carbonaceous solid used, other solid carbonaceous material and liquid hydrocarbonaceous materials may serve as charge to the process. In operation, a carbonization coal in finely divided form, for example, of the order of 50% having a size of less than 100 mesh, is fed through pipe 1 and line 7 to the lower conical portion of coker 10. Any conventional feeding device for finely divided solids, such as an aerated standpipe, a pressurized feed hopper or mechanical conveyor, may be used to feed the coal to the system. The coal is picked up in pipe 3 by a fluidizing gas, such as steam, flue gas, or the like, supplied to line 3 by compressor 5.

The dilute suspension formed passes into line 7 and through a distributing device, such as a perforated grid 9, into the carbonization zone 12 of coker 10 where the coal is subjected in the form of a dense, ebullient, fluidized mass forming a well defined upper level L10 to coking temperatures of between 800° and 2000°F.; low carbonization temperatures of 850° to 1200°F. are preferred to produce a highly reactive coke for gasification. The heat required for the carbonization reaction is supplied by highly heated solid combustion residue recirculated from heater 50 through line 55 as will appear more clearly hereinafter. The superficial velocity and amount of the fluidizing gas admitted through line 3 to coker 10 are so chosen that within carbonization zone 12 a superficial gas velocity of about 0.3 to 3 feet per second and a fluidized bed density of about 10 to 50 pounds per cubic foot are established. Product vapors containing small amounts of carbonaceous fines are passed overhead from level L10 through line 14 and a conventional gas solids separation system such as cyclone separator 16. Vapors and gases substantially free of solids are withdrawn through line 18 for further treatment in a conventional recovery system (not shown) for the production of such carbonization products as coal gas, oil, tar, chemicals, etc. Solids separated in separator 16 may be recycled through pipe 20 or discarded from the system through line 22.

Fluidized coke admixed with combustion residue is withdrawn downwardly from carbonization zone 12 from a point above grid 9 through line 24 which may be a standpipe aerated and stripped with steam through one or more taps 25 and provided with a control valve, such as a slide valve 26. The fluidized solids are then passed to line 28 wherein they are suspended in steam supplied from line 27. The so diluted suspension is passed under the pseudo-hydrostatic pressure of standpipe 24 to the lower conical portion of gas generator 30 and through a distributing grid 32 into gas generation zone 34.

The relative and absolute proportions of steam and solids in line 28 and the superficial gas velocity within zone 34 are so chosen that a dense fluidized mass with an upper level L30 forms above grid 32, in a manner similar to that described in connection with coker 10. Gas generation zone 34 is maintained at a temperature of between 1400° and 2400°F., preferably about 1600° to 1800°F. at about atmospheric to 400 pounds per square inch pressure to permit the water gas reaction to take place between the steam and the carbon of the fluidized solids bed.

The heat required for the water gas reaction is supplied by highly heated carbonaceous solids recirculated from heater 50 through line 59 at the desired temperature, as will appear more clearly hereinafter. The carbon concentration within zone 34 is maintained at about 10 to 50% or higher by a proper adjustment of the ash withdrawal or ash loss overhead, for instance, through lines 42, 43 and/or 64, which is adjusted so as to hold the carbon at the desired concentration in generator 30 as determined by the economic balance of the process.

A gas consisting mainly of CO and H_2 is taken overhead from generator 30 through line 36 and gas solids separator 38. Separated solids may be returned through line 40 to zone 34 or discarded from the system through line 42. Water gas substantially free of solids is withdrawn through line 44 to be passed, if desired after heat exchange with process gases and/or solids, to any suitable use as a fuel gas, for hydrocarbon synthesis and others. Solid gasification residue comprising a mixture of carbon and ash is withdrawn downwardly through line 45 which may be a conventional standpipe aerated and stripped with steam or air through one or more taps 46 and provided with a slide valve 47. The fluidized solids pass into line 48 wherein they are picked up by air supplied from compressor 49.

Combustion zone 54 contains a dense fluidized bed of a noncombustible diluent material, such as sand, having a particle size appreciably coarser than that of the solid admitted through grid 52. The particle size depends on the density and the character of the noncombustible material. When sand is used, particle mesh sizes varying from 8 to 180, preferably from 20 to 40, are usually suitable depending on the size of the coke particles fed. The dimensions of the noncombustible solids bed in zone 54 are such that combustion takes place at an average carbon concentration of not more than about 1%, preferably of about 0.1 to 0.5%. Combustion temperatures of 1500°F. and above may be maintained in this manner.

The linear velocity of the gas within zone 54 is so chosen that the coarse noncombustible fluids are maintained in a highly turbulent state without being entrained in and carried away with the upwardly flowing gases to any substantial extent. The gas velocity should, however, be high enough fully to entrain the smaller sized solids fed through grid 52. Such velocities may range from about 1 to 20 feet per second depending on the character and particle size of the solids used. Velocities of 3 to 10 feet per second are generally suitable for sand particles larger than 60 mesh and process solids particles of 20 to 60 mesh. In this manner, the coarse noncombustible solids are caused to stay within zone 54 while the solids introduced through grid 52 and their solid residue are carried overhead into a phase 56 of fine carbonaceous solids in flue gases, having an upper level L56. In general, it is desirable to maintain zone 56 which has a relatively high carbon concentration as thin as feasible in order to prevent appreciable formation of CO.

Hot flue gases pass overhead from level L56 through line 60 into a conventional gas solids separator 61. Separated fines may be returned to zone 56 through line 62 or discarded through line 64. Flue gases substantially free of solids are withdrawn through line 66 to be vented, if desired, after heat exchange with feed gases and/or solids, or to be used for fluidization, aeration and/or stripping purposes in the process.

The temperature in combustion zone 54 is preferably so maintained that the solids collecting in zone 56 have the highest possible temperature commensurate with economical construction materials and the fusion or softening point of the ash. This temperature lies generally between 1600° and 2300°F. If the ash fusion point restricts the upper temperature limit the feed coal may be treated with materials increasing the fusion point of the ash, such as silica or alumina to permit a temperature increase of about 100° to 200°F.

Fluidized carbonaceous solids from zone 56 are returned through line 55 to coker 10, if desired, via line 7. Line 55 may be a conventional standpipe aerated through one or more taps 53 and provided with a slide valve 57. The amount of solids flowing through pipe 55 depends on the desired temperature differential between zones 12 and 56, the temperature and quantity of coal entering in line 1, the specific heat of the solids and the heat required for coking the coal.

Another considerably larger amount of solids is withdrawn from zone 56 through standpipe 59, aerated through taps 61 and provided with control valve 63. This quantity of hot solids is returned to gas generator 30, if desired, via line 28, as shown in the drawing, to supply the heat required in zone 34. In accordance with the higher temperature and the normally larger dimensions of gas generator 30, the amount of solids recycled to generator 30 is many times that recycled to coker 10, and amounts to about 200 pounds of recirculated solids per pound of carbon consumed in zone 34 when the temperature is 100°F. lower in zone 34 than in zone 54. If desired or necessary, these solids returned from zone 56 may be subjected to further classification and more inert diluent solids separated out and returned to zone 56 before the carbonaceous solids are carried over to zone 34.

Treatment of Hydrocarbonaceous Solids

This description by R.B. Day; U.S. Patent 2,406,810; September 3, 1946; assigned to Universal Oil Products Company relates to a process and apparatus for the production of normally liquid and normally gaseous hydrocarbons, by distillation and pyrolytic conversion, from hydrocarbonaceous solids, such as for example, oil shales, tar sands, coal, lignite and materials of a similar nature.

This process involves the following combination of features: maintaining a bed of the solid hydrocarbonaceous material to be treated in a confined distilling zone; continuously supplying material in subdivided form to the upper portion of the bed; causing the particles or lumps of solid material to move continuously downwardly through the distilling zone; effecting substantial devolatilization of the solid material within the distilling zone by supplying heat; removing the evolved volatile hydrocarbons from the distilling zone and separating the same into selected relatively light and relatively heavy liquid fractions and gases.

The process then involves heating the relatively heavy liquid fractions to a temperature suitable for their pyrolytic conversion and supplying the heated material to an intermediate point in the distilling zone and into direct contact with the upper portion of the bed to supply heat for the distilling operation; separately heating relatively light, normally liquid and/or gaseous fractions to a substantially higher temperature than that to which the heavy fractions are heated and introducing the highly heated material into the lower portion of the distilling zone and into direct contact with the bed to supply additional heat for further distillation of volatile fractions from the solid material.

The process continues by directing solid material from the lower portion of the bed in the distilling zone into a combustion zone and burning residual combustibles from the solid material; employing heat thus evolved in the combustion zone to heat relatively light normally liquid and/or gaseous fractions to the desired high temperature prior to their introduction into the distilling zone; removing solid material from which the residual combustibles have been burned and in which a portion of the heat of combustion is stored from the combustion zone; passing the same in indirect contact with air to preheat the latter and cool the solid material and discharging the thus cooled solid material from the system and supplying air thus preheated to the combustion zone to effect the burning of the residual combustibles from the solid material.

Referring to Figure 4.5, after any required pretreatment the solid charging material is fed by a suitable elevator or the like not shown to hopper 1 from which it passes downwardly through conduit 2 and a suitable sealing and flow-regulating device, for example, the star feeder indicated at 3, into retort 4 and into the bed 5 of solid material maintained within the retort.

The distilling retort 5 is a vertically elongated vessel preferably having an outer metal wall or casing and lined with suitable high temperature refractory material not illustrated. The retort is preferably constructed with a gradually increasing internal diameter from its upper to its lower portion so as to accommodate some swelling of the bed of solid material undergoing distillation without sticking and plugging of the retort. The solid particles of the bed 5 pass continually downwardly through the retort and a large portion of their volatile components is driven off by the direct application of heat thereto as they pass through the bed. This is accomplished by introducing highly heated hydrocarbons into the retort and into direct contact with the solid particles of the bed.

The temperature employed in the distilling retort is preferably within the range which will give pyrolytic conversion or cracking of a considerable portion of the volatiles driven off and the temperature maintained in the lower portion of the bed 5 in the retort is sufficiently high to cause substantial coking of any residual tar-like materials remaining on the solid particles, including those formed and deposited as a result of the preceding distilling and cracking operation.

Thus, the solid particles of the bed leaving the distilling zone will carry a substantial quantity of residual combustibles of the nature of petroleum coke or the like. These residual combustibles represent the least valuable components of the hydrocarbonaceous materials originally contained in the charge and formed in the cracking operation. In the process all or a substantial portion of these residual combustibles are burned from the remaining incombustible solid material subsequent to their discharge from the distilling retort, as will now be described. The solid particles from which all or a substantial portion of the volatiles have been driven in the distilling, cracking and coking operation are directed in the case illustrated through the hopper-like bottom section 6 of the retort onto a moving grate or conveyer 11 disposed within

FIGURE 4.5:   TREATMENT OF HYDROCARBONACEOUS SOLIDS

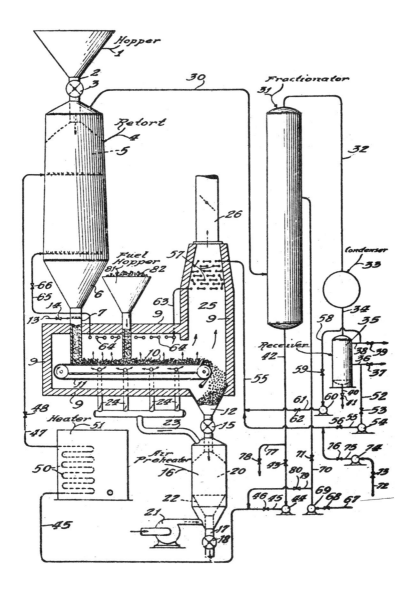

Source: R.B. Day; U.S. Patent 2,406,810; September 3, 1946

a combustion zone defined by refractory walls 9. The solid material is distributed on the moving grate or conveyer in the form of a relatively thin bed 10 which moves continuously away from the point at which the solid material is supplied, to the opposite discharge end of the combustion zone where it falls into the discharge hopper 12 to pass therefrom, preferably through a suitable cooling zone and from the system, as will be later described.

The length and speed of the chain grate or conveyer 11 are correlated to give sufficient time for the solid material in the combustion zone to burn all or a major portion of the residual combustibles therefrom while keeping a relatively thin bed 10 on the grate. Air is admitted, as will be later described, to the combustion zone, preferably at spaced points along and beneath the moving grate and passes upwardly through the latter into contact with the bed 10 wherein it supports combustion of the residual carbon and heavy hydrocarbonaceous material carried from the distilling retort by the solid particles. The temperature attained in the combustion zone may be kept at the desired value by regulation of the amount of air supplied, a relatively large amount of excess air being ordinarily employed to dilute and cool the evolved combustion gases. The gaseous products of combustion are discharged from the combustion zone through a heating chamber 25 to a suitable stack 26. To prevent any substantial passage of combustion gases from the combustion zone into the distilling retort 4, steam or any other suitable relatively inert gas is supplied as a blanketing and stripping medium to the hopper bottom 6 of the retort or into the conduit 7 which connects this portion with the combustion zone. Line 13 and valve 14 is provided for this purpose in the case illustrated and a portion of the steam thus introduced into contact with the solid material passing from the distilling retort passes into the combustion zone, while another protion passes upwardly into the distilling retort and displaces or substantially strips occluded volatile hydrocarbons from the solid material so that no substantial quantity of the latter pass into the combustion zone.

To substantially seal the opposite end of the combustion zone and prevent the escape of any substantial quantity of combustion gases with the solid particles being discharged, a suitable sealing device, such as the star feeder indicated at 15, is provided at the discharge end of hopper 12.

The hot solid particles from which all or a substantial portion of the residual combustibles have been burned in the combustion zone are directed from the latter through hopper 12 and member 15 to a separate confined vessel 16 which, in the case illustrated, serves as an air preheater, where the solid material is cooled, as will be later described, by direct contact with air and is then discharged through conduit 17 and a sealing and flow-regulating device, such as the star feeder 18, to suitable conveying means, as a dump car or the like not shown.

A downwardly moving bed 20 of the solid particles is maintained within vessel 16 and air is supplied by a suitable blower or the like indicated at 21 to the lower portion of vessel 16 beneath a suitable substantially cone shaped perforate member or the like indicated at 22, through which it passes into the bed 20 and is there heated by direct contact with the hot solid material. The preheated air is directed from above the bed in vessel 16 through conduit 23 and preferably through a plurality of suitable branch conduits 24 into the combustion zone beneath bed 10 where it is used to support combustion and control the temperature in the combustion zone.

Vapors and gases supplied to and evolved in the distilling retort are directed from the upper portion above bed 5 through line 30 to fractionator 31 where their high-boiling normally liquid components are condensed and from the upper portion of which fractionated vapors and gases of the desired end-boiling point are directed through line 32 to condenser 33. The resulting condensate and uncondensed normally gaseous fractions are supplied from the condenser through line 34 to the receiver and gas separator 35, where the distillate product may be withdrawn to storage or to any desired further treatment through line 36 and valve 37 and where the normally gaseous fractions are directed through line 38 and valve 39 to storage or to suitable fractionating and gas concentrating equipment not illustrated. Steam supplied to the distilling retort and that formed by the vaporization of moisture in the solid charging material charged to the retort is condensed in condenser 33 and the water which separates from the distillate in receiver 35 is withdrawn through line 40 and valve 41.

Direct Conversion of Carbonaceous Material to Hydrocarbons

Coal or other naturally occurring bituminous carbonaceous materials, or carbon, coke, or carbonaceous petroleum materials are converted directly to hydrocarbons and oxygen-containing organic compounds by reacting the carbonaceous material with steam in the presence of a two component catalyst system which is proposed by E.J. Hoffman; U.S. Patent 3,505,204; April 7, 1970; assigned to The University of Wyoming. The first catalyst component is a compound of an alkali or alkaline earth metal and the second component is a compound of a group VIII transition metal. By utilizing these catalysts, good yields of hydrocarbons are obtained in a single stage reaction at temperatures of from 800° to 1000° or 1200°F.

Figure 4.6 is a flow sheet diagram of the process utilizing a fluidized bed reactor. By the use of a suitable two component catalyst system it is possible to reduce the temperature levels of the initial carbon steam reaction to those for the Fischer-Tropsch reactions, thus making possible the direct, single stage overall conversion with the attendant savings in investment and processing costs. The endothermicity of the initiation reactions tends to be balanced by the exothermicity of the completion reaction, thus eliminating most of the heat transfer problems ordinarily encountered.

In this process, carbonaceous material and steam are reacted in a single stage reactor. A multiple catalyst is also present in the reactor and can be introduced pulverized or in a slurry. The reactor is operable in the temperature range of approximately 800° to 1200°F., and at pressures of from near atmospheric to around 500 psi, depending upon the nature of the product desired. The overhead product from the reactor is passed through a solid-gas separator to remove entrained solids, and then partially condensed to yield a hydrocarbon phase and an aqueous phase containing predominately the oxygenated compounds, though some are also partitioned in the hydrocarbon phase. The uncondensed vapors contain the more volatile hydrocarbons (principally methane, ethane, etc.), as well as carbon dioxide.

The condensed hydrocarbon liquid phase may be further refined according to conventional refinery procedures to yield gasoline and diesel fuels, and higher molecular weight residues. Some gas and LPG will also be dissolved in the liquid layer, depending upon the phase equilibria of the separation. The aqueous layer will contain principally dissolved oxygenated compounds such as the lower alcohols, aldehydes and ketones, and organic acids.

FIGURE 4.6: DIRECT CONVERSION OF CARBONACEOUS MATERIAL TO HYDROCARBONS

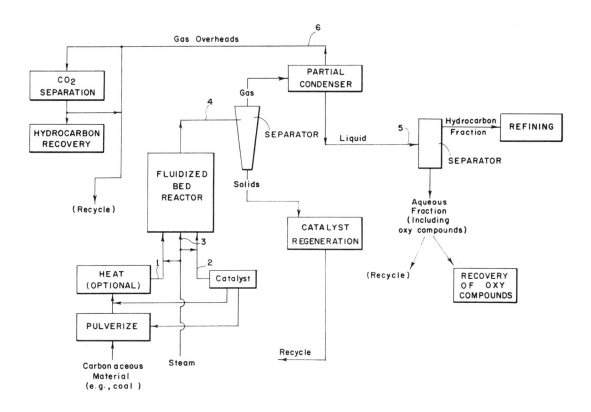

Source: E.J. Hoffman; U.S. Patent 3,505,204; April 7, 1970

These may be subjected to further separation by means of the techniques of azeotropic and extractive distillation, solvent extraction, etc. The aqueous layer can be recycled as a source of steam for the reaction and fluidization. If all or part of the oxygenated compounds are left in the recycle, these compounds will act to suppress further oxy formation.

The catalyst system includes two components. The first component is a compound of an alkali metal or an alkaline earth metal. Oxides and carbonates of sodium and potassium are preferred, but other compounds, such as chlorides, hydroxides, sulfates, silicates, sulfides, etc., can be used. The compounds can be used directly in an impure state. For example, the hydrated sodium carbonate ore, trona, can be used directly. The second catalyst is a Fischer-Tropsch type catalyst containing a transitional metal of group VIII of the Periodic Table. Compounds of iron, nickel and cobalt are preferred, and of these, iron compounds, particularly the iron oxides, are the most preferable.

Other metals belonging to the group are Ru, Rh, Pd, Os, Ir and Pt. The compounds may be oxides or other compounds such as carbonates, nitrates, carbides, chlorides, sulfates, etc., and the second component may include compounds of metals in different valence states.

For example, the second component may comprise ferrous and ferric oxide. The second component need not be pure. Iron catalyst, for example, may consist of nitrided steel wool, steel turnings, iron ore, roasted pyrites, fused iron, mill scale, iron alloys, steel shot, lathe turnings, magnetite, hematite, Luxmasse, Lautamasse, siderite, goethite, ferrosilicon, limonite, and sandstone (with Fe present). The more active catalysts for the completion of the reaction would be Ni or Co. However, these are not only more expensive than Fe, but are quite reactive at the reactor conditions, and tend to produce gases (greater degree of hydrogenation) preferentially to liquids. The nickel and cobalt will also tend to be lost from the system due to the production of volatile carbonyls. With reference to Figure 4.6, an operation utilizing a fluidized bed system will be described in detail. Coal pulverized to an average particle size of 35 mesh (Tyler) on a roller mill is preheated to a temperature of about 800°F. and continuously introduced into a fluidized bed reactor such as a simple refractory lined column including means to introduce a fluidizing gas. Steam is introduced into the coal feed stream 1 and is used to motivate the coal into the reactor. Pulverized catalyst is introduced to the reactor and additional steam is used to motivate the catalyst through feed stream 2. The catalyst contains about 10% by weight sodium carbonate of an average size of 65 mesh and 90% impure iron ore of an average size of about 40 mesh made up of Fe_3O_4, Fe_2O_3, FeO, Fe, and other materials, principally iron carbides. About 40% of the catalyst is in a reduced state which state can be achieved by subjecting spent catalyst to a regenerating step to be described subsequently.

Steam is introduced at a rate of about 1.5 mols per mol of carbon to maintain fluidized conditions at space velocities to 400 hr.$^{-1}$ and the reaction is maintained at a temperature of from 800° to 1000°F. at a pressure of from 100 to 200 psi. Steam can also be introduced directly to the reactor at 3 as shown in Figure 4.6. The catalyst may conveniently be ground with the carbonaceous material and introduced into the reactor through the same feed stream and, of course, the catalyst may be preheated.

Solids are separated from the overhead stream 4 by one or more cyclone separators. Other separators can be used and provision can be made to remove solids from a point below the top of the reactor which may be desirable in the event that the carbonaceous material includes a good deal of inert substances. Solids removed from the overhead include catalyst, unreacted coal, ash, and any inerts not otherwise separated from the reactor. The solids may be recycled to the reactor unless they include a substantial amount of inerts in which case these materials are separated in any convenient manner such as by fluidizers and the like. If the iron catalyst is recycled, it may require regeneration in which case the catalyst, together with unreacted coal, is treated with hydrogen or synthesis gas at temperatures of from 500° to 700°F. or higher.

The gaseous overhead is partially condensed to form a liquid stream 5 and a gaseous overhead stream 6. The gaseous stream includes CO_2, C_1, C_2, LPG and H_2S. This stream can be treated to remove CO_2 and H_2S and processed for the LPG and other hydrocarbons present. The stream may be partially recycled to the reactor before or after CO_2 removal to suppress gas formation in the reactor and to provide temperature control.

The liquid product stream 5 contains an aqueous fraction and a hydrocarbon fraction which are mutually insoluble and thus easily divided. The hydrocarbon fraction may be refined by conventional refinery procedures to yield gasoline, diesel fuel and other useful petroleum fractions. The aqueous layer will include oxygenated compounds such as alcohols, aldehydes, ketones, acids and the like which are valuable in themselves and can be recovered by conventional separation techniques such as distillation.

Preparation of Hydrocarbon Oils by Thermal Cracking of Bituminous Materials

The process proposed by C.T. Harding; U.S. Patent 2,379,077; June 26, 1945; assigned to Standard Oil Development Company relates to treating bituminous material such as shale, oil sands, coal and the like to recover therefrom valuable hydrocarbons, including gasoline, heating oils, etc.

In Figure 4.7, 1 represents a supply hopper in which raw shale is contained, and this shale is discharged into a grinder 2 where it is ground to a particle size of from 60 to 200 mesh or finer. The grinder is motivated by a suitable motor or other driving means 5, a projection of whose shaft 7 extends into the grinding means 2. Simultaneously steam, flue gas or hydrocarbon vapors either produced from the process or supplied from extraneous source are also discharged into the grinding means 2 and these serve as a carrier gas to form a suspension of the ground shale in the gas. In some cases it is desirable to heat these gases or vapors prior to introduction into the grinder.

In the drawing no specific means for dispersing a powder in a gas or vapor is shown, but it will be understood that any suitable means for effecting the formation of a suspension may be employed. The suspension is withdrawn through line 10 and discharged into a preheating coil 11 disposed in a suitable furnace 12 where the suspension is heated up to a temperature below 1000°F., preferably from 700° to 900°F.

The effect of heating the ground shale is to liberate a portion of the hydrocarbons formed or contained within the shale, and the heated suspension is withdrawn through line 16 and discharged into a dust separator or a cyclone separator 18 where the vapors are separated from the shale and then discharged through an overhead pipe 22 into a fractionator 25. From fractionator 25 an overhead fraction is recovered through line 30, and this fraction may be delivered to equipment (not shown) to recover hydrocarbons boiling within the gas oil range and gasoline range and lighter hydrocarbons.

Referring again to the cyclone separator 18, it is pointed out that two or more may be used in series to effect efficient separation of the dust or powdered shale from the gases, if that is necessary, and one or more Cottrell precipitators may be so employed. The separated shale is withdrawn from the bottom of cyclone separator 18 through pipe 40 and delivered into a second hopper 45 and then discharged into a secondary grinder 47 where it is ground to a particle size of from 200 to 400 mesh or finer. The grinding means 41 may be similar in all details to grinding means 2, except that the shale is reduced to a finer state of subdivision. Also there is discharged into grinder 47 or other mixing device therein contained or associated with steam, flue gas, or hydrocarbon vapors through line 50 to form with the ground shale a suspension.

FIGURE 4.7: PREPARATION OF HYDROCARBON OILS BY THERMAL CRACKING OF BITUMINOUS MATERIALS

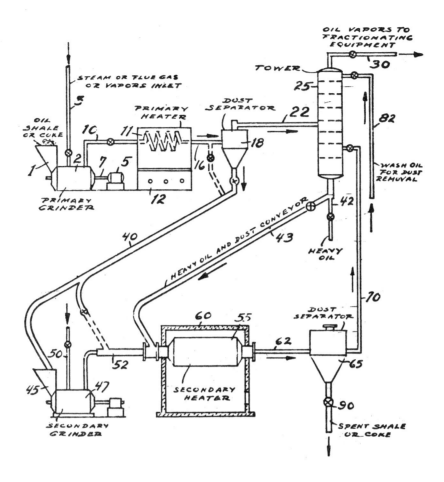

Source: C.T. Harding; U.S. Patent 2,379,077; June 26, 1945

A suitable grinding device that may be employed here is, for example, the commonly known Raymond kiln mill. As is generally known, in this type of mill a material may be powdered and suspended in a gas. Of course, any other suitable equipment may be employed for this purpose. The suspension formed is withdrawn through line 52 and discharged into a second heating coil or drum 55 disposed within a suitable furnace 60 where the shale is heated up to a temperature of from 1000° to 1800°F. In this secondary heater, a further quantity of hydrocarbon oil is formed and/or distilled from the shale, and thereafter the suspension is withdrawn through line 62 and delivered to a second cyclone separator 65 where the shale is separated from the vapors.

The vapors are withdrawn through line 70 and discharged into fractionator 25 where they are subjected to fractionation, together with vapors from line 22. The vapors from line 70 contain normally gaseous hydrocarbons, gasoline hydrocarbons, gas oil hydrocarbons, and a minor quantity of heavier hydrocarbons. The lighter hydrocarbons, of course, pass overhead through line 30, while the heavier fractions may be withdrawn through line 42 or they may be withdrawn through line 43 and discharged into a secondary heater 55 where they may be subjected to further treatment to produce increased quantities of gasoline.

Method of Producing Motor Fuel

W.G. Scharmann and F.T. Barr; U.S. Patent 2,436,938; March 2, 1948; assigned to Standard Oil Development Company provide a method for production of liquid motor fuels from solid carbonaceous materials. It relates to improvements in the production of liquid motor fuels, such as gasoline, from solid carbonaceous materials containing volatile hydrocarbon constituents, such as coal, lignite, oil shale, and certain cellulosic materials, by subjecting the starting material to a distillation extraction treatment in the presence of a hydrocarbon oil of suitable boiling characteristics and recovering liquid motor fuels from the distillate.

Referring to Figure 4.8, fresh ground coal, of which any type but anthracite may be used, including peat, lignite brown coal, bituminous coal, etc., enters the system through line 1 by any suitable means (not shown), for instance, by means of a screw feeder in communication with a suitable supply hopper. The coal is discharged into line 2 and mixed there with a hydrocarbon oil predominantly paraffinic, with an initial boiling point of about 300° to 400°F., and having an end boiling point of not higher than 700° to 800°F. Where other solid carbonaceous materials are charged, this end boiling point may be somewhat higher or lower, the best operation being obtained when it is about the same as the end point of the volatile constituents to be extracted from the carbonaceous material. This oil is normally produced in a later stage of the process and supplied through recycle line 17 to the mixing zone of line 2, as will appear hereafter in more detail.

During the starting period of the process, any extraneous hydrocarbon oil having the specified boiling characteristics may be introduced into the mixing zone of line 2 through supply line 3. The coal and/or oil supplied to line 2 may be preheated, if desired, sufficiently beyond the initial boiling point of the oil so that the mixture of coal and oil consists at least to a substantial part of a suspension of powdered coal in oil vapor. The relative proportions of coal and oil in this mixture are maintained at about 1 pound of coal per 0.2 to 1 pound of oil. If sufficient oil is vaporized at this point to suspend the solid material, operation may be in the lower range of the proportions given, e.g., 0.3 to 0.5 pound of oil per 1 pound of coal; if nearly all the oil remains liquid at this point, the greater amount of oil is required, e.g., 0.6 to 0.8 pound of oil per 1 pound of coal, but the treating time may be reduced in the latter case.

FIGURE 4.8:   METHOD OF PRODUCING MOTOR FUEL

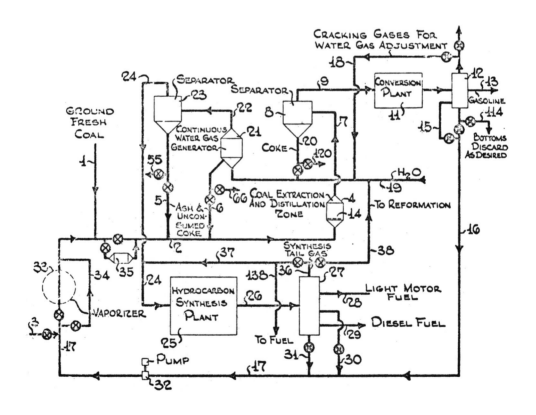

Source: W.G. Scharmann and F.T. Barr; U.S. Patent 2,436,938; March 2, 1948

The mixture of coal and oil is passed from line 2 into the distillation extraction zone 4, where it is maintained at a temperature of the order of 700° to 800°F. for a sufficient length of time to secure substantially complete vaporization of the oil and the volatile constituents of the coal. Heat for this reaction may be supplied by charging recycled coke and/or ash obtained at a high temperature of, for instance, 1600° to 1800°F. in a later stage of the process through either or both of lines 5 and 6 into line 2.

If desired, the reaction may be carried out in a vessel designed to transmit heat through the retaining walls to the reaction zone. Such equipment may consist of a tube-like furnace if continuous operation is required or it may involve the use of a drum type retort. If heat supply through the walls of the distillation extraction chamber is contemplated, the heat required may be supplied by direct firing or may be obtained by indirect heat transfer with the gas generated at temperatures as high as 1600° to 1800°F. in the water gas reactor   One or more of the above methods of retorting may be used in the same system.

As indicated before, the oil may be present in line 2 either in the liquid or in the vapor phase. However this may be, the oil is completely vaporized in zone 4 to form there a suspension of powdered coal in oil vapors. In order to secure optimum heat conduction and a proper time of residence of the powdered coal in zone 4, the vapor velocity and the particle size of the coal in zone 4 may be so controlled as to cause the phenomenon of hindered settling and the formation of a dense suspension of powdered coal in the oil vapor.

This is accomplished in known manner by maintaining vapor velocities in zone 4 of 1/2 to 10 feet per second, preferably 3/4 to 3 feet per second, and coal particle sizes of from 50 to 400 mesh. To aid in the distribution of the entering gas suspension, a perforated member 14 may be disposed near the bottom of distillation extraction zone 4. The average residence time of the powdered coal in zone 4 may range from 3 to 30 minutes, a longer treating period giving somewhat greater percent extraction.

A suspension of coked distillation residue in a mixture of oil vapors and vaporous volatile constituents from the coal is continuously withdrawn overhead from zone 4 and passed through line 7 into a vapor solid separator 8, which may be of any suitable known design, such as a cyclone separator, a Cottrell precipitator, or the like. Alternatively, the functions of vessels 4 and 8 may be carried out in a single vessel, in accordance with improvements in the fluid solids technique known to the art.

From separator 8 hydrocarbon vapors are taken overhead and passed through line 9 to a gasoline recovering plant which may comprise a conversion plant 11 and a fractionating column 12. In conversion plant 11 the distillate vapors may be subjected to thermal or catalytic cracking to increase the yield of high octane motor fuels. It should be understood, however, that any other desired refining treatment, such as thermal or catalytic reforming, may follow or take the place of the cracking treatments in plant 11.

The cracked and/or reformed distillate is fractionated in column 12 into a gasoline fraction withdrawn and passed to storage through line 13 and a bottom fraction which may be either withdrawn for further treatment or otherwise disposed of through line 114, recycled to column 12 through line 15, or recycled through lines 16 and 17 to the mixing zone of line 2 to furnish at least a portion of the hydrocarbon oil used in the distillation extraction zone. Normally gaseous products are withdrawn overhead from column 12 and may be either discarded or passed through line 18 into line 19 which carries steam and oxygen.

Production of Chemical Products from Coal Carbonization

The process described by R.T. Joseph and J.B. Maguire; U.S. Patent 2,977,299; March 28, 1961; assigned to Allied Chemical Corporation relates to a method for the production of valuable chemical products from coal products; that is from coal and related carbonaceous materials such as lignite and peat, as well as tars derived therefrom, especially by low temperature carbonization processes, and fractions, especially residues, obtained in the recovery of valuable products from coal tars of various types.

Thus it includes processes for the production of (1) gaseous products valuable for their heat content and chemical composition, and (2) a light oil tar product containing valuable aromatic chemicals in quantity and quality similar to those present in tars produced by high temperature carbonization of bituminous coal, from such raw materials as coals, lignites, peats, and products derived from the high and low temperature carbonization of these substances, including low temperature tars, middle oils from high temperature tars, residual oils, pitches, and the like. It relates especially to the production of valuable gases and organic aromatic chemical compounds from tars and oils obtained in the low temperature carbonization of lignites, from oils, pitches and residues obtained in the distillation of high temperature coal tar, and from residues from the refining of tar acids and tar bases. The process is based upon the discovery that low temperature coal tars, lignite tars, coal tar distillates and residues, and other coal products, including coal itself, can be converted to products similar to those obtained in the high temperature coking of coal by subjecting the low temperature coal tar, lignite tar, or other coal products to extremely rapid pyrolysis at temperatures above 600°C. and especially at 800° to 1000°C., preferably in the presence of steam, followed by rapid passage of the resulting pyrolysis products through a heated reforming chamber maintained at a temperature above 600°C., and preferably containing coke, followed by cooling of the resulting reformed products, preferably below 100°C. When coke is employed, the preferred size is such that the coke is maintained in a fluidized state by the passage of the products therethrough.

Referring to Figure 4.9, 1 and 1A represent storage tanks for the feed stock, which are suitably provided with the heating jackets to maintain their contents in fluid form, and which are adapted to be alternately connected to the feed line 3 by suitable valved connections 2. The line 3 is connected to the inlet of a pump 4 for the feed stock, which in turn is connected by a suitable conduit 5 to the inlet 6 of the jacketed spray nozzle 7 which is mounted with its spray tip 8 within a heating chamber 9.

The heating chamber 9 is adapted to be heated to temperatures above 600°C. by external heat such as hot flue gases, gas flame, or the like, contacting the outer walls 10 of the chamber within a suitable furnace 11. The heating chamber is formed of suitable material to withstand the temperature, such as steel, the inner surface of which is lined with a thin lining of refractory material such as alumina or an alumina-silica fire clay, which functions as a cracking catalyst.

Heating chamber 9 is also supplied with an inlet for superheated steam 15 which is supplied through conduit 16 from a steam superheater 17 adapted to superheat by indirect contact with a suitable source of heat, such as flue gases, electrical resistance heating and the like, steam supplied to the superheater by a conduit 18 from a steam generator 19. Water for generation of the steam is supplied from a suitable reservoir 22 thru valved connection 23 by a pump 24 and a conduit 25.

The heating chamber 9 communicates directly with an elongated reforming column 30 which is suitably heated to temperatures above 600°C. by indirect heat, as for example, by furnace gases, flue gases, electrical resistance heating or the like, within a heating jacket 31. The chamber 30 is formed of suitable material capable of withstanding the elevated temperatures, such as stainless steel containing iron, chromium and nickel, e.g., stainless steel No. 304.

The outlet 32 of column 30 is connected to the inlet 33 of a condenser 34 adapted to be cooled by a suitable fluid flowing through a jacket 35, such as water, steam or oil. The outlet 36 of the condenser is connected to a primary liquid product receiver 37 which leads to a reflux condenser 38. The vapor outlet 39 of the reflux condenser is connected by a conduit 40 to a condenser 41, the outlet 42 of which is connected by a dip pipe 43 which leads into oil scrubber 44 which is partially filled with mineral oil adapted to scrub the gases and vapors passing through it.

FIGURE 4.9:   PRODUCTION OF CHEMICAL PRODUCTS FROM COAL CARBONIZATION

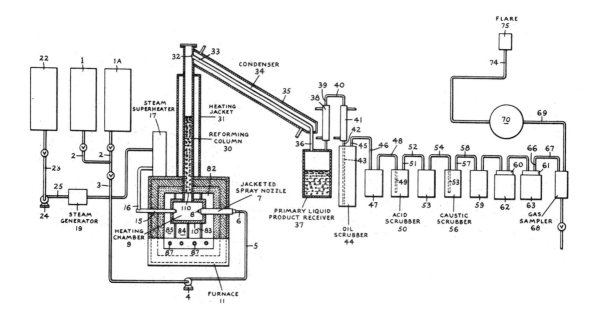

Source: R.T. Joseph and J.B. Maguire; U.S. Patent 2,977,299; March 28, 1961

The mineral oil is of the type normally employed in the benzol scrubber of the usual coal gas by-product recovery processes. The outlet 45 of the scrubber is connected by a conduit 46 to an empty overflow chamber 47 which, in turn, is connected by conduit 48 with a dip pipe 49 which leads into a scrubber 50 partially filled with a suitable mineral acid adapted to remove ammonia and organic bases present in the gas and vapor mixture passing through it, for example, 20% aqueous hydrochloric acid.

The outlet 51 of the scrubber 50 is connected by a conduit 52 with an overflow chamber 53 which, in turn, is connected through conduit 54 with a dip pipe 55 which leads into a scrubber 56 partially filled with dilute aqueous caustic alkali or other scrubbing liquid adapted to remove sulfur present as H_2S from the gases or vapors passing through it, for example, 20% aqueous sodium hydroxide. The outlet 57 of the caustic scrubber 56 is connected by a conduit 58 to an overflow chamber 59 which, in turn, is connected in series with two vessels 60 and 61 which are surrounded by solid carbon dioxide (Dry Ice) jackets 62 and 63 to reduce the temperature of the chambers to that of solid carbon dioxide. The outlet 66 of the chamber 61 is connected by a conduit 67 with a gas sampler 68 which, in turn, is connected by a conduit 69 to a wet test meter 70, the outlet of which is connected to a flare 75 by a conduit 74. The process will be illustrated by the following example.

Example: The starting material employed in this example was lignite tar produced from Texas lignite at the Rockdale plant of the Texas Power and Light Company by low temperature carbonization of lignite. After filtration to remove 1 to 1.5% finely divided solids, it was a viscous, sticky mass at 25°C. having the following characteristics.

Specific gravity at 15.5°C.	1.025
Water content	0.2%
Matter insoluble in benzene	0.9%

At 100°C. it had the consistency of a thin oil. When subjected to the usual tar analysis by distillation in a 1" x 36" Stedman fractionation apparatus at 760 mm. mercury pressure and a 2" water pressure drop, the following percentages of the tar were obtained as distillates.

	Percent
Up to 80°C.	0.00
80° to 100°C.	1.20
100° to 125°C.	0.00
125° to 150°C.	0.00
150° to 200°C.	8.80
200° to 230°C. (no naphthalene)	12.00
230° to 250°C.	4.00

On further distillation of the residue according to ASTM Standard Method D20-56, the following percentages of tar were obtained as distillates.

	Percent
250° to 270°C.	6.70
270° to 300°C.	10.20
300° to 325°C.	22.90

The residue which amounted to 33% of the tar, consisted of coke and carbon. The filtered tar was subjected to pyrolysis and reforming in the presence of steam in accordance with the process in the following manner. The cracking chamber 9 shown in Figure 4.9 was heated to a temperature of 925°C. and superheated steam was introduced into the chamber. The column 30 was filled about one-half with coke particles 1 inch in size and was heated to 850°C. The oil burner nozzle 8 was rated at one gallon per hour at 100 pounds pressure. The feeds of filtered lignite tar and superheated steam were then adjusted to introduce equal parts by weight of superheated steam and lignite tar into the cracking chamber. The pressure on the steam jet was 2 psig and in chamber 9 was 1 psig. The pressure on the tar feed was 50 pounds.

After preliminary operation as set out above, to establish the desired conditions, the tar was pyrolyzed continuously at a rate giving a residence time in the pyrolyzer and reformer of about 0.1 second. The products consisted of gas, a tar and some coke. The analysis of the principal components of the product were as follows, in terms of percent by weight, based on the lignite tar charged.

	Yield Percent
Total gas product	41.7
Principal components of gas product:	
Hydrogen	1.65

	Yield Percent
Methane	9.79
Nitrogen	10.42
Ethylene	8.73
Ethane	1.16
Propylene	2.70
Carbon dioxide	4.23
Benzene	1.60

The tar separated from receiver 37, after removal of water condensed from unreacted steam, was a viscous fluid of which 11% was insoluble in benzene.

	Yield Percent
Total tar product	54
Tar analysis by distillation	
(1" x 36", Stedman frac-	
tionation as above)	
Up to 80°C.	0.0
80° to 100°C.	5.0
100° to 125°C.	1.8
125° to 150°C.	0.0
150° to 200°C.	2.7
200° to 230°C.	7.0
230° to 250°C.	2.0

The residue had a softening point (shouldered ring and ball) of 60°C., and 28.5 percent was insoluble in benzene.

	Yield Percent
Distillation of residue	
(ASTM D20-56)	
250° to 270°C.	0.0
270° to 300°C.	0.09
300° to 325°C.	2.1
325° to 360°C.	6.1
Residue	33.1

The residue had a softening point (shouldered ring and ball) of 188°C., and 54.8 percent was insoluble in benzene. The fraction boiling below 200°C. contained benzene, toluene, higher solvents and resin monomers.

Production of Synthetic Crude Oil from Low Temperature Carbonization of Coal Tars

H.L. Bennett; U.S. Patent 3,576,734; April 27, 1971; assigned to Bennett Engineering Company describes a process for the production of synthetic crude oil from low temperature coal tars which have been obtained by careful temperature control during the carbonization of various cool materials, such as coal.

In the process carbonaceous material, such as bituminous coal and the like, is introduced into a suitable roaster, such as multihearth vertical roaster, under controlled temperature with the gases removed at each level to avoid overheating. The solid material is retained in the roaster from two to four hours at a temperature of from between 400° to 600°C. The rotation speed of the roaster arms and the feed is regulated to assure the desired retention time. The roaster arms preferably move the material along with a plow type action. The roaster preferably has a heat exchange and induction center at the bottom thereof for the introduction of the superheated steam. The exhaust resulting from the introduction of the superheated steam contains hydrogen, carbon dioxide, steam and other trace gases. This exhaust is treated to separate the hydrogen and carbon materials and the hydrogen is retained for subsequent use.

After the hot gases have been removed the remaining solid material, high volatile char, are removed mechanically from the roaster, cooled, and marketed or further processed into producer gas which in turn is marketed for heating or refined into light end products. The hot distillation gases emitted at the various levels of the roaster are cleaned and condensed into low temperature tars with the remaining gases sent to the light end plant. At this point approximately 1,200 to 1,500 cubic feet of hydrogen is added to each barrel of low temperature tar and salvaged bottoms and the mixture is brought into contact with a fixed bed catalyst under controlled pressure, heat and time.

A single autoclave type batch unit having a void to catalyst ratio of from 1:1 to 4:1 can be advantageously used, or a continuous flowthrough unit with a liquid hourly space velocity (oil to catalyst volume ratio) of from 1.5 to 4.0 can be used. The pressure in the units is maintained from between 700 to 2,000 psi and the temperature is maintained between 350° to 500°C. Generally, the tars are passed through a primary reactor at a temperature between 350° and 370°C., and are then passed through a second reactor at a temperature of from 450° to 490°C. The resulting effluent is then cooled into synthetic crude oil and gases. After cooling, the gases containing hydrogen sulfide, hydrogen, various light end hydrocarbons and nitrogen compounds are removed and further processed.

The hydrogen gas can be recycled and introduced into the low temperature tar stream entering the reaction chamber or burned as a flare gas. The hydrogen sulfides can be processed to produce a commercial sulfur or processed with hydrogen to produce commercial acids. The light hydrocarbons can further be refined in light end units where yielded off-gases are returned for production heat. The nitrogen compounds can be converted into commercial fertilizer, acids and other products.

The low temperature tar which has been converted into a synthetic crude stock is then processed in a conventional petroleum distillation unit to yield a naphtha product boiling below 250°C. and a series of gases which are utilized in light ends plant or burned as excess. The synthetic crude after removal of the naphtha and light end gases becomes residual and can be recycled with low temperature tars or further treated to form various grades of asphaltic material, fuel oils and lubricating stock.

The material removed from the distillation unit as a naphtha cut can be further processed into regular petroleum products or petrochemicals utilizing any number of refining processes known. The light ends plant consist of polymerization, alkylation and/or isomerization units. The phenols can also be processed into commercial units.

The Hydrovisbreaking of Coal to Motor Fuels

This process by N.J. Paterson; U.S. Patent 3,518,182; June 30, 1970; assigned to Chevron Research Company relates to converting coal primarily to motor fuels by a process combination wherein (a) coal particles are mixed with solvent, such as a gas oil boiling between about 300° and 750°F.; (b) the mixture of coal particles and solvent is hydrovisbroken and hydrocarbons are extracted from the coal by passing the mixture through a heated coil together with H_2 and H_2O; (c) the hydrovisbreaker coil effluent is fractionated into several cuts; and (d) these several cuts are selectively subjected to hydrogenation and coking as interconnected processing steps to obtain a high yield of motor fuel with relatively low hydrogen consumption per ton of coal.

A method is provided for converting coal to motor fuels which comprises the following steps in combination: (a) mixing coal particles with a solvent comprised of a gas oil to obtain a coal-gas oil slurry; (b) hydrovisbreaking the coal-gas oil slurry by passing the coal-gas oil slurry through a heated tubular coil together with H_2 and H_2O under the following conditions: (1) 100 to 1,000 scf of H_2 per barrel of slurry; (2) 0.1 to 5.0 weight percent H_2O based on slurry weight; (3) coil outlet temperature between 600° and 900°F.; (4) residence time in the coil between 10 and 500 seconds, whereby there is obtained a hydrovisbreaker effluent.

The process continues with (c) distilling the hydrovisbreaker effluent to obtain a first gas oil, a heavy gas oil, and a pitch; (d) reacting the heavy gas oil and a first heavy bottoms oil obtained as hereinbelow described with hydrogen under catalytic hydrogenation conditions in a hydroconversion zone to obtain hydrogen enriched oil and distilling the hydrogen enriched oil to obtain a second gas oil and a second heavy bottoms oil; (e) coking the pitch and the second heavy bottoms oil in a coking unit to obtain coke and coker vapors and distilling the coker vapors to obtain a third gas oil and the first heavy bottoms oil; and (f) converting at least a substantial portion (i.e., between 50 and 100 percent) of the first, second and third gas oils to motor fuels by catalyzed reaction of the gas oils with hydrogen at elevated temperature and pressure.

Figure 4.10 is a schematic process flow diagram of the basic processing steps. Coal particles and solvent circulated via line 15 are mixed together in slurry tank 2. Typical coals used in the process contain 20 to 50 weight percent volatiles, 70 to 85 weight percent carbon, and 2 to 15 weight percent ash. If the moisture content of the coal is between 1 and 3 weight percent, then no drying is required. However, if the moisture content of the coal is excessive, say 5 to 10 weight percent, then it is desirable to dry the coal previous to introducing the coal into the slurry tank.

The coal is preferably bituminous coal which has been freshly mined to thus avoid oxidation by prolonged exposure to air. The coal, which is fed to the slurry tank in line 1, is of a particle size less than about 1/4 inch in diameter or length. In the process it is not required to grind the coal into very fine particles, such as 100 or 200 mesh, because in the hydrovisbreaking extracting step of the process the coal rapidly disintegrates due to the action of the solvent gas oil and the turbulent conditions existing in the hydrovisbreaker coil. Although in this specification, for simplicity, the hydrovisbreaking extraction zone 7 is generally referred to as a hydrovisbreaker, it is to be understood that in addition to reduction of viscosity of the liquid portion of the slurry feed, the hydrovisbreaker serves the important function of extracting

FIGURE 4.10: HYDROVISBREAKING OF COAL TO MOTOR FUELS

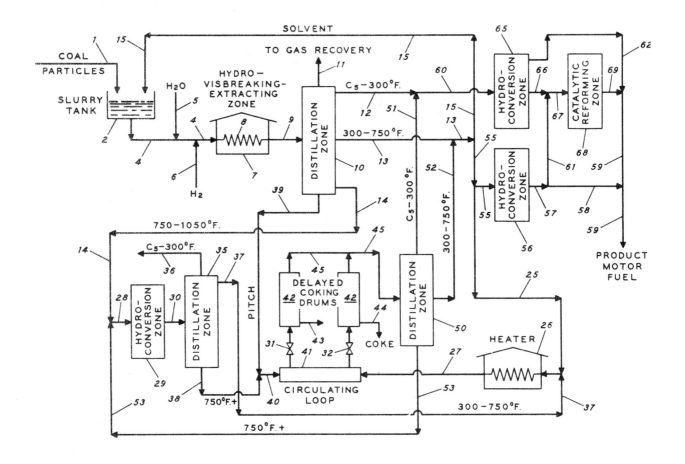

Source: N.J. Paterson; U.S. Patent 3,518,182; June 30, 1970

hydrocarbons from the coal in the slurry. Temperature in the slurry tank is maintained at about 225° to 275°F. by preheating the solvent and/or steam jacketing the slurry tank. It is advantageous to continuously agitate the coal and extractant mixture in the slurry tank by the introduction of an oxygen-free inert gas in addition to mechanical mixing of the contents of the slurry tank.

The slurry of coal and solvent is withdrawn from the slurry tank in line 5 and is passed together with water or steam introduced in line 5 and hydrogen introduced in line 6 to coil 8. Coil 8 is located in a furnace so that the coil and its contents may be heated to high temperatures. In the process, gas oils are the preferred solvents for the extraction of hydrocarbons from the coal. According to the process, the solvent is generated from one or more of the several processing steps in the overall processing scheme. Accordingly, the composition of the solvent will vary somewhat with the type of coal being processed, the extraction conditions, and the particular processing steps from which the solvent is derived. However, the preferred solvent for use in the process boils in the range 300° to 750°F. and is composed of a mixture of aromatics and naphthenes comprised of dialkylbenzenes, naphthalenes, anthracene, alpha-methylnaphthalene, alpha-naphthylamine, phenanthrene, Tetralin, alpha-methylphenanthrene, fluorenes, 9,10-dihydrophenathrene, 1-methylisopropylphenanthrene and naphthene.

The slurry of coal and extractant is passed at high velocity together with 100 to 1,000 standard cubic feet of hydrogen per barrel of slurry and 0.1 to 5.0 weight percent H_2O through tubular coil 8. The presence of H_2O, which is mostly steam at the temperatures existing in the coil, serves to increase the velocity of the stream flowing through the coil and also to increase the turbulence of the stream flowing through the coil. The temperature at the inlet of the coil is about 200° to 300°F., and the outlet of the coil is generally maintained in the range 600° to 900°F., preferably 700° to 825°F.

Inlet pressure for the coil is preferably maintained in the range 1,000 to 1,200 psig; and outlet pressure from 200 to 300 pounds per square inch gauge. The addition of hydrogen in line 6 to the slurry fed to tubular coil 8 serves to permit longer sustained operation of the hydrovisbreaker by inhibiting the formation of olefinic coke precursors. Also, with respect to the extraction effected in the hydrovisbreaker, the added hydrogen serves to aid in the dissolving of the coal in the solvent. Thus the presence of hydrogen tends to speed up the initial dissolving of the coal and serves to enhance depolymerization which is effected under the conditions maintained in the hydrovisbreaker.

The material from tubular coil 8 is passed in line 9 to distillation zone 10. Distillation zone 10 may suitably be comprised of three distillation columns. The first distillation column serves to separate hydrogen, CO_2, H_2S, NH_3 and light hydrocarbons, such as methane through butane, from the heavier material in the hydrovisbreaker effluent. This first distillation column is preferably operated at a pressure of from 50 to 100 psig. The light gases obtained as overhead in this first distillation column are passed to gas recovery processing. The heavier material is withdrawn from the lower part of the first distillation column and passed to a second distillation column operating at 20 to 50 psig.

A hydrocarbon cut boiling in the range pentane (C_5) to 300°F. is withdrawn from the overhead of the second distillation column and then passed, as indicated by lines 12 and 60, to hydroconversion zone 65. Material heavier than a normal boiling point of 300°F. is withdrawn from the lower part of the second distillation column and passed to a vacuum distillation column. From the upper part of the vacuum distillation column a gas oil, preferably boiling in the range 300° to 750°F., is withdrawn as indicated by line 13 from distillation zone 10. This gas oil is combined with gas oil from distillation zone 50 and/or 35. A portion of the combined gas oil is preferably recycled via line 15 for use as a solvent in slurry tank 2.

As an intermediate fraction or cut from the vacuum distillation column, a heavy gas oil is withdrawn. Preferably the heavy gas oil boils over the range 750° to 1050°F. However, since the heavy gas oil is next passed via lines 14 and 28 to hydroconversion zone 29 for reaction with hydrogen in the presence of the catalyst, in some cases it is preferable to lower the upper cut point to 1000° or 900°F. to insure low ash and metals content in the heavy gas oil. Small amounts of ash will reduce the activity of the hydroconversion catalyst. Thus, it is necessary to design and operate the vacuum distillation column so that there is only a small amount of ash and/or metallic contaminants in the heavy gas oil. The ash contaminants in the heavy gas oil should be no more than 100 ppm by weight as metals, preferably less than 10 ppm, and still more preferably less than 3 ppm. By careful design of the vacuum distillation column so as to minimize entrainment of pitch into the heavy gas oil, these low ash contents may be achieved without excessive expense.

Hydroconversion zone 29 is preferably composed of a single stage, once through hydrocracker. Preferred catalysts are nickel-molybdenum or nickel-tungsten on an alumina-silica base. Suitable temperatures are 600° to 900°F. and preferred temperatures are from 725° to 825°F. Suitable pressures are 1,500 to 5,000 psig and preferred pressures are 2,500 to 3,500 psig. Suitable liquid hourly space velocities are 0.1 to 10.0. Suitable hydrogen recycle rates are 1,000 to 15,000 scf per barrel of oil feed. Suitable fresh hydrogen replenishing rates are 1,000 to 2,000 scf per barrel of oil feed.

As shown in Figure 4.10, preferably a 750° to 1050°F. heavy gas oil cut is withdrawn from distillation zone 10 in line 14 and passed to hydroconversion zone 29 together with a heavy bottoms stream that is 750°+F. boiling range hydrocarbons obtained from distillation zone 50. The 750° to 1050°F. cut from distillation zone 10, which may be referred to more generally as a heavy gas oil cut, and the 750°+F. bottoms withdrawn from distillation zone 50, which may be referred to as a heavy bottoms oil, are converted by hydrocracking, preferably to the extent of 25 to 35 volume percent material boiling below 750°F.

Also, the material fed to hydroconversion zone 29 is enriched in hydrogen content by catalytic hydrogenation of cracked (i.e., severed) hydrocarbon molecules as well as catalytic hydrogenation of uncracked hydrocarbon molecules (i.e., molecules where nitrogen or sulfur is removed without cracking and molecules where unsaturated bonds are saturated without cracking). The hydrogen enriched hydrocarbons obtained from hydroconversion zone 29 boiling in the gas oil and in the heavy gas oil and above ranges are advantageously used as hydrogen donors in the coking step of the process.

The effluent from the hydrocracker reactor of hydroconversion zone 29, after separation of recycle hydrogen and light hydrocarbons, is withdrawn in line 30 and passed to distillation zone 35. In distillation zone 35 the C_5-300°F. cut is separated and withdrawn in line 36 and passed, for example, to hydroconversion zone 65. The gas oil cut, preferably boiling between 300° and 750°F., is withdrawn in line 37, and at least a portion of this gas oil is preferably used as a hydrogen donor and heating medium in the coking step of the process. A heavy bottoms oil, preferably boiling from 750°F. upwards, is withdrawn from distillation zone 35 in line 38 for processing in the coking unit.

After leaving hydroconversion zone 29, the 750°+F. boiling hydrocarbons go to a delayed coking drum followed by further hydrocracking treatment resulting in a reformate which is mixed with other hydroconversion fractions to form the product motor fuel.

Process for Hydrocoking Coal to Liquid Hydrocarbons

W.I. Gilbert and C.W. Montgomery; U.S. Patent 2,654,695; October 6, 1953; assigned to Gulf Research & Development Company provides an improved procedure for converting coal into liquid hydrocarbons suitable as fuel which also improves the economics of the conversion of coal into liquid hydrocarbon fuel. This includes liquefying a first portion of coal by treatment with hydrogen at elevated temperature and pressure to obtain a liquid product, separating this liquid product into a hydrocarbon fraction and a phenolic fraction, extracting a second portion of coal with the phenolic fraction and subjecting a mixture of the hydrocarbon fraction, the phenolic fraction and the material extracted from the second portion of coal by the extraction treatment to a treatment with hydrogen while at elevated temperature and while in the presence of a metalliferous substance having the property of promoting hydrogenation.

In Figure 4.11, a diagrammatic flow sheet of the process, powdered coal, such as powdered lignite flows from hopper 1 into reactor A by way of metering device 2. Fresh hydrogen is introduced into reactor A by way of conduit 4 and recycle hydrogen by way of conduit 6. In reactor A the coal is converted in known manner at elevated temperature and pressure into a liquid product and a solid residue. The residue is withdrawn intermittently from char receiver 8 and can be used as a fuel. The liquid product is removed from reactor A by way of conduit 10 and is introduced into neutralizer B. An aqueous solution of caustic is introduced into neutralizer B through conduit 12 and the materials therein are agitated and are then stratified, the hydrocarbon upper layer being withdrawn through conduit 14.

The lower layer constituting an aqueous solution of phenolic salts is withdrawn through conduit 16 and introduced into tank C. Acid is then introduced through conduit 18 into tank C to split the phenolic salts. The contents of tank C are then stratified and the upper phenolic layer is introduced by way of conduit 20 into reactor D while the aqueous lower layer is withdrawn by way of conduit 22 and discarded or employed to make caustic for further use in the process.

FIGURE 4.11: PROCESS FOR HYDROCOKING COAL TO LIQUID HYDROCARBONS

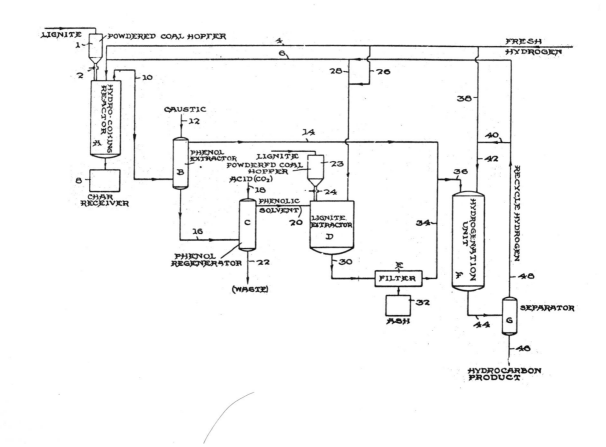

Source: W.I. Gilbert and C.W. Montgomery; U.S. Patent 2,654,695; October 6, 1953

A second portion of coal such as lignite in particulate form flows from hopper 23 into reactor D by way of metering device 24 while recycle and fresh hydrogen are introduced into reactor D through conduits 26 and 28. In reactor D the coal is subjected at elevated temperature to a combined extraction and hydrogenation, resulting in liquefaction of a considerable portion of the coal. The product, including the phenolic solvent from reactor A is withdrawn from reactor D by way of conduit 30 and is introduced into filter E where the ash and carbonaceous residue from the coal is removed by filtration.

The filtrate is withdrawn through conduit 34 and the ash is collected in 32. After heating to remove the solvent the ash or residue may be pulverized for use as fuel since this material contains only 30 to 50% actual ash. The filtrate flows through conduit 34 and is combined with the liquid hydrocarbons flowing through conduit 14 and derived from neutralizer B, i.e. the hydrocarbon from the neutralizing stage B is combined with the phenol solvent and coal extract from the D extraction stage and is introduced by way of conduit 36 into reactor F. Hydrogen in the form of fresh hydrogen is introduced into reactor F through conduit 38 while recycle hydrogen is introduced through conduit 40.

This combined mixture of hydrogen flows through conduit 42 into reactor F which contains a body of pellets comprising a hydrogenating catalyst on a porous carrier. The conditions in reactor F are selected so that hydrogenation of the mixture with concomitant upgrading takes place. Conversion of the phenols to hydrocarbons and desulfurization also takes place under conditions which result in such upgrading. The hydrogenated product is then withdrawn by way of conduit 44 and is introduced into separator G where the liquid product is separated from hydrogen. The liquid product is removed through conduit 46 and the separated hydrogen is recycled through conduit 48.

Process and System for Producing Synthetic Crude from Coal

A process is described by L.L. Ludlam, M. Skripek and K.E. Whitehead; U.S. Patent 3,503,867; March 31, 1970; assigned to Atlantic Richfield Company for producing synthetic petroleum crude from coal for use in a petroleum refining system, which includes low temperature carbonization of dried pulverized coal, hydrocracking of the combination of middle oil, tar and naphtha, vacuum distillation and secondary hydroheating of the low volatility components derived from the hydrocracking process and fractionation of the high volatility hydrocarbons from the hydrocracking unit and the secondarily hydrogenated low volatility components derived from the hydrocracking process.

The process may be described, in its principal steps, as including the low temperature carbonization of coal for converting the more valuable carbonaceous components to liquid hydrocarbon materials, feeding the liquid hydrocarbon materials and naphtha through a hydrocracking step, vacuum distilling the heavier components from the hydrocracking step and recycling the solid and low volatility components to the carbonizer, secondarily hydrotreating the volatile components from the vacuum distillation step and combining the more volatile components from the hydrocracking step and the secondarily hydrotreated components for fractionation to produce a synthetic petroleum crude for being handled according to conventional petroleum refining techniques.

Referring to Figure 4.12, the major components of the system for carrying out this process comprise a low temperature carbonizer 10, a hydrocracking unit 20, a vacuum still 30, a hydrotreater unit 40, and a fractionator 50. Auxiliary units which comprise important elements in the system include a char pulverizer 60, a phenol extractor 70, an ammonia stripper 80, a naphtha recovery unit 90, an acid gas removal unit 100, and a hydrogen generator 110.

Dried coal, which may include recycled hot char, passes from line 9 through a vapor lock into the low temperature carbonizer 10. Nonvolatilized coal components pass by gravity through a pressure seal to exit line 11. The tar components of the volatilized coal products comprise the heavier liquid fractions and entrained solid particulate matter and are transferred through line 12 to the hydrocracking unit 20. The middle oil fractions are also fed to the hydrocracking unit 20 through line 13. It will, of course, be remembered that in the process using a different type of carbonizer only one liquid stream, light tar, which may include entrained particles, will be produced or a light tar may be produced by combining the tar and middle oil fractions from the Lurgi carbonizer.

The more volatile components, including the highly volatile hydrocarbons and fixed gases produced or released by the low temperature carbonization process exit through line 14. The aqueous components are condensed and are withdrawn from the carbonizer through line 15 carrying the water-soluble components, primarily phenols and ammonia. Fractions of the flue gas from the carbonizer may be recycled through the coal dryer as shown at line 16 to conserve heat values.

The low vapor pressure liquids and entrained solids are removed from the hydrocracker 20 through line 21 to the vacuum still 30. The high vapor pressure hydrocarbons leave through line 22 to the fractionator as will be described more specifically hereinafter. Gaseous components and the very light hydrocarbons are carried through line 23 to the naphtha recovery system as will be described. Ammonia-rich waste water is condensed and is withdrawn through line 24 to the ammonia recovery and water treatment system. The major portion of the synthetic crude hydrocarbon fractions exit through line 31 from the vacuum still 30 to the hydrotreater 40. The still bottoms, including the solid material, are recycled through line 32 to the low temperature carbonizer 10.

FIGURE 4.12:   PROCESS AND SYSTEM FOR PRODUCING SYNTHETIC CRUDE FROM COAL

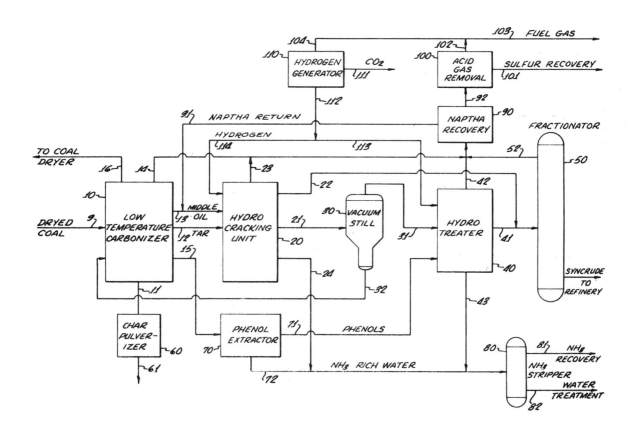

Source: L.L. Ludlam, M. Skripek and K.E. Whitehead; U.S. Patent 3,503,867; March 31, 1970

The upgraded synthetic crude is transferred from the hydrotreater 40 through line 41 where it is combined with the high vapor pressure hydrocarbons exiting from the hydrocracking unit 20 through line 22 and fed to the fractionator 50 which separates the syncrude (synthetic petroleum crude) which exits through line 51 and may be transported to the refinery, and the light hydrocarbons together with small quantities of the more highly volatile naphtha components which are returned through line 52 to the system. Returning again to the first steps in the process, the char from the low temperature carbonizer 10 is removed through line 11 to the char pulverizer 60 and then through a conveyor line indicated at 61 for recycling or for combustion as conventional coke.

Phenols from the phenol extractor 70 are conveyed through line 71 to the hydrotreater 40 for being upgraded, along with the hydrocarbon components from the vacuum still 30, to form the synthetic crude. The aqueous phase from the phenol extractor is combined with the aqueous phase from the hydrocracking unit 20 and from the secondary hydrotreater 40 and flows through line 72 to the ammonia stripper 80. Ammonia is removed through line 81 to any desired type of ammonia recovery system for the production of fertilizer, industrial chemicals, etc. Waste water from the system exits through line 82 to a water treatment plant and is discharged.

The light hydrocarbons, naphtha and fixed gas streams are collected from the low temperature carbonizer 10 through line 14, the hydrocracking unit 20 through line 23, the hydrotreater 40 through line 42 and the fractionator 50 through line 52 and enter the naphtha recovery unit 90. As previously described, the naphtha is removed by scrubbing with middle oil and recycled through line 91 where it is combined with middle oil or light tar output of the low temperature carbonizer and fed to the hydrocracking unit 20. Recycling the naphtha in the manner described provides several important advantages. The hydrocracking step of the process may be more easily and efficiently conducted by recycling the naphtha in the manner described and the quality of the synthetic crude is improved. It is entirely possible that the recycle step in the process described may make the difference between an economically practical system and a system which, while being technically feasible, is not economically attractive. The light hydrocarbons and fixed gases flow from the naphtha recovery unit through line 92 to the acid gas removal system. The sulfur-containing components are carried through line 101 to the sulfur recovery unit. The remaining gases, primarily carbon monoxide, hydrogen, and gaseous hydrocarbons, exit through line 102. Fuel gas for providing heat at the necessary points throughout the entire system and for distribution to public utility gas companies is drawn off through line 103. Enough of the hydrogen-containing gas is drawn through line 104 to the hydrogen generator 110 to operate the hydrocracking unit 20 and the hydrotreater 40.

As previously described, the hydrogen generator converts substantially all of the gas components to carbon dioxide and hydrogen with only traces of methane remaining. The carbon dioxide is drawn off at 111 for purification and sale as an industrial gas or solidification and sale for refrigeration purposes. The hydrogen, containing the traces of methane, is drawn off through line 112 and distributed through lines 113 and 114 to the secondary hydrotreater 40 and the hydrocracking unit 20.

Low Temperature Carbonization for the Production of Synthetic Crude Oil from Coal

M. Skripek, L.L. Ludlam and K.E. Whitehead; U.S. Patent 3,503,866; March 31, 1970; assigned to Atlantic Richfield Company describe a process for producing synthetic petroleum crude from coal for use in a petroleum refining system. The process may be described, in its principal steps, as including the low temperature carbonization of coal for converting more valuable carbonaceous components to liquid hydrocarbon materials, feeding the liquid hydrocarbon materials to a liquid recovery system which may be a scrubbing or distillation system for separating out the very low boiling point and the very high boiling point materials and the entrained solid materials from the usable middle oil and tar fractions.

The middle oil and tar fractions are hydrotreated and the hydrogenated liquid material is fractionated to produce a stream of synthetic crude for use in a refinery. Naphtha is recovered from the carbonization, liquid recovery and hydrotreating steps and is recirculated to the hydrotreater. Hydrogen is generated from the low molecular weight hydrocarbons for use in the hydrotreater. It is, accordingly, a principal object of the process to provide an improved method for producing synthetic crude of a quality comparable to petroleum crude by low temperature carbonization of coal to produce a liquid fraction and hydrotreating of the liquid fraction. A more specific object of this process includes a process and system for adding naphtha components with middle oil and tar in the hydrotreating of the liquid carbonization products. (See also U.S. Patent 3,503,867.)

Method for the Production of Gasoline

E.J. Gohr, F.T. Barr and B.E. Roetheli; U.S. Patent 2,697,718; December 21, 1954; assigned to Standard Oil Development Company describes a process which utilizes coal for the production of gasoline. The coal is subjected to coking temperatures to form fixed carbon or coke and volatile constituents; thereafter, the coke is converted to water gas which, after adjustment of the hydrogen to CO ratio, is subjected to a conversion in the presence of a suitable catalyst which forms normally liquid hydrocarbons, from which hydrocarbons including gasoline may be obtained by further treatment. The volatile constituents from the original coking operation may be treated to recover ammonia, light aromatic spirits and normally gaseous olefins which may be polymerized and/or alkylated, according to known procedure, to form further quantities of gasoline; and the tar is hydrogenated to form a quantity of gasoline.

The process comprises establishing a first, second and third fluidized bed of hot, finely divided coke, each in a separate zone by passing a gasiform fluid upwardly through each of the beds. The fluidizing gas in the second bed is a combustion supporting gas and the fluidizing gas in the third bed comprises a gas reactant with the coke to produce hydrogen and carbon monoxide. The process comprises preheating finely divided coal to a temperature between about 250° and 600°F., continuously feeding the preheated coal into mixture with the coke in the first bed and maintaining the mixture of coke and coal at coal-carbonizing temperature in the first bed to distill off volatile constituents including tar from the coal. Thereby the coal is converted to a residue coke. Coke is continuously fed from the first bed to the second bed. Combustion is carried out in the second bed to raise bed temperature substantially above the temperature in the first bed, and a stream of hot coke from the second bed is continuously fed to the first bed. A stream of hot coke is continuously fed from the second bed to the third bed.

A gas containing hydrogen and carbon monoxide is recovered from the third bed. Liquid hydrocarbons are catalytically synthesized from part of the last mentioned gas. An unconverted residual part of this last mentioned gas is recycled to hydrogenate the coal tar and thereby increase the yield of liquid product.

In the manner of operation described above, it is possible to produce gasoline in an integrated operation starting wholly from coal to give a yield of commercial motor fuel of satisfactory quality of the order of 2 1/2 barrels per ton of coal charged. To explain this further, starting with a ton of powdered medium grade Pennsylvania bituminous coal, by this process, 2.5 barrels of gasoline per ton of coal could be obtained. If the ton of coal is used in other processes gasoline yields would be obtained as shown on the following page.

Type of Process	Yields per Ton of Coal, Barrels
(1) Coal hydrogenation	2.0
(2) Fischer-Tropsch synthesis	1.4
(3) Low temperature carbonization	0.7

Depolymerization of Bituminous Coal Utilizing Friable Metal Reactants

This process by J. Winkler; U.S. Patent 3,282,826; November 1, 1966 relates to depolymerization of bituminous coal and products derived therefrom, where a solid-solid reaction between coal particles and particles of a friable, solid metal, metal mixtures and/or alloys of metals being distinguished by good reactivity with oxygen and sulfur atoms, is induced and effected by heat generating grinding of mixture, leading to the cleavage of the coal macromolecule between the

$$-C \overset{\downarrow}{-} O \overset{\downarrow}{-} C- \quad \text{and} \quad -C \overset{\downarrow}{-} S \overset{\downarrow}{-} C-$$

molecular bridges. The expression "grinding operation" is being used in the generic sense and covering repetitious, intimate surface frictional contact of the coal with the metal particles, as well as a more vigorous mutual abrading action resulting in a continuous reduction of the coal and metal particle size.

The basic theoretical idea of this process is to utilize predominantly surface imperfections of bituminous coal for solid-solid selective reactions between oxygen and sulfur scavenging metal powders at temperatures as low as possible. Preground coal, and preferably low priced coal fines are thoroughly mixed with any sufficiently friable metal possessing high heat of formation with oxygen and sulfur, preferably with preground or preformed particles of iron, aluminum, zinc, magnesium, titanium, manganese, copper, lithium, sodium, cadmium, potassium, calcium, barium, etc., any alloys and/or mixtures thereof.

This mixture is further ground at temperatures preferably not exceeding 400°C., until an equilibrium is established in which the oxygen and sulfur bridges in the coal macromolecule become abstracted by the metal particles and converted into metal oxides and metal sulfides. As the majority of volatile bituminous coals contain less than 10% of oxygen and sulfur combined, even when using high molecular metals like iron, the necessary amount of the metal will rarely amount to more than 15% of the coal used. When the bridging oxygen and sulfur atoms are abstracted from the coal macromolecule it becomes fragmentized into a predominantly liquid mixture of various hydrocarbons containing some quantitites of liquid nitrogenous and oxygenated hydrocarbons.

It has been found that during the abovedescribed chemical reaction, even at temperatures approaching 400°C., only small amounts of gaseous products are produced. This demonstrates the novelty of this process; that a solid-solid reaction between particles of coal and an oxygen and sulfur scavenging metal which are involved in a mutually grinding reaction provides the only practical way to depolymerize coal to valuable liquid compounds. This grinding operation, combined with the exothermic reaction between the metal and the coal-bound oxygen and sulfur generates sufficient well distributed heat of reaction, and can be readily kept at the desired level by external cooling. The following example should illustrate the process more clearly.

Example: This process is depicted schematically in Figure 4.13. A high volatile bituminous Cannel coal, analyzed as before indicated, from Morgan, Ky., was predried to a moisture content of 1.0%, and further preground to an average particle size of 20 mesh. Eighty weight parts of the coal were premixed with 20 weight parts of zinc dust, regenerated from a previous run, were fed continuously into grinder-reactor A_1 kept at an average temperature of 325°C. and pressure of 50 psi.

Into the center of this reactor-grinder, approximately 50 weight parts of a solvent S_1 were introduced. The solvent was derived from the same process, as a distillate fraction boiling from 200° to 360°C. The residence time of the mixture was kept at one hour. From A_1 the slurry passed to a screw-type solid-liquid separator B_1 where a filtrate F_1 was separated from a solid residue R_1. The filtrate F_1 went to a solvent regeneration and liquid coal depolymerization recovery unit. The solid residue R_1 was conveyed into reactor-grinder A_2. Here at a temperature of 350°C. and pressure of 75 psi the solid residue R_1 was again ground in the presence of additional 50 weight parts of fresh solvent S_2.

The ground mass passes to the screw separator B_2, where again a filtrate F_2 and a residue R_2 was obtained. Residue R_2 passed to reactor A_3. Here at 375°C. and a pressure of 100 psi, it was finally ground in the presence of an additional 50 weight parts of fresh solvent S_3. This slurry passed into a screw-separator B_3 where a final solid residue R_3 and a filtrate F_3 was obtained. Filtrates F_2 and F_3 together with the previously made F_1 went to processing where the used solvents

FIGURE 4.13:   DEPOLYMERIZATION OF BITUMINOUS COAL UTILIZING FRIABLE METAL REACTANTS

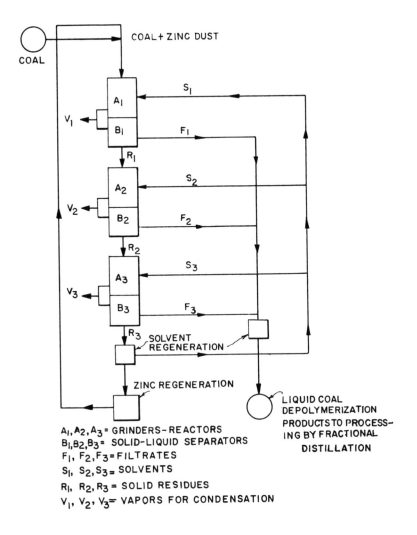

A_1, A_2, A_3 = GRINDERS-REACTORS
B_1, B_2, B_3 = SOLID-LIQUID SEPARATORS
F_1, F_2, F_3 = FILTRATES
S_1, S_2, S_3 = SOLVENTS
R_1, R_2, R_3 = SOLID RESIDUES
V_1, V_2, V_3 = VAPORS FOR CONDENSATION

Source: J. Winkler; U.S. Patent 3,282,826; November 1, 1966

S_1, S_2 and S_3 were regenerated.   The balance of the used solvents were regenerated from the residue R_3 by conventional means of vacuum and steam distillation, and returned into the process.   The solvent-free residue went to a conventional regeneration of the used zinc dust by a retort distillation-reduction with coke.   Solvent-free filtrates F_1, F_2, and F_3 are processed into liquid coal depolymerization products.   In addition, more volatile products are recovered from vapors and gases vented from $A_1 + B_1$; $A_2 + B_2$; $A_3 + B_3$ as V_1, V_2 and V_3.   The material balance from processing of 80 weight parts of the mentioned coal and 20 weight parts of zinc dust is as follows:

Volatiles	Percent
(1) Water condensible and washing oil absorbed vapors; (mainly hydrocarbons C_4 and up)	10.0
(2) Noncondensible hydrocarbon vapors and gases; (up to C_3, NH_3 and traces of CH_4)	1.5

(continued)

Organic Products from Filtrates F_2 and F_3	Percent
(1) Phenolic and organic acids	traces
(2) Basic organic compounds; (pyridines, quinolines, etc.)	5.0
(3) Hydrocarbons boiling up to 200° C. (gasolines etc.)	6.0
(4) Hydrocarbons boiling up to 360° C. (Kerosenes, jet fuel, etc.)	10.0
(5) Hydrocarbons boiling over 360° C. (gas and diesel oils, etc.)	9.0
(6) Residue (fuel oil, etc.)	10.0

Solid Inorganic Matter	
(1) ZnO, ZnS	27.0
(2) Unreacted zinc	0.5
(3) Other ash constituents from the coal	.11.0

Solid Organic Matter	
Unreacted coal, coke, asphaltenes, etc.	5.0

It can be calculated from above material balance that from 80 weight parts of this coal and 20 weight parts of zinc dust not less than 50.5 weight parts of hydrocarbons and 5.0 weight parts of valuable nitrogeneous bases were produced.

PYROLYSIS OF COAL

Continuous Distillation of Coal and Other Hydrocarbonaceous Materials and Autogenous Hydrogenation of the Condensible Volatiles

The process by M. G. Huntington; U.S. Patent 3,107,985; October 22, 1963; assigned to Huntington Chemical Corp. relates to the continuous drying, destructive distillation, gasification and carbonization of coal and other solid hydrocarbonaceous material. More particularly, it relates to a continuous multistage pressurized coal distillation and gasification system in a single vertical vessel; including the functions of coal drying, preheating, distillation with coincidental mild hydrogenation and subsequent severe hydrogenation of the condensible volatiles, and coincidental hydrogenation of recycled heavy bottoms, internal combustion of char to furnish the heat for the system, and selective total gasification of the balance of the char.

This process provides a coal destructive distillation system operating at substantial pressures in which practically all of the distillable, uncombined hydrogen which was originally present in the coal is conserved without dilution with combustion gases and is available at system pressures. That is, since the products of combustion utilized to heat the system are not mixed with the coal being distilled, they do not mix with the primary volatile matter evolved. The uncondensible gases of the primary volatile matter principally include methane, C_2 and C_3 gases and hydrogen. These hydrocarbon gases, including methane, may then be cracked in the heat exchange portion of the system as the thermal carrier gases are recycled through the hot char below the combustion zone.

It also provides for hydrogenation coincidental with the destructive distillation to produce a tar which is much higher in hydrogen and is almost completely free of sulfur, while at the same time the spent char itself will be desulfurized and a substantial part of its nitrogen content recovered as ammonia.

Since hydrogen is actually the thermal carrier fluid which, in the system of this process, must raise the temperature of the preheated, dried coal from about 650° to about 1300°F., and since the thermal carrier hydrogen mixes with the primary and secondary volatiles and with nothing else, the total hydrogen leaving the retort is two to four times by weight that of the combined primary and secondary (volatiles from contact coking of the recycled heavy bottoms) volatile matter, this will provide at a system pressure of 15 to 30 atmospheres, the net effect of coincidental hydrogenation. Also, in this coincidental hydrogenation and destructive distillation, the generation of uncondensible gases and the disassociation of ammonia (NH_3) are retarded because of the high partial pressure of hydrogen in the distillation zone.

Pyrolyzing a Solid or Liquid Hydrocarbonaceous Fuel in a Fluidized Bed

In a process by A.M. Squires; U.S. Patent 3,597,327; August 3, 1971 a solid or liquid hydrocarbonaceous fuel, such as bituminous coal or residual oil, is charged to a lower zone of a fluidized bed, this zone comprising coke pellets, where the fuel is carbonized or cracked (i.e., pyrolyzed) to form gaseous products and a fresh coke accreting upon the pellets. The gaseous products fluidize a superposed, contiguous, upper zone of the fluidized bed, comprising a solid of smaller size and being fluidized at lower velocity.

The velocity of the lower zone is sufficient to prevent the smaller solid from penetrating deeply into the zone. Heat is supplied to the lower zone by heat conduction from the upper zone. The heat is either generated within the upper zone (e.g., by combustion or other chemical reaction or by supply of a hot solid to the upper zone and withdrawal of solid therefrom) or supplied thereto by indirect heat exchange from a heating medium. Alternatively, if the fuel carbonization or cracking is conducted in an atmosphere of hydrogen at a sufficiently high partial pressure, so that the reaction of the fuel is exothermic, heat is withdrawn from the lower zone by heat conduction to the upper zone, and the heat is removed from the upper zone, e.g., by indirect heat exchange to a cooling medium.

Figure 4.14 is a schematic diagram illustrating a process and apparatus for carbonization of coal in a manner such that the fuel gas and coke products are substantially free of sulfur. The agglomerating zone is endothermic, and heat is imparted to the second zone both by supplying a hot solid to this zone and by reaction of CaO with CO_2 to form $CaCO_3$ therein. The process is described with reference to a specific example for clarification.

Example: Bituminous coal, of a type representative of coals widely used in United States industry, is supplied to the process at 80°F. through conduit 1 in an amount comprising 489,488 pounds per hour of moisture- and ash-free (maf) coal and 51,221 pounds per hour of ash. The maf coal has the following analysis (expressed in weight percent):

Carbon	80.70
Hydrogen	5.47
Sulfur	3.72
Nitrogen	1.62
Oxygen	8.49

Grinding equipment 2 reduces the coal to a particle size such that substantially all of the coal passes through a 100-mesh screen (U.S. Standard). Coal is supplied from equipment 2 via conduit 3 to heating equipment 4, where the coal is dried and its temperature is raised to 300°F. The coal is transferred from equipment 4 via line 5 to lock system 6. The coal in line 5 carries 28,456 pounds per hour of intrinsic moisture, and is accompanied by steam at 300°F. and 25 pounds per square inch absolute (psia). Gas is supplied to the process at 397 psia and 700°F. via line 7. The rates of supply of the several constituents in the gas are as follows, expressed in pound-mols per hour:

CO	1,251.9
H_2	1,815.6
CO_2	644.2
H_2O	1,359.9
H_2S	3.64
COS	0.12
N_2	3,962.3
A	49.4

A fraction 0.31684 of the gas is supplied via line 8 to lock system 6, where the gas is used to raise the pressure of the coal to 397 psia, and the gas and coal are injected together at a substantially constant rate into coal-carbonization vessel 9 via a multiplicity of lines 10 and nozzles 11. For simplicity of the drawing, only one line 10 and one nozzle 11 are shown. The remaining gas from line 7 is supplied via line 12 to gas-heating equipment 13 and then at 1300°F. to the bottom of vessel 9, to provide (together with gas from lines 10 and nozzles 11) the fluidizing gas for fluidized bed 14 housed in a lower part of vessel 9.

Coal-carbonization vessel 9 houses two regions in which particulate solids are maintained in the fluidized state: fluidized-bed 14 at 1400°F. occupies a lower part of vessel 9, and fluidized region 15 at 1740°F. occupies an upper part of vessel 9. Particulate solids are maintained in the dense-phase fluidized condition in bed 14, and they are maintained in the dilute-phase fluidized condition in region 15. The pressure at the bottom of bed 14 is 350 psia.

Bed 14 comprises two superposed, contiguous fluidized-bed zones: a lower zone 16 comprising pellets of coke of a size suitably ranging from about 1/12 inch in diameter to about 3/4 inch, and an upper zone 17 comprising a solid derived from naturally-occurring dolomite rock of a particle size suitably ranging from about 40-mesh to about 325-mesh. Off-gases from zone 17 convey the dolomite-derived solid across void space 18 and into region 15.

FIGURE 4.14:   PYROLYZING A SOLID OR LIQUID HYDROCARBONACEOUS FUEL IN A FLUIDIZED BED

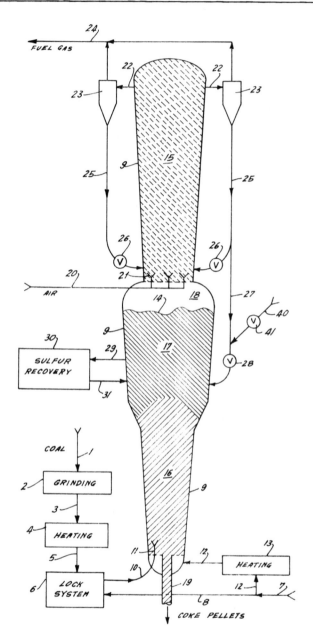

Source: A.M. Squires; U.S. Patent 3,597,327; August 3, 1971

Zone 16 is an agglomerating coal-carbonization zone, which preferably has the form of a frusto-conical chamber with a gradual taper and the smaller end at the bottom. The fluidizing-gas velocity is suitably 20 ft./sec. at the bottom of zone 16, and is suitably 15 ft./sec. at the top. Coal entering zone 16 is heated almost instantaneously to substantially the bed temperature, and carbonization of the coal is initiated practically instantaneously. Almost at once, the coal is split into a gaseous fraction, comprising mainly methane and hydrogen, and a sticky, semifluid residue. The latter is "captured" by a coke pellet, sticking thereto to form a "smear" upon the surface of the pellet.

Zone 16 of coke pellets serves as a "dust trap" for the sticky initial carbonization residue. Further coking reactions, which occur more slowly, transform the sticky smear into dry coke and cause additional gases and vapors to be evolved. However, the residue of carbonization remains sticky for only a time on the order of a very few seconds. Coke product is withdrawn from zone 16, to maintain the inventory of coke pellets therein substantially constant, via pipe 19 at the bottom. The maf coke has the following analysis (expressed in weight percent):

Carbon	95.92
Hydrogen	1.33
Sulfur	0.30
Nitrogen	1.43
Oxygen	1.02

The rate of coke production is 333,057 pounds per hour on an maf basis.

The dolomite-derived solid of zone 17 comprises an intimate intermingling of microscopic crystallites of $CaCO_3$, CaO, CaS, and MgO. Natural dolomite, the double carbonate of calcium and magnesium, seldom contains these two elements in precisely one-to-one atomic ratio, the calcium usually being present in excess. Ideally, however, dolomite may be written $CaCO_3 \cdot MgCO_3$. Solids derived by half-calcining or fully-calcining dolomite may be written $[CaCO_3 + MgO]$ and $[CaO + MgO]$ respectively, to signify the fact that neither of these solids is a true chemical species, but comprises an intimate intermingling of crystallites of the chemical species included between the brackets. The solid derived by allowing one of these solids to absorb sulfur may be written $[CaS + MgO]$. The dolomite-derived solid in zone 17 suitably comprises 2 parts $CaCO_3$, 1 part CaO, 1 part CaS, and 4 parts MgO, on a molar basis. Sulfur in form of H_2S arises in vessel 9 not only as a direct result of carbonization of the coal but also as an indirect result of cracking of tar species and of attack by hydrogen upon coke. Substantially all of the H_2S reacts with the dolomite-derived solid in zone 17.

Solid separated from the gas in each line 22 is delivered from each cyclone 23 to a standpipe 25 fitted with a solid-flow regulating valve 26. The flows of solid through the several valves 26 are suitably regulated so that a return of solid via pipes 25 and valves 26 to the bottom of region 15 produces a loading of solid in the gas rising upward through region 15 and also in each line 22 on the order of one pound or more of solid per actual cubic foot of gas.

The effect of cyclones 23, standpipes 25, and valves 26 is to recirculate a large flow of solid from the top to the bottom of region 15. This recirculation of solid serves to maintain the temperature throughout region 15 substantially uniform and thereby to reduce the likelihood of the occurrence of small zones wherein the temperature might rise to a level such that the dolomite-derived solid would sinter and lose its chemical reactivity toward H_2S and CO_2.

One of the standpipes 25 is fitted with a branch standpipe 27, which delivers solid via solid-flow regulating valve 28 to zone 17 of fluidized bed 14. The solid passing through branch standpipe 27 and valve 28 comprises (expressed in pound-mols per hour:

CaS	1,646.1
CaO	4,990.7
MgO	6,636.8

Hydrocarbon Fuels by the Pyrolysis of Coal in a Fuel Cell

N.P. Cochran; U.S. Patent 3,477,942; November 11, 1969; assigned to U.S. Secretary of the Interior describes a process for the pyrolysis or hydrogasification of coal wherein the coal is converted to fluid products and hot solid char, the improvement comprising passing a first portion of char to a fuel cell or magneto-hydrodynamic device to produce DC current and passing a second portion of char to an internal resistant reactor wherein the char is reacted with steam to form a producer gas containing hydrogen using a portion of the DC current produced to control the heat input to the reactor.

Referring to Figure 4.15, there is shown a process for the production of a variety of valuable fuels from coal. Numeral 1 is a pulverized or finely divided coal feed which if necessary is heated in a fluid bed at from about 600° to 750°F. to prevent subsequent agglomeration. The size of the coal should permit fluidization in bed 2 where the coal is treated at from about 800° to 950°F. for a residence time of about 10 to 60 minutes with a gas stream 3 consisting predominately of nitrogen. This treatment results in a dried and preheated coal stream 6 and an overhead 4 which may be either vented, or collected and condensed, or recycled as 5 to bed 2.

The predried coal stream 6 is led to a second fluidized bed 7, operating in a range of from about 1100° to 1200°F. There it is held for a residence time of from 10 to 60 minutes so that pyrolysis occurs and volatiles 9 are driven off as the predried feed 6 is contacted with a hot gas stream 8. A partially pyrolyzed coal stream 10 is fed from fluidized bed 7 to fluidized bed 11 where it is contacted with a high temperature hydrogen stream 12 at about 1500° to 1600°F. again for a residence time of from 10 to 60 minutes. The volatiles driven off in this bed form stream 8 which is sent back to bed 7.

A portion 14 of the char product from bed 11 is fed into fluidized reactor 15 where it is in contact with a steam input 16 at about 2500°F. to produce a gas stream 17 comprising carbon monoxide and hydrogen. Reactor 15 is of the internal resistance type, that is, the reactor is equipped with electrodes across which an electrical potential is maintained.

FIGURE 4.15:   HYDROCARBON FUELS BY THE PYROLYSIS OF COAL IN A FUEL CELL

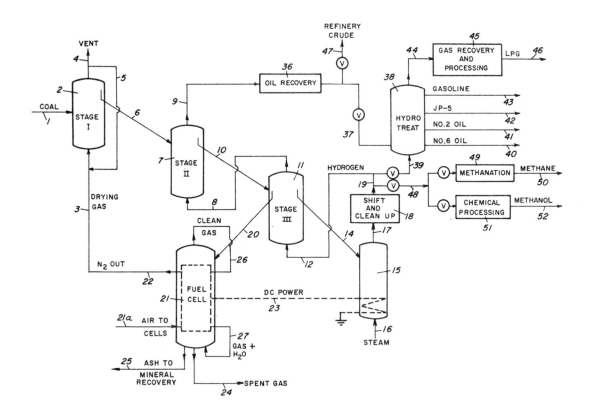

Source: N.P. Cochran; U.S. Patent 3,477,942; November 11, 1969

When the reactor is fluidized with conductive char particles electric energy is supplied and the temperature of the bed can be raised to a reactive level and a high degree of temperature control can be maintained.   Reactors of this type are described in U.S. Patents 1,857,799; 2,921,840; 2,968,683 and 2,978,315.   Exiting reactor 15, stream 17 is sent to a treatment at 18 where it is cleaned in a conventional manner such as by condensing and separating to remove impurities, shifted with steam to carbon dioxide and hydrogen and then passed through a conventional carbon dioxide absorber resulting in a stream 19 consisting of carbon monoxide and of hydrogen.   A portion of 19 is sent back as stream 12 to bed 11.

The remaining portion 20 of the char product from bed 11 serves as the input to a high temperature fuel cell 21 which operates in the range of from about 1000° to 1100°C.   In this cell, which is described in Office of Coal Research Report No. 17 entitled, "Review and Evaluation of Project Fuel Cell," char 20 and air 21a are in the inputs and a nitrogen containing gas 22, power 23, spent gas 24 and ash 25 are the outputs.   Clean gas 26 is recycled as well as a partially spent gas 27.

The refining of hydrocarbons takes places as volatiles 9 from bed 7 are sent to an oil recovery 36 where they undergo condensation and separation by a water quench.   Depending upon the condition of the stream at that point, it may also be subjected to an acid treatment, an alkali treatment, or both.   Following such treatments the petroleum extract may be sent via 47 to a refining stage or via 37 to a hydrocracking unit 38 where it is contacted with hydrogen-containing stream 39.   Depending upon the extent of cracking and the use of other conversion processes such as reforming, hydrogenation, isomerization, etc., a variety of products can be recovered.   Gaseous products exit via 44 and are sent to a gas recovery unit 45 where they undergo cleanup condensation and if necessary separation into propane and butane fractions by distillation.   Other recoverable products include number 6 oil, 40, number 2, oil, 41, JP-5 fuel, 42, and gasoline, 43.

Alternatively, hydrogen and carbon monoxide from stream 19 may be diverted to form methane or methanol.   To produce methane at 50, the carbon monoxide and hydrogen in stream 48 are contacted at elevated temperatures over a methanation catalyst such as Raney nickel in a tube wall reactor 49.

If a methanol product 52 is desired, the gases in line 48 are passed over a conventional hydrogenation catalyst in a reactor 51 causing the following reaction to occur.

$$CO + 2H_2 \longrightarrow CH_3OH$$

When large amounts of methane or methanol are desired, the product from oil recovery 36 will generally be sent to a refinery as crude via 47 unless some alternative source of hydrogen is available for refining purposes.

CONCOMITANT PRODUCTION OF COKE

Chemical Modification of Coal into Hydrocarbon Oils and Coke

This process by E. Bluemner; U.S. Patent 2,714,086; July 26, 1955 relates to the chemical modification of coal. One of the objects of this process is to provide a method for the treatment of bituminous coal, which permits considerable amounts of liquid hydrocarbons to be obtained per unit of coal. Another object is to provide a method for the production of liquid hydrocarbons from bituminous coal in which the solid residues are obtained in the form of hard, marketable coke, and to provide a method for preparing a liquid extract from bituminous coal. It also provides a method for transforming the greater part of bituminous coal into a substance which is soluble in oil.

The extract is subjected to conditions of a pressure thermic treatment analogous to the pressure cracking of oils. When this process is completed, the pressure is released to obtain separation into on the one hand the mineral oils of high hydrogen content obtained from the mixture of coal and carrier oil, these being further separated by fractional separation (condensation) and on the other hand the residues poorest in hydrogen and being pitch substances, which latter are then subjected to a heat treatment without pressure for obtaining coke.

This process also provides a continuous process for the production of hard coke and simultaneous production of a high output of light and medium hydrocarbons from bituminous coal of any kind and more particularly from bituminous coal having such chemical and physical characteristics as would prevent a marketable hard coke from being obtained in the customary low temperature carbonizing methods. The process is described more in detail by way of example with reference to Figure 4.16. Figure 4.16 is a diagrammatic view of the apparatus.

FIGURE 4.16: CHEMICAL MODIFICATION OF COAL INTO HYDROCARBON OILS AND COKE

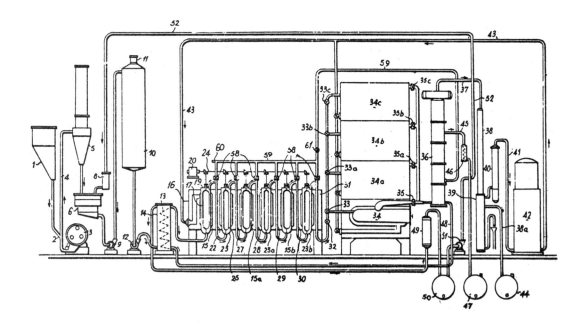

Source: E. Bluemner; U.S. Patent 2,714,086; July 26, 1955

Coal from a bunker 1 is admitted through a pipe 2 to a pulverizing mill 3, which converts the coal into a fine powder preferably a powder passing through a 1000 to 1300 mesh (150 to 200 per sq. cm.), no appreciable advantages being obtainable by comminution beyond this degree of fineness. The powder obtained in the mill 3 flows through a pipe line 4 to a container 5 for the pulverized coal; the latter supplies the pulverized coal to a mixing device 6, to which heavy mineral oil measured by a device 8 is simultaneously admitted to produce suspension of the coal in the oil.

In accordance with the process, the paste-like mixture of coal and oil is subjected to the gentlest possible resolving transformation to produce a selected extract. For this purpose the mixture obtained in the mixer 6, which by means of a pump 9 has been transferred to a storage tank 10, in which it is stirred by a motor 11, is forced by a pressure pump 12 working against a pressure of more than 20 kg./cm.^{2} through the coil 13 of a heat exchanger 14 into the lower end of a first heating cylinder 15 which forms one of a battery of cylinders in a suitably heated reaction furnace 16. The cylinder 15 contains a cylindrical rotor 17 which, fills the cylinder except for a narrow annular space along the wall thereof.

The rotor 17 is mounted on a shaft 18 which extends through the upper cover 19 of the cylinder and is driven for rotation jointly with similar rotors in all remaining cylinders of the furnace 16, by means of a geared motor 20 and a transmission shaft 24. The rotor 17 carries three longitudinally extending scrapers 21 which move in contact with the cylinder wall and force the material in the cylinder to participate in the rotation of the rotor while passing upwardly between the latter and the wall of the cylinder. The heating of the cylinder 15 is so controlled in relation to the rate of movement of the mixture into each cylinder, the distance between the rotor and the cylinder wall and the speed of rotation of the rotor, that the temperature of the mixture will rise in the cylinder 15 to the first reaction temperature of 290° to 300°C., the arrangement being such that, owing to the small cross-section of the annular space between the cylinder wall and the rotor, this heating takes place at a rapid rate as to be completed, for example, within 7 minutes.

From the upper end of the cylinder 15 the heated mixture is conducted through a pipe connection including a vertical gas-separator pipe 22, which will be described further on, to the lower end of the next following cylinder 23. The latter is generally of similar construction as the cylinder 15 and likewise contains a rotor driven synchronously with the rotor 17 by the common transmission shaft 24 but, this rotor 25, has a substantially smaller diameter than the rotor 17, while the cylinder 23 has the same diameter as the cylinder 15. As a consequence the annular space between the rotor 25 and the cylinder 23 has a much greater cross-section area than the annular space between the first cylinder 15 and its rotor 17, and as a consequence the speed at which the mixture arriving from the pipe 22 rises through the cylinder 23 is substantially less than the speed at which the mass rises through the cylinder 15, the dimensions being such that the material remains in cylinder 23 for a period of approximately 30 minutes.

Scraper arms 26 making contact with the wall of the cylinder 23 are provided on the rotor 25 similarly to the scrapers 21 on the rotor 17, these scrapers being however modified in dimensions and construction in accordance with the greater width of the gap between the rotor and cylinder wall. The circumferential speed at which the scrapers move over the surface of the cylinder wall is substantially greater than the speed at which the material rises in the cylinder, so that, in spite of the difference in the rate of vertical movement of the material in the two cylinders which corresponds to the different periods in which the material is intended to stay in each of these, the speed at which the material is moved along the wall, which is of great importance for the transfer of heat, is substantially the same.

The heating of the cylinder 23 is so controlled that during the 30 minutes period in which the material remains in this cylinder its temperature rises only to 310°C. From the upper end of the cylinder 23 the material is conducted through a pipe connection 27, similar to pipe connection 22, to a further cylinder 15a which is of substantially the same construction as cylinder 15, and from the upper end of which a pipe connection 28 leads the material to a further cylinder 23a, substantially identical in construction with cylinder 23.

Further pipe connections 29 and 30 respectively serve to conduct the material from cylinder 23a to a cylinder 15b, substantially identical with cylinder 15 and then to a last cylinder 23b, substantially identical with cylinder 23. In cylinder 15a the material is rapidly heated to 390°C., while in cylinder 23a it remains for a period of about 30 minutes, during which its temperature is raised from 400° to 410°C.

The treatment in cylinder 23a completes the conversion of the coal into oil-soluble extract substances dissolved in the carrier oil, and the solution thus obtained is ready to be subjected to treatment corresponding to the cracking of liquid hydrocarbons. To this end the material coming from cylinder 23a, after being freed from gases during its passage through gas separator pipe 29, is rapidly heated in cylinder 15b to a temperature of about 450°C. to remain in cylinder 23b for a further period of 30 minutes during which it is gradually heated to 470°C.

A further pipe connection 31 leads from cylinder 23b to a pressure-release valve 32 in which the pressure of the treated material is reduced from its previous value of approximately 20 kg./sq. cm. to atmospheric pressure, at which it is allowed, through a stop valve 33, to enter a coking retort 34 which has previously been brought to a temperature of about 400° to 500°C. Owing to the sudden reduction of pressure, on entering the retort 34 the volatile components will at once evaporate, the temperature of these components being prevented by the evaporation from rising above 400°C.

The vapor mixture, which in practice will have a temperature of 350° to 400°C., passes through a further stop valve 35 to enter a separating column or dephlegmator 36. The lightest fraction containing benzene and permanent gases is led off through a pipe 37 at the top of the column to a benzene condenser 38, a water remover 39 and gas washer 40, when the permanent gases are led through a pipe 41 to the gasometer 42.

Gas from this gasometer is utilized for heating the reaction furnace 16 and the retort 34, to which it is supplied through a pipe system 43. Crude benzene from the benzene condenser 38 is collected in a tank 44. The heavier fractions are conducted from the column 36 through different pipe connections, viz. medium oil (diesel oil) through a pipe connection 45 to a cooler 46 and a medium oil tank 47, while heavy oil, which has the highest condensation temperature, is conducted through a pipe 48 and through the body of the heat exchanger 13 before being finally cooled in a cooler 49 and stored in the heavy oil storage tank 50.

Carbonization of Coal to Coke and Recovery of Volatile Constituents

This process of E.F. Pevere, G.B. Arnold and H.V. Hess; U.S. Patent 2,664,390; December 29, 1953; assigned to The Texas Company relates to the production of finely divided particles of coke from coal. The process may be applied to coals of various types, especially bituminous coals and lignite. The process is particularly applicable to the treatment of bituminous coals.

At temperatures above about 700°F., there is a condensation of free radicals or unsaturated compounds (generated by thermal decomposition of coal substance) into materials more stable than the original coal substance. At temperatures above about 825°F., the rate of precipitation of insoluble polymer may exceed the rate of liquefaction. The coal is kept at a temperature as low as possible during liquefaction and subsequent handling in the liquid state to prevent excessive precipitation of the solid polymer. The optimum temperature for liquefaction is dependent upon the type and source of the coal, and the period of time the coal must be kept in liquid state, and is best determined by trial for any given coal.

The atomized coal may be carbonized under conditions of temperature satisfactory for conventional carbonization of coal. In general, the temperatures used for distillation of coal range from about 900° to about 2000°F. or higher. The lower temperatures within this range are preferred, as the yield of valuable products from the coal is favored by low temperature distillation. In the conventional processes it is difficult to carbonize coal at temperatures on the order of 900° to 1000°F.

Carbonization may be carried out efficiently at the lower temperatures by the process. In atomized form the coal particles are more readily distilled than in conventional particle form. The oil also aids in the distillation of the coal. An oil fraction obtained from the process and having a boiling range of from about 400° to about 500°F., for example, is readily vaporized at the coal distillation temperature.

Such volatile oils used for plasticizing or liquefying the coal in the process aid in the distillation of the coal and recovery of desirable volatilizable constituents therefrom by reducing the effective partial pressure of the volatilizable constituents. Distillation is also favored by the passage of gases through the distillation zone. The coke particles may be maintained in the carbonization zone as a fluid bed. The particle size of the product may be controlled by regulation of the droplet size produced on atomization.

Figure 4.17 is a diagrammatic view illustrating the process. Coal is supplied to a hopper 5 through a conduit 6. From the hopper, the coal may be fed through conduit 7 into liquefaction vessel 8 or through conduit 9 into liquefaction vessel 10. Any number of such vessels may be employed. While coal and oil are charged to one of the vessels to prepare a liquefied coal feed stream for carbonization, another is discharged to the carbonization step. When a vessel has been filled with coal from the hopper, inert gas may be admitted from line 12 to the vessel to purge it of air and other gases. Valve 13 associated with vessel 8, and valve 14, associated with vessel 10, are provided for this purpose. The purged gases may be vented from the vessels 8 and 10 through valves 15 and 16 respectively.

Preheated oil from line 18 may be admitted to vessel 8 through valve 19 and to vessel 10 through valve 20. When a vessel is charged with coal and hot oil, the valves are closed and the coal at least partially liquefied due to the combined effect of heating the coal and the solvent or plasticizing action of the oil.

Mechanical mixers 21 and 22 are provided to disintegrate and disperse any undissolved residue or precipitated solid material from the coal. A substantially homogeneous liquid mixture of coal substance and oil is thus obtained. Generally, sufficient heat for the liquefaction may be supplied by preheating the oil stream. Additional heat may be supplied directly to the liquefaction vessels by suitable means not illustrated in the drawing. The oil may be supplied to the vessel at least partially in vapor form under a pressure sufficient to cause condensation in the liquefaction vessel and thereby furnishing additional heat for heating the coal. The resulting liquid coal feed is discharged from the vessel 8 through valve 23 and from vessel 10 through valve 24 to a charge pump 25. Inert gas from line 12 may be admitted to the vessel during the period of discharge of the liquefied coal therefrom. The inert gas may be supplied under sufficient pressure

FIGURE 4.17:   CARBONIZATION OF COAL TO COKE AND RECOVERY OF VOLATILE CONSTITUENTS

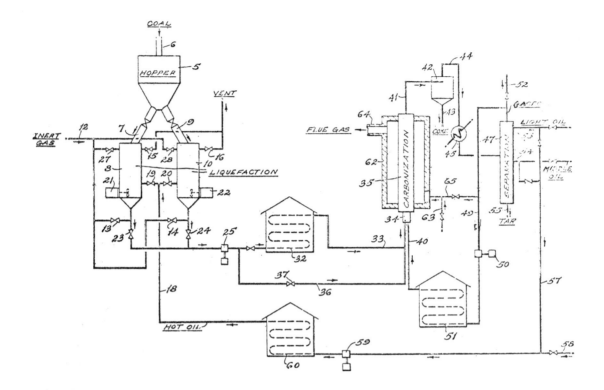

Source: E.F. Pevere, G.B. Arnold and H.V. Hess; U.S. Patent 2,664,390; December 29, 1953

to maintain the desired pressure within the vessel to prevent substantial flashing of volatile hydrocarbons and aid in discharging the liquefied coal therefrom. From the charge pump 25, the liquefied coal feed stream is passed through a heating coil 32 wherein it is heated to a temperature within the range required for carbonization. The liquefied coal feed is charged through line 33 into an atomizer 34 associated with carbonization zone 35. Alternatively, part or all of the coal feed stream may be fed without preheating directly from the charge pump 25 to the atomizer 34 through line 36 as controlled by valve 37.

The atomizer 34 may be of conventional type and is constructed of materials which are resistant to erosion. A suitable atomizer may be one of the spray type wherein the liquid is forced under pressure through an orifice of small diameter. The atomized particles are dispersed in a stream of hot inert gases supplied to the carbonization zone through line 40.

The carbonized particles of coal, or coke, are entrained in the hot gas stream and discharged through line 41 into a cyclone separator 42. The coke is separated from the hot gas stream and discharged from the cyclone separator through line 43. The hot gas stream, which contains vapors of the oil used in the preparation of the feed stream and volatilized constituents from the fresh coal feed, is discharged from the cyclone separator through line 44, cooled in a cooler 45, and passed to a separation system 47.

In the separation system, a gaseous fraction comprising methane and other gases resulting from distillation of the coal is separated from the normally liquid products of distillation comprising, for example, light oil, middle oil and tar fractions. A portion of the gases from the separation zone is recycled through line 49 and pump 50 to a heating coil 51 wherein the gases are heated and introduced into the carbonization zone through line 40. Part or all of the remaining portion of the gases may be discharged from the system through line 52 for use as fuel or other purposes. A light oil fraction is withdrawn from the separation zone through line 53, a middle oil fraction, through line 54, and a tar fraction through line 55.

Example: Pittsburgh bed coal containing about 2% water, 31% volatile matter, 58% fixed carbon and 9% ash, as received, is subjected to carbonization. The coal is charged to a liquefaction vessel in the form of lumps ranging from about 1/2" to about 1/4" in average diameter. This coal is mixed with a middle oil fraction obtained from the distillation of coal. Approximately equal parts by weight of coal and oil are charged to the liquefaction vessel. The oil has a boiling range from about 450° to about 550°F., and is preheated to a temperature of about 825°F. prior to mixture with the coal.

A pressure of about 300 pounds per square inch gauge is maintained on the liquefaction vessel to insure liquid phase conditions. The coal and oil are subjected to mechanical agitation to insure dispersion of carbonaceous residue. About 65% by weight of the coal is taken into solution by the oil and the remaining 35% dispersed in the form of minute particles. The resulting liquid coal stream, at a temperature of 600°F., is atomized with an inert gas comprising largely methane. The atomized particles are suspended in the inert gas at a temperature of about 1000°F.

The gases and dispersed coal particles are passed through an elongated tubular retort which is externally heated where they are further heated to a temperature of about 1200°F. Coke particles resulting from distillation and carbonization of the coal are separated from the entrained gas stream as a granular product of relatively uniform particle size.

COMPANY INDEX

The company names listed below are given exactly as they appear in the patents, despite name changes, mergers and acquisitions which have, at times, resulted in the revision of a company name.

Allied Chemical Corp. – 201
Ashland Oil & Refining Co. – 183
Atlantic Richfield Co. – 134, 209, 211
Bennett Engineering Co. – 204
Chevron Research Co. – 205
Compagnie Francaise des Essences Synthetiques
    Societe Anonyme – 76
Consolidation Coal Co. – 4, 9, 13, 16, 20,
    36, 45, 50, 57, 60, 174
Esso Research and Engineering Co. – 54, 114,
    132, 135, 191
FMC Corp. – 149, 190
Fossil Fuels, Inc. – 117, 124
Great Lakes Carbon Corp. – 69
Gulf Oil Corp. – 65
Gulf Research & Development Co. – 208
Huntington Chemical Corp. – 214
Hydrocarbon Research, Inc. – 103, 156, 158,
    159, 163, 164, 167, 169, 172, 179

Kerr-McGee Corp. – 128
Koppers Company, Inc. – 119
Lummus Co. – 69, 72
Phillips Petroleum Co. – 146
Pyrochem Corp. – 121, 175
Research Council of Alberta, Canada – 96
Shell Development Co. – 144
Shell Oil Co. – 138, 140, 141, 148, 153
Standard Oil Development Co. – 186, 188, 198, 199, 211
Sun Oil Co. – 94, 161, 166
Texaco Development Corp. – 110, 131
Texaco Inc. – 106
Texas Co. – 48, 101, 183, 221
Union Carbide Corp. – 108, 112, 182
U.S. Secretary of the Interior – 36, 49, 65, 93, 117, 151,
    152, 172, 174, 178, 217
Universal Oil Products – 30, 32, 35, 38, 41, 42, 47, 75,
    79, 85, 89, 93, 123, 145, 194
University of Wyoming – 196

INVENTOR INDEX

Albright, C.W., 108
Alpert, S.B., 163, 169
Arnold, G.B., 101, 183, 221
Bailey, W.A., Jr., 144
Barr, F.T., 199, 211
Becke, F., 145
Bennett, H.L., 204
Bloomer, W.J., 69, 72
Bleumner, E., 219
Broche, H., 53
Bull, W.C., 65
Calderon, M., 159, 179
Campbell, D.R., 75
Chervenak, M.C., 158
Cochran, N.P., 217
Corey, R.S., 47, 75, 85, 89
Day, R.B., 194
Doughty, E.W., 112
Eastman, D., 106
Eccles, M.A., 112
Eddinger, R.T., 149, 190
Frese, E.L., 119
Friedel, R.A., 93
Friedman, L.D., 149
Gatsis, J.G., 35, 41, 79
Gilbert, W.I., 208
Gleim, W.K.T., 85, 89
Gohr, E.J., 211
Gorin, E., 4, 9, 13, 16, 20, 36, 50,
    57, 60, 174
Greensfelder, B.S., 144
Harding, C.T., 198
Harris, G.W., 135
Herédy, L.A., 45
Hess, H.V., 101, 221
Hirst, L.L., 178
Hiteshue, R.W., 152
Hodgson, G.W., 96
Hodgson, R.L., 138, 140, 141, 148
Hoffman, E.J., 196
Howell, J.H., 112
Huntington, M.G., 121, 175, 214
Johanson, E.S., 156, 163, 164, 169, 172
Johnson, C.A., 159, 167
Jones, J.F., Jr., 190
Joseph, R.T., 201
Kawa, W., 152

Keith, P.C., 103, 163
Kessler, T., 93
Keunecke, E., 145
Kirk, M.C., Jr., 161, 166
Kloepper, D.L., 65
Kruyer, J., 96
Leaders, W.M., 128
Leas, A.M., 183
Ludlam, L.L., 209, 211
Maguire, J.B., 201
Malli, J., Jr., 93
Martin, S.W., 69
Mayland, B.J., 146
Montgomery, C.W., 208
Nelson, E.F., 30, 32, 38, 42, 123
Neuworth, M.B., 16, 45
Noel, H.M., 186
Odell, W.W., 188
Orchin, M., 49
Overholt, D.C., 182
Paterson, N.J., 205
Pelipetz, M.G., 117, 151
Perry, R.C., 108
Pevere, E.F., 48, 101, 183, 221
Phinney, J.A., 36
Pott, A., 53
Reichl, E.H., 36
Riedl, F.J., 47, 75, 85, 89
Rieve, R.W., 134
Ringer, F., 103
Roach, J.W., 128
Roetheli, B.E., 211
Rogers, T.F., 65
Round, G.F., 96
Roy, G.D., 182
Ruidisch, L.E., 48
Russell, F.R., 191
Schappert, H.M., 119
Scharmann, W.G., 199
Schlinger, W.G., 106
Schroeder, W.C., 117, 124
Schulman, B.L., 54, 114
Schuman, S.C., 158, 163, 164
Seglin, L., 190
Seitzer, W.H., 94, 161
Sellers, F.B., 110, 131
Shalit, H., 134

Sharkey, A.G., Jr., 93
Shinn, R.W., 94
Simmat, W.E., 119
Skripek, M., 209, 211
Sprow, F.B., 135
Squires, A.M., 215
Stephenson, T.G., 117
Stevenson, L.G., 65, 117
Stoewener, F., 145
Stone, R.D., 93
Storch, H.H., 151, 178
Stotler, H.H., 159, 164, 179
Struck, R.T., 60, 174

Sunagel, G.R., 85, 89
Syacha, R.E., 47
Thibaut, L., 76
Thomas, C.L., 145
Wadley, E.F., 132
Wald, M.M., 153
Warren, R.R., 182
Whitehead, K.E., 209, 211
Wilson, E.L., Jr., 132
Winkler, J., 212
Wolk, R.H., 158, 163, 164, 169, 172
Zielke, C.W., 60, 174

U.S. PATENT NUMBER INDEX

2,308,247 - 53	3,107,985 - 214	3,514,394 - 132
2,337,944 - 145	3,117,921 - 13	3,518,182 - 205
2,377,728 - 145	3,120,474 - 16	3,519,553 - 164
2,379,077 - 198	3,143,489 - 20	3,519,554 - 179
2,392,588 - 144	3,152,063 - 117	3,519,555 - 163
2,406,810 - 194	3,158,561 - 45	3,520,794 - 35
2,436,938 - 199	3,162,594 - 50	3,523,886 - 36
2,464,271 - 178	3,184,401 - 57	3,527,691 - 138
2,476,999 - 49	3,231,486 - 108	3,532,617 - 141
2,557,680 - 188	3,232,861 - 60	3,533,938 - 183
2,572,061 - 131	3,244,615 - 121	3,535,224 - 75
2,595,979 - 183	3,247,092 - 175	3,536,608 - 47
2,606,142 - 151	3,282,826 - 212	3,540,995 - 172
2,654,695 - 208	3,321,393 - 158	3,543,665 - 153
2,658,861 - 101	3,341,447 - 65	3,549,512 - 140
2,664,390 - 221	3,355,376 - 174	3,556,978 - 152
2,676,908 - 186	3,375,188 - 72	3,574,065 - 190
2,681,300 - 48	3,379,638 - 69	3,575,847 - 135
2,697,718 - 211	3,453,202 - 149	3,576,734 - 204
2,707,163 - 76	3,477,941 - 42	3,577,337 - 93
2,714,086 - 219	3,477,942 - 217	3,583,900 - 79
2,738,311 - 119	3,488,278 - 123	3,594,303 - 161
2,741,549 - 191	3,488,279 - 54	3,594,304 - 94
2,753,296 - 110	3,488,280 - 114	3,594,305 - 166
2,756,194 - 146	3,502,564 - 148	3,597,327 - 215
2,832,724 - 112	3,503,863 - 41	3,598,717 - 89
2,860,101, - 117	3,503,864 - 38	3,598,718 - 85
2,885,337 - 103	3,503,865 - 92	3,607,718 - 128
2,977,299 - 201	3,503,866 - 211	3,607,719 - 167
3,018,241 - 4	3,503,867 - 209	3,617,465 - 169
3,018,242 - 9	3,505,201 - 96	3,617,474 - 159
3,030,297 - 124	3,505,202 - 30	3,619,404 - 134
3,075,919 - 106	3,505,203 - 32	
3,084,118 - 182	3,505,204 - 196	Reissue 25,770 - 156

NOTICE

Nothing contained in this Review shall be construed to constitute a permission or recommendation to practice any invention covered by any patent without a license from the patent owners. Further, neither the author nor the publisher assumes any liability with respect to the use of, or for damages resulting from the use of, any information, apparatus, method or process described in this Review.

1

ADHESIVES
GUIDEBOOK AND DIRECTORY 1972
Blue Book No. 2

This Guidebook and Directory to adhesives and their producers is the second volume in our comprehensive Blue Book Series. In keeping with our policy, this book attempts to provide a reasonably complete listing of commercially available, standardized products offered by American industry. The book describes the "on the line" adhesive products of U.S. manufacturers arranged according to company names.

All the information in this volume is taken directly from the manufacturers' hard-to-get data sheets and technical bulletins. In each case enough information is provided to enable the researcher to judge from the data presented whether or not a given adhesive will do the job for the intended applications and purposes.

The data appearing in this book were selected by the publisher from each manufacturer's literature at no cost to, nor influence from, the manufacturers of the materials.

One of the primary purposes of this book is to present the significant, first line information about adhesives all in one place—saving you many hours of work trying to obtain specific information and facts regarding any particular adhesive or class of adhesives.

The book will answer questions regarding the commercial availability and suitability of glues and adhesives for:

Bonding Paper and Paperboard
Metal to Metal Bonding
Fiber to Rubber Bonding (Tiremaking)
Adhesives for Glass and Ceramics
Polymer to Polymer Bonding
Plastic to Metal Bonding
Special Adhesives for Paper and Wood
Pressure Sensitive Adhesives
Pressure Sensitive Adhesive Tapes
Water-Soluble Adhesives
Water-Insoluble Adhesives
Hot Melt Adhesives
Special Purpose Adhesives for
  Shoemaking
  Paper Coating
  Tiremaking
  Rubber Goods

Furniture Making
Housing Construction
Aeroplane Construction
Pipe Joining and Sealing
Flexible Laminates
Rigid Laminates
and many more purposes.

Find out about the chemical nature of commercial adhesives. Are they based on:
Starch
Dextrins
Other Natural Substances
or like most adhesive products offered today, are they polymer based, and if so, on which one.
Are they based on:
Epoxy Resins and Curing Agents,
or is no catalyst required.
Other bases are:
Acrylics
Polyvinyl Acetate
Polyvinyl Alcohol
Polyurethanes and Isocyanates
Ethylene Copolymers
Styrene-Butadienes
Silicones-Polysiloxanes
and many more.

This is a guide to U.S. manufacturers with standard product lines and gives precise, complete, up-to-date and pertinent information.

This guidebook and directory is intended for the end user, whom it can serve as a constant source of reference and a real timesaver. The advantage of having all key facts in one convenient reference volume is important to the engineering executive, research chemist, company director, and purchasing agent, who may want to choose among competitive items or must select new adhesives for new applications.

By listing the intended uses and physical properties, as well as the manufacturers and suppliers, this book is intended to be a substantial contribution and to furnish a comprehensive service to the science and art of applying adhesives. It should be in every technical library.

407 pages

$36

ENVIRONMENTAL CONTROL IN THE INORGANIC CHEMICAL INDUSTRY 1972
by H. R. Jones
Pollution Control Review No. 6

Except for radioactive wastes, inorganic pollution control is still a field that must receive greater attention and action. Because of the nature of the industry, obsolete units remain sufficiently profitable to continue in use.

Contaminated wastewaters come from electrolysis and crystallization brines, washings from filter cakes, and spent acids and alkalis. In addition, thermal pollution occurs. Waste treatment methods require neutralization, sedimentation, lagooning, and segregation of uncontaminated cooling waters. Biological treatment is seldom applicable.

Air pollution problems are considerable and arise from chlor-alkali, nitric, sulfuric, and hydrofluoric acid manufacture, etc. In-plant control of atmospheric emissions is essential and mandatory.

The present book provides helpful directions for adequate pollution control. Commercial processes are shown, as well as detailed technology from the U.S. patent literature. Partial list of contents follows:

1. WASTEWATER CHARACTERISTICS
2. WATER POLLUTION PROBLEMS IN THE MANUFACTURE OF 33 SPECIFIC CHEMICALS
3. ACTUAL POLLUTION CONTROL PROCESSES FOR WASTEWATERS CONTAINING:
  Phosphoric Acid—U.S. Steel Corp.
  Radioactive Materials—
    Halliburton Co.; U.S.A.E.C.
  Soda Ash—I.C.I.
  Titanium Dioxide—Ishihara Sangyo
  Refinery Acid Sludges—
    Container Corp.; Gulf Oil
  Steel Mill Pickle Liquors—
    Horizons, Inc., Allied Chemical;
    Crucible Steel; Simon-Carves, Ltd.
  Paper Mill Bleach Liquors—
    T. Niwa et al.; Kimberly-Clark
  Acid Mine Wastewaters—
    C. E. Baer et al.
  Paper Mill Waste Liquors—
    Lummus Co.
  Boiler Blow-Down Water—
    Petro-Tex Chem. Corp.
  Industrial Alkali Wastes—
    Crane Co.
  Iron-Containing Wastewaters—
    Johns-Manville Corp.
    Coal Industry Patents, Ltd.
    General Services Co.

Hungerford & Terry, Inc.
Manganese-Containing Wastewaters—
  Calgon Corp.
  Johns-Manville Corp.
Tin & Fluorides in Wastewaters—
  National Steel Corp.
Chromium-Containing Wastewaters—
  R. Richards; Crane Co.;
  Lancy Laboratories
Strontium-Containing Wastewaters—
  U. S. Atomic Energy Commission
Copper-Containing Wastewaters—
  Du Pont
Cyanides in Wastewaters—
  Western Electric Co.
Sulfides in Wastewaters—
  British Petroleum Co.
Phosphates in Wastewaters—
  General Mills, Inc.

4. AIR POLLUTION PROBLEMS IN THE MANUFACTURE OF 15 SPECIFIC CHEMICALS
5. ACTUAL POLLUTION CONTROL PROCESSES FOR ATMOSPHERIC EMISSIONS CONTAINING:
  Ammonia—W. J. Sackett
  Ammonium Sulfate—Inventa AG
  Chlorine—Allied Chemical;
    M.E.J. Cathala; Du Pont
  Fluorine & Compounds—
    Hooker Chem. Corp.; L. A. Mitchell,
    Ltd.; W. J. Sackett; Wellman-Lord, Inc.;
    Whiting Corp.
  Hydrogen Sulfide—
    Gewerkschaft Auguste Viktoria
  Iodine—U. S. Atomic Energy Commission
  Magnesium Chloride—Am. Magnesium Co.
  Nitrogen Oxides—F. Schulze; Du Pont;
    W. R. Grace; Mine Safety Appliance
  Phosphorus and Its Compounds—
    Knapsack-Griesheim AG
  Sulfur and Sulfur Oxides—
    Pacific Foundry Co.; Chem. Construction Corp.; Furukawa Mining Co.;
    W. R. Grace; Ionics, Inc.; Shell Oil
  Tellurium Hexafluoride—
    U. S. Atomic Energy Commission
  Titanium Dioxide—National Lead Co.

6. INCREASED TECHNOLOGICAL AWARENESS AND FUTURE TRENDS

255 pages

$36

SAUSAGE PROCESSING 1972
by Dr. E. Karmas
Food Processing Review No. 24

The detailed, descriptive process information included in this Food Processing Review is based on U.S. patents relating to sausage production. The material involving 136 processes, developed since 1960, has been divided into two parts—Emulsion Ingredients and Processing Methods. The first part emphasizes various emulsion additives from the viewpoint of cured flavor, emulsion stability, and ingredient control. The second part deals with sausage processes such as stuffing, linking, cooking, and peeling; as well as the production of conventional and some novel sausage products.

Partial Table of Contents showing process examples:

1. ACCELERATED DEVELOPMENT AND STABILIZATION OF CURED COLOR (18)
  Glucono Delta Lactone
  Methyl 2-Ketogluconate
  Soluble Calcium Salts
  2,3-Dihydroxy-1-cyclohexenone
  1,2,3-Cyclohexanetrione
  Nitric Oxide Gas
  Dialuric Acid
  Fumaric Acid
  Ethylenediaminetetraacetic Acid
  Acid Phosphates
  Citrates and Ascorbates
  Sorbitol
2. FLAVORING & COLORING ADDITIVES (3)
3. PREVENTION OF RANCIDITY (4)
  Hot Carcass Processing
  Oxygen-Impermeable Casings
  Ground Mustard Seed
  NaCl Coated with Antioxidants
4. FERMENTED FLAVORS (3)
5. TEXTURIZING AGENTS (13)
  Phosphate Gels
  Calcium Caseinate
  Methyl Cellulose
  Wheat Flour-Base Binder
  Milk Solids with Enzyme
  Bovine Blood Plasma
  Salt-Soluble Protein
6. EMULSION STABILIZERS (5)
  Magnesium Ions

Polymeric Phosphates
Other Phosphates
7. LOW TEMPERATURE DEFATTING OF MEAT (3)
8. LOW TEMPERATURE DEFATTING OF ADIPOSE TISSUE (3)
9. FATTY TISSUE RENDERING (2)
10. MEAT RECOVERY FROM BONES (4)
11. COMPOSITION CONTROL (2)
12. PRODUCT AND INGREDIENT IDENTIFICATION (2)
13. STUFFING OPERATIONS (10)
  Deaerated Emulsion
  Controlled Stuffing Rate
  Continuous Stuffing
  Metered Stuffing
14. LINKING AND TYING (13)
15. FORMING AND SHAPING (3)
  Calcium Alginate Coating
  Surface Treatment in Acid
16. MISCELLANEOUS METHODS (4)
  Smoking Meat While Comminuting
  Pumping Meat Emulsion
17. HOT AIR COOKING (6)
  Static Air Heating
  Control of Humidity
18. COOKING IN LIQUID (3)
19. COOKING WITH HEAT EXCHANGER
20. ELECTRICAL COOKING (14)
  Forming and Cooking
  Forming Devices
  Skin-Forming and Dyeing
  Heating of Flowing Emulsion
21. RELEASING THE CASING (2)
22. REMOVING THE CASING (3)
23. FRESH PORK SAUSAGE (3)
24. DRY SAUSAGE (8)
  Buffered Humidity Zone
  Cellulose Casings
  Reduction of Drying Time
25. VARIOUS PRODUCTS (2)
  Continuous Method of Making Small Smoked Sausages
  Liver Sausage in Laminate Casing
26. NOVELTY PRODUCTS (2)
  Annular Sausages
  Multicolored Sausages

218 pages

$36

FLOCKED MATERIALS 1972
Technology and Applications
by E. L. Barden

Demand for flocked materials and articles covered with fibers or similar substances is increasing steadily. Fibers and flakes are used extensively to flock walls and ceilings, not only for decorative purposes, but also because the flocking soundproofs, waterproofs, acts as insulator, and is highly durable.

The flocked covering can vary between a heavy finish for a plush toy and a short finish to simulate suede or velvet on greeting cards or on the insides of an automobile. Synthetic turfs and storage battery plates are readily made by flocking procedures. Good quality carpeting can be produced rapidly and in enormous quantities in contrast to traditional carpet weaving.

The book describes 111 processes from U.S. patents. Partial Table of Contents showing examples:

1. ELECTROSTATIC PROCESSES (23)
  Production of Flocked Articles
  Production of Piled Fabrics
  Production of Flocked Filaments
2. MECHANICAL FLOCKING (4)
  Flexible Vibrator
  Suction
  Supersonic Compression
  Pneumatic Vibrator
3. TYPES OF FLOCK (3)
  Crimpable Fibers
  Hollow Filaments
  Long Curled Filaments
4. FLOCK TREATMENTS (8)
  Silica & Magnesium Oxide
  Antistatic Agents
  Tannins and Antimony
  Amphoteric Compounds
  Titanium Dioxide
  Diallyl Ammonium Polymers
  Quaternary Ammonium Compounds
5. ADHESIVES (13)
  Water-Insoluble Polymers
  Diisocyanate-Modified Polymer
  Latex Foam
  N-Methylol Polyether
  Acrylic Melamine
  Alkyl Acrylate

Pressure-Sensitive Adhesive
Binding Nonwovens
Fluorescent Adhesive
Reactive Diamine
Polyolefins
Aminoplast
Aminoplast & Catalyst

6. DECORATIVE EFFECTS (12)
  Patterning with Air Jets
  Multicolored Design
  Iron-On Design
  Panne Effect
  Varied Textures
  Patterning with Flock Solvent
  Dyed Flock Design
  On Polyester
  On Cellulose Fabric
  Beading Designs
  Opacifying Nonwovens
  Flock Granule Pattern
7. WEARING APPAREL (16)
  Garment Fabrics
  Shoes
  Hats
  Hosiery
  Rubber Gloves
8. HOME FURNISHINGS (11)
  Floor Coverings & Carpets
  Bedding & Blankets
  Other Materials
9. AUTOMOBILE MANUFACTURE (7)
  Floor Coverings
  Thick Pile Density
  Window Channel Strips
  Upholstery
  Stretchable Suede
10. OTHER APPLICATIONS (14)
  Battery Plates
  Colored Pictures
  Electrical Insulators
  Golf Greens
  Paint Rollers
  Paper Towels
  Wall Flocking
  Paneling

294 pages

$36

ANTISTATIC AGENTS 1972
Technology and Applications
by K. Johnson

Antistatic agents are used in plastics such as phonograph records, bottles, and film wraps to reduce pickup of dust and dirt.

In the textile industry, charged fibers interfere with the spinning process, and the attraction of dust particles produces marks and soiling in weaving. The clinging tendencies of garments and the electrical shocks experienced when walking on dry carpets are familiar to everyone.

Antistatic agents described in 160 U.S. patents since 1965 are covered in this book with specific sections devoted to two large volume applications—Plastics and Textiles. Partial Table of Contents showing examples:

1. POLYOLEFINS (27 processes)
   Polyethylene Plastics Treatment
   Polypropylene Plastics Treatment
   Polystyrene Plastics Treatment

2. RECORDS & FILMS (17)
   Polyvinyl Chloride Phonograph Records
   Cellulose Triacetate Photographic Applications
   Other Photographic Applications
   Acrylics
   Miscellaneous Plastics

3. FIBERS & FABRICS TREATMENT (29)
   Nylon Treatment
   Polyester Treatment
   Nylon Yarn Finishes
   Lubricants
   Polyesters in General

4. FURTHER FIBERS AND FABRICS TREATMENT (27)
   Polyacrylonitrile Treatments in General
   Polyacrylonitrile Yarns
   Lubricants for Polyacrylonitriles
   Polypropylene Treatments
   Polyethylene Treatments
   General Treatments

5. TECHNIQUES OF TREATMENT (22)
   Polyamines
   Other Nitrogen-Containing Compounds
   Phosphorus-Containing Compounds
   Silicones
   Other Antistatic Agents

6. SOFTENER & LUBRICANT FORMULATIONS (20)
   Yarn Treatments
   Lubricants
   Miscellaneous

7. OTHER APPLICATIONS—SYNTHESES (18)
   Fuels
   Miscellaneous Applications
   Syntheses of Antistatics in General

To indicate the detailed information given in the book, a breakdown of Chapter 5 follows:

Polyalkylene Glycol-Polyamines Reacted with N,N'-Methylenebis(acrylamide)
Water-Soluble Oxide-Containing Polyamine-Epoxide Reaction Products
Polyamine-Polyalkoxy Addition Products and Epoxy Curatives (2)
Hydrazinium Hydroxypolyalkoxy Alkylenediamines
Aziridine Compounds from Ethylenimine and Organic Halides
Fatty Acid Esters, Amide-Amine Reaction Products
Polymeric Quaternary Ammonium Compounds
Polyamide, Halogenated Polyoxyalkylene and Epihalohydrin Reaction Products
Quaternary Ammonium Carbamate
Fatty Esters of N-Hydroxyalkylpyrrolidone
Zwitterions of 1-(2-Aminoethylimidazolines)
Cyclic Imide Addition Products with Incidental Biocidal Properties
Polyoxazines
Amine Salts of 2-Carboxyalkyl Alkylphosphonic Acids
N-Alkyl-Substituted Phosphoric Amides
Polymeric Quaternary Phosphorus Compounds
Sulfopropylated Organofunctional Siloxanes
Siloxane-Oxyalkylene Block Copolymers Containing SiH
Copolymers of Alkali Metal Ethylene Sulfonates
Ethylene Methacrylyl Chloride Copolymers
Polyglycolacrylate-Epoxy Copolymers

307 pages

$36

RIGID FOAM LAMINATES 1972
by M. G. Halpern

It is estimated that the output of foamed polymers will more than double in the next few years. By 1975 the U.S. production of urethane polymers, for example, is expected to approach 2,000 million pounds annually. One third of this will be in the form of rigid foams. The development and utilization of rigid, foamed materials in the building and construction industry is constantly increasing. These foamed composites have excellent insulative properties, are themselves of low density, but at the same time exhibit good strength-to-weight ratios, and if needed, can be molded to any desired shape.

This book concerns itself with processes for the manufacture of rigid foam laminates, in which the foam cores are bonded to a great variety of outer coatings. Most processes involve the plastic foams, but other expanded materials are discussed also. Included too, are important techniques for strengthening and reinforcing the foam cores.

Additional processes deal with specific applications of these foam laminates for making refrigerated cars, insulated containers and packaging materials, as well as their utilization in roofing composites, acoustical panels and other building components.

Describes 134 processes based on U.S. patents. The information included can be deduced from the partial Table of Contents where the numbers in parentheses indicate how many processes are covered in each area. Examples are shown for each chapter. Also contains company, author, and patent number indexes which will help you make the greatest use of the information.

1. CHEMICAL PROCESSES FOR THE PREPARATION OF PLASTIC FOAMS (7)
   Polyurethanes
   Polystyrenes
   Polyolefins

2. NONPLASTIC EXPANDED MATERIALS (5)

3. PLASTIC SKIN-PLASTIC FOAM LAMINATES (15)
   Foam and Skin from One Plastic Sheet
   Nonspecific Foam Cores
   Foamed Polystyrene Cores
   Foamed Polyvinyl Chloride Cores
   Other Cores

4. POLYURETHANE FOAM COMPOSITIONS (10)
   Plastic Facings with Polyurethane Foam Cores
   Other Processes Involving Polyurethane Foams

5. NONPLASTIC SKIN AND FOAMED PLASTIC CORE LAMINATES (9)
   Metal-Foam Laminates
   Asbestos-Foam Laminate
   Glass-Foam Laminates
   Wood-Wool-Foam Laminates
   Nonspecific Skin-Foam Laminates

6. PAPER-FOAM COMPOSITIONS (6)

7. CONTAINERS AND PACKAGING MATERIALS (9)

8. REFRIGERATED CONTAINERS (9)
   Door and Wall Panels for Refrigerated Cars
   Floor Panels for Refrigerated Cars
   Insulated Cabinets
   Insulation for Cryogenic Temperatures

9. ACOUSTICAL PANELS (5)

10. ROOFING APPLICATIONS (12)
    Roofs
    Skylights

11. OTHER STRUCTURAL PANELS (14)
    Concrete Form Boards
    Fire Retardant Panels
    Door and Wall Panels
    Unusual Cores

12. INTERNAL REINFORCEMENTS (12)
    Metal Reinforcements
    Fibrous Reinforcements
    Paper Reinforcements
    Strengthening Edges

13. ADHESIVE TECHNIQUES (8)

14. EMBOSSING & DECORATING (4)

15. MISCELLANEOUS PROCESSES (9)
    In Situ Foaming

271 pages

$36

OPTICAL BRIGHTENERS 1972
Technology and Applications
by T. Rubel

Optical brighteners are defined as fluorescent dyes that have the property of absorbing ultraviolet radiant energy and emitting energy in the visible range. The emission is usually in the green, blue, or blue-violet regions, but can also be toward the red region. To the unaided human eye the fluorescence in itself is not noticeable. However, its presence has the effect of "brightening" colors or making whites "white". This property can be turned into the very useful purpose of imparting a brighter or whiter appearance to a variety of materials.

Since this book is intended primarily as a practical one, its arrangement emphasizes the applications of the brighteners rather than their chemical nature, although methods of synthesis are given throughout the volume. Much attention and detail is spent on the question of just how compatible and stable a brightener is in relation to a given polymer or other material.

The book is based on 136 U.S. patents issued since January 1965. Partial contents include:

1. OPTICAL BRIGHTENERS ADDED TO NATURAL MATERIALS (6 Processes)
   Fluorescent Brightening Agents of the Pyrazoline, Stilbene, Coumarin, and Triazine Types for Wool and Silk Fibers
   Pyridotriazole Brighteners in Weft Straightening During Weaving

2. TO SYNTHETIC POLYMERS (52 Processes)
   Pyrazolo[3,4b]quinoline Compounds for Polyesters and Cellulose Acetates
   Pyrazolylnaphthalimides for Polyamides, Polyacrylonitriles, Polyesters, Cellulose Acetates
   Brighteners Containing Groups Capable of Reacting with Synthetic Polymers esp. Polyamides, Polyurethanes, Polyesters
   4,4'-Dibenzoxazol-2-ylstilbene for Polyethylenes and Polypropylenes

3. TO NATURAL AND SYNTHETIC SUBSTANCES, SINGLY OR IN COMBINATION (42 Processes)
   Bis[triazinylamino]stilbenesulfonic Acid Compounds for Paper, Wool, Synthetic Polyamides
   4,4'-Bis[4,6-di(chloroanilino)-s-triazin-2-ylamino]-2,2'-stilbenedisulfonic Acid for Cottons, Polyesters, Mixtures
   Bis[β-hydroxyethylsulfonylphenylaminotriazinyl]stilbenes for Wool, Silk, Synthetic Protein Fibers, Cotton, Hemp, Linen, Synthetic Polymers, Leather, and Paper

4. TO DETERGENTS (8 Processes)
   Chlorinated Stilbenenaphthotriazoles Stable to Chlorine Bleaches
   sym.-1,2-(5-Methylbenzoxazolyl) ethylene in Dispersion for Nylon and Dacron
   Graying Inhibitors for Semi-Synthetic Textiles

5. TO FABRIC SOFTENERS (5 Processes)
   4,4'-Bis[anilino-6-[N-(3-aminopropyl)diethanolamino]-1,3,5'triazin-2-yl]amino]stilbene-2,2'-disulfonic Acid to Maintain Brightness After Softening Treatment

6. BRIGHTENERS FOR PAPERS AND PHOTOGRAPHIC MATERIALS (19 Processes)
   Sugar-Containing Brightening Agent for Diazotype Heat Process
   Compositions of Hydrophobic Polymers and Nonmigrating Optical Brighteners
   Cycloalkylamine Substituted Stilbenes Applied to Sulfite Pulps

7. OTHERS (4)

280 pages

$36

FOOD GUIDE TO EUROPE 1972
Second Edition

This greatly expanded second edition of the "Food Guide to Europe" describes approximately 1,500 of the leading food processing companies located in eighteen countries of Western Europe.

Where available and pertinent, the following information is given:

Name	Number of Employees
Address	Plant Locations
Telephone Number	Principal Executives
Telex Number	Products
Ownership	Domestic Subsidiaries
Sales	Foreign Subsidiaries

For easy reference companies are arranged alphabetically under the following eighteen country headings:

Austria	Italy
Belgium	Luxembourg
Denmark	Netherlands
Finland	Norway
France	Portugal
Germany	Spain
Greece	Sweden
Iceland	Switzerland
Ireland	United Kingdom

In addition to the information on companies, each chapter includes a short resume of the food industry in the country concerned, giving the salient features of the industry and production and trade statistics.

The food processing industry of Western Europe, while not as advanced as that of the United States, has been developing rapidly in recent years. It is now true that the manufacture of processed foods in Europe can be considered a substantial growth industry.

In some European countries extensive consolidation has resulted in sections of the industry being controlled by a small number of large groups which can take advantage of the latest food processing techniques. In other countries the more traditional pattern of family firms has been maintained. This book will help you to understand this complex and diverse market.

"Food Guide to Europe" concentrates on the most important food companies, those firms which have the most to offer in the way of sales contracts, licensing arrangements, joint ventures, and research and development know-how. It will help you to increase sales, concentrate on the important buyers, plan joint ventures, make licensing arrangements, contact company officials, prepare market reports, and talk intelligently about the European food processing industry.

This book was prepared in our London office. Our London office is a focal point for the gathering of commercial intelligence regarding European processing industries.

325 pages

$24

ENZYMES IN FOOD PROCESSING AND PRODUCTS 1972
by H. Wieland
Food Processing Review No. 23

Commercial availability of enzymes has increased considerably. Enzymes applicable to food processing are now plentiful, and the alert food processor is urged not to miss this opportunity to improve his products in many ways. 101 Processes. The numbers in ( ) indicate the number of processes allocated to each topic.

FRUIT & VEGETABLE PROCESSING (13)
STARCH & SUGAR CONVERSION (9)
BAKED GOODS APPLICATIONS (12)
CHEESE MAKING (11)
MEAT TENDERIZATION (18)
SPECIAL APPLICATIONS (13)
FLAVORS THROUGH ENZYMES (13)
DEOXYGENATING AND DESUGARING (6)
ENZYME STABILIZATION (6)

269 pages. **$36**

SEAFOOD PROCESSING 1971
by M. Gillies
Food Processing Review No. 22

Describes 84 processes based on U.S. patents issued since 1960. Numbers in ( ) denotes numbers of processes in each chapter.

1. PRESERVATION (13)
   On Fishing Vessels
   Chemical Methods
   Edible Coatings
   Various Preservatives
2. CANNING PROCEDURES
   Tuna and Similar Fish
   Sardines
   Forestalling Struvite
3. PROTEIN CONCENTRATES (14)
   Mechanical Means
   Chemical Means
   Biological Means
   Stickwater Proteins
4. MOLLUSKS & SHELLFISH (18)
   Squid
   Bivalves
   Crustaceans
5. CONSUMER PRODUCTS (17)
6. ANIMAL FOODS (11)

206 pages. **$36**

FRUIT PROCESSING 1971
by M. Gutterson
Food Processing Review No. 21

All 140 processes (mostly developed since 1960) were selected with the purpose of providing fruits and fruit products retaining the characteristics of freshly picked fruit, yet capable of being shipped the world over and being highly acceptable by organoleptic tests. Preventing the growth of microorganisms with a minimum of chemicals and processing equipment was another goal.

1. GENERAL TECHNIQUES (34 processes)
   Heat Treatments, Increasing Cellular Permeability, Inhibiting Discoloration, Ripening, Dehydration
2. TREATMENT OF POMES (23)
3. CITRUS FRUITS (18)
4. BERRIES (20)
5. DRUPES (16)
6. DRIED FRUITS (10)
7. OTHER FRUITS (19)
   Flavor Improvement, Delaying Senescence, Use of Enzymes and Freezing Techniques. 223 pages. **$36**

POULTRY PROCESSING 1971
by G. H. Weiss
Food Processing Review No. 20

Poultry is the most efficient and effective means for converting grain to protein. This book discusses in detail the different methods devised to assure excellent flavor, texture and tenderness concomitant with easy preservation, maximum storage time, easy handling, and consumer acceptance. 55 processes in 8 chapters:

1. **Preservation (11 processes)**
2. **Chilling and Freezing (6)**
3. **Enhancing Palatability (10)**
4. **Stuffed Products (3)**
5. **Molded Rolls and Loaves (19)**
6. **Batter-Coated Products (2)**
7. **Cooking Procedures (2)**
8. **Poultry Concentrates (2)**

168 pages. **$24**

VEGETABLE PROCESSING 1971
by M. Gutterson
Food Processing Review No. 19

Shipping vegetables from one continent to another has become a normal means of supply. But such transporting is possible only by adequate processing of the perishable vegetable goods. Many of the 184 process descriptions in this book are concerned with just such treatments. Processes for improving the stability of vegetables in regard to time, temperature and moisture are numerous. So are those where the emphasis is in making vegetables more digestible and more acceptable to children and adults:

1. **General (27 processes)**
2. **Potatoes (59)**
3. **Other Roots (12)**
4. **Bulbs (13)**
5. **Leaves & Stems (8)**
6. **Tomatoes & Others (30)**
7. **Corn (6)**
8. **Legumes (23)**
9. **Olives & Mushrooms (6)**

335 pages. **$36**

FLAVOR TECHNOLOGY 1971
by Dr. N. D. Pintauro

Scientific and trade journals contain only limited information on practical and applied flavor research and technology. Industry and commercial operators wish to keep such information confidential. This book reviews such technology from U.S. patents since 1960. There are 99 processes in 9 chapters:

1. **Spice Technology** (11)
2. **Peppermint & Citrus** (11)
3. **Fruit Essences** (9)
4. **Dairy Flavors** (6)
5. **Bread Flavors** (8)
6. **Vanilla** (9)
7. **Meat Flavors** (17)
8. **Meat Seasonings** (10)
9. **Fixation** (18)

228 pages. **$35**

CONFECTIONARY PRODUCTS MANUFACTURING PROCESSES 1969
by M. Gutterson
Food Processing Review No. 6

This book is of technological significance in that it details over 200 processes for producing confections, based on the U.S. patent literature since 1960.

Based solely on new technology, this book offers substantial manufacturing information relating to this field. The wide scope of detailed data can be seen by the chapter headings indicated below:

Candy
Chocolate Products
Whipped Products
Icings
Gels
Coatings and Glazes
Gums and Stabilizers
Egg Products
Marshmallows and Meringues
Puddings
Frozen Confections
Chewing Gum
Other Confections
Indexes

Illustrations. 321 pages. **$35**

EDIBLE OILS AND FATS 1969
by Dr. N. E. Bednarcyk
Food Processing Review No. 5

This book describes in detail 225 recent process developments.

Shortenings; Fluid, Plastic, Miscellaneous: Margarine and Spreads; Margarine Oils, Highly Nutritional Oil Blends, Antispattering Agents, Fluid and Whipped Margarines, Flavor, Color, and Texture Modifications, Low Calorie Spreads: Salad Oils, Mayonnaise and Emulsified Dressings; Crystallization Inhibitors, Emulsified Dressings, Flavored Salad Oils, Low Calorie Dressings: Frying and Cooking Oils; Equipment, Breakdown Inhibitors, Antispattering Additives, Other Additives: Hard Butters; Preparation by Fractional Crystallization, Preparation by Ester Exchange, Miscellaneous: Oil Processing; Antioxidants and Stabilizers; Emulsifiers and Emulsions; Mixed Ester Emulsifiers, Dried Emulsion, Miscellaneous: Peanut Butter and Spreads; Chocolate Products; Indexes. Illustrations. 404 pages. **$35**

SNACKS AND FRIED PRODUCTS 1969
by Dr. A. Lachmann
Food Processing Review No. 4

The sales of snack foods in the U.S. may reach the two billion dollar mark in 1969. Many companies are actively working on new snack foods or on improved processes. The patent literature on french fried potatoes, potato chips, corn chips and other crisps is continually growing and it is the purpose of this book to present this literature in easy readable form.

French fried potatoes and their methods of production are described in the second chapter. The next chapter deals with potato chips, still the most popular product of the snack food industry. The U.S. market for potato chips is estimated to be approximately 600 million dollars in 1969. In Chapter Four the processes for corn chips are covered; in Chapter Five, apple crisps. Chapter Six describes processes for expanded chips and some specialty items; and the last chapter deals with batter mixes. Many illustrations. 181 pages. **$35**

PROTEIN FOOD SUPPLEMENTS 1969
by R. Noyes
Food Processing Review No. 3

The 126 Processes in this book are organized in 8 chapters by raw material source including the important newer processes for producing protein by fermentation of hydrocarbons. Another chapter on textured foods describes in detail a number of processes for producing these products that simulate meat. Indexes by company, inventors and patent number help in providing easily obtainable information.

This book is based upon the patent literature and serves a double purpose in that it supplies detailed technical information and can be used as a guide to the U.S. Patent literature on processes to obtain protein materials.

Contents: Hydrocarbon Fermentation, Fish-Based Protein, Soybeans, Cottonseed, Other Oilseeds and Legumes, Wheat and Gluten, Milk-Based Protein, Textured Foods, Miscellaneous, Indexes. Many illustrations. 412 pages. **$35**

DEHYDRATION PROCESSES FOR CONVENIENCE FOODS 1969
by R. Noyes
Food Processing Review No. 2

Describes 236 up-to-date dehydration processes for producing specific foods. Most detailed body of information ever published.

The detailed, descriptive process information in this book is based on 236 U.S. patents in the food dehydration field—issued between January 1960 and May 1968. This book serves a double purpose in that it supplies detailed technical information, and can be used as a guide to the U.S. patent literature on dehydration of foods. By indicating only information that is significant, and eliminating much of the legal jargon in the patents; this book then becomes an advanced commercially oriented review of food dehydration processes.

Dry Milk Products, Cheese and Yoghurt, Eggs, Fruit and Vegetable Juices, Fruits, Potatoes, Vegetables, Coffee, Tea, Miscellaneous. Many illustrations. 367 pages. **$35**

ALCOHOLIC MALT BEVERAGES 1969
by M. Gutcho
Food Processing Review No. 7

157 Patent-based processes in the brewing field: Malting, Wort, Hops, Fermentation, Freeze Concentration and Reconstitution of Beer, Chillproofing, Preservation against Microbiological Spoilage, Foam, Indexes. 333 pages. **$35**

FREEZE DRYING OF FOODS AND BIOLOGICALS 1968
by R. Noyes
Food Processing Review No. 1

The descriptive process information in this book is based on 105 U. S. patents in the freeze drying field—issued between January 1960 and May 1968. Supplies detailed technical information, and can be used as a guide to the patent literature on freeze drying. 313 pages. **$35**

MILK, CREAM AND BUTTER TECHNOLOGY 1971
by G. Wilcox
Food Processing Review No. 18

In these days of heightened consumer awareness, the alert dairy processor cannot afford to bypass the latest developments in his field. Much emphasis now is on modified milk products which contain numerous proteins of high nutritional value. The even distribution of essential amino acids bestows on modified milk a great enticement for use with otherwise deficient diets. Methods for low sodium milk products, hypoallergenic dietary prepns. and infant milk products are given special attention. 181 Processes are described: 1. Pasteurization and Sterilization (15 processes). 2. Removal of Radioactive Contaminants (8). 3. Buttermilk and Allied Products (10). 4. Modified Milk Products (21). 5. Dehydration of Skim Milk (28). 6. Dehydration of Whole Milk, Whey and Milk Blends (47). 7. Concentrated Milk (19). 8. Cream (22). 9. Butter (11). 313 pages. **$35**

EGGS, CHEESE AND YOGURT PROCESSING 1971
by G. Wilcox
Food Processing Review No. 17

One route to discovering the latest technology is via this Food Processing Review which serves to bring you timely, useful information. Brought to you in this one easy-to-use, comprehensive volume is commercial research and development done in the field from 1960 to 1970, gathered from the U.S. patent literature.

The Table of Contents shows the processes discussed in this book. The numbers in parentheses indicate the number of processes covered for each particular process, equipment or product.

Section I—Eggs: Whole Eggs (18); Egg Yolks (7); Egg Whites (27); Egg Products (10). Section II—Cheese and Yogurt: Cottage Cheese (26); Cheddar Type and Process Cheeses (45); Cream Cheese and Bakers' Cheese (8); Mozzarella, Provolone and Parmesan Cheeses (8); Miscellaneous Cheese Processes (17); Manufacture of Yogurt (5).

280 pages. **$35**

RICE AND BULGUR QUICK-COOKING PROCESSES 1970
by R. Daniels
Food Processing Review No. 16

This salient report in our Food Processing Review series summarizes with detailed process information the pertinent U.S. patent literature relating to quick-cooking processes for both rice and bulgur. The information provides needed know-how concerning processing of raw rice and wheat to obtain the more desirable refined forms.

63 specific processes covered. The numbers in ( ) indicate their distribution.

Rice Milling—Extraction—Polishing (13)
Quick-Cooking Rice (17)
Special Rice Processes (6)
Brown and Parboiled Rice (6)
Specialty Products with Rice (9)
Quick-Cooking Wheat Bulgur Products (12)

267 pages. **$35**

STARCHES AND CORN SYRUPS 1970
by Dr. A. Lachmann

This report covers the field of starch production from many standpoints.

Wet milling is the primary method of starch production, therefore much of the material is concerned with this route to starch. Dry milling processes are also covered.

In addition, coverage of the current technological progress in hydrolyzing starches into dextrins, corn syrups and dextrose and starch fractionation into amylose is covered.

Contains 139 processes covering: The Manufacture of Starch, Treatment of Starch, Modified Starch, Pregelatinized Starch, Acid Hydrolysis of Starch to Sweeteners, Starch Hydrolyzing Enzymes, Enzymatic Starch Hydrolysates, Starch Hydrolysates Produced by Acid and Enzyme Treatments, Starch Fractionation. 275 pages. **$35**

FRESH MEAT PROCESSING 1970
by Dr. E. Karmas
Food Processing Review No. 12

This Food Processing Review, deals with 106 detailed processes covering essential developments in the fresh meat processing industry since 1960. The book provides a well-organized tour through the field; the processes included are well researched and presented as an easy-to-use guide to what is being done in this vital field today.

The material has been divided into two parts; processes for enhancing palatability, and preservation processes. The numbers in ( ) after each heading indicate the number of processes for each entry.

A. Palatability: Tenderness (33), Flavor and Tenderness (8), Flavoring (12), Color (13), Integral Texture (6). B. Preservation: Moisture Retention (9), Antimicrobial Treatment (10), Ionizing Radiation (7), Other Methods of Preservation (8). 236 pages. **$35**

SOLUBLE TEA PRODUCTION PROCESSES 1970
by Dr. N. Pintauro
Food Processing Review No. 11

This book describes production processes for producing soluble tea and offers a wealth of detailed practical information based primarily on the U.S. patent literature. Describes 73 specific processes in this field with substantial background information. The Table of Contents is listed below. The numbers in ( ) indicate the number of processes in that category.

Withering and Rolling (4)
Fermentation, Firing and Sorting (8)
Extraction (13)
Recovery of Aroma (10)
Tannin-Caffeine Precipitate (Cream) (15)
Filtration and Concentration (8)
Dehydration Process (6)
Agglomeration and Aromatization (9)

Illustrations. 183 pages. **$35**

FRUIT JUICE TECHNOLOGY 1970
by M. Gutterson
Food Processing Review No. 15

This publication deals with the technology of the noncarbonated fruit juice industry from 1960 through 1970 as covered in the U.S. patent literature. Modern technology has studied and overcome many processing problems, resulting in a vast output of new and improved processing methods. It is oftentimes difficult to keep up with the latest technology. This book is designed to offer you such help.

In the abbreviated Table of Contents shown below, you can see the large amount of valuable material included. The numbers in ( ) indicate the number of processes discussed.

1. Manufacturing Techniques (23), 2. Concentration of Fruit Juices (37), 3. Stabilization Processes (19), 4. Dehydration (18), 5. Freeze Drying (24), 6. Flavors from Fruit Juices (10), 7. Miscellaneous Processes (9).

206 pages. **$35**

MEAT PRODUCT MANUFACTURE 1970
by Dr. E. Karmas
Food Processing Review No. 14

This Review concerns latest technology in preparing packaged meats in ready-to-cook and ready-to-eat forms.

The Table of Contents below indicates the many areas covered in this survey.

General Processing: Curing Methods and Ingredients, Increased Water Binding and Yield, Improved Curing Formulations, Integral Meats, Smoking, Thermal Processing and Sterilization, Miscellaneous Processing Methods.

Products: Bacon Production, Patty Type Products, Dehydrated Convenience and Snack Products, Modified and Novel Products.

273 pages. **$35**

MODERN BREAKFAST CEREAL PROCESSES 1970
by R. Daniels
Food Processing Review No. 13

Describes in detail production processes and equipment for the manufacture of modern breakfast cereals. These include both ready-to-eat and quick-cooking products.

Offers detailed practical information for the manufacture and production of these cereal products based on the U.S. patent literature. 61 processes included. Abbreviated Table of Contents follows.

Dough Cooking and Extrusion Processes
Treatment Prior To Puffing
Puffing Processes
Processes For Whole Cereal Grains
Cereal Shaping Processes
Sugarcoating Process
Fruit Incorporation and Nutritional Enrichment
Quick Cooking Cereal Products

217 pages. **$35**

ANIMAL FEEDS 1970
by M. Gutcho
Food Processing Review No. 10

This is a significant work, based on the patent literature, that shows you how to prepare a wide variety of modern feed products from numerous sources. It discusses the use of many chemicals, additives, and supplements used for animal feeds.

The 278 processes covered in this book are listed in the Table of Contents below. The numbers in ( ) indicate the number of processes described under that heading.

Introduction; Forage and Fodder (32), Fats and Oils (21), Molasses and Flavoring (15), Estrogens as Growth Stimulators (17), Antibiotics as Anabolic Stimulators (33), Antioxidants in Feeds (6), Minerals and Vitamins (13), Growth-Promoting Chemical Additives (24), Poultry Feeds (40), Ruminant Feeds (23), Feed for Swine (10), Pet and Other Feeds (19), Feed Products from Industrial Waste and By-Products (25). Indexes. 350 pages. **$35**

BAKED GOODS PRODUCTION PROCESSES 1969
by M. Gutterson
Food Processing Review No. 9

This book describes 201 recent processes for the production of baked goods. Based on the patent literature, it offers an up-to-date comprehensive publication of manufacturing processes.

There is a substantial amount of information in this book relating to the use of various chemicals and related additives.

Contents: Bread, Yeast Leavened Products, Chemically Leavened Products, Leavening Agents, Air Leavened Products, Non-Leavened Products, Refrigerated Doughs, Emulsifiers and Dough Improvers, Miscellaneous, Indexes. Illustrations. 353 pages. **$35**

SOLUBLE COFFEE MANUFACTURING PROCESSES 1969
by Dr. N. Pintauro
Food Processing Review No. 8

This book describes significant manufacturing processes for producing soluble coffee, and offers a wealth of detailed practical information based primarily on the U.S. patent literature. Describes 114 specific processes in this field with substantial background information.

Introduction: Roasting, Extraction, Filtration and Concentration, Recovery of Aromatic Volatiles, Spray Drying and Other Dehydration Processes, Freeze Drying Processes, Aromatization of Soluble Coffee Powder, Agglomeration Techniques for Soluble Coffee, Decaffeinated Soluble Coffee, Packaging of Soluble Coffee. Illustrations, Indexes, 254 pages. **$35**

CHEMICAL PROCESSING

SULFURIC ACID MANUFACTURE AND EFFLUENT CONTROL 1971
by M. Sittig
Chemical Process Review No. 55

102 processes of manufacture and 39 pollution control measures are outlined in this encyclopedic survey:

SO_2 from Sulfur (11 processes)
SO_2 from Waste Gases (11)
SO_2 from Hydrogen Sulfide (2)
SO_2 from Sulfide Ores (8)
SOx and H_2SO_4 from Sulfates (12)
H_2SO_4 from SO_2 HC1 (2)
The Chamber Process (4)
Conversion of SO_2 to SO_3 (9)
SO_3 to H_2SO_4 and Oleum (5)
Integrated Contact Processes (14)
Unconventional Processes (2)
Concentration of H_2SO_4 (2)
Dilution of H_2SO_4 (1)
Purification of H_2SO_4 (2)
Recovery of Spent H_2SO_4 (17)
Removal and Recovery of SOx from Tail Gases (30)
Recovery of Acid Mists (9)
Future Trends

423 pages. **$48**

TRIMELLITIC ANHYDRIDE AND PYROMELLITIC DIANHYDRIDE 1971
by P. Stecher
Chemical Process Review No. 53

Trimellitic anhydride (TMA) being an anhydride and a carboxylic acid, can undergo many useful reactions; it can form esters and polyimides. Demand is rising sharply. Pyromellitic dianhydride (PMDA) yields polyimides and cured epoxy resins having very high temperature stability. This book gives 61 manufacturing processes and all the technology involved in making TMA and PMDA:

1. TM-Acid Synthesis (17)
2. TM-Acid Purification (3)
3. TMA Preparation (8)
4. TMA Purification (2)
5. TM-Double Anhydride (2)
6. PM-Acid Synthesis (6)
7. PMDA Preparation (5)
8. PMDA Purification (4)
9. Non-Hazardous Oxidations (1)
10. Derivatives of TMA & PMDA (13)

233 pages. **$35**

PHTHALOCYANINE TECHNOLOGY 1970
by Y. L. Meltzer
Chemical Process Review No. 42

Advances in phthalocyanine technology have been truly explosive during the past few years. New phthalocyanine products, processes and applications have poured forth from industrial, governmental and academic laboratories at a rapid pace. These advances in technology have made themselves felt in the market place and in government programs, and have contributed to corporate sales and profits. At the same time, however, competition has become more intense in the phthalocyanine field making it imperative to keep up with the latest technological advances.

Examines recent developments in phthalocyanine technology as reflected in U.S. patents and other literature. The first 23 chapters discuss up-to-date manufacturing processes for phthalocyanine pigments and dyes. Chapters 24 through 31 discuss unusual new applications for phthalocyanines. 390 pages. $35

SYNTHETIC PERFUMERY MATERIALS 1970
by M. Gutcho
Chemical Process Review No. 45

This Review shows you how to produce synthetic perfumery materials. It contains a valuable odor index.

The 152 U.S. patents included in this book are distributed among the 11 areas as shown below:

From Terpenic Materials (28)
Alcohols (11)
Esters (18)
Ethers (19)
Aldehydes (10)
Ketones (18)
Lactones, Pyrones, Substituted Phenols and Quinones (12)
Other Structures (7)
Naphthalene and Indene Derivatives (17)
Compounds with Scent of Ambergris or Irone (9)
Product Application (13)

273 pages. **$35**

ION EXCHANGE RESINS 1970
by C. Placek
Chemical Process Review No. 44

This report on ion exchange resins provides detailed information on 126 U.S. patents issued since 1960 concerning the composition and manufacture of ion exchange materials. This Review, by its organization, also provides a guide to these ion exchange resins by grouping them according to physical form, behavior characteristics, etc.

1. Anion Exchange Resins
2. Cation Exchange Resins
3. Resins For Removing Metals
4. Resins Having Mixed Properties
5. Specific Use Resins
6. Unconventional Materials
7. Process Emphasis
8. Properties of Ion Exchange
9. Ion Exchange Membranes
10. Emphasis on Shapes

329 pages. **$35**

RADIATION CHEMICAL PROCESSING 1969
by R. Whiting
Chemical Process Review No. 41

A number of radiation induced chemical processes are already operating commercially. The radiation processing of chemicals has been growing at an annual rate of about 25% per year. Currently, \$100 to 150 million worth of irradiated products are produced in the United States per year, however, it has been forecast that by 1980, the value of products receiving radiation treatment will be close to \$1,000 million per year.

This book surveys the radiation processing field and is based on the U.S. patent literature since 1960. Over 250 separate processes are described in detail in the chemical, polymer, rubber, petroleum, textile and other fields.

Contents: Polyolefins, Other Polymers, Elastomers, Hydrocarbons, Organic Chemicals, Inorganic and Organo-Metallic Compounds, Other Processes, Indexes. 377 pages. **$35**

CHEMICAL PROCESSING

PHOTOCHEMICAL PROCESSES 1969
by B. Albertson
Chemical Process Review No. 36

Describes 210 photochemical production processes in detail.

Introduction, Photohalogenation, Photonitrosation, Organic Photochemical Reactions, Inorganic Photochemical Reactions, Photopolymerization, Indexes. Illustrations. 185 pages. **$35**

CHLORINE AND CAUSTIC SODA MANUFACTURE RECENT DEVELOPMENTS 1969
by Dr. R. Powell
Chemical Process Review No. 33

Brine Electrolysis
Diaphragm and Mercury Cells
Recovery of Mercury
NaOH Production
Titanium Anodes
Sea Water Electrolysis
Cl_2 Production
Deacon Process Modifications
Numerous Illustrations,
48 processes, 265 pages. **$35**

ALKALI METAL PHOSPHATES 1969
by Dr. M. W. Ranney
Chemical Process Review No. 34

The 97 processes described are based on U.S. patents issued since 1960 and offer a comprehensive treatment of up-to-date technical information.

Contents: Orthophosphates, Metaphosphates, Pyrophosphates, Tripolyphosphates, Phosphites/Hypophosphites.

Numerous illustrations. 344 pages. **$35**

AMINES, NITRILES AND ISOCYANATES PROCESSES AND PRODUCTS 1969
by M. Sittig
Chemical Process Review No. 31

Material covered includes: Manufacture of Amines, Manufacture of Mono-Nitriles, Acrylonitrile Derivatives, Isocyanate Manufacture, Future Trends. 62 illustrations. 201 pages. **$35**

NITRIC ACID TECHNOLOGY RECENT DEVELOPMENTS 1969
by Dr. R. Powell
Chemical Process Review No. 30

Ammonia Oxidation Process, Wisconsin Thermal Process, Nitrogen Fixation by Shock Waves, Nitrogen Fixation in a Nuclear Reactor, Absorption of Nitrogen Oxides in Water, Concentration of Dilute Nitric Acid Solutions, Direct Production of Concentrated Nitric Acid, Purification of Nitric Acid, Stabilizers for Nitric Acid. Numerous illustrations. 245 pages. **$35**

CITRIC ACID PRODUCTION PROCESSES 1969
by R. Noyes
Chemical Process Review No. 37

Detailed descriptions of production processes for citric acid, based on the patent literature.

The Table of Contents is indicated below:

Processing, Iron Impurities Other Microorganisms, Recovery and Purification, Other Processes. Indexes. 157 pages. **$24**

CARBON BLACK TECHNOLOGY RECENT DEVELOPMENTS 1968
by Dr. R. Powell
Chemical Process Review No. 21

Introduction; Feedstocks, Channel Blacks, Furnace Blacks, Thermal Blacks, Acetylene Blacks, High Structure Carbon Blacks, Low Structure Carbon Blacks, Unconventional Processes, Carbon Black Pelletizing, Other Finishing Treatments. Numerous illustrations. 242 pages. **$35**

ELECTRO-ORGANIC CHEMICAL PROCESSING 1968
by Dr. C. Mantell
Chemical Process Review No. 14

This volume has been written from the viewpoint of the chemical engineer, with emphasis on plant processes, operating data, and plant design. The commercial successes in this field have been attained by the chemical engineering approach. 186 pages. **$35**

AROMATICS MANUFACTURE AND DERIVATIVES 1968
by M. Sittig
Chemical Process Review No. 17

Contents: Introduction, Production of Aromatics, Separation of Aromatics, Purification of Aromatics, Reactions giving Hydrocarbon Products, Other Reactions, Phenol Production, Styrene Manufacture and Derivatives, Future Trends. 73 illustrations. 232 pages. **$35**

CATALYSTS AND CATALYTIC PROCESSES 1967
by M. Sittig
Chemical Process Review No. 7

Contents: Hydrocarbon Conversion Processes, Hydrocarbon Polymerization Processes, Hydrocarbon Oxidation Processes, Future Trends. 109 illustrations. 303 pages. **$35**

SUGAR ESTERS 1968
by Research Corporation

Already approved for use in foods in a number of countries, use of sugar esters in food in the United States awaits FDA clearance.

Sugar esters are an important new raw material for the food industry.

Contains papers presented at California Symposium 1967. 134 pages. **$15**

INDUSTRIAL GASES MANUFACTURE AND APPLICATIONS 1967
by M. Sittig
Chemical Process Review No. 4

This book discusses conventional cryogenic air separation and purification techniques in considerable detail.

This book also discusses newer techniques such as adsorption using molecular sieves, and permeation using various membrane materials. 313 pages. 103 illustrations. **$35**

POLYMERS AND ADHESIVES

POLYMER ADDITIVES GUIDEBOOK AND DIRECTORY 1972
Blue Book No. 1

Perhaps the most comprehensive listing of commercially available, protective additives ever offered to the plastics industry. Gives products of 86 U.S. manufacturers arranged according to company name. Each product is carefully indexed by chemical, generic, trivial, and trade name or registered trademark in the "one alphabet" index at the end of the book.

Abounds with antioxidants and stabilizers plus countless other protective aids. By listing the intended uses and physical properties, as well as the manufacturers and suppliers, this book intends to furnish a real service to the advancing polymer technology.

The data appearing in this book were selected by the publisher from manufacturers' literature at no cost to, nor influence from the manufacturers of the materials. 472 pages. **$36**

SEALING AND POTTING COMPOUNDS 1972
by J. A. Szilard

Sealing and potting compounds are used to protect against ingress or egress of liquids or gases. In most cases the desired protection is against the penetration of moisture. Describes 166 sealant manufacturing processes based on polymer technology including silicones.

Products intended for:
General Use
Soil Treatment
Highways and Runways
Building Construction
Aircraft Construction
Pipe Joint Sealing
Automotive Use
Shoemaking
Swimming Pool & Aquarium Sealing
Shafts & Stuffing Boxes
Carton & Container Sealing
Electrical & Electronic Instruments

Also discusses special sealants for extremely high and low temperatures, lubricating sealants, encapsulants for printed and high frequency circuits, and many more. 288 pages. **$36**

REINFORCED COMPOSITES FROM POLYESTER RESINS 1972
by Dr. M. W. Ranney

1. POLYESTER INTERMEDIATES
   Hydroxy Intermediates (9)
   Carboxylic Acids-Anhydrides (14)
   Diels-Alder Adducts (8)
   Others (10)
2. ADDITIVES
   Catalysts (9)
   Accelerators-Promoters (12)
   Inhibitors (12)
   Thickeners (16)
   Color Controllers (10)
   Miscellaneous (3)
3. FLAME RETARDANTS
   Acid-Anhydrides (9)
   Hydroxy Intermediates (6)
   Other Reactants (16)
4. FORMULATIONS
   Acrylics (3)
   Nitrogen Compounds (4)
   Other Thermoplastics (6)
   Reactive Solvents (4)
   Low Profile Shrinkage (3)
5. PROCESSING
   Glass Fiber Treating (4)
   Other Processes (8)

166 Patent-based Processes on 324 pages. **$36**

PLASTIC PRINTING PLATES MANUFACTURE AND TECHNOLOGY 1971
by M. G. Halpern

Shows easy adaptation to traditional letterpress practice and automated equipment for plastic 3-dimensional relief plates.

1. PHOTOPOLYMERIZED PRINTING PLATES (2)
2. CELLULOSE POLYMERS (5)
3. OTHER POLYMERS (6)
4. ANCHOR LAYERS (6)
5. PHOTOINITIATORS (10)
6. MODIFICATIONS (22)
   Afterexposure Treatments
   Calendering Aids
   Speed & Contrast Aids
   Increasing Sensitivity
7. PHOTOCHEMICAL CROSSLINKING (9)
8. POLYAMIDE PLATES (12)
   Sensitizers
   Photomechanical Processes
9. PHOTOREPRODUCTION LAYERS (20)
10. INTAGLIO IMAGES AND ETCHABLE PLASTIC PLATES (7)
11. MOLDED PLATES (4)

294 pages. **$36**

VINYL AND ACRYLIC ADHESIVES INCLUDING PRESSURE SENSITIVES 1971
by K. Johnson

Includes 123 processes.

1. ACRYLICS (51)
   Pressure Sensitives
   Laminates
   Tire Cord Adhesives
   Anaerobics
2. POLYVINYL ACETATE (14)
   Hot Melts
   Wood Bonding
3. POLYVINYL ALCOHOL (10)
   Paper and Corrugated Board
   Water-Soluble Pressure Sensitives
   Cement Compositions
4. ETHYLENE COPOLYMERS (13)
   Hot Melts
   Atactic Polypropylene
5. OTHER VINYL POLYMERS (25)
   Iron-On Adhesives
   Fabric Bonding
   Pressure Sensitive Phenol-Aldehyde Resins
6. PRESSURE SENSITIVE TAPES (10)
   Release Coatings

287 pages. **$36**

FLEXIBLE FOAM LAMINATES 1971
by M. McDonald

Reviews the U.S. patent literature on the technology of flexible foam laminates from 1960 through early 1971. Altogether 101 processes in 6 chapters. In 1970 about 75 million pounds of polyurethane foam in the U.S. alone were bonded, mostly to fabrics, to form flexible laminates.

1. THERMAL METHODS (16 processes)
2. ADHESIVE METHODS (15)
3. FOAM-IN-PLACE METHODS (19)
4. FABRIC TO FOAM (17)
5. FLOOR COVERINGS (14)
6. MISCELLANEOUS (20)
   Packaging Materials, Foam on Cardboard, Sealing Strips, Sound Insulation, Polyester Foam Laminates, Polypropylene Foam to Metal, Deforming Foam Surfaces, Stretchable Foam Laminates.

265 pages. **$36**

COATINGS

POLYURETHANE COATINGS 1972
by K. Johnson

Reviews 157 U.S. patents issued mostly since 1960 related to paint vehicles, wet look, highly glossy fabric coatings, microporous products, etc.

1. COATING VEHICLES
   Isocyanates (9 processes)
   Carboxyl, Polyols (16)
   Modified Resins (13)
   Aqueous Systems (9)
   Catalysts & Crosslinking (5)
   Miscellaneous (17)
2. MICROPOROUS MATERIALS
   Solvent Processes (22)
   Pore-Forming Agents (9)
   Suede Substitutes (3)
   Others (3)
3. COATED FABRICS & PAPERS
   Water Repellency & Ability to Dryclean (8)
   Coated Fabrics (13)
   Papers (3)
4. MAGNETIC TAPES & OTHER SUBSTRATES
   Magnetic Tapes (6)
   Wire Coatings (3)
   Other Applications (18)

338 pages. **$36**

POWDER COATINGS AND FLUIDIZED BED TECHNIQUES 1971
by Dr. M. W. Ranney

Describes 166 processes. Due to the actuality of the subject all have been developed very recently. Numbers in ( ) indicate number of processes per chapter.

1. FLUIDIZED BED—SPRAY-POURING TECHNIQUES (27)
   Fluidized Bed Designs
   Spray-Powder, etc.
2. ELECTROSTATIC PROCESSES (8)
3. EPOXIES (19)
   Curing Agents
   Modified Epoxies
   Powdering Techniques
4. POLYOLEFINS (10)
   Primers & Surface Treatment
   Use of Copolymers
5. VINYLS (6)
6. OTHER RESINS (10)
7. PIPE COATINGS (28)
8. ELECTRICAL COMPONENTS (19)
9. OTHER APPLICATIONS (24)
10. INORGANIC & PARTICLE COATINGS (15)

249 pages. **$36**

PAPER COATINGS BASED ON POLYMERS 1971
by K. Johnson

178 Processes for coating paper stock elaborated during the last 10 years. Pigment binder and barrier coatings are discussed in detail e.g. acrylics give high gloss and good ink holdout, while silicone and solvent-based coatings allow considerable latitude in formulations.

1. POLYETHYLENE ETHYLENE COPOLYMERS—HOT MELTS (34 processes)
2. POLYVINYLIDENE CHLORIDE BARRIER COATINGS (10)
3. WATER-SOLUBLE COATINGS (30)
4. STYRENE-BUTADIENE ETHYLENE-PROPYLENE LATICES (27)
5. VINYL ACETATE LATICES (13)
6. ACRYLIC LATICES (23)
7. SILICONE AND SOLVENT-BASED COATINGS (24)
8. SPECIALTY COATINGS (17)
   Photographic Paper Coatings, Opaque Coatings, Metallized Coatings, Chemical Watermark Paper, Coatings for Erasable Paper, Mulch Sheets.

313 pages. **$36**

WIRE COATINGS 1971
by D. J. De Renzo

The good insulating properties of many thermoplastic and thermosetting polymers make them suitable for coating wires to be used as conductors in electrical apparatus. Other properties include abrasion resistance, impact strength, flexibility, solvent resistance, and high temperature stability.

The U.S. patent literature of the past ten years provides an excellent description of the many types of processes for organic wire coatings. Numbers in ( ) indicate the number of processes described in each chapter. 180 processes in all.

Acrylics (12), Epoxy Resins (9), Fluorinated Resins (4), Polycarbonates (5), Polyesters (31), Polyimides and Polyamides (26), Polyolefins (41), Polyspirones (5), Polyurethanes (8), PVA Resins (15), Silicones (7), Vinyl Chloride Polymers and Copolymers (13), Other Resins (4).
232 pages. **$35**

PAINT ADDITIVES 1970
by H. Preuss

This publication surveys the field of paint additives offered for sale by manufacturers in the United States. It gathers together for you in one useful volume a series of articles written by Mr. Preuss for METAL FINISHING from 1965 through 1970. It is designed to help lead the paint formulator through the maze of modern additives; placing at his fingertips needed information about their chemistry, properties, specifications, uses and applications.

Additives form an integral part of a coating. Some of the additives discussed in this book are: antiskinning, antifoaming, antifouling, antifreezing, dispersing, destaticizing, antilivering, antisagging, curing, antisettling or suspension and moisture resistant agents; plasticizers; antioxidants; fire retardants; corrosion inhibitors; odorants and deodorants; and many others. 249 pages. **$18**

METAL COATING OF PLASTICS 1970
by Dr. F. Lowenheim

Describes 125 processes for applying metallic coatings to plastic articles on a production basis with reasonable reliability, and in such fashion that the metal is acceptably adherent to the substrate, and that the resulting products are useful for decorative or functional purposes. 254 pages. **$35**

ELECTRODEPOSITION AND RADIATION CURING OF COATINGS 1970
by Dr. M. W. Ranney

The advantages of electrodeposition: Pinhole-free coating, eliminating of fire hazards and air pollution problems, automated operation and fast throughput make this an attractive method. Radiation curing is quick, eliminates ovens and uses solvent-free vehicles. 96 Patent-based process on 170 pages. **$35**

POLYMERS AND ADHESIVES

POLYMERS IN LITHOGRAPHY 1971
by D. J. De Renzo

About 50% of all printing today is done by lithography, also named the planographic method. This has led to an extensive use of polymers for making the base plates and the sensitized plate coatings. Polymers are used also in etching solutions, lacquers, deletion fluids, inks, etc. 145 processes from the U.S. patent literature since 1965.

1. DIAZO TYPE PRESENSITIZERS (46 processes)
2. NONDIAZO PHOTOSENSITIVE LAYERS (17)
3. BASE PLATES AND COATINGS (32)
4. OTHER POLYMERS FOR PLATES (9)
5. LACQUERS, ETCHANTS, ETC. (18)
6. THERMOGRAPHIC PROCESSES (13)
7. ELECTROPHOTOGRAPHIC PROCESSES (9)
8. THE DRIOGRAPHIC PROCESS.

216 pages. **$36**

URETHANE FOAMS TECHNOLOGY AND APPLICATIONS 1971
by Y. Meltzer

Urethane foam production is growing at about twice the annual growth rate of the overall plastics industry. Rigid foams are used in refrigerators and freezers, and in sophisticated and efficient types of food processing and preserving equipment. By far the largest consumer is the building and construction industry; while flexible foams are leading the demand in the furniture, aviation and automotive industries. The book contains descriptions of 148 manufacturing processes of which 42 deal with application technology:

Raw Materials (39)
Special Additives (30)
Product Types (29)
Processing (8)
Applications (42)

448 pages. **$36**

EPOXY AND URETHANE ADHESIVES 1971
by Dr. M. W. Ranney

An ever increasing demand for epoxy adhesives makes them the leader of the industry. Urethane polymers and intermediates are also augmenting the adhesives market. Isocyanate monomers are applied to textile fibers, metals, and elastomers as primers for adhesion. Polymethylene polyphenyl isocyanates are used in formulations for bonding glass, metal, elastomers and wood to a variety of substrates. Polyurethanes with polyesters, polyamides, and elastomers meet many high performance requirements. 111 processes in 7 chapters:

Metal to Metal (25)
Fiber to Rubber (22)
Glass & Ceramics to Metal (18)
Polymer to Polymer (12)
Plastic to Metal (10)
Paper and Wood (13)
General Purpose Adhesives (11)

280 pages. **$36**

POLYIMIDE MANUFACTURE 1971
by Dr. M. W. Ranney
Chemical Process Review No. 54

The U.S. patent literature of the past ten years provides an excellent description of the many types of polyimides and their syntheses. This book is an attempt to collate and summarize those processes pertaining to the manufacture of polymers containing an imide grouping. Emphasis has been placed on practical, technically useful information. About 90 distinct processes of manufacture are described in eight chapters.

1. Polyamide Acids (20)
2. Polyimide-Esters from TMA (7)
3. Polyimide-Amides (11)
4. Modified Polyimides and Cross-Linking (11)
5. Specialty Intermediates (15)
6. Silicone-Fluorocarbon-Polysulfone Modifications (11)
7. Cellular Polyimides (5)
8. General Processing Techniques (9)

243 pages. **$35**

HOT-MELT ADHESIVES 1971
by M. McDonald

Reviews the U.S. patent literature from 1950 through early 1971. Hot-melts set fast enough to accommodate high-speed machinery in shoemaking, paper converting, bonding textiles (replacing hand and machine sewing), metal container sealing, etc. 63 processes:

1. **Hot-Melts for Shoemaking** (14)
2. **Bonding Paper & Paperboard** (23)
3. **Bonding Metals** (7)
4. **Bonding Plastics** (6)
5. **Bonding 2 or more Materials** (7)
6. **Textiles and Coated Substrates** (6)

238 pages. **$35**

FLUOROCARBON RESINS 1971
by Dr. M. W. Ranney
Chemical Process Review No. 51

1. Polytetrafluoroethylene (42). 2. Vinylidene Fluoride Elastomers (38). 3. Vinyl Fluoride. 4. Trifluorochloroethylene (15). 5. Fluorodienes (16). 6. Fluoroethers (13). 7. Fluorinated Nitroso Polymers (6). 8. Others (23). 9. General Processing Techniques (14). 226 pages. **$35**

POLYSULFIDE MANUFACTURE 1970
by C. Placek
Chemical Process Review No. 50

This report covers 73 processes dealing with polymers possessing the disulfide (-SS-) group. Basic Processes (14); Modified Polysulfide Polymers (13); Curing (12); Process Control (4); Physical Form (3); Single-Package Compositions (6). 141 pages. **$35**

TEXTILES

SPANDEX MANUFACTURE 1970
by M. McDonald
Chemical Process Review No. 48

This book covers methods of making spandex fibers, that is, the conversion of polyurethanes into fibers, as described in the U.S. patent literature. The U.S. patent literature has the most complete and comprehensive process information available, and as such, this publication will give you key processing information for this fast-growing fiber. The Table of Contents below gives the scope of this volume. The numbers in ( ) represent the number of processes included.

Wet Spinning Processes (13), Solvent Spinning Processes (19), Melt Spinning Processes (3), Chemical Composition and Raw Materials (19), Improving Resistance to Ultraviolet Light and Oxidation (9), Improving Dyeability of Spandex (9), Miscellaneous (8).

191 pages. **$35**

SOIL RESISTANT TEXTILES 1970
by Dr. M. W. Ranney
Textile Processing Review No. 5

Ideal soil release finishes must be capable of releasing stains readily and preventing redeposition of soil during laundering. Treatments should render manmade fibers and durable press reactants less attractive to oily stains and should be more easily wetted.

This report summarizes the developments in soil retardant and soil release finishes in both the carpet industry and in textile manufacture. It includes the newest technology associated with the use of acrylates and fluorochemical treatments. The numbers in ( ) following each treating agent indicate the number of processes covered for that particular compound.

Introduction: Metal Oxides and Salts For Carpet Treatment (15), Acrylic and Vinyl Polymers (10), Silicones (6), Fluorochemical Compounds (72), General Treatments (14). 216 pages. **$35**

WATERPROOFING TEXTILES 1970
by Dr. M. W. Ranney
Textile Processing Review No. 4

This Textile Processing Review summarizes the technology of water resistant treatments for textiles and fabrics as described in the U.S. patent literature since the early 1950's. 246 waterproofing processes are included—64 relate to use of fluorochemicals.

The numbers in ( ) after each entry in the Table of Contents, where the treatment processes are organized by the agent used, indicates the number of production processes for each agent.

Production Processes for Waterproofing Textiles using the following Agents: Metal Salts and Wax-Containing Formulations (44), Silicones and Alkyl Polysiloxanes (53), Organofunctional Silicones and Fluorosilanes (20), Acrylics (8), Nitrogen Containing Compounds (30), Fluorochemical Compounds (64), Elastomer, Vinyl, Polyolefin Vapor Permeable Fabrics (27), Miscellaneous Treatments (9). 353 pages. **$35**

FLAME RETARDANT TEXTILES 1970
by Dr. M. W. Ranney
Textile Processing Review No. 3

Describes 177 commercial processes to produce flame retardant textiles and fabrics.

Most activity is based on chemical modification of cellulose through hydroxyl groups. Use of phosphoric acid, urea-phosphates, and other phosphorylating agents all confer flame retardant properties to cellulose. A significant portion of this book is devoted to the latest in application of phosphorus containing materials.

Numbers in ( ) indicate the number of processes described.

Ammonium Salts, Borates (12); Antimony, Titanium Metal Oxides (25); Amine-Phosphorus Products (21); Aziridines, APO, APS (21); Methylol-Phosphorus Polymers, THPC (27); Phosphonitrilic Chlorides (9); Triallyl Phosphates and Phosphonates (26); Silicones Isocyanates, Miscellaneous (10); Nylon, Acrylics (18). 373 pages. **$35**

CREASEPROOFING TEXTILES 1970
by Dr. M. W. Ranney
Textile Processing Review No. 2

Summarizes detailed process information relating to textile creaseproofing agents used to obtain wash and wear, or permanent press fabrics. Over 300,000 words, describes 343 processes in this field. Shows you chemical agents used, and processes by which they are applied.

Dimethylolethylene Urea and Related Compounds, Aldehyde-Urea Condensates, Uron Resins, Aminoplasts—Catalyst Performance, Melamine Derivatives, Triazones, Carbamates, Other Nitrogen-Containing Compounds, Phosphorus-Amino Compounds—Aziridines, Aminoplast-Thermoplastic Resin Compositions, General Processing Techniques and Formulations, Aldehydes, Acetals, Epoxies, Epiholohydrins, Sulfones, Sulfonium Salts, Cross-Linking Agents, Miscellaneous, Polymeric Coatings—Rubber, Vinyl, Silicones, Radiation Curing, Wool, Nylon, and Others. Indexes. 460 pages. **$35**

DYEING OF SYNTHETIC FIBERS 1969
by C. Whiting
Textile Processing Review No. 1

The dyeing of synthetic fibers continues to be a challenge. Successful methods however, have been developed. Chapters 2 through 7 of this Review are divided into two sections. The first presents various new dyes and dyeing processes which are applicable to synthetic fibers. The second section concerns many auxiliary products available to aid in production of an acceptably dyed product. These include dye improving agents, leveling and retarding agents, agents used in after treatment to achieve optimum fastness properties.

Introduction: Dyeing Polyolefin and Polypropylene Fibers, Dyeing Polyamide Fibers, Dyeing Polyester Fibers, Dyeing Acrylic Fibers, Dyeing Hydrophobic Fibers, Dyeing Glass Fibers, Dyeing Miscellaneous Fibers, Dyes Applicable to More than One Type of Fiber, Dyeing Fiber Blends. 257 pages. **$35**

POLYMERS AND ADHESIVES

ETHYLENE-PROPYLENE-DIENE RUBBERS 1970
by Dr. M. W. Ranney
Chemical Process Review No. 49

Summarizes patent literature relating to: Polyene Monomers—Polymer Synthesis; Catalysts and Activators; MW Regulators; Process Technology; Recovery Techniques; Modified Terpolymers; Adhesives; Miscellaneous Vulcanizates; Cross-Linking Agents. 272 pages. **$35**

POLYCARBONATES—RECENT DEVELOPMENTS 1970
by K. Johnson
Chemical Process Review No. 47

Part I—Aromatic Polycarbonates: Synthesis and Polymerization (17); Halogen-Containing Polycarbonates (9); Processing (20); Modified Polycarbonates (23); Applications (5). Part II—Aliphatic Polycarbonates: Cycloaliphatics (8); Linear Aliphatics (6). 298 pages. **$35**

ABS RESIN MANUFACTURE 1970
by C. Placek
Chemical Process Review No. 46

ABS (acrylonitrile-butadiene-styrene) resins make up one of the most rapidly growing segments of the polymer industry. **Straight ABS Materials; ABS Modified with Acrylic Derivatives; ABS from Alpha-Methylstyrene; Miscellaneous Modifiers; Modification of Properties; Process Variations.** 233 pages. **$35**

FLAME RETARDANT POLYMERS 1970
by M. Ranney

Summarizes 144 processes for fire retardant additives and reactive intermediates for major plastic materials. Polyethylene and Polypropylene (15); Polystyrene (19); Polyurethanes (50); Polyesters (13); Other Polymer Systems (26); General Utility Additives (21). 263 pages. **$35**

AGRICULTURAL

AGRICULTURAL CHEMICALS MANUFACTURE 1971
by M. Sittig
Chemical Process Review No. 52

Agricultural chemicals, properly used, are essential for supplying the food requirements of the world's evergrowing population. Current attacks on the toxicity of today's pesticides notwithstanding, our agriculture saves about 5 dollars worth of produce for every dollar spent on the war against harmful pests. 172 manufacturing process and product descriptions are given:

1. **Environmental Control in Manufacture**
2. **Manufacture of Intermediates** (4)
3. **Insecticides** (80)
4. **Herbicides** (48)
5. **Fungicides** (25)
6. **Nematocides** (5)
7. **Plant Growth Regulators** (9)
8. **Fertilizer Additives** (1)
9. **Future Trends**

264 pages. **$35**

HORMONAL AND ATTRACTANT PESTICIDE TECHNOLOGY 1971
by Y. L. Meltzer

The need for non-chemical pesticides which are highly selective, nonpolluting and nontoxic, is urgent. Encouraging results are being obtained with insect hormones and hormonelike substances that interfere with the life cycle of noxious insects. 23 chapters based on the world's patent literature and technical articles: 1. Scope of the Problem. 2. Insect Hormones as Pesticides. 3. Insect Development and Hormones. 4. Juvenile Hormone. 5 Ecdysone. 6. Brain Hormone. Attractants for 7. Insects. 8. Bees. 9. Boll Weevils. 10. Cabbage Looper Moths. 11. Cockroaches. 12. Bombyx mori. 13. Flies. 14. Gypsy Moths. 15. Pink Bollworms. 16. Termites. 17. Yellow Jackets. 18. 10,12-Hexadecadiene Derivs. 19. Aliphatic Hydroxy Attractants. 20. Polyenols. 21. Review Articles. 22. Regulations. 23. Future Trends. 281 pages. **$35**

CELLULAR PLASTICS RECENT DEVELOPMENTS 1970
by K. Johnson

Describes 189 processes:
Polyolefins (15)
Polyvinyl Chloride (15)
Polystyrene (22)
Rubber (15)
Polyurethanes (71)
Polyesters and Epoxides (15)
Urea-Formaldehyde and Phenolic Resins (9)
Other Cellular Products (27)

280 pages. **$35**

COMPATIBILITY AND SOLUBILITY 1968
by I. Mellon

Normally, it requires laborious testing to determine compatibility of polymers, resins, elastomers, plasticizers, and solvents. Predictions made without testing or literature searching, are usually unreliable.

This book helps you evaluate proper materials by the use of 224 tables. 304 pages. **$20**

AQUATIC HERBICIDES AND ALGAECIDES 1971
by J. H. Meyer

There is a growing need for control of aquatic weeds and algae. This vegetation destroys natural waterways and water supplies. The most effective control is by chemicals. This book gathers the latest technology for producing or using aquatic herbicides and algaecides, based on U.S. patent literature. Numbers in ( ) indicate the number of processes described, 108 in all.

Metal Compounds (22)
Chlorinated Hydrocarbons (7)
Other Halogenated Compounds (16)
The Halogens Themselves (4)
Sulfur-Containing Materials (12)
Quaternary Ammonium Compounds (8)
Amides and Imides (10)
Amines (6)
Acids and Their Derivatives (8)
Miscellaneous Organic Compounds (9)
Carriers (6)

177 pages. **$35**

AGRICULTURAL

FERTILIZER DEVELOPMENTS AND TRENDS 1968
by A. V. Slack

R&D Trends, Ammonia, Ammonium Nitrate, Sulfate, Urea, Slow Release Nitrogen, Other Nitrogen Fertilizers, Phosphoric Acid, Ammonium Phosphate, Nitric & Superphosphates, Thermal and Other Phosphate Processes, Potassium Fertilizers, Fluid Fertilizers, Bulk Blending, Minor Nutrients. 98 illustrations. 406 pages. **$35**

NEW FERTILIZER MATERIALS 1968
by C. I. E. C.

Ureaform, Crotonylidene & Isobutylidene Diurea, Triple Superphosphate, Ammonium Phosphates, Nitrophosphates, Nitrate of Potash, Potassium Phosphates and Metaphosphates, Magnesium, Sulfur Fertilizers, Oxamide, Urea Nitrate and Phosphate, Hydrides of Phosphorus, Red Phosphorus. Applications. 430 pages. **$35**

AMMONIUM PHOSPHATES 1969
by Dr. M. W. Ranney
Chemical Process Review No. 35

This book describes recent pro cesses for production of ammonium phosphates.

Introduction; Ammonium Orthophosphates, Diammonium Orthophosphates, Ammonium Polyphosphates, Metal Ammonium Phosphates, Ammonium Phosphate—Ammonium Nitrate Mixtures. Many illustrations. 278 pages. **$35**

CONTROLLED RELEASE FERTILIZERS 1968
by Dr. R. Powell
Chemical Process Review No. 15

This book offers you complete technical data on numerous processes and products in this field. The two major approaches are (a) compounds of low solubility, and (b) coated granules.

Introduction; Compounds of Low Solubility, Coated Granules, Prevention of Nitrogen Losses, Rapid-Release Fertilizer. 279 pages. **$35**

TEXTILES

POLYESTER FIBER MANUFACTURE 1971
by M. Sittig

In 1970 polyester became the number one U.S. fiber, surpassing the consumption figure for nylon by another 100 million pounds. Predictions are that continuous processing from polymerization to finished yarn will be common in 1975. A total of 116 processes is given.

1. INTRODUCTION
2. ECONOMICS
3. VARIOUS POLYESTER COMPOSITIONS (6)
4. RAW MATERIALS AND PURIFICATION (9)
5. DIMETHYL TEREPHTHALATE (8)
6. INTEGRATED POLYESTER PRODUCTION (5)
7. BIS (HYDROXYETHYL) TEREPHTHALATE (23)
8. PREPOLYMER PRODUCTION (8)
9. POLYCONDENSATION (28)
10. POLYMER AFTER-TREATMENT (2)
11. SCRAP RECOVERY (3)
12. FIBER PRODUCTION (24)
13. FUTURE TRENDS

214 pages. **$36**

NONWOVEN FABRIC TECHNOLOGY 1971
by M. McDonald

Nonwovens are structures produced by bonding or interlocking of fibers, accomplished by mechanical, chemical, thermal, or solvent means. Low cost is the primary advantage over woven or knitted products, resulting in a wide variety of disposable items from flush-away diapers to industrial uniforms. U.S. hospitals and other medical organizations bought over $100 millions worth of disposable hospital gowns and other nonwovens in 1970 of what is thought to be a $800 million market. This book emphasizes those processes that turn out materials for making garments, draperies, upholstery, sheets, etc. 121 processes are described:

1. Resin Bonding (22 processes). 2. Spunbonding (23). 3. Needle Punching (28). 4. Fluid Pressure (13). 5. Heat Bonding (10). 6. Web Formation (7). 7. Miscellaneous (18). 240 pages. **$35**

SYNTHETIC PAPER FROM SYNTHETIC FIBERS 1971
by K. Johnson

This book provides a summary of the U.S. patent literature through 1970, relating to 74 processes for producing synthetic papers on conventional papermaking machinery:

1. **Cellulosics** (37 processes)
   Cellulose Derivatives (15)
   Cross-Linked Cellulose (4)
   Blends with Other Fibers (10)
   General (8)
2. **Polyamides** (8)
   General (5)
   Nylon + Cellulose (3)
3. **Polyacrylonitrile** (13)
   Bonding (7)
   General (4)
   Blends (2)
4. **Synthetic Fibers** (16)
   General Processing (10)
   Specialty Papers (2)
   Polytetrafluoroethylene (3)
   Polyester (1)

236 pages. **$35**

MULTICOMPONENT FIBERS 1971
by C. Placek

Discusses processes for producing multicomponent fibers, that is, those fibers that consist of two or more polymeric compounds spun together. The spinning of multicomponent fibers is one method used to produce bulked or crimped fibers. The difference in physical properties of the two filaments results in a bulked yarn.

This report covers 106 patents issued since 1960. The processes range over a wide spectrum of fiber technology—composition, properties, physical forms and spinning techniques. Numbers in ( ) indicate the number of processes described in each chapter.

Variations of the Same Polymer (24), Chemically Unrelated Components (10), Spontaneous Crimp (2), Permanent Crimp (12), Specific Properties of Fibers (8), Production of Sheath-Core Structures (10), Side-by-Side Components (7), Spinning Technology (33).

225 pages. **$35**

PHARMACEUTICAL AND COSMETIC

X-RAY CONTRAST AGENTS 1971
by M. Gutcho

Deals with the preparation of new x-ray contrast agents which are economical to produce and offer the desirable property of sharper radiographs without increased toxicity. Formulations are given for use in cholecystography, urology, myelography, lymphography, and bronchography. A special chapter is devoted to process improvements in the preparation of barium sulfate and injectable iodine contrast media. A total of 55 preparative processes is described. An abbreviated Table of Contents is shown, where the number in ( ) indicates the number of agents in each area:

1. Polyiodobenzoic Acid Derivatives (16). 2. Polyiodophthalic Acid Derivatives (5). 3. Iodophenyl Derivatives (12). 4. Radiopaque Formulations (9). 5. Miscellaneous Contrast Media (4). 6. Process Improvements (9). 7. Other Medical Uses For Radiopaque Materials. 130 pages. **$20**

ARTIFICIAL KIDNEY SYSTEMS 1970
by M. Gutcho

The processes and apparatus reported here are concerned with the wide range of components which in one way or another form the parts of a complete hemodialysis system. Some deal with the dialyzer; others with the mechanics of the dialysate solution.

Contains significant, detailed technical data, based on the patent literature relating to manufacturing, assembly, and operation of artificial kidney systems. Numerous illustrations are included. The accompanying Table of Contents, indicates the coverage offered and by the numbers in ( ), the processes covered.

Dialyzers in Artificial Kidney Systems (17); The Design of Dialyzer Parts (9); Dialysate Modifications (12); Lung and Kidney Machines (6); Dialyzers (6); Miscellaneous Blood Purification Processes (2). 320 pages. **$35**

SUSTAINED RELEASE PHARMACEUTICALS 1969
by A. Williams

This book is based on the U.S. patent literature, and presents substantial technical information for production of these products.

TABLETS-PILLS
- Cellulosic Coatings
- Lipid Coating
- Gels-Gums
- Specific Medicaments
- Tablet Design
- Miscellaneous

CAPSULES
- General Coatings
- Particle Size Control
- Capsule Design & Manufacture

INJECTABLES
- Antibiotics
- Miscellaneous

MISCELLANEOUS RELEASE PREPARATIONS
- Suppositories
- Powders
- General

Indexes. 273 pages. **$35**

ANTIOBESITY DRUG MANUFACTURE 1970
by Dr. B. Idson
Chemical Process Review No. 43

This book discusses 162 processes in the field of anorectic drug production technology. The numbers in ( ) in the Table of Contents show the number of preparations discussed for each heading.

N-Alkyl Amines (2), Substituted Aminopropanes—Arylaminopropanes (17), Substituted Aminopropanes—1-Heterocyclic-2-Aminopropanes (2), Substituted Aminopropanes—Bicyclic Aminopropane (1), Substituted Aminopropanes—1-Heterocyclic Oxoaminopropanes (1), Substituted Aminoalkenes (2), Aralkyl Amines (22), Aralkyl Hydrocarbon (1), Ring Substituted Heterocyclic Compounds (20), Nitrogen Substituted Heterocyclic Compounds (43), Bicyclic Compounds (2), Azacyclic Compounds (5), Miscellaneous Functional Substitutions (24), Alkaloids (1), Antibiotic (1), Resins (3), Steroids (6), Amphetamine Salts (2), Compositions (8), Appendix. 193 pages. **$35**

COSMETIC FILMS 1970
by M. Gutcho

The 62 processes included in this book are concerned with methods of forming cosmetic films and other related preparations.

The abbreviated Table of Contents indicates the four major films and the distribution of the patents within each area — the numbers in ( ).

- Powders (21)
- Creams and Lotions (12)
- Nail Preparations (19)
- Lipsticks (14)

143 pages. **$20**

TETRACYCLINE MANUFACTURING PROCESSES 1969
(2 Volumes)

CTC, Oxytetracycline, TC, DMTC and DMCTC, 2N-Derivatives, Position 4 Derivatives, 6-Methylene Derivatives, 6-Deoxy Derivatives, Anhydrotetracyclines, 7-and/or 9-Derivatives, 11a-Halo Derivatives, 5a, 11a-Dehydrotetracyclines, 12a-Derivatives, Epimers, Mechanism Study intermediates. Indexes. 931 pages. **(2 Volumes) $45**

NUCLEOTIDES AND NUCLEOSIDES 1970
by S. Gutcho

Organic Synthesis of Nucleotides in General, and of Specific Nucleotides, Fermentation Procedures for Nucleotides in General and for Specific Nucleotides, Enzymatic Digestion of Nucleic Acids, Nucleotides Coenzymes, Cyclic Nucleotides, Dinucleoside Phosphates, Purification Techniques, General Procedures, Nucleotides as Flavor Enhancers. 200 pages. **$35**

DENTIFRICES 1970
by T. Jefopoulos

A guide to information available from U.S. Patent literature to therapeutic and cosmetic agents in dentifrices.

The numbers in ( ) indicate the number of processes covered.

- Cleaning Agents (17)
- Polishing Agents (14)
- Prophylactic Compositions (27)
- Fluorides (30)
- Dentifrices for Dentists (6)
- Other Dentifrices (30)
- Improved Processing (2)

191 pages. **$35**

PHARMACEUTICAL AND COSMETIC

HAIR PREPARATIONS 1969
by A. Williams

Provides a detailed technological summary of recent developments based on 138 U.S. patents, since 1960, covering all aspects of hair preparations for the head, beard, eyelashes, and eyebrows.

Introduction, Dyeing, Bleaching, Waving, Setting, Shampoos-Rinses, Grooming-Tonics, Shaving Assistants, Other, Indexes. 208 pages. **$35**

FIBRINOLYTIC ENZYME MANUFACTURING 1969
by T. Rubel
Chemical Process Review No. 38

Methods for production and purification of fibrinolytic agents, their precursors and activators. Emphasis is on urokinase and streptokinase which activate plasminogen to form plasmin.

Plasminogen and Fibrinolysin, Urokinase, Streptokinase and Streptodornase, Other Fibrinolytic Enzymes. Indexes. 139 pages. **$24**

VITAMIN B_{12} MANUFACTURE 1969
by R. Noyes
Chemical Process Review No. 40

Vitamin B_{12} active substances are important therapeutic products for treatment of pernicious anemia. Also used for treatment of various other human ailments, and as a veterinary growth factor. This book offers various methods of producing vitamin B_{12} active substances. 327 pages. $35

VITAMIN E MANUFACTURE 1969
by T. Rubel
Chemical Process Review No. 39

This review relates the known methods for the preparation of tocopherols from natural products or by synthetic means, and conversion of non-alpha tocopherols.

Introduction; Tocopherols From Deodorizer Sludge, Conversions to Alpha Tocopherol, Synthesis of Tocopherols, Miscellaneous Related Processes, Indexes. 114 pages. $24

U. S. MARKETS

POLLUTION CONTROL COMPANIES U.S.A. 1972

Provides a marketing guide to the U.S. pollution control industry.

The first section is an alphabetical listing of ca. 1,500 companies or company units (divisions, subsidiaries, etc.) which manufacture or supply products useful in the areas of air, water, noise, and radiation pollution control and waste management.

The second section lists more than 500 companies and company units which provide such professional services as consulting, design engineering, and analyses of air or water pollutants.

The address and telephone number of each company is listed together with a brief description of the company's pollution control products or services, although these may constitute only a small portion of the company's business. 239 pages. **$24**

CHEMICAL GUIDE TO THE UNITED STATES 1971
Sixth Edition

Describes over 400 of the largest chemical firms in the U.S.: Those who actually carry out chemical syntheses in their plants. Companies and factual data about them are listed in alphabetic order, followed by an index which gives companies, subsidiaries and divisions, again by strict alphabetic arrangement.

Whenever available the following information is given in detail:

- **Name and Address with Zip Code**
- **Ownership**
- **Annual Sales**
- **Number of Employees**
- **Principal Executives and Titles**
- **Plant Locations**
- **Products**
- **Subsidiaries and Affiliates**
- **Internal Structure**

Also gives information on closely held firms, joint ventures, and others that do not publish annual reports. 191 pages. **$20**

FOOD AND BEVERAGE PROCESSING INDUSTRIES 1971

The usefulness of this book derives from its organization. It is divided into 2 sections. The first section is an alphabetical listing of approximately 3,500 U.S. food firms giving the correct name, address and zip code. Also concise, pertinent information (where available) such as:

- (a) Annual Sales
- (b) Number of Employees
- (c) Name of Chief Executive
- (d) Product Types

The second section is arranged numerically according to zip code with the companies once again listed alphabetically within their proper zip code numbers, thereby providing you with an easy-to-use geographical index to the U.S. food industry.

It is a great help in marketing efforts by providing the means for forward geographical planning.

169 pages. **$20**

PHARMACEUTICAL AND COSMETIC FIRMS U.S.A. 1970

Describes the 700 leading pharmaceutical and cosmetic firms in the United States. Includes (1) ethical, (2) proprietary, (3) veterinary, (4) private formula, (5) cosmetics, and (6) toiletries firms.

Contains (where available): name, address, and telephone; ownership, annual sales figure; number of employees; names of executives; subsidiaries and affiliates; plant locations; products.

Has two indexes—a subsidiary and division index and a zip code index. The zip code index is an extremely important sales tool; lists companies in numerical order by zip code, providing an easy-to-use, invaluable, geographical index.

This guide will help you; concentrate on the big buyers, prepare market reports, increase sales effectiveness, research potential acquisitions and divestitures, and serve as an employment and personnel guide. 212 pages. $20

ELECTRONIC AND ELECTRICAL MATERIALS

RESISTOR MATERIALS 1971
by P. Conrad
Electronics Materials Review No. 12

A helpful guide to new resistor materials.

- **Metals and Other Elements and Alloys (48)**
- **Metal-Metal Oxide Mixtures (9)**
- **Inorganic Oxide Compositions (32)**
- **Other Inorganic Compounds (21)**
- **Organic Compositions (12)**

217 pages. **$35**

SUPERCONDUCTING MATERIALS 1970
by P. Conrad
Electronics Materials Review No. 11

Gives 99 detailed manufacturing and fabrication processes. Superconductive materials can improve long distance transmission of electric power, provide more compact memories for computers, improve magnets for physics research and thermonuclear power reactors. 135 pages. **$35**

BATTERY MATERIALS 1970
by P. Conrad
Electronics Materials Review No. 10

Describes 162 processes useful in the manufacture of modern batteries:

- **Aqueous Battery Systems (89)**
- **"Dry" Battery Systems (29)**
- **Inorganic Electrolyte Systems (6)**
- **Organic Electrolyte Systems (6)**
- **Solid Electrolyte Systems (18)**
- **Molten Electrolyte Systems (11)**
- **Radioactive Batteries (3)**

171 pages. **$35**

MAGNETIC MATERIALS 1970
by M. Sittig
Electronics Materials Review No. 9

Surveys the empirical state of the art as revealed in recent U.S. patents.

1. **Simple Oxides (2)**
2. **Ferrites and Other Complex Oxides (66)**
3. **Metallic Magnetic Materials (37)**

Index of Companies, Authors and Patents. 286 pages. **$35**

PHOTOCONDUCTIVE MATERIALS 1970
by M. Sittig
Electronic Materials Review No. 8

Photoconductors have a number of important applications, such as television camera tubes, solar cells, photoelectric cells, solid state light amplifiers, electrophotographic copying machines. 86 processes. 288 pages. **$35**

THERMOELECTRIC MATERIALS 1970
by M. Sittig
Electronics Materials Review No. 7

Deals with thermocouples which convert thermal energy into electrical energy. 112 processes for isolating and making thermoelectric substances with descriptions of power-type thermocouples. Precise physical and electrical data. 235 pages. **$35**

ELECTROLUMINESCENT MATERIALS 1970
by M. Sittig
Electronics Materials Review No. 6

Illustrates and describes 113 manufacturing processes for making cathode ray tube phosphors (black & white & color), fluorescent lamp materials, and luminous diodes. Discusses future trends, e.g. diode-based lamps and flat TV screens. 306 pages. **$35**

PRODUCING FILMS OF ELECTRONIC MATERIALS 1970
by M. Sittig
Electronics Materials Review No. 5

Reviews commercially developed techniques for film production useful in the manufacture of integrated circuits and discrete components. Practically every method with practical applications is discussed, e.g. Electron Deposition, Ion Beam Deposition, Carrier Transport in Vapor Phase, etc. 113 processes. 295 pages. **$35**

DOPING AND SEMICONDUCTOR JUNCTION FORMATION 1970
by M. Sittig
Electronics Materials Review No. 4

Alloyed Junctions, Diffusion Processes, Melt Grown Junctions, Doping During Melting, Simultaneous Dopant and Substrate Deposition, Spark Doping Processes, Doping by Particle Bombardment, Hydrothermally Grown Junctions, Doping Epitaxial Layers, Future Trends. Indexes. 115 Processes. 132 illustrations. 318 pages. **$35**

SEMICONDUCTOR CRYSTAL MANUFACTURE 1969
by M. Sittig
Electronics Materials Review No. 3

Verneuil Method, Other Fusion Processes, Spark Discharge Processes, Single Crystal Pulling, Zone Melting, Other Melts, Dendritic Crystals, Single Crystals by Sintering, Melting, Crystals from Vapor Phase, Hydrothermal Growth, Solution Melts, Shaped Crystals, Films, Future Trends, Indexes. 100 processes. 106 illustrations. 303 pages. **$35**

MANUFACTURE OF SEMICONDUCTOR COMPOUNDS 1969
by M. Sittig
Electronics Materials Review No. 2

Manufacturing processes to produce semiconductor compounds based on Aluminum, Bismuth, Boron, Cadmium, Calcium, Gadolinium, Gallium, Indium, Iron, Lead, Magnesium, Silicon, Silver, Thallium, Titanium, Vanadium, Zinc, and Organics. 114 processes. 106 illustrations. 326 pages. **$35**

PURE CHEMICAL ELEMENTS FOR SEMICONDUCTORS 1969
by M. Sittig
Electronics Materials Review No. 1

Detailed manufacturing techniques for producing pure chemical elements for semiconductors.

Antimony, Arsenic, Bismuth, Boron, Gallium, Germanium, Indium, Phosphorus, Selenium, Silicon, Tellurium, Thallium, Zinc, Future Trends. 105 processes. 112 illustrations. 335 pages. **$35**

OVERSEAS MARKETS

WORLD PHARMACEUTICAL FIRMS 1972

Lists alphabetically by country the names and full addresses of over 6,000 manufacturers of ethical drugs, pharmaceutical specialties and basic pharmaceutical materials in all the major producing areas of the world.

For easy reference the 52 countries are arranged in geographical areas:

- **North America**
- **South America**
- **Western Europe**
- **Eastern Europe**
- **Africa**
- **Australasia**
- **Asia**
- **North Africa and Middle East**

This book will enable companies dealing with the pharmaceutical sector to mail sales literature, help plan and evaluate area representation, assist in the preparation of market reports and provide useful references.

Prepared in our London office. 122 pages. **$24**

EUROPEAN PAINT MANUFACTURERS 1971

Developing technology in the field of polymer-based and solventless coatings has resulted in European acquisitions and mergers. Describes about 1,000 of the most important paint manufacturers in 17 countries of Western Europe. Entries are listed alphabetically by country and the following data are presented as fully as they were obtainable:

- Name
- Address
- Telephone Numbers
- Telex Numbers
- Number of Employees
- Principal Executives
- Products
- Plant Locations
- Domestic Subsidiaries
- Foreign Subsidiaries
- Sales Volume

Prepared in our London Office. 155 pages. **$24**

EUROPEAN CHEMICAL DISTRIBUTORS 1971

A considerable proportion of the sales of the world's major chemical companies are made through distributors, particularly in foreign countries. The book is divided into a main section, arranged by European distributors, and an index of worldwide companies the 1,300 distributors are representing.

Includes:

Austria	Luxembourg
Belgium	Netherlands
Denmark	Norway
Finland	Portugal
France	Spain
Germany	Sweden
Greece	Switzerland
Iceland	Turkey
Ireland	United Kingdom
Italy	

The chemical companies represented by the distributors are cross-referenced in the index. 264 pages. **$24**

EUROPEAN PHARMACEUTICAL MARKET REPORT 1971
Second Edition

Gives statistical information from 1960 to the end of 1969 on the 5,000 million dollar drug industry of the EEC (European Economic Community) and of the EFTA (European Free Trade Association). Type of information included:

- **General and Historical Growth Potentials**
- **Production and Sales**
- **Domestic and Foreign Trade**
- **Distribution—Pricing**
- **Market Structure**
- **Structure of the Industry**
- **Names and Addresses of Trade Associations and of over 1,000 Manufacturers**
- **Research and Development**
- **Government Legislation**
- **Health Service Expenditures**

This book, a greatly expanded version of the earlier successful study, will bring you up to date with the European pharmaceutical scene and will give you a coherent picture of this complex market. 158 pages. **$36**

TEXTILE INDUSTRY OF JAPAN 1971

Relates significant developments of nearly 900 companies:

- **Name and Address**
- **Principal Officers**
- **Employees**
- **Capital and Sales**
- **Total Assets**
- **Bankers & Stockholders**

Statistically analyzes the whole Japanese textile industry:

- **Production**
- **Trade**
- **Raw Materials**
- **Consumption**
- **Employment Pattern**
- **Wages & Productivity**
- **Important Trademarks**

Increasing pressures from expanding developing countries and restricted imports by the U.S. are producing many changes evaluated here.

205 pages. **$35**

CHEMICAL GUIDE TO EUROPE 1971
Fifth Edition

Prepared in our London Office to give on-the-spot coverage. Describes ca. 1,100 companies in the 19 countries of Western Europe which together constitute a market almost as large as that of the U.S. Includes all major European Chemical Companies. Gives this information (where pertinent and available):

- **Name and Address**
- **Telephone and Telex Numbers**
- **Ownership**
- **Plant Locations and Products**
- **Internal Structure**
- **Local Subsidiaries and Affiliates**
- **Foreign Subsidiaries and Affiliates**
- **Principal Executives**
- **Annual Sales**
- **Number of Employees**

Also companies which are predominantly non-chemical, but have important chemical interests, are included. 288 pages. **$20**

OVERSEAS MARKETS

KEY EUROPEAN INDUSTRIALS 1970

This important new directory describes 1,000 leading manufacturers in 19 countries of Western Europe. Prepared by our London office, it will provide the hard-pressed executive with a unique, on-the-spot guide to the activities of Europe's key industrial companies and groups. Find out who owns whom.

Full name and address
Telephone and telex numbers
Share capital, sales, profit
Number of employees
Principal executives
Range of products and activities
Domestic and foreign subsidiaries

Volume I — (EFTA) — Austria, Denmark, Finland, Iceland, Ireland, Norway, Portugal, Sweden, Switzerland, United Kingdom. 180 pages.
Volume II — (EEC) — Belgium, France, Germany, Greece, Italy, Luxembourg, Netherlands, Spain, Turkey. 182 pages.
2 Volumes—**$35**

ELECTRONICS MANUFACTURERS OF WESTERN EUROPE AND U.S.A. 1970

This book provides the reader with a comprehensive and up-to-date guide to names and addresses of electronics manufacturers in the following 16 countries:

Austria	Netherlands
Belgium	Norway
Denmark	Portugal
Finland	Spain
France	Sweden
Germany	Switzerland
Ireland	United Kingdom
Italy	United States

It will enable companies dealing with the electronics sector to: mail sales literature and promotional material as effectively as possible; help plan and evaluate area representation more accurately; assist in the preparation of market reports; and provide a useful day-to-day work of reference. 131 pages. **$19**

PETROCHEMICAL INDUSTRY OF JAPAN 1970

Japanese petrochemical industry output by 1969 reached a record level of $2,500 million. Japanese petrochemicals now constitute a major force in the world chemical market.

The bulk of the book is a detailed guide to the 205 manufacturers in the industry. Companies are listed alphabetically, giving their address, capital, sales, number of employees, president and, where relevant, ownership. For every company, the existing and planned capacity of each product is listed, together with its plant location and expected completion date.

To those associated with developments in the petrochemical sector, this important new guide to one of the world's leading producers will be both a convenient source of reference and an invaluable marketing aid. 147 pages. **$35**

EUROPEAN FOOD MARKET RESEARCH SOURCES 1970

Enables you to pinpoint publications most likely to be of assistance.

References are classified by Government statistics and reports, other statistics and reports, trade associations, food trade journals; other newspapers and periodicals, directories, advertising statistics, bank reviews. 111 pages. **$19**

KNITWEAR AND HOSIERY GUIDE TO EUROPE 1970

Entries are listed alphabetically under country and are accompanied, wherever possible, by the following key data: full name and address; telephone and telex numbers; principal executives; product range; domestic and foreign subsidiaries and affiliates; plant location; latest sales figures and number of employees. 201 pages. **$20**

EUROPEAN KNITWEAR AND HOSIERY MARKET REPORT 1970

17 countries included. Trend of activity established. Size structure of domestic market determined. Information on yarn consumption, knitwear and hosiery production, foreign trade, number of companies and employees engaged in manufacture. Comprehensive selection of statistical material. 166 pages. **$35**

TEXTILE GUIDE TO EUROPE 1970

Describes the 1,300 largest textile firms in Western Europe. Part 1 lists companies alphabetically under each country. Part 2 lists types of textile products manufactured. Company listings include full name and address, principal executives, product range, domestic and foreign subsidiaries, plant locations, no. of employees, latest sales figures. 200 pages. **$20**

EUROPEAN CHEMICAL MARKET RESEARCH SOURCES 1969

Each country is treated separately, sources being grouped under the following headings: Government Statistics and Reports, Other Statistics and Reports, Trade Associations, Trade Journals, Other Newspapers and Magazines, Directories, Advertising Statistics, Bank Reviews. 102 pages. **$19**

ELECTRONICS GUIDE TO EUROPE 1969

Contains company profiles of over 600 leading electronics manufacturers in 14 countries. Arranged for easy comparison: Full name and address, ownership, principal executives, product range, domestic and overseas subsidiaries, plant location, latest sales figures, number of employees. 150 pages. **$20**

ENVIRONMENT AND POLLUTION

HYDROGEN SULFIDE REMOVAL PROCESSES 1972
by P. G. Stecher
Pollution Control Review No. 5

Furnishes reliable and efficient methods of H_2S removal from gases, air, and liquids. 80 Patent-based processes.

1. ABSORPTION FROM GASES WITH INORGANICS
2. WITH ORGANICS
Alkanolamines
Other Amines
Esters and Ethers
Other Compounds
Recycling Absorbents
3. REMOVAL FROM GASES BY OTHER METHODS
Oxidation
Adsorption
Hydrotreating
Use of Electrolysis
H_2S Recycle in White Liquor Regeneration
Ion Exchange Resins
Molecular Sieves
Adsorption plus Oxidation
4. REMOVAL FROM LIQUIDS
From Fluid Hydrocarbons
From Aqueous Solutions

288 pages. **$36**

SULFUR DIOXIDE REMOVAL FROM WASTE GASES 1971
by A. V. Slack
Pollution Control Review No. 4

Reviews the problems of smelter operators, power plants, refineries, sulfur acid plants, and Claus process sulfur plants.

1. THE PROBLEM
Alternatives of Control
2.-3. THROWAWAY PROCESSES
Dry Systems
Wet Systems
4. ECONOMIC FACTORS IN RECOVERY
5. RECOVERY PROCESSES
6. ALKALIS AS ABSORBENTS
7. ALKALINE EARTH ABSORBENTS
8. METAL OXIDE SORPTION
9. ADSORPTION PROCESSES
10. CATALYTIC OXIDATION & REDUCTION
11. OTHER RECOVERY METHODS
Organic Sorbents
Fuel Gasification
Gas Cleaning

200 pages. **$36**

ENVIRONMENTAL CONTROL IN THE ORGANIC AND PETROCHEMICAL INDUSTRIES 1971
by H. R. Jones
Pollution Control Review No. 3

1. WASTE SOURCES
2. WATER USE
3. WATER POLLUTION
4. RECEIVING WATERS
5. REUSE OF WATER
6. PHYSIOLOGICAL EFFECTS
7. POLLUTION PARAMETERS
8. MONITORING
9. CHEMICAL CLASSIFICATION
10. SPECIFIC PRODUCTS
11. WASTE WATERS
12. INDUSTRIAL-MUNICIPAL TREATMENT PLANTS
13. INTERNAL IMPROVEMENTS
14. PHYSICAL TREATMENTS
15. CHEMICAL TREATMENTS
16. BIOLOGICAL TREATMENTS
17. OTHER DISPOSAL METHODS
18. WATER ECONOMICS
19. AIR POLLUTION
20. AIR POLLUTANTS REMOVAL
21. IMMEDIATE RECOMMENDATIONS
22. REFERENCES-INDEXES

257 pages. **$36**

PAPER RECYCLING AND THE USE OF CHEMICALS 1971
by M. McDonald

Paper accounts for almost half of our solid waste (ca. 40 million tons per year accumulate in the U.S. alone). But paper can be reused. Treatment is mechanical and chemical, using many substances for removing printer's ink, plastic coatings, wax, adhesives, etc. The secondary fibers industry, on the threshold of an era of expanded growth, is consuming a steadily increasing amount of solvents, bleaches, and other chemicals discussed in this book. 68 processes.

Removing Ink (23)
Removing Coatings and Impregnants (19)
Dispersing Coatings (11)
Repulpable Adhesives and Coatings (5)
Miscellaneous (10)

304 pages. **$36**

CATALYTIC CONVERSION OF AUTOMOBILE EXHAUST 1971
by J. McDermott
Pollution Control Review No. 2

The need for controlling the exhaust gas emissions from gasoline, diesel, and jet engines is becoming increasingly urgent. The emission of carbon monoxide, nitrogen oxides, lead compounds, reactive olefins, and even of carcinogens such as benzopyrene, has become the concern of almost every legislature.

This book summarizes the U.S. patent literature relating to combustion catalysts, such as various metal oxides, platinum, and palladium. In general, the catalytic unit, mounted after the exhaust manifold, completes the oxidation of unburned hydrocarbons and converts the carbon monoxide to carbon dioxide. 94 processes and devices are described.

Catalytic Converter Design (31)
Catalyst Bed Design (17)
Catalysts (32)
Catalytic Units (14)

208 pages. **$36**

CORROSION RESISTANT MATERIALS HANDBOOK 1971
Second Edition
by I. Mellan

Corrosion, always an urgent and persistent problem, bothers and baffles us even more today, because of the quantity and complexity of chemicals in our polluted biosphere. This book will help you cut losses by enabling you to choose the proper commercially available corrosion resistant material. The index lists thousands of corrosive substances and refers you to specific recommendations in the 147 tables:

Synthetic Resins (90 tables)
Elastomers (17 tables)
Cements (11 tables)
Glass & Ceramics (4 tables)
Wood (3 tables)
Metals & Alloys (22 tables)

487 pages. **$25**

ENVIRONMENT AND POLLUTION

MERCURY POLLUTION CONTROL 1971
by H. R. Jones
Pollution Control Review No. 1

In 1970 mercury pollution hit the headlines. Mercury ions were expected to react with other inorganic ions in the water, form precipitates, and sink harmlessly to the bottom. But when organic molecules from sewage or dead organisms are present, mercury reacts with these molecules to form toxic methyl mercury compounds which are excreted very slowly by fish and man. This book explains in detail what measures can be taken to prevent further pollution and to remove existing contamination. 13 Chapters: 1. The Fish Episode. 2. Production of Mercury. 3. Its Properties. 4. Uses of Mercury. 5. Its Toxicology. 6. Detection and Determination. 7. Air Pollution by Mercury. 8. Cleanup of Spilled Mercury. 9. Removal from Gases. 10. From Liquids. 11. From other Materials. 12. Legislation. 13. Trends and Problems. 251 pages. **$35**

HAZARDOUS CHEMICALS HANDLING AND DISPOSAL 1970
The Institute of Advanced Sanitation Research International

This publication is the record of a symposium of hazardous chemicals handling and disposal.
Hygiene Control—Handling Certain Hazardous Chemicals
Hazardous Chemicals Handling in "The Pharmaceutical Chemical Industry"
Effects of Hazardous Chemicals on Biochemical Oxygen Demand Tests of Stream Water Samples
Pesticide Handling in an Industrial Plant
Thermal Method for the Disposal of Hazardous Wastes
Land Disposal of Hazardous Chemicals
Hazardous Chemicals Disposal in a Large Chemical Complex
Research, Development and Application of New Biological Methods for Toxic Wastes Degradation and Disposal
Design and Tests of a Portable Cask for Explosive Chemicals

130 pages. **$15**

HAZARDOUS CHEMICALS HANDLING AND DISPOSAL 1970
The Institute of Advanced Sanitation Research International

This is the record of the Second Symposium.
Pesticide Container Decontamination
Fate and Effects of Pesticides
Separation of Organic and Inorganic Chemicals in a Waste Stream
Vector Problems in Waste Disposal
Plants Poisonous to Livestock
Land Application and Anaerobic Lagoon Disposal of Waste
Reverse Osmosis for Reclamation and Reuse of Chemical and Metal Waste Solutions
Thermal Methods for Destruction of Chemical Waste
Specialty Gases and Hazardous Wastes
Education of the Public
Hazardous Chemicals from Natural Sources
Maximum Allowable Concentrations and Water Quality
Biochemical Oxygen Demand and its Meaning

163 pages. **$20**

WASTE WATER CLEANUP EQUIPMENT 1971
by C. Pazar
Pollution Control Handbook No. 2

This book describes commercial equipment used for water pollution control. It is based directly on information supplied by manufacturers. Appropriate, detailed, technical information and illustrations were selected by the author (at no cost to, nor influence from, the manufacturers of this equipment). An abbreviated Table of Contents is shown below. The numbers in ( ) indicate the number of companies whose equipment is described.

Sewage Pretreatment (8), Clarification—Flocculation—Sludge Collection (25), Aerobic Treatment (28), Sludge Processing and Handling (28), Treatment of Plant Effluents (14), Treatment for Specific Contaminants (40), Sewage Systems and Hydraulic Components (20), Packaged and Prefabricated Treatment Plants (11), Anaerobic Processing (4), Tertiary Treatment (22). 551 pages. **$35**

DESALINIZATION BY REVERSE OSMOSIS 1970
by J. McDermott

Summarizes the patent literature through June 1970 relating to reverse osmosis processes with particular emphasis on membrane technology and equipment design. The abbreviated Table of Contents shows material covered. The numbers in ( ) indicate number of patents.

MEMBRANE PREPARATION
Cellulosic (6)
Discrete Particles (4)
Miscellaneous Membrane Systems (5)
Membrane Supports (8)
EQUIPMENT DESIGN
Tubular Units (7)
Spirally Wound Membrane Modules (7)
Miscellaneous (5)
MODIFIED REVERSE OSMOSIS TECHNIQUES
Vapor Permeation (2)
Other Energy Sources (6)
Solution Modifications (3)
SPECIAL UNITS
Submerged Units (4)
Portable Units (3)
General (3)

-209 pages **$35**.

DESALINIZATION BY DISTILLATION 1971 RECENT DEVELOPMENTS
by J. McDermott

The prospect of revitalizing arid areas, together with the problem of providing increased quantities of potable water for the developed areas has produced considerable research in desalinization processes. In the past two years alone, over one hundred patents relating to distillation processes have been issued in the U.S.

Flash Evaporators: Multistage Multieffect Evaporators, Direct Contact Condensation, Use of Combustion Gases. Flash Evaporation and Power Generation. Vapor Compression: General Process, Contact Condensation. Control of Scale Formation: Process Techniques, Chemical and Miscellaneous Techniques. Membranes and Refrigerant Circuits: Semiporous Membrane, Silicone Rubber, Distilland Heating, Heat Exchange Circuits. Miscellaneous: Latent Heat Distillation, Partially Submerged Unit, Water Purification Units. 194 pages. $35

ENVIRONMENT AND POLLUTION

DESALINIZATION BY FREEZE CONCENTRATION 1971
by J. McDermott

This volume is the second of a series of three, dealing with the major desalinization processes. The information contained will provide needed know-how concerning the renewed interest in freeze concentration processes.

The Table of Contents indicates the coverage of processes and equipment offered by this volume. The numbers in ( ) indicate the processes in a particular area.

Direct Contact Volatile Refrigerants
General Processes (24)
Crystal Washing Techniques (11)
Direct Contact Low Volatility Heat Transfer Mediums
Kerosene and Other Hydrocarbons (9)
Other Coolants (2)
Vacuum Freezing
Zarchin Process (9)
Other Processes (6)
Hydrate Processes (11)
Surface Freezing
General Processes (7)
Other Processes (7)

207 pages. **$35**

AIR AND GAS CLEANUP EQUIPMENT 1970
by C. Pazar
Pollution Control Handbook No. 1

Supplies detailed, technical data, diagrams and specifications for air pollution control equipment.

An abbreviated Table of Contents is shown. The number of companies whose equipment is described is the number in ( ).

DRY DUST COLLECTORS
Electrostatic Precipitators (9)
Inertial Separators (25)
Filtration Through Fabric (35)
Components, Auxiliaries (20)
WET SCRUBBERS
Packed Towers and Beds (13)
Cyclones (12)
Venturi Scrubbers (20)
Impingement—Inertial—Capillary (18)
Gas Coolers, Separators (6)
INCINERATION AND GAS PROCESSING
Incineration of Gases (10)
Sludge, Liquid Incineration (6)
Solid Refuse (15)
Incineration Components (7)
Oxidation (10)
Carbon Adsorption, Gases (4)

637 pages. **$35**

SOUNDPROOF BUILDING MATERIALS 1970
by Dr. M. W. Ranney

Table of Contents shows scope of this volume.

Fibrous Glass and Mineral Wool
Fibrous Glass
Surface Coating Techniques for Fibrous Glass
Mineral Wool
Flake Glass Panels
Fiberboard
Perforation Techniques
Panel Design
Surface Coatings
Miscellaneous
Gypsum—Ceramic—Perlite
Gypsum
Ceramic
Perlite, Vermiculite and Silicate
Miscellaneous
Plastic Products
Polystyrene
Polyurethane
Miscellaneous
General Processes
Flexible Partitions
General Construction

217 pages. **$35**

WATER POLLUTION CONTROL AND SOLID WASTES DISPOSAL 1969
by M. Sittig

Types of Water Contaminants. Removing Specific Inorganic Water Contaminants, Removing Specific Organic Water Contaminants, Removing Specific Solid Contaminants from Water, Handling Liquid and Solid Radioactive Wastes, Sewage Disposal, Solid Waste Disposal Processes, Future Trends. 78 illustrations. 244 pages. **$35**

AIR POLLUTION CONTROL PROCESSES AND EQUIPMENT 1968
by M. Sittig

Sources of Air Pollution, Air Pollution Control Devices, Removing Specific Gases and Vapors from Air, Equipment for Removing Solids and Liquids from Air, Removing Specific Solids and Liquids from Air, Removing Automotive Exhaust Fumes from Air. Future Trends. 102 illustrations. 260 pages. **$35**

OTHERS

CONTINUOUS CASTING OF STEEL 1970
33 Magazine

It is probably true that all new steelmaking installations are going to be based on continuous casting. By 1972, 38 countries will be producing primary steel by this process. This volume of highly technical and economic data and information on continuous casting fulfills the need for a common reference work on the subject. The material originally appeared as a series of articles over the years in 33 Magazine. Continuous Casting of Steel 1970 is as current as the world continuous casting Round/up of August-September 1970.

An abbreviated Table of Contents is given where the numbers in ( ) indicate the number of articles in each chapter.

Theoretical Aspects and Historical Development (9); Design Concepts and Engineering Parameters (10); Studies in Continuous Casting (23). 341 pages. **$20**

INDUSTRIAL SOLVENTS HANDBOOK 1970
by I. Mellan

A handbook with complete, up-to-date, pertinent data regarding industrial solvents.

821 tables contain pertinent data concerning physical properties of solvents and degrees of solubility of materials in these solvents. Numerous graphs included giving a great deal of data concerning various parameters. Also includes phase diagrams for multi-component products.

The vast amount of information contained in this book is shown in the abbreviated Table of Contents in the next column. The numbers in ( ) after each entry indicate the number of tables.

Hydrocarbon Solvents (14); Halogenated Hydrocarbons (130); Nitroparaffins (5); Organic Sulfur Compounds (5); Monohydric Alcohols (122); Polyhydric Alcohols (150); Phenols (6); Aldehydes (10); Ethers (53); Glycol Ethers (79); Ketones (44); Acids (18); Amines (124); Esters (61). 478 pages. **$25**

8

FIRE RETARDANT BUILDING PRODUCTS AND COATINGS 1970
by Dr. M. W. Ranney

Imparting fire retardancy presents a many-sided challenge to the industry. The fire retardant chemicals must be relatively inexpensive because of the economics of the building trade. In addition the coatings must also be able to maintain the generally desirable characteristics of good building materials such as paintability and hygroscopicity.

These needs, which are present in the search for good fire retardants, are surveyed in this Review. The value of this report is indicated by the number of chemicals and processes covered for all the building materials here.
1. Wood Impregnation
2. Fiberboard
3. Ceiling Tile and Panel Construction
4. Asphaltic Products
5. Intumescent Coatings
6. General Coating Formulations
7. Adhesives
186 pages. $35

ELECTRON BEAM WELDING 1971
by Dr. R. Bakish

The material has been arranged for easy use in the seven broad areas shown, with the number of developments indicated. 1. Processes and Equipment (41), 2. Alternate Beam Generating System (8), 3. Beam Control (20), 4. Moveable Chambers (8), 5. Beam Protective Devices (6), 6. Viewing Devices (10), 7. End Products (13). 150 pages $35

ORGANIC CHEMICAL PROCESS ENCYCLOPEDIA
by M. Sittig

Second Edition 1969

A handy desk-top reference to organic chemicals and their industrial manufacturing processes.

Gives the key processing facts for instant reference to 711 industrial organic chemical processes—with 711 large flow diagrams. 712 pages—8½" x 11"—hard cover. $35

ANTIOXIDANTS 1971
by G. Bayern

This book is a guide to antioxidants manufactured in the U.S. and their trade names, chemical classification, and suppliers. This publication gives you quick access to pertinent information relating to commercial antioxidants by correlating trade names and generic names of any particular antioxidant. 63 pages. $18

INORGANIC CHEMICAL AND METALLURGICAL PROCESS ENCYCLOPEDIA 1968
by M. Sittig

This book is organized in an unusual format. There is one inorganic chemical or metallurgical process on each page. At the top of the page an equipment drawing or flow diagram is shown, and underneath a description of the process is given. 883 pages—8½" x 11"—hard cover. $35

MICROENCAPSULATION TECHNOLOGY 1969
by Dr. M. W. Ranney

This book is based on U.S. patent technology in the microencapsulation field. Detailed descriptions and illustrations of processes and products are given. An abbreviated table of contents is outlined below:

Phase Separation Methods; Coacervation-Aqueous Phase Separation, Organic Phase Separation, Spray Drying, Miscellaneous: Interface Reactions—Polymerization; Dissolved Monomer Polymerization, Interfacial Polymerization, In-situ-Polymerization, Vapor Deposition: Physical Methods; Fluidized Bed, Electrostatic, Multi-Orifice Centrifugal, Vacuum Metallizing, Coating Fusible Material: Applications; Xerographic Toner, Light Sensitive-Photographic Materials, Heat Sensitive, Transfer Sheets—Dyes, Miscellaneous, Indexes. Illustrations. 275 pages. $35

POLYMETHYLBENZENES 1969
by H. W. Earhart

Presents physical property data. Discusses the chemistry of the PMB's established chemical reactions, relative kinetic rate data, yields, etc. Known as well as suggested end-uses for numerous PMB's and derivatives are given, e.g. for benzene, toluene, xylene, mesitylene, pseudocumene, hemimellitene, durene, isodurene, prehnitene, penta-and hexamethylbenzene. 63 tables. 549 references. 158 pages. $20

FUEL CELLS RECENT DEVELOPMENTS 1969
by Dr. M. W. Ranney

Fuels, Hydrocarbons, Nitrogen Compounds, Solid Electrolytes, Electrolyte Additives, Liquid Electrolytes, High Temperature Electrolytes, Ion-Exchange Membranes, Fuel Cell Construction, Water Removal-Control, Pressure Variation and Control, Biochemical and Thermocells, Regeneration, Reactivation, Indexes. Many illustrations. 325 pages. $35

MEMBRANES TECHNOLOGY AND ECONOMICS 1967
by Dr. R. Rickles

This book will assist you in undertaking profitable projects in this field that appears to have a brilliant future.

Chapters: Membranes Theory, Electrodialysis, Ultrafiltration, Dialysis and Diffusion Control, Membrane Filtration, Gas Permeation, Medical Applications, Preparation of Synthetic Polymeric Membranes. 197 pages. $24

SOLAR CELLS 1969
by Dr. M. W. Ranney

Summarizes recent process development and applications on the use of photoresponsive materials in solar cells. While commercial development has centered on silicon type cells, advances in the use of other inorganic and organic semiconductors as well as photoemissive devices for solar cell application are included.

Indexes, 85 illustrations, 271 pages. $35